The Mammals of Eastern Canada

The Mammals
of Eastern Canada

Randolph L. Peterson

Curator, Department of Mammalogy
Royal Ontario Museum, University of Toronto

Toronto, Oxford University Press, 1966

Printed and bound in England by
HAZELL WATSON AND VINEY LTD
AYLESBURY, BUCKS

Contents

COLOUR ILLUSTRATIONS xviii

LINE ILLUSTRATIONS xix

DISTRIBUTION MAPS xxiv

TABLES xxvii

PREFACE xxix

ACKNOWLEDGEMENTS xxxi

MAMMALS AND MAN 2

THE CLASS MAMMALIA 6

THE ORIGIN AND CLASSIFICATION OF MAMMALS 9

THE MAMMALIAN SKELETON 20

THE REGION OF EASTERN CANADA 25

KEY TO THE ORDERS OF EASTERN-CANADIAN RECENT MAMMALS 26

Order MARSUPIALIA 27

Family DIDELPHIDAE, 27

DIDELPHIS MARSUPIALIS. Common Opossum. *Opossum.* 27
* *D. m. virginiana* Kerr. Virginia.

Order INSECTIVORA 30

Family SORICIDAE, 31

SOREX CINEREUS. Common or Masked Shrew. *Musaraigne cendrée.* 34
  S. c. acadicus Gilpin. Nova Scotia (Halifax ?).
  S. c. cinereus Kerr. Fort Severn, Ontario.
  S. c. miscix Bangs. Black Bay, Strait of Belle Isle, Labrador.

SOREX FUMEUS. Smoky Shrew. *Musaraigne fuligineuse.* 36
  S. f. fumeus Miller. Peterboro, Madison County, New York.
  S. f. umbrosus Jackson. James River, Antigonish County, Nova Scotia.

SOREX ARCTICUS. Arctic or Saddle-back Shrew. *Musaraigne arctique.* 38
  S. a. arcticus Kerr. Fort Severn, Ontario.
  S. a. laricorum Jackson. Elk River, Sherburne County, Minnesota.
  S. a. maritimensis R. W. Smith. Wolfville, Kings County, Nova Scotia.

SOREX GASPENSIS. Gaspé Shrew. *Musaraigne de Gaspé.* 40
  S. gaspensis Anthony and Goodwin. Mount Albert, Gaspé County, Quebec.

SOREX DISPAR. Gray Long-tailed Shrew. *Musaraigne gris longicaude.* 41
  S. d. dispar Batchelder. Beedes, Essex County, New York.

SOREX PALUSTRIS. Water Shrew. *Musaraigne palustre.* 42
  S. p. albibarbis (Cope). Profile Lake, Grafton County, New Hampshire.
  S. p. gloveralleni Jackson. Digby, Digby County, Nova Scotia.
  S. p. hydrobadistes Jackson. Withee, Clark County, Wisconsin.
  S. p. labradorensis Burt. Red Bay, Strait of Belle Isle, Labrador.
  S. p. palustris Richardson. Hudson's Bay to Rocky Mountains.
  S. p. turneri Johnson. Fort Chimo, Quebec.

MICROSOREX HOYI. Pygmy Shrew. *Musaraigne pygmée.* 44
  M. h. alnorum (Preble). Robinson Portage, Manitoba.
  M. h. intervectus Jackson. Lakewood, Oconto County, Wisconsin.
  M. h. thompsoni (Baird). Burlington, Chittenden County, Vermont.

BLARINA BREVICAUDA. Big Short-tailed Shrew. *Grande musaraigne.* 47
  B. b. angusta Anderson. Kelly's Camp, Berry Mountain Brook, Gaspé County, Quebec.
  B. b. hooperi Bole and Moulthrop. Lyndon, Caledonia County, Vermont.

* Geographic races are followed by type localities.

B. b. pallida Smith. Wolfville, Kings County, Nova Scotia.
B. b. talpoides (Gapper). Between York and Lake Simcoe, Ontario.

CRYPTOTIS PARVA. Little Short-tailed Shrew. *Petite musaraigne.* 50
C. p. parva (Say). Near Blair, Washington County, Nebraska.

Family TALPIDAE, 52

SCALOPUS AQUATICUS. Eastern Mole. *Taupe à queue glabre.* 52
S. a. machrinus (Rafinesque). Near Lexington, Fayette County, Kentucky.

PARASCALOPS BREWERI. Hairy-tailed Mole. *Taupe à queue velue.* 54
P. breweri (Backman). Eastern North America.

CONDYLURA CRISTATA. Star-nosed Mole. *Condylure étoilé.* 56
C. c. cristata (Linnaeus). Eastern Pennsylvania.
C. c. nigra Smith. Wolfville, Kings County, Nova Scotia.

Order CHIROPTERA 59

Family VESPERTILIONIDAE, 60

MYOTIS LUCIFUGUS. Little Brown Bat. *Chauve-souris brune.* 63
M. l. lucifugus (LeConte). Georgia (near Riceboro, Liberty County ?).

MYOTIS KEENII. Eastern Long-eared Bat or Keen Bat. *Chauve-souris de Keen.* 66
M. k. septentrionalis (Trouessart). Halifax, Nova Scotia.

MYOTIS SUBULATUS. Least Bat or Small-footed Bat. *Chauve-souris pygmée.* 68
M. s. leibii (Audubon and Bachman). Erie County, Ohio.

LASIONYCTERIS NOCTIVAGANS. Silver-haired Bat. *Chauve-souris argentée.* 70
L. noctivagans (LeConte). Eastern United States.

PIPISTRELLUS SUBFLAVUS. Eastern Pipistrelle. *Pipistrelle de l'Est.* 72
P. s. obscurus Miller. Lake George, Warren County, New York.

EPTESICUS FUSCUS. Big Brown Bat. *Grande chauve-souris brune.* 74
E. f. fuscus (Beauvois). Philadelphia, Pennsylvania.
E. f. pallidus Young. Boulder, Boulder County, Colorado.

NYCTICEIUS HUMERALIS. Evening Bat. *Chauve-souris vespérale.* 77
N. h. humeralis (Rafinesque). Kentucky.

LASIURUS BOREALIS. Red Bat. *Chauve-souris rousse.* 78
L. b. borealis (Müller). New York.

LASIURUS CINEREUS. Hoary Bat. *Chauve-souris cendrée.* 81
L. c. cinereus (Beauvois). Philadelphia, Pennsylvania.

Order LAGOMORPHA 83

Family LEPORIDAE, 84

LEPUS AMERICANUS. Varying Hare, Snowshoe Hare. *Lièvre d'Amérique.* 87
  L. a. americanus Erxleben. Hudson Bay, Canada.
  L. a. phaeonotus J. A. Allen. Hallock, Kittson County, Minnesota.
  L. a. struthopus Bangs. Digby, Nova Scotia.
  L. a. virginianus Harlan. Blue Mountains, N.E. of Harrisburg, Pennsylvania.

LEPUS ARCTICUS. Arctic Hare. *Lièvre arctique.* 89
  L. a. bangsii Rhoads. Codroy, Newfoundland.
  L. a. labradorius Miller. Fort Chimo, Quebec.

LEPUS TOWNSENDII. White-tailed Jack Rabbit. *Lièvre de Townsend.* 92
  L. t. campanius Hollister. Plains of Saskatchewan (near Carlton House ?).

LEPUS EUROPAEUS. European Hare. *Lièvre d'Europe.* 95
  L. e. hybridus Desmarest. Central Russia.

SYLVILAGUS FLORIDANUS. Cottontail. *Lapin à queue blanche.* 97
  S. f. mearnsii (J. A. Allen). Fort Snelling, Hennepin County, Minnesota.

SYLVILAGUS TRANSITIONALIS. New England Cottontail. *Lapin de Nouvelle-Angleterre.* 100
  S. transitionalis (Bangs). Liberty Hill, New London County, Connecticut.

ORYCTOLAGUS CUNICULUS. Domestic Rabbit. *Lapin de garenne.* 102
  O. cuniculus (Linnaeus). Germany.

Order RODENTIA 103

Suborder SCIUROMORPHA 105

Family SCIURIDAE, 105

SCIURUS CAROLINENSIS. Eastern Gray Squirrel. *Ecureuil gris.* 108
  S. c. hypophaeus Merriam. Elk River, Sherburne County, Minnesota.
  S. c. pennsylvanicus Ord. Pennsylvania, west of the Alleghany Ridge.

SCIURUS NIGER. Eastern Fox Squirrel. *Ecureuil fauve.* 110
  S. n. rufiventor E. Geoffroy Saint-Hilaire. Mississippi Valley.

TAMIASCIURUS HUDSONICUS. Red Squirrel. *Ecureuil roux.* 112
  T. h. gymnicus (Bangs). Greenville, Piscataquis County, Maine.
  T. h. hudsonicus (Erxleben). Fort Severn, Ontario.
  T. h. laurentianus Anderson. Lac Marchant, Saguenay County, Quebec.
  T. h. loquax (Bangs). Liberty Hill, New London County, Connecticut.
  T. h. minnesota J. A. Allen. Fort Snelling, Hennepin County, Minnesota.
  T. h. regalis A. H. Howell. Belle Isle, Isle Royale, Michigan.
  T. h. ungavensis Anderson (= *T. h. regalis*). Lake Waswanipi, Abitibi District, Quebec.

MARMOTA MONAX. Woodchuck. *Marmotte commune.* 115
 M. m. canadensis (Erxleben). Quebec City, Quebec.
 M. m. ignava (Bangs). Black Bay, Strait of Belle Isle, Labrador.
 M. m. johnsoni Anderson. Percé, Gaspé County, Quebec.
 M. m. rufescens A. H. Howell. Elk River, Sherburne County, Minnesota.

CITELLUS FRANKLINII. Franklin Ground Squirrel. *Spermophile de Franklin.* 118
 C. franklinii (Sabine). Vicinity of Carlton House, Saskatchewan.

TAMIAS STRIATUS. Eastern Chipmunk. *Suisse.* 121
 T. s. griseus Mearns. Fort Snelling, Hennepin County, Minnesota.
 T. s. lysteri (Richardson). Penetanguishene, Georgian Bay, Ontario.
 T. s. quebecensis Cameron. St Félicien, Lake St John County, Quebec.

EUTAMIAS MINIMUS. Least or Western Chipmunk. *Tamia mineur.* 124
 E. m. neglectus J. A. (Allen). Mouth of Montreal River, Lake Superior, Ontario.
 E. m. hudsonius Anderson and Rand. Bird (Mile 349) Hudson Bay Railway, Manitoba.

GLAUCOMYS VOLANS. Eastern Flying Squirrel. *Petit polatouche.* 128
 G. v. volans (Linnaeus). Virginia.

GLAUCOMYS SABRINUS. Northern Flying Squirrel. *Grand polatouche.* 129
 G. s. canescens A. H. Howell. Portage la Prairie, Manitoba.
 G. s. goodwini Anderson. Berry Mountain Camp, Matane County, Quebec.
 G. s. gouldi Anderson. Frizzleton, Inverness County, Cape Breton Island, N.S.
 G. s. macrotis (Mearns). Hunter Mountain, Greene County, New York.
 G. s. makkovikensis (Sornborger). Makkovik, Labrador.
 G. s. sabrinus (Shaw). Fort Severn, Ontario.

Family CASTORIDAE, 133

CASTOR CANADENSIS. Beaver. *Castor.* 133
 C. c. acadicus V. Bailey and Doutt. Nepisiquit River, New Brunswick.
 C. c. caecator Bangs. Near Bay St George, Newfoundland.
 C. c. canadensis Kuhl. Hudson Bay.
 C. c. labradorensis V. Bailey and Doutt. 5 mi. above Grand Falls, Hamilton R., Labrador.
 C. c. michiganensis V. Bailey. Tahquamenaw River, Luce County, Michigan.

Suborder MYOMORPHA 138

Family CRICETIDAE, 138

PEROMYSCUS MANICULATUS. Deer Mouse. *Souris sylvestre.* 140
 P. m. abietorum Bangs. James River, Nova Scotia.
 P. m. anticostiensis Moulthrop. Fox Bay, Anticosti Island, Quebec.
 P. m. argentatus Copeland and Church. Grand Harbour, Grand Manan Island, N.B.
 P. m. bairdii (Hoy and Kennicott). Bloomington, McLean County, Illinois.

P. m. eremus Osgood. Pleasant Bay, Grindstone Island, Magdalen Islands, Quebec.

P. m. gracilis (LeConte). Michigan.

P. m. maniculatus (Wagner). The Moravian Settlements, Labrador.

P. m. plumbeus C. F. Jackson. Pigou River, Saguenay County, Quebec.

PEROMYSCUS LEUCOPUS. White-footed Mouse. *Souris à pattes blanches.* 144

P. l. caudatus Smith. Wolfville, Kings County, Nova Scotia.

P. l. noveboracensis (Fischer). New York.

DICROSTONYX HUDSONIUS. Ungava Varying Lemming. *Lemming d'Ungava.* 147

D. hudsonius (Pallas). Labrador.

SYNAPTOMYS COOPERI. Southern Lemming Mouse or Bog Lemming. *Campagnol-lemming de Cooper.* 150

S. c. cooperi Baird. Unknown (New England ?).

SYNAPTOMYS BOREALIS. Northern Lemming Mouse. *Campagnol-lemming boréal.* 152

S. b. innuitus (True). Fort Chimo, Quebec.

S. b. medioximus Bangs. L'Anse au Loup, Strait of Belle Isle, Labrador.

S. b. smithi Anderson and Rand. Thicket Portage, (Mile 165), Hudson Bay Railway, Man.

S. b. sphagnicola Preble. Fabyans, Coos County, New Hampshire.

CLETHRIONOMYS GAPPERI. Red-backed Mouse. *Campagnol à dos roux de Gapper.* 155

C. g. gapperi (Vigors). Between York and Lake Simcoe, Ontario.

C. g. gaspeanus Anderson. Berry Mountain Camp, Matane County, Quebec.

C. g. hudsonius Anderson. Kapuskasing, Cochrane District, Ontario.

C. g. loringi (Bailey). Portland, Traill County, North Dakota.

C. g. ochraceus (Miller). Mount Washington, Coos County, New Hampshire.

C. g. pallescens Hall and Cockrum. Wolfville, Kings County, Nova Scotia.

C. g. proteus (Bangs). Hamilton Inlet, Labrador.

C. g. ungava (Bailey). Fort Chimo, Quebec.

PHENACOMYS UNGAVA. Eastern Phenacomys. *Phenacomys d'Ungava.* 158

P. u. crassus Bangs. Rigolet, Hamilton Inlet, Labrador.

P. u. mackenzii Preble. Fort Smith, Mackenzie District, Northwest Territories.

P. u. soperi Anderson. Clear Lake, Riding Mountain National Park, Manitoba.

P. u. ungava Merriam. Fort Chimo, Quebec.

MICROTUS PENNSYLVANICUS. Meadow Vole. *Campagnol des champs.* 161

M. p. acadicus Bangs. Digby, Nova Scotia.

M. p. drummondii (Audubon and Bachman). Valley of the Rocky Mts, (Jasper House, Alta ?).

M. p. enixus Bangs. Hamilton Inlet, Labrador.

M. p. fontigenus Bangs (= *M. p. pennsylvanicus*). Lake Edward, Quebec.

M. p. labradorius Bailey. Fort Chimo, Quebec.

M. p. pennsylvanicus (Ord). Philadelphia, Pennsylvania.

M. p. terraenovae (Bangs). Codroy, Newfoundland.

MICROTUS CHROTORRHINUS. Yellow-nosed Vole or Rock Vole. *Campagnol des rochers.* 164

M. c. chrotorrhinus (Miller). Mount Washington, Coos County, New Hampshire.

M. c. ravus Bangs. Black Bay, Strait of Belle Isle, Labrador.

MICROTUS PINETORUM. Pine Mouse or Pine Vole. *Campagnol sylvestre.* 167
  M. p. scalopsoides (Audubon and Bachman). Long Island, New York.

ONDATRA ZIBETHICUS. Common Muskrat. *Rat musqué.* 169
  O. z. albus (Sabine). Cumberland House, Saskatchewan.
  O. z. aquilonius (Bangs). Rigolet, Hamilton Inlet, Labrador.
  O. z. obscurus (Bangs). Codroy, Newfoundland.
  O. z. zibethicus (Linnaeus). Eastern Canada.

Family MURIDAE, 173

RATTUS NORVEGICUS. Norway Rat. *Rat surmulot.* 174
  R. norvegicus (Berkenhout). Norway.

RATTUS RATTUS. Roof Rat and Black Rat. *Rat des toits et Rat noir.* 177
  R. r. alexandrinus (E. Geoffroy Saint-Hilaire). Alexandria, Egypt.
  R. r. rattus (Linnaeus). Upsala, Sweden.

MUS MUSCULUS. House Mouse. *Souris commune.* 178
  M. m. domesticus Rutty. Dublin, Ireland.

Family ZAPODIDAE, 181

ZAPUS HUDSONIUS. Meadow Jumping Mouse. *Souris sauteuse des champs.* 181
  Z. h. acadicus (Dawson). Nova Scotia.
  Z. h. canadensis (Davies). Near Quebec City, Quebec.
  Z. h. hudsonius (Zimmermann). Hudson Bay (Fort Severn, Ontario ?).
  Z. h. ladas Bangs. Rigolet, Hamilton Inlet, Labrador.

NAPAEOZAPUS INSIGNIS. Woodland Jumping Mouse. *Souris sauteuse des bois.* 185
  N. i. abietorum (Preble). Peninsula Harbour, Lake Superior, Ontario.
  N. i. algonquinensis Prince. Smoke Lake, Algonquin Park, Ontario.
  N. i. frutectanus Jackson. Crescent Lake, Oneida County, Wisconsin.
  N. i. gaspensis Anderson. Berry Mountain Brook, Gaspé County, Quebec.
  N. i. insignis (Miller). Restigouche River, New Brunswick.
  N. i. saguenayensis Anderson. Trout Lake, near Moisie Bay, Saguenay County, Quebec.

Suborder HYSTRICOMORPHA 188

Family ERETHIZONTIDAE, 188

ERETHIZON DORSATUM. Porcupine. *Porc-épic.* 188
  E. d. dorsatum (Linnaeus). Eastern Canada.
  E. d. picinum Bangs. L'Anse au Loup, Strait of Belle Isle, Labrador.

Family CAPROMYIDAE, 192

MYOCASTOR COYPUS. Coypu or Nutria. *Nutria.* 192
  M. c. bonariensis (E. Geoffroy Saint-Hilaire). Argentina.

Order CARNIVORA 194

Family CANIDAE, 195

CANIS LATRANS. Brush Wolf or Coyote. *Coyote.* 197
    C. l. thamnos Jackson. Basswood Island, Apostle Islands, Ashland County, Wis.

CANIS LUPUS. Timber Wolf. *Loup.* 200
    C. l. beothucus G. M. Allen and Barbour. Newfoundland.
    C. l. hudsonicus Goldman. Schultz Lake, Keewatin District, Northwest Territories.
    C. l. labradorius Goldman. Fort Chimo, Quebec.
    C. l. lycaon Schreber. Vicinity of Quebec City, Quebec.

CANIS FAMILIARIS. Domestic Dog. *Chien.* 203

ALOPEX LAGOPUS. Arctic Fox. *Renard arctique.* 205
    A. l. innuitus (Merriam). Karogar River, Point Barrow, Alaska.
    A. l. ungava (Merriam). Fort Chimo, Quebec.

VULPES VULPES. Red Fox. *Renard roux.* 210
    V. v. abietorum Merriam. Stuart Lake, British Columbia.
    V. v. fulva (Desmarest). Virginia.
    V. v. rubricosa Bangs. Digby, Nova Scotia.

UROCYON CINEREOARGENTEUS. Gray Fox. *Renard gris.* 215
    U. c. borealis Merriam. Marlboro, 7 mi. from Monadnock, Cheshire County, N.H.
    U. c. cinereoargenteus (Schreber). Eastern North America.
    U. c. ocythous Bangs. Platteville, Grant County, Wisconsin.

Family URSIDAE, 218

URSUS AMERICANUS. Black Bear. *Ours noir.* 219
    U. a. americanus Pallas. Eastern North America.
    U. a. hamiltoni Cameron. Big Falls, Humber River, Newfoundland.

THALARCTOS MARITIMUS. Polar Bear. *Ours polaire.* 222
    T. m. maritimus (Phipps). Spitzbergen.

Family PROCYONIDAE, 226

PROCYON LOTOR. Raccoon. *Raton laveur.* 226
    P. l. hirtus Nelson and Goldman. Elk River, Sherburne County, Minnesota.
    P. l. lotor (Linnaeus). Eastern United States.

Family MUSTELIDAE, 231

MUSTELA ERMINEA. Ermine. *Hermine.* 233
    M. e. bangsi Hall. Elk River, Sherburne County, Minnesota.
    M. e. cicognanii Bonaparte. Northeastern North America.
    M. e. richardsonii Bonaparte. Fort Franklin, Mackenzie District, N.W.T.

MUSTELA FRENATA. Long-tailed Weasel. *Belette à longue queue.* 239
  M. f. noveboracensis (Emmons). Williamstown, Berkshire County, Massachusetts.
  M. f. occisor (Bangs). Bucksport, Hancock County, Maine.

MUSTELA RIXOSA. Least Weasel. *Petite belette.* 241
  M. r. rixosa (Bangs). Osler, Saskatchewan.

MUSTELA VISON. Mink. *Vison.* 245
  M. v. lacustris (Preble). Echimamish River, near Painted Stone Portage, Manitoba.
  M. v. lowii Anderson. Mistassini Post, Mistassini Lake, Quebec.
  M. v. vison Schreber. Eastern Canada.

MUSTELA MACRODON. Sea Mink. *Vison de mer.* 250
  M. macrodon (Prentiss). Shell heaps at Brooklin, Hancock, Maine.

MUSTELA PUTORIUS. Domesticated Ferret. *Putois.* 251
  M. p. furo (Linnaeus). 'Africa'.

MARTES AMERICANA. Marten. *Martre.* 252
  M. a. americana (Turton). Eastern North America.
  M. a. atrata (Bangs). Bay St George, Newfoundland.
  M. a. brumalis (Bangs). Okkak, Labrador.

MARTES PENNANTI. Fisher. *Pékan.* 256
  M. p. pennanti (Erxleben). Eastern Canada.

GULO LUSCUS. Wolverine. *Carcajou.* 260
  G. l. luscus (Linnaeus). Hudson Bay, Canada.

TAXIDEA TAXUS. Badger. *Blaireau.* 263
  T. t. taxus (Schreber). South west of Hudson Bay, Canada.

MEPHITIS MEPHITIS. Striped Skunk. *Mouffette rayée.* 267
  M. m. hudsonica Richardson. Plains of Saskatchewan.
  M. m. mephitis (Schreber). Eastern Canada.
  M. m. nigra (Peale and Beauvois). Maryland.

LUTRA CANADENSIS. Otter. *Loutre de rivière.* 271
  L. c. canadensis (Schreber). Eastern Canada.
  L. c. chimo Anderson. Fort Chimo, Quebec.
  L. c. degener Bangs. Bay St George, Newfoundland.
  L. c. preblei Goldman. Near McTavish Bay, Great Bear Lake, Northwest Territories.

Family FELIDAE, 275

FELIS CONCOLOR. Cougar. Puma. *Couguar.* 276
  F. c. cougar Kerr. Pennsylvania.

FELIS CATUS. Domestic Cat. *Chat domestique.* 279

LYNX CANADENSIS. Canada Lynx. *Lynx du Canada.* 280
  L. c. canadensis Kerr. Eastern Canada.
  L. c. subsolanus Bangs. Codroy, Newfoundland.

LYNX RUFUS. Bobcat. *Lynx roux.* 284
   L. r. gigas Bangs. Fifteen miles back of Bear River, Nova Scotia.
   L. r. rufus (Schreber). New York.
   L. r. superiorensis Peterson and Downing. McIntyre Twp, near Pt Arthur, Ontario.

Order PINNIPEDIA 288

Family ODOBENIDAE, 288

ODOBENUS ROSMARUS. Walrus. *Morse.* 289
   O. r. rosmarus (Linnaeus). Arctic Regions.

Family PHOCIDAE, 292

PHOCA VITULINA. Harbour Seal. *Phoque commun.* 294
   P. v. concolor DeKay. Long Island Sound, Nassau County, New York.
   P. v. mellonae Doutt. Lower Seal Lake, 90 miles east of Richmond Gulf, Quebec.

PHOCA (PUSA) HISPIDA. Ringed Seal. *Phoque annelé.* 296
   P. h. hispida Schreber. Coasts of Greenland and Labrador.

PHOCA (PAGOPHILUS) GROENLANDICA. Harp or Greenland Seal. *Phoque du Groenland.* 299
   P. groenlandica Erxleben. Greenland and Newfoundland.

ERIGNATHUS BARBATUS. Bearded Seal, Square-Flipper. *Phoque barbu.* 302
   E. barbatus (Erxleben). Coasts of Scotland, southern Greenland, and Iceland.

HALICHOERUS GRYPUS. Gray Seal, Horsehead Seal. *Phoque gris.* 305
   H. grypus (Fabricius). Greenland.

CYSTOPHORA CRISTATA. Hooded Seal, Bladdernose Seal. *Phoque à capuchon.* 309
   C. cristata (Erxleben). Southern Greenland and Newfoundland.

Order PERISSODACTYLA 312

Family EQUIDAE, 312

EQUUS CABALLUS. Domestic Horse. *Cheval domestique.* 313

EQUUS ASINUS. Ass, Donkey, Burro. *Âne.* 314

Order ARTIODACTYLA 315

Suborder SUIFORMES 315

Family SUIDAE, 315

SUS SCROFA. Domestic Pig. *Cochon domestique.* 316

Suborder RUMINANTIA 317

Family CERVIDAE, 317

CERVUS CANADENSIS. Wapiti, American Elk. *Wapiti.* 318
  C. c. canadensis Erxleben. Eastern Canada (Quebec).
  C. c. manitobensis Millais. Manitoba and eastern Saskatchewan.
  C. c. nelsoni V. Bailey. Yellowstone National Park, Wyoming.

ODOCOILEUS VIRGINIANUS. White-tailed Deer. *Cerf du Viriginie.* 322
  O. v. borealis Miller. Bucksport, Hancock County, Maine.
  O. v. dacotensis Goldman and Kellogg. White Earth R., Mountrail Co., North Dakota.

ALCES ALCES. Moose. *Orignal.* 326
  A. a. americana (Clinton). Country north of Whitestown, New York.
  A. a. andersoni Peterson. Fifteen miles east of Brandon, Manitoba.

RANGIFER TARANDUS. Caribou. *Caribou.* 330
  R. t. caribou (Gmelin). Eastern Canada.
  R. t. groenlandicus (Linnaeus). Southwest coast of Greenland.

Family BOVIDAE, 335

BISON BISON. Bison. *Bison d'Amérique.* 336
BOS TAURUS. Domestic Cow. *Vache domestique.* 337
OVIS ARIES. Domestic Sheep. *Mouton domestique.* 338
CAPRA HIRCUS. Domestic Goat. *Chèvre domestique.* 339

Order CETACEA 340

Suborder ODONTOCETI 341

Family ZIPHIIDAE, 342

MESOPLODON BIDENS. Sowerby Beaked Whale. *Baleine à bec de Sowerby.* 343
  M. bidens (Sowerby). Coast of Elginshire (Moray), Scotland.

MESOPLODON DENSIROSTRIS. Blainville Beaked Whale. *Baleine à bec de Blainville.* 345
  M. densirostris (Blainville). Type locality unknown.

MESOPLODON MIRUS. True Beaked Whale. *Baleine à bec de True.* 347
  M. mirus True. Beaufort Harbour, Carteret County, North Carolina.

HYPEROODON AMPULLATUS. Bottlenose Whale. *Baleine à bec commune.* 349
  H. ampullatus (Forster). Maldon, Essex, England.

Family PHYSETERIDAE, 351

PHYSETER CATODON. Sperm Whale. *Cachalot macrocéphale.* 351
  P. catodon Linnaeus. North Atlantic.

Family KOGIIDAE, 354

KOGIA BREVICEPS. Pygmy Sperm Whale. *Cachalot pygmée.* 354
  K. breviceps (Blainville). Region of Cape of Good Hope, South Africa.

Family MONODONTIDAE, 357

DELPHINAPTERUS LEUCAS. White Whale, Beluga. *Béluga ou Marsouin blanc.* 357
  D. leucas (Pallas). Mouth of Ob River, northeastern Siberia, U.S.S.R.

MONODON MONOCEROS. Narwhal. *Narval.* 360
  M. monoceros Linnaeus. Arctic Seas.

Family DELPHINIDAE, 362

DELPHINUS DELPHIS. Common Dolphin. *Dauphin commun.* 364
  D. delphis Linnaeus. European Seas.

TURSIOPS TRUNCATUS. Bottle-nosed Dolphin. *Dauphin à gros nez.* 366
  T. truncatus (Montagu). Totnes, Devonshire, England.

LAGENORHYNCHUS ALBIROSTRIS. White-beaked Dolphin. *Dauphin à nez blanc.* 369
  L. albirostris Gray. Great Yarmouth, Norfolk, England.

LAGENORHYNCHUS ACUTUS. White-sided Dolphin. *Dauphin à flancs blancs.* 371
  L. acutus (Gray). Type locality unknown.

ORCINUS ORCA. Atlantic Killer Whale. *Épaulard.* 373
  O. orca Linnaeus. European Seas.

GLOBICEPHALA MELAENA. Pilot Whale, Blackfish, Pothead Whale. *Globicéphale noir.* 376
  G. melaena (Traill). Scapay Bay, Pomona, Orkney Islands, Scotland.

PHOCOENA PHOCOENA. Harbour Porpoise. *Marsouin commun.* 379
  P. phocoena (Linnaeus). Swedish Seas.

Suborder MYSTICETI 381

Family BALAENOPTERIDAE, 382

BALAENOPTERA PHYSALUS. Common Finback or Fin Whale. *Rorqual commun.* 383
  B. physalus (Linnaeus). European Seas.

BALAENOPTERA BOREALIS. Sei or Pollack Whale. *Rorqual sei.* 386
  B. borealis Lesson. Gromitz, Lübeck Bay, Schleswig-Holstein, Germany.

BALAENOPTERA ACUTOROSTRATA. Little Piked or Minke Whale. *Petit rorqual.* 388
  B. acutorostrata Lacépède. European Seas.

SIBBALDUS MUSCULUS. Blue or Sulphur-bottom Whale. *Baleine bleue.* 391
  S. musculus (Linnaeus). Firth of Forth, Scotland.

MEGAPTERA NOVAEANGLIAE. Humpback Whale. *Baleine à bosse, Mégaptère.* 394
 M. *novaeangliae* (Borowski). Coast of New England.

Family BALAENIDAE, 397

EUBALAENA GLACIALIS. North Atlantic Right Whale. *Baleine noire.* 398
 E. *glacialis* (Borowski). North Cape, Norway.

BALAENA MYSTICETUS. Bowhead or Greenland Right Whale. *Baleine boréale.* 400
 B. *mysticetus* Linnaeus. Greenland Seas.

GLOSSARY 404

BIBLIOGRAPHY 409

INDEX 451

Colour Illustrations

Following page 240

I. SOME EASTERN-CANADIAN BATS: Hoary Bat, Silver-haired Bat, Little Brown Bat, Big Brown Bat, Red Bat, Eastern Pipistrelle

II. SOME EASTERN-CANADIAN *Sciuridae:* Eastern Chipmunk, Red Squirrel, Western Chipmunk, Franklin Ground Squirrel

III. SOME EASTERN-CANADIAN MICROTINE RODENTS: Meadow Vole, Eastern Phenacomys, Rock Vole, Red-backed Mouse, Northern Lemming Mouse

IV. EASTERN-CANADIAN FOXES: Arctic Fox, Gray Fox, Red Fox

V. SOME EASTERN-CANADIAN *Mustelidae:* Ermine, Marten, Mink, Fisher

VI. CANADA LYNX AND BOBCAT

VII. MOOSE

VIII. CARIBOU

Line Illustrations

Fig.

1. Skull of the DOMESTIC RABBIT. 21
2. Skull of the DOMESTIC CAT. 23
3. Skeleton of the DOMESTIC CAT. 24
4. COMMON OPOSSUM, *Didelphis marsupialis.* 28
5. Skull of *Didelphis marsupialis.* 29
6. LONG-TAILED SHREWS. 33
7. SHREW TEETH compared. 34
8. Skull of *Sorex cinereus.* 34
9. Skull of *Sorex fumeus.* 37
10. Skull of *Sorex arcticus.* 39
11. Skull of *Sorex dispar.* 42
12. Skull of *Sorex palustris.* 43
13. Skull of *Microsorex hoyi.* 45
14. BIG SHORT-TAILED SHREW, *Blarina brevicauda.* 47
15. Skull of *Blarina brevicauda.* 48
16. LITTLE SHORT-TAILED SHREW, *Cryptotis parva.* 51
17. Skull of *Cryptotis parva.* 51
18. EASTERN MOLE, *Scalopus aquaticus.* 53
19. Skull of *Scalopus aquaticus.* 53
20. HAIRY-TAILED MOLE, *Parascalops breweri.* 55
21. Skull of *Parascalops breweri.* 55
22. STAR-NOSED MOLE, *Condylura cristata.* 57

23. Skull of *Condylura cristata.* 57
24. BAT EARS compared. 61
25. LITTLE BROWN BAT, *Myotis lucifugus.* 63
26. Skull of *Myotis lucifugus.* 63
27. EASTERN LONG-EARED BAT, *Myotis keenii.* 66
28. Skull of *Myotis keenii.* 66
29. LEAST BAT, *Myotis subulatus.* 68
30. Skull of *Myotis subulatus.* 68
31. SILVER-HAIRED BAT, *Lasionycteris noctivagans.* 71
32. Skull of *Lasionycteris noctivagans.* 71
33. EASTERN PIPISTRELLE, *Pipistrellus subflavus.* 73
34. Skull of *Pipistrellus subflavus.* 73
35. BIG BROWN BAT, *Eptesicus fuscus.* 75
36. Skull of *Eptesicus fuscus.* 75
37. Skull of *Nycticeius humeralis.* 77
38. RED BAT, *Lasiurus borealis.* 79
39. Skull of *Lasiurus borealis.* 79
40. HOARY BAT, *Lasiurus cinereus.* 81
41. Skull of *Lasiurus cinereus.* 82
42. Unusual growth of incisor teeth of an ARCTIC HARE. 85
43. VARYING HARE, *Lepus americanus.* 86

44. Skull of *Lepus americanus*. 87

45. ARCTIC HARE, *Lepus arcticus*. 90

46. Skull of *Lepus arcticus*. 91

47. WHITE-TAILED JACK RABBIT, *Lepus townsendii*. 92

48. Skull of *Lepus townsendii*. 93

49. EUROPEAN HARE, *Lepus europaeus*. 94

50. Skull of *Lepus europaeus*. 95

51. COTTONTAIL, *Sylvilagus floridanus*. 98

52. Skull of *Sylvilagus floridanus*. 99

53. NEW ENGLAND COTTONTAIL, *Sylvilagus transitionalis*. 100

54. Skull of *Sylvilagus transitionalis*. 101

55. Skull of DOMESTIC RABBIT, *Oryctolagus cuniculus*. 102

56. Examples of malocclusions in BEAVER, WOODCHUCK, and NORWAY RAT. 103

57. EASTERN GRAY SQUIRREL, *Sciurus carolinensis*. 107

58. Skull of *Sciurus carolinensis*. 109

59. EASTERN FOX SQUIRREL, *Sciurus niger*. 110.

60. Skull of *Sciurus niger*. 111

61. RED SQUIRREL, *Tamiasciurus hudsonicus*. 112

62. Skull of *Tamiasciurus hudsonicus*. 113

63. WOODCHUCK, *Marmota monax*. 115

64. Skull of *Marmota monax*. 117

65. FRANKLIN GROUND SQUIRREL, *Citellus franklinii*. 119

66. Skull of *Citellus franklinii*. 119

67. EASTERN CHIPMUNK, *Tamias striatus*. 121

68. Skull of *Tamias striatus*. 122

69. WESTERN CHIPMUNK, *Eutamias minimus*. 124

70. Skull of *Eutamias minimus*. 125

71. EASTERN FLYING SQUIRREL, *Glaucomys volans*. 127

72. Skull of *Glaucomys volans*. 128

73. NORTHERN FLYING SQUIRREL, *Glaucomys sabrinus*. 130

74. Skull of *Glaucomys sabrinus*. 131

75. BEAVER, *Castor canadensis*. 134

76. Skull of *Castor canadensis*. 135

77. Tooth enamel patterns of MICROTINE RODENTS (uppers above). 138

78. PRAIRIE DEER MOUSE, *Peromyscus maniculatus bairdii*. 141

79. WOODLAND DEER MOUSE, *Peromyscus maniculatus gracilis*. 141

80. Skull of *Peromyscus maniculatus bairdii*. 142

81. Skull of *Peromyscus maniculatus gracilis*. 143

82. WHITE-FOOTED MOUSE, *Peromyscus leucopus*. 145

83. Skull of *Peromyscus leucopus*. 146

84. UNGAVA VARYING LEMMING, *Dicrostonyx hudsonius*. 147

85. Skull of *Dicrostonyx hudsonius*. 148

86. Feet of *Dicrostonyx hudsonius*. 148

87. SOUTHERN LEMMING MOUSE, *Synaptomys cooperi*. 150

88. Skull of *Synaptomys cooperi*. 151

89. Feet of NORTHERN LEMMING MOUSE, *Synaptomys borealis*. 153

90. Skull of *Synaptomys borealis*. 154

91. RED-BACKED MOUSE, *Clethrionomys gapperi*. 156

92. Skull of *Clethrionomys gapperi*. 157

93. EASTERN PHENACOMYS, *Phenacomys ungava.* 158

94. Skull of *Phenacomys ungava.* 159

95. MEADOW VOLE, *Microtus pennsylvanicus.* 162

96. Skull of *Microtus pennsylvanicus.* 163

97. YELLOW-NOSED VOLE, *Microtus chrotorrhinus.* 165

98. Skull of *Microtus chrotorrhinus.* 166

99. PINE MOUSE, *Microtus pinetorum.* 167

100. Skull of *Microtus pinetorum.* 168

101. COMMON MUSKRAT, *Ondatra zibethicus.* 169

102. Skull of *Ondatra zibethicus.* 170

103. NORWAY RAT, *Rattus norvegicus.* 174

104. Skull of *Rattus norvegicus.* 175

105. Upper cheek teeth of *Rattus.* 176

106. HOUSE MOUSE, *Mus musculus.* 178

107. Skull of *Mus musculus.* 179

108. MEADOW JUMPING MOUSE, *Zapus hudsonius.* 182

109. Skull of *Zapus hudsonius.* 183

110. WOODLAND JUMPING MOUSE, *Napaeozapus insignis.* 185

111. Skull of *Napaeozapus insignis.* 186

112. PORCUPINE, *Erethizon dorsatum.* 189

113. Skull of *Erethizon dorsatum.* 190

114. Skull of NUTRIA, *Myocastor coypus.* 193

115. BRUSH WOLF, *Canis latrans.* 198

116. Skull of *Canis latrans.* 199

117. TIMBER WOLF, *Canis lupus.* 201

118. Skull of *Canis lupus.* 202

119. Skull of DOMESTIC DOG, *Canis familiaris.* 204

120. Arctic fox, *Alopex lagopus.* 206

121. Skull of *Alopex lagopus.* 207

122. RED FOX, *Vulpes vulpes.* 211

123. Skull of *Vulpes vulpes.* 212

124. GRAY FOX, *Urocyon cinereoargenteus.* 215

125. Skull of *Urocyon cinereoargenteus.* 216

126. BLACK BEAR, *Ursus americanus.* 219

127. Skull of *Ursus americanus.* 220

128. POLAR BEAR, *Thalarctos maritimus.* 223

129. Skull of *Thalarctos maritimus.* 224

130. RACCOON, *Procyon lotor.* 227

131. Skull of *Procyon lotor.* 228

132. ERMINE, *Mustela erminea.* 234

133. Skull of *Mustela erminea.* 235

134. LONG-TAILED WEASEL, *Mustela frenata.* 238

135. Skull of *Mustela frenata.* 239

136. LEAST WEASEL, *Mustela rixosa.* 241

137. Skull of *Mustela rixosa.* 242

138. MINK, *Mustela vison.* 244

139. Skull of *Mustela vison.* 246

140. Skull of SEA MINK, *Mustela macrodon* (Type specimen). 250

141. Skull of DOMESTICATED FERRET, *Mustela putorius.* 251

142. MARTEN, *Martes americana.* 253

143. Skull of *Martes americana.* 254

144. FISHER, *Martes pennanti.* 256

145. Skull of *Martes pennanti* (male). 257

146. Skull of *Martes pennanti* (female). 257

147. WOLVERINE, *Gulo luscus.* 260

148. Skull of *Gulo luscus.* 261

149. BADGER, *Taxidea taxus.* 263

150. Skull of *Taxidea taxus.* 264

151. STRIPED SKUNK, *Mephitis mephitis.* 266

152. Skull of *Mephitis mephitis.* 268

153. OTTER, *Lutra canadensis.* 271

154. Skull of *Lutra canadensis.* 272

155. COUGAR, *Felis concolor.* 276

156. Skull of *Felis concolor.* 277

157. Skull of DOMESTIC CAT, *Felis catus.* 279

158. CANADA LYNX, *Lynx canadensis.* 281

159. Skull of *Lynx canadensis.* 281

160. BOBCAT, *Lynx rufus.* 284

161. Skull of *Lynx rufus.* 285

162. WALRUS, *Odobenus rosmarus.* 289

163. Skull of *Odobenus rosmarus.* 290

164. HARBOUR SEAL, *Phoca vitulina.* 294

165. Skull of *Phoca vitulina.* 295

166. RINGED SEAL, *Phoca hispida.* 297

167. Skull of *Phoca hispida.* 298

168. HARP SEAL, *Phoca groenlandica.* 300

169. Skull of *Phoca groenlandica.* 301

170. BEARDED SEAL, *Erignathus barbatus.* 303

171. Skull of *Erignathus barbatus.* 303

172. GRAY SEAL, *Halichoerus grypus.* 306

173. Skull of *Halichoerus grypus.* 306

174. HOODED SEAL, *Cystophora cristata.* 308

175. Skull of *Cystophora cristata.* 310

176. Skull of DOMESTIC HORSE, *Equus caballus.* 313

177. Skull of DOMESTIC PIG, *Sus scrofa.* 316

178. WAPITI, *Cervus canadensis.* 319

179. Skull of *Cervus canadensis.* 320

180. WHITE-TAILED DEER, *Odocoileus virginianus.* 323

181. Skull of *Odocoileus virginianus.* 324

182. MOOSE, *Alces alces.* 327

183. Skull of *Alces alces.* 328

184. WOODLAND CARIBOU, *Rangifer tarandus caribou.* 331

185. Skull of *Rangifer tarandus caribou.* 332

186. Skull of BISON, *Bison bison.* 336

187. Skull of DOMESTIC COW, *Bos taurus.* 337

188. Skull of DOMESTIC SHEEP, *Ovis aries.* 338

189. Skull of DOMESTIC GOAT, *Capra hircus.* 339

190. SOWERBY BEAKED WHALE, *Mesoplodon bidens.* 343

191. Skull of *Mesoplodon bidens.* 343

192. BLAINVILLE BEAKED WHALE, *Mesoplodon densirostris.* 345

193. Skull of *Mesoplodon densirostris.* 345

194. TRUE BEAKED WHALE, *Mesoplodon mirus.* 347

195. Skull of *Mesoplodon mirus.* 347

196. BOTTLENOSE WHALE, *Hyperoodon ampullatus.* 349

197. Skull of *Hyperoodon ampullatus.* 350

198. SPERM WHALE, *Physeter catodon.* 352

199. Skull of *Physeter catodon.* 353

200. PYGMY SPERM WHALE, *Kogia breviceps.* 355

201. Skull of *Kogia breviceps.* 355

202. WHITE WHALE, *Delphinapterus leucas.* 358

203. Skull of *Delphinapterus leucas.* 358

204. NARWHAL, *Monodon monoceros.* 360

205. Skull of *Monodon monoceros.* 361

206. COMMON DOLPHIN, *Delphinus delphis.* 364

207. Skull of *Delphinus delphis.* 365

208. BOTTLE-NOSED DOLPHIN, *Tursiops truncatus.* 366

209. Skull of *Tursiops truncatus.* 367

210. WHITE-BEAKED DOLPHIN, *Lagenorhynchus albirostris.* 370

211. Skull of *Lagenorhynchus albirostris.* 370

212. WHITE-SIDED DOLPHIN, *Lagenorhynchus acutus.* 371

213. Skull of *Lagenorhynchus acutus.* 372

214. ATLANTIC KILLER WHALE, *Orcinus orca.* 374

215. Skull of *Orcinus orca.* 375

216. PILOT WHALE, *Globicephala melaena.* 376

217. Skull of *Globicephala melaena.* 377

218. HARBOUR PORPOISE, *Phocoena phocoena.* 379

219. Skull of *Phocoena phocoena.* 380

220. COMMON FINBACK WHALE, *Balaenoptera physalus.* 384

221. Skull of *Balaenoptera physalus.* 384

222. SEI WHALE, *Balaenoptera borealis.* 387

223. Skull of *Balaenoptera borealis.* 387

224. LITTLE PIKED WHALE, *Balaenoptera acutorostrata.* 389

225. Skull of *Balaenoptera acutorostrata.* 389

226. BLUE WHALE, *Sibbaldus musculus.* 391

227. Skull of *Sibbaldus musculus.* 392

228. HUMPBACK WHALE, *Megaptera novaeangliae.* 394

229. Skull of *Megaptera novaeangliae.* 395

230. NORTH ATLANTIC RIGHT WHALE, *Eubalaena glacialis.* 398

231. Skull of *Eubalaena glacialis.* 399

232. BOWHEAD WHALE, *Balaena mysticetus.* 401

233. Skull of *Balaena mysticetus.* 401

Distribution Maps

1. COMMON OPOSSUM, *Didelphis marsupialis.* 28

2. COMMON SHREW, *Sorex cinereus.* 35

3. SMOKY SHREW, *Sorex fumeus.* 37

4. ARCTIC SHREW, *Sorex arcticus.* 39

5. GASPÉ SHREW, *Sorex gaspensis* and GRAY LONG-TAILED SHREW, *Sorex dispar.* 41

6. WATER SHREW, *Sorex palustris.* 43

7. PYGMY SHREW, *Microsorex hoyi.* 45

8. BIG SHORT-TAILED SHREW, *Blarina brevicauda.* 48

9. LITTLE SHORT-TAILED SHREW, *Cryptotis parva.* 51

10. EASTERN MOLE, *Scalopus aquaticus.* 53

11. HAIRY-TAILED MOLE, *Parascalops breweri.* 56

12. STAR-NOSED MOLE, *Condylura cristata.* 58

13. LITTLE BROWN BAT, *Myotis lucifugus.* 64

14. EASTERN LONG-EARED BAT, *Myotis keenii.* 67

15. LEAST BAT, *Myotis subulatus.* 69

16. SILVER-HAIRED BAT, *Lasionycteris noctivagans.* 71

17. EASTERN PIPISTRELLE, *Pipistrellus subflavus.* 73

18. BIG BROWN BAT, *Eptesicus fuscus.* 76

19. EVENING BAT, *Nycticeius humeralis.* 77

20. RED BAT, *Lasiurus borealis.* 80

21. HOARY BAT, *Lasiurus cinereus.* 82

22. VARYING HARE, *Lepus americanus.* 88

23. ARCTIC HARE, *Lepus arcticus.* 91

24. WHITE-TAILED JACK RABBIT, *Lepus townsendii.* 93

25. EUROPEAN HARE, *Lepus europaeus.* 96

26. COTTONTAIL, *Sylvilagus floridanus.* 99

27. NEW ENGLAND COTTONTAIL, *Sylvilagus transitionalis.* 101

28. EASTERN GRAY SQUIRREL, *Sciurus carolinensis.* 109

29. EASTERN FOX SQUIRREL, *Sciurus niger.* 111

30. RED SQUIRREL, *Tamiasciurus hudsonicus.* 113

31. WOODCHUCK, *Marmota monax.* 117

32. FRANKLIN GROUND SQUIRREL, *Citellus franklinii.* 120

33. EASTERN CHIPMUNK, *Tamias striatus.* 122

34. WESTERN CHIPMUNK, *Eutamias minimus.* 125

35. EASTERN FLYING SQUIRREL, *Glaucomys volans.* 129

36. NORTHERN FLYING SQUIRREL, *Glaucomys sabrinus.* 131

37. BEAVER, *Castor canadensis.* 135

38. DEER MOUSE, *Peromyscus maniculatus.* 142

39. WHITE-FOOTED MOUSE, *Peromyscus leucopus.* 145

40. UNGAVA VARYING LEMMING, *Dicrostonyx hudsonius*. 148

41. SOUTHERN LEMMING MOUSE, *Synaptomys cooperi*. 151

42. NORTHERN LEMMING MOUSE, *Synaptomys borealis*. 154

43. RED-BACKED MOUSE, *Clethrionomys gapperi*. 156

44. EASTERN PHENACOMYS, *Phenacomys ungava*. 159

45. MEADOW VOLE, *Microtus pennsylvanicus*. 163

46. YELLOW-NOSED VOLE, *Microtus chrotorrhinus*. 165

47. PINE MOUSE, *Microtus pinetorum*. 168

48. COMMON MUSKRAT, *Ondatra zibethicus*. 170

49. NORWAY RAT, *Rattus norvegicus* and BLACK RAT, *Rattus rattus*. 175

50. HOUSE MOUSE, *Mus musculus*. 179

51. MEADOW JUMPING MOUSE, *Zapus hudsonius*. 183

52. WOODLAND JUMPING MOUSE, *Napaeozapus insignis*. 186

53. PORCUPINE, *Erethizon dorsatum*. 190

54. BRUSH WOLF, *Canis latrans*. 199

55. TIMBER WOLF, *Canis lupus*. 202

56. ARCTIC FOX, *Alopex lagopus*. 207

57. RED FOX, *Vulpes vulpes*. 212

58. GRAY FOX, *Urocyon cinereoargenteus*. 216

59. BLACK BEAR, *Ursus americanus*. 220

60. POLAR BEAR, *Thalarctos maritimus*. 224

61. RACCOON, *Procyon lotor*. 228

62. ERMINE, *Mustela erminea*. 235

63. LONG-TAILED WEASEL, *Mustela frenata*. 239

64. LEAST WEASEL, *Mustela rixosa*. 242

65. MINK, *Mustela vison*. 246

66. MARTEN, *Martes americana*. 254

67. FISHER, *Martes pennanti*. 258

68. WOLVERINE, *Gulo luscus*. 261

69. BADGER, *Taxidea taxus*. 264

70. STRIPED SKUNK, *Mephitis mephitis*. 268

71. OTTER, *Lutra canadensis*. 272

72. COUGAR, *Felis concolor*. 277

73. CANADA LYNX, *Lynx canadensis*. 282

74. BOBCAT, *Lynx rufus*. 285

75. WALRUS, *Odobenus rosmarus*. 290

76. HARBOUR SEAL, *Phoca vitulina*. 295

77. RINGED SEAL, *Phoca hispida*. 298

78. HARP SEAL, *Phoca groenlandica*. 301

79. BEARDED SEAL, *Erignathus barbatus*. 304

80. GRAY SEAL, *Halichoerus grypus*. 307

81. HOODED SEAL, *Cystophora cristata*. 310

82. WAPITI, *Cervus canadensis*. 320

83. WHITE-TAILED DEER, *Odocoileus virginianus*. 325

84. MOOSE, *Alces alces*. 329

85. CARIBOU, *Rangifer tarandus*. 333

86. SOWERBY BEAKED WHALE, *Mesoplodon bidens*. 344

87. BLAINVILLE BEAKED WHALE, *Mesoplodon densirostris*. 346

88. TRUE BEAKED WHALE, *Mesoplodon mirus*. 348

89. BOTTLENOSE WHALE, *Hyperoodon ampullatus*. 350

90. SPERM WHALE, *Physeter catodon*. 353

91. PYGMY SPERM WHALE, *Kogia breviceps*. 356

92. WHITE WHALE, *Delphinapterus leucas*. 359

93. NARWHAL, *Monodon monoceros*. 361

94. COMMON DOLPHIN, *Delphinus delphis*. 365

95. BOTTLE-NOSED DOLPHIN, *Tursiops truncatus*. 368

96. WHITE-BEAKED DOLPHIN, *Lagenorhynchus albirostris*. 370

97. WHITE-SIDED DOLPHIN, *Lagenorhynchus acutus*. 372

98. ATLANTIC KILLER WHALE, *Orcinus orca*. 375

99. PILOT WHALE, *Globicephala melaena*. 377

100. HARBOUR PORPOISE, *Phocoena phocoena*. 380

101. COMMON FINBACK WHALE, *Balaenoptera physalus*. 385

102. SEI WHALE, *Balaenoptera borealis*. 387

103. LITTLE PIKED WHALE, *Balaenoptera acutorostrata*. 389

104. BLUE WHALE, *Sibbaldus musculus*. 393

105. HUMPBACK WHALE, *Megaptera novaeangliae*. 395

106. RIGHT WHALE, *Eubalaena glacialis*. 399

107. BOWHEAD WHALE, *Balaena mysticetus*. 402

Tables

		Page
1.	PRODUCTION OF BEAVER PELTS IN EASTERN CANADA, 1950–60	137
2.	PRODUCTION OF MUSKRAT PELTS IN EASTERN CANADA, 1950–60	172
3.	PRODUCTION OF ARCTIC FOX PELTS (WHITE COLOUR-PHASE) IN EASTERN CANADA, 1950–60	209
4.	PRODUCTION OF WILD RED, CROSS, AND SILVER FOX PELTS IN EASTERN CANADA, 1950–60	214
5.	PRODUCTION OF RACCOON PELTS IN EASTERN CANADA, 1950–60	230
6.	PRODUCTION OF ERMINE PELTS IN EASTERN CANADA, 1950–60	237
7.	PRODUCTION OF RANCH MINK PELTS IN EASTERN CANADA, 1950–60	248
8.	PRODUCTION OF WILD MINK PELTS IN EASTERN CANADA, 1950–60	249
9.	PRODUCTION OF MARTEN PELTS IN EASTERN CANADA, 1950–60	255
10.	PRODUCTION OF FISHER PELTS IN EASTERN CANADA, 1950–60	259
11.	PRODUCTION OF STRIPED SKUNK PELTS IN EASTERN CANADA, 1950–60	270
12.	PRODUCTION OF OTTER PELTS IN EASTERN CANADA, 1950–60	274
13.	PRODUCTION OF LYNX PELTS IN EASTERN CANADA, 1950–60	283
14.	PRODUCTION OF BOBCAT PELTS IN EASTERN CANADA, 1950–60	287

Preface

This book was started with the aim of providing a treatise suitable for high-school and university use; but in its finished form, which combines essential scientific details with descriptive information that can be easily understood by the layman, it will, I hope, be of value to everyone with a serious interest in mammals. In organizing the enormous mass of data available to me, I have tried to make the book useful to a wide audience without sacrificing accuracy and readability on the one hand and scientific detail and substantiating evidence on the other.

Since many of the readers of this work will not have ready access to some of the standard reference books on mammals, I have included an introduction on the classification of mammals, the mammalian skull, and the mammalian skeleton, and a Glosary of terms that may not be familiar to the beginning student of mammalogy. There is also an extensive Bibliography.

Full trinomial names with authorities and type localities have been listed in the Contents. No attempt has been made to revise or validate the subspecies listed; in some species it seems quite apparent that a thorough study will reduce the number of racial names that are currently recognized. The treatment of geographic races or subspecies has been limited to a listing of the generally recognized forms under the heading of Distribution and Variation.

The skull alone, or the whole animal, may be identified as far as possible by the keys. As a Curator in a museum that receives a steady stream of requests to identify finds that turn out to be the bones of domestic animals, I have included a treatment of the skulls of domestic and introduced species.

For many species the detailed distribution maps are the first available and in the majority of cases they differ substantially from those published in the past. Many species reach their northern limits of distribution in eastern Canada and it is hoped that the details given here will serve as a basis for further study. Each solid dot represents one or more specimens currently preserved in a permanent museum collection. Open squares represent other records not substantiated by specimens. To list the names of these mapped localities would perhaps double the size of this volume; they are preserved in the files of the Department of Mammalogy of the Royal Ontario Museum, University of Toronto, and are available for further use.

The total fauna treated here consists of 122 species of which 102 are native, 9 are introduced, 10 are domestic, and one has become extinct (the sea mink). The wapiti has been extirpated as a native species and the original geographic race has become extinct; existing wapiti have been introduced. Counting the geographic races, there are 234 forms listed, including 213 native, 9 introduced, 10 domestic, and 2 extinct forms. These are distributed among 10 orders (9 native, 1 domestic), 30 families (26 native, 2 introduced, 2 domestic), and 85 genera (75 native, 4 introduced, and 6 domestic). While I have summarized, as briefly as was practicable, the information provided by many authors in my synopsis of each species, I have added personal knowledge and a considerable amount of original data.

Direct quotations and literature citations have been deleted for brevity and ease of reading and selected references have been provided for each species instead.

Eastern Canada is considered in this study to include the provinces of Ontario, Quebec, New Brunswick, Nova Scotia, Prince Edward Island, and Newfoundland (including Labrador),* and the adjacent off-shore waters. The islands in James Bay and eastern Hudson Bay, politically a part of the Northwest Territories, are also included. The land area—approximately 1,215,590 square miles—extends about 1800 miles from east to west and 1400 miles from north to south.

* All references to Newfoundland refer to the island; that part of Newfoundland on the mainland is called Labrador.

Acknowledgements

As this book has been ten years in preparation, it is not possible to acknowledge all the assistance I have received. I have been aided by too many people to thank everyone and I must express my gratitude collectively for much of the help that was given to me.

A good deal of the book was written as part of the research program of the Department of Mammalogy in the Royal Ontario Museum, University of Toronto, whose collections provided the foundation for my work. My former secretary, Mrs Shirley Heenan, deserves special thanks for carrying a heavy burden in preparing, organizing, and transcribing a vast amount of data. I am also grateful to Stuart C. Downing and A. A. Outram of the Department of Mammalogy and to the librarians of the Museum for many hours of labour on my behalf. I am aware of my good fortune in obtaining the artistic skills of Karl S. Pogany, who drew most of the illustrations while he was a staff member of my department, and of Terry M. Shortt, Erik Thorn, John Crosby, and Paul Geraghty.

I am also much obliged to Dr William E. Schivill who checked the manuscript of the whale section and provided many valuable suggestions for its improvement, though any deficiencies in this part of the book must be attributed to me.

The staff and facilities of the following institutions assisted immeasurably in providing me with information about specimens of the eastern-Canadian mammals in their collections:

Arctic Unit, Fisheries Research Board of Canada, Montreal
American Museum of Natural History, New York
British Museum (Natural History), London
Carnegie Museum, Pittsburgh
Chicago Natural History Museum

Department of Conservation, Cornell University
Museum of Comparative Zoology, Harvard University
Museum of Natural History, University of Kansas
Museum of Zoology, University of Michigan
National Museum of Canada
Ontario Department of Lands and Forests
Philadelphia Academy of Science
United States Fish and Wildlife Service
United States National Museum

I am most grateful to Mr Vianney Legendre and Mr Claude Minguy of the Department of Fish and Game, Quebec Wildlife Service, and to the Comité des noms français de mammifères du Québec of the Société zoologique de Québec, Incorporée, for providing an approved list of French names for the species of mammals in eastern Canada. The Comité—consisting of Richard Bernard, Raymond Cayouette, Clément Delisle, Pierre Desmeules, and Gaston Moisan—very kindly held special meetings at Laval University to complete this task for me.

During the research that preceded the final organization of my material, I received grants from the National Research Council of Canada, the Ontario Research Council, and the Canadian National Sportsmen's Show; without this financial aid I could not have continued in my work. The last-named organization, through the good offices of its President, Frank H. Kortright, generously provided funds to underwrite the cost of coloured illustrations, making their inclusion in this book possible.

I would like to express my appreciation to the Oxford University Press and especially to William Toye, my editor, who turned a vast amount of technical information into a readable text and whose design for the book has made the material it contains easy of access.

Like most authors I owe much to the patience of my family. My largest share of gratitude, then, belongs to my wife whose help sometimes included being a research assistant and typing parts of the manuscript. Without the support of her unflagging interest and encouragement, this book might have taken not ten but fifteen years to reach completion.

RANDOLPH L. PETERSON

The Mammals of Eastern Canada

Mammals and Man

Mammalogy, the scientific study of mammals, is a specialized branch of zoology in that it is primarily concerned with only one class of animals, yet it encompasses, or integrates with, many other scientific disciplines. The general field of mammalogy is so broad and the various specialized facets of research within it are so numerous that it is difficult to comprehend the true role of mammals and mammalogy in the complex web of life. The difficulty in regarding the subject whole is further compounded by the fact that man himself, with all his human complexities, is also a member of the Class *Mammalia*. The interrelations of man and other mammals had their beginning with common prehuman ancestors in the early evolution of mammals. While man tends to set himself apart from other mammals, there are many ways in which mammals have played a vital role in the history and development of human civilization unrelated to the evolution of *Homo sapiens*.

From prehistoric times mammal flesh has been an important source of man's food. Hides and fur have provided clothing, and bones have been used to fashion tools. Blubber and fat were used for food and fuel (and still are by Eskimos). Mammals were domesticated long before the dawn of written history, perhaps over 9000 years ago. There is evidence that dogs were kept by the inhabitants of what is now Denmark about 6000 years ago and of Jericho about 6800 years ago; the Chinese are thought to have started swine husbandry more than 5000 years ago; the Egyptians kept cats prior to 2100 B.C. Mammals have been used as guardians and as aids in hunting and killing other forms of life, as beasts of burden, as draft animals, and in warfare. Some species even assumed a holy role and were worshipped or were assumed to be sacred.

With the advance of civilization, mammal products became prime articles of commerce and played a major role in man's exploration and settlement of new lands. Early land transportation was almost wholly dependent on horses, cattle, and camels. The early development of agriculture was built around mammals for draft animals and animal husbandry in many forms. Many mammal by-products came into use as civilization developed. They now include milk, cheese, butter, fat, oils, blood products, felt, leather products, wool, bristles, ivory, wax, whalebone, and fertilizers.

Some mammals play an increasingly important role in the search for knowledge by which man may better understand himself. Mammals have been used in various experiments to help shed light on the psychology of human behaviour. Surgery and most forms of medical research have been advanced immeasurably by the use of laboratory mammals. Mammals and mammal products are used in the development and production of serums, vaccines, hormones, and other biological products such as insulin, that are now used in modern medicine. As specimens for dissection, mammals are indispensable in training science students—particularly in medicine and other branches of biology. Mammals are also fundamentally involved in research in many divisions of the biological sciences such as anatomy, physiology, genetics, palaeontology, embryology, ecology, histology, cytology, endocrinology, neurology, haematology, parasitology, psychology, behaviour, population dynamics, wildlife management, and other specialized disciplines.

However, not all of man's relations with other mammals have been beneficial. The fear of actually being killed and eaten by them was very real to early man. There have always been species that plagued man by consuming or damaging his stores of food, his crops, his livestock, or his equipment. Some species became carriers of infectious diseases or parasites that were transmitted either to man himself or to his livestock; some competed with domesticated livestock for grass or other foods.

Native mammals are an integral part of the renewable natural resources—soil, water, forest, and wildlife—and sound conservation (wise utilization) of any one of these resources calls for some understanding and appreciation of the interrelations of the multitude of facets of the total environment. A major disturbance of the equilibrium that has become established within an environment has many far-reaching and complex results. For example, in man's attempt to modify or control the land for his own use, there is frequently a conflict with the wild native fauna. When man introduced domestic cattle, sheep, or goats to an area and attempted to eliminate native grass-eating ungulates such as bison, pronghorn, deer or wapiti (to reduce the competition for food), he found that native carnivores began to prey on his livestock instead of on the native ungulates. When he attempted to eliminate these predators he found his land plagued with rabbits and rodents, which provided just as much competition for the vegetation needed as food for the livestock as did the original native ungulates. Viewed in relation to man's own interest, no species of mammal is entirely beneficial or entirely detrimental.

Each species attains a state of harmony with its environment through gradual adaptations, modifications, and evolution, and must adjust to continual changes. Now that man has become capable of making profound and rapid alterations in the environment, the future survival of most species is becoming more and more dependent upon man's actions.

While the vital role that mammals have played in man's past and their many contributions to his present well-being leave no doubt of their basic importance and economic worth, mammals should also be considered in a cultural or aesthetic context. They have played a part in the history of religion, art, mythology, and literature. The comradeship and bond between man and his pet dog, cat, or other mammal is legendary. In the sphere of recreation and entertainment one hardly needs to attempt to catalogue the enjoyments provided by zoos, natural parks, nature trails, and wilderness areas where naturalists, photography enthusiasts, Nimrods, and countless other people merely seeking recreation or relaxation can encounter living mammals.

A person who observes mammals in their native habitat even casually cannot help but be attracted to them in one way or another. He may be fascinated by their behaviour and activities; enthralled by their beauty of form and their speed, power, agility, and grace of movement; envious of their apparent sense of purpose and self-sufficiency; curious about their adaptations for survival or their vocal sounds and other means of communication. Their appeal for some may be in the mystery and excitement of the unknown, the unpredictable, and the unexpected; or in the satisfaction that comes from discovering a new experience or new knowledge. Whatever the attractions of mammals, they arouse an emotional response in man that cannot be adequately described, though it can be illustrated by the warmth of feeling universally shown by man toward the young of almost any mammal, be it kitten, cub, pup, fawn, lamb, or baby mouse or squirrel. The overall association of man with other mammals contributes immeasurably to his cultural development and to his enjoyment, relaxation, and emotional stability.

For the serious student of mammals—whether amateur, undergraduate, graduate, or professional—there are still further attractions, challenges, and rewards. As one builds on the existing knowledge of mammals by searching for answers to the unknown, each problem solved reveals new questions to intensify a growing thirst for knowledge and understanding. The thrill of discovery and the satisfaction of sharing new knowledge with others are extremely powerful motivations for further effort. Mammalogy offers almost unlimited opportunity for those willing to accept its challenges—there is so much yet to be learned.

The Class Mammalia

Among the animals that have developed an internal skeleton (Subphylum *Vertebrata*), the earliest types were fish-like and lived in the sea. One group, the amphibia, progressed to dry land but returned to water for part of the life cycle (the development of the egg). In time an egg developed that did not have to be laid in water, and the group known as reptiles evolved. One group of reptiles developed feathers and the power of flight and evolved as birds. Another group developed fur and mammary glands. In time these evolving mammals no longer laid their eggs for external hatching but instead retained them inside the uterus for full development after fertilization. After birth, the young were provided with food from the mammary glands; this gave them much greater security and more opportunity for survival. Thus the Class *Mammalia* was evolved.

The one characteristic that is shared by all mammals and is absent in all other groups of vertebrates is mammary glands. The next most universal character is the presence of hair as a body covering, although in some whales the hair has been drastically reduced and in others only the developing foetus exhibits hair, which is usually shed before birth. Typically mammals are viviparous—that is, the young are developed in the uterus, with the monotremes (egg-layers) being the only known exceptions. Mammals maintain a constant body temperature: they are homeothermic or 'warm-blooded', a characteristic they share with birds. The body cavity of mammals is divided into two chambers by a diaphragm. As in birds, the heart has four chambers, with a closed circulation; but only the left aortic arch is present, whereas birds have only the right. Mammal blood cells are without a nucleus.

The mammalian skeleton is characterized as follows:

(1) a single bone in each side of the lower jaw that articulates directly with the cranium;

(2) teeth that are typically heterodont—differentiated into incisors, canines, premolars, and molars (in some, this condition is secondarily masked by the modification, reduction, or loss of teeth);

(3) permanent teeth that are preceded by a set of deciduous or milk teeth in the incisors, canines, and premolars only;

(4) a skull that articulates with the vertebral column with paired or two occipital condyles;

(5) vertebrae that are differentiated into cervicals, thoracics, lumbars, sacrals, and caudals;

(6) seven cervical vertebrae, except in the sloths (*Choloepus*, six or seven; *Bradypus*, nine) and the manatee (*Trichechus*, six);

(7) long bones that have epiphyses on the ends;

(8) a shoulder girdle that is reduced and partly or wholly free from the sternum;

(9) a pelvic girdle that is consolidated into a pair of innominate bones;

(10) feet that are primarily made up of five digits, although the lateral ones may be reduced or lost;

(11) a phalangeal formula consisting of two in the first digit (thumb or big toe) and three in all other digits;

(12) a palate that is roofed over between the upper toothrows;

(13) a quadrate group of bones that is reduced and modified into the bones of the inner ear;

(14) a tympanic bulla that is usually formed partially or entirely from the tympanic bone, although it may sometimes be absent.

Mammals range in size from the tiny pygmy shrew, which measures as little as three to four inches including tail and weighs about the same as a ten-cent piece, up to the blue whale which may exceed 100 feet in length and weigh more than 100 tons.

Geographically mammals have occupied most of the earth's surface, both land and sea. Inland Antarctica is the largest land-mass devoid of native mammal fauna, although whales and seals commonly frequent its shores. Special adaptations allow certain species to occupy all climatic regions, from the Arctic to the tropics, including deserts, grasslands, and forests. Some orders have become adapted for a marine existence: two are wholly marine—*Cetacea* and *Sirenia*—while *Pinnipedia* and some carnivora spend only a part of their life at sea and regularly return to land to breed. Only one order, the *Chiroptera*, has developed true flight to become as aerial as birds, but several species within the Orders *Marsupialia, Dermoptera,* and *Rodentia* have become volant or gliders. Of the mammals that have become specialized for an arboreal existence, the sloths, which live almost entirely above ground, are the extreme example. Several species have become adapted for a fossorial or subterranean existence: moles (*Insectivora*) and pocket gophers (*Rodentia*) are example of species that rarely venture above ground. No mammal is completely aquatic—living entirely in fresh water— unless the *Sirenia* is so classified; those mammals that have become strongly adapted for an aquatic existence retain a terrestrial base of operations. Most mammals are adapted for a terrestrial existence and have many specialized modifications for specific habitat requirements.

Mammals have also developed many modifications in food habits. Most mammals depend on plant foods—grass, herbs, shrubs, and trees, fruit or seeds, roots (rhizomes or tubers), and even the nectar of flowers (the food of several tropical bats). Among those mammals dependent on animal sources of food, the largest of the whales is adapted for feeding on plankton (a number of quite small organisms). Insects and other invertebrates provide food for several groups, particularly shrews and moles, bats, anteaters, and some rodents and carnivores. Among the vertebrates, fish provide the basic diet of some mammals; reptiles and amphibians, as well as birds, are usually only a portion of the diet of many species commonly grouped as carnivores. The flesh of mammals forms the basic food of some species, particularly within the *Carnivora*. One family has become specialized to the point that it requires nothing but fresh blood for food (*Desmodontidae*—Vampire bats). Another has become dependent upon scavenging for an existence (*Hyaenidae*), although many species indulge in it from time to time. Still other mammals must be classed as omnivores—they will eat almost anything readily available. The opossum, the raccoon, the bear, and man belong in this category.

Countless other modifications and adaptations are exhibited within the Class *Mammalia*. Many of them will be noted in the accounts of the species treated.

The Origin and Classification of Mammals

Modern mammals represent only a surviving fraction of the great number that have evolved since the earliest transition from the mammal-like reptiles at about the end of the Triassic period some 200 million years ago. Unfortunately the fossil records of the earliest mammals are sketchy, especially from the Mesozoic era; they are based on isolated and mostly fragmentary teeth. Among the mammal-like reptiles of the Subclass *Synapsida*, there were many that acquired characters normally associated with mammals, but none of these reptiles that have been discovered can be accepted as *the* progenitor of true mammals. The absence of information concerning both the ancestors of the most primitive of living mammals, the Monotremes or egg-laying mammals, and of the next most primitive living order, the marsupials, leaves room for speculation that modern mammals may have had a polyphyletic origin—that is, there may have been more than one ancestral line of evolution—and that the true placental mammals (all the remaining orders) derive from one evolutionary line and the non-placentals from another. Unfortunately it is difficult to classify the earliest mammals according to their mode of reproduction because this is unknown.

The most complete and widely accepted classifications of all mammals, both extinct and living, is the work of Simpson (1945), whose arrangements are followed in this book with only a few modifications. (An outline of the major orders and families will be found on pages 13 to 19.) The Class *Mammalia* has been divided in various ways, with most authorities agreeing that the Subclass *Prototheria* includes only the Order *Monotremata*, the egg-laying mammals represented by the duck-billed platypus and the spiny anteaters (also called echidnas), both restricted to the Australasian region. The fossil record for this order extends only as far back as the Pleistocene age; the known prehistoric forms do not differ from those living today.

The classification of the remaining primitive mammals—the so-called Multituber-culates, Triconodonts, Pantotheres, and Symmetrodonts—has been handled in different ways by different authors. The first and sometimes the second are treated as represent-ing a Subclass *Allotheria*, and Pantotheres and Symmetrodonts (and sometimes Tri-conodonts) as an Infraclass *Metatheria* of the Subclass *Theria*. In this arrangement the Subclass *Theria* would include both the Infraclass *Metatheria* (the marsupials) and the Infraclass *Eutheria* (the true placental mammals).

The modern system of classification is based on the work of the famous Swedish naturalist Carl von Linnaeus (1707–1778) and dates from the tenth edition of Linnaeus's *Systema Naturae* (1758). The scientific names have been derived from Latin or Greek in order to establish a nomenclature that is universally understood. Family names always have the ending *-idae* and subfamily names the ending *-inae*. Most other group names—with the exception of the less commonly used groups of tribe (*-ini*) and sub-tribe (*ina*)—lack universally accepted endings. In order to avoid duplication and con-fusion, a detailed set of rules has been established by an International Commission on Zoological Nomenclature. This body considers and rules on new problems in nomen-clature as they arise from time to time.

The animal kingdom has been subdivided on the basis of a hierarchy of smaller and smaller units beginning with Kingdom, Phylum, Class, Order, Family, Genus, and Species. Thus, the classification of a domestic cat can be illustrated as follows:

Kingdom ANIMAL

Phylum CHORDATA

Subphylum VERTEBRATA

Class MAMMALIA

Order CARNIVORA

Family FELIDAE

Genus FELIS

Species FELIS CATUS

One of the basic aims of the modern system of classification is to illustrate the phylogenetic relations of various groups and the relationships of one kind or one group of kinds to another. This system also attempts to begin with the most primitive or generalized forms and to proceed to the more advanced or specialized. But no workable system can adequately express all the complex and changing variations inherent in the evolution of living organisms: a system of classification for a particular group of animals based on one set of criteria could be different from another system based on a different set. At best the goal of an ideal 'natural' classification must of necessity become an artificial one in order to simplify the system sufficiently to keep it workable. Among the taxonomists—that group of scientists concerned with classifying living (or extinct) organisms—there are some who prefer to emphasize the *differences* between groups or kinds; they tend to erect an increasing number of names and categories, and within the profession they are called 'splitters'. There are also taxonomists who prefer to emphasize the *similarities* between groups and kinds; they tend to combine names and categories to reduce their number and are known as 'lumpers'. Obviously a flexible system is required, one that is somewhere between these two extremes.

In order to express better the complex relations of various kinds of animals, it will be useful to study an expansion of the basic hierarchy given above. The additional categories are not mandatory and are not applicable to all groups. Nevertheless they are useful in many large, complex groups, especially as a tool for the specialist. The most commonly accepted full hierarchy is shown on page 12.

The origin, development, radiation, modification (speciation), and extinction or survival of animals of the Class *Mammalia* is a most interesting and complex study that lies beyond the scope of this work. Classification is inherently concerned with the process of evolution as it was outlined by Darwin in his theories of evolution through natural selection. Perhaps some appreciation of the evolution of mammals can be obtained by comparing the number of kinds of mammals that evolved and became extinct with the number that have survived to make up our modern fauna. The Class *Mammalia* is generally divided into thirty-two or thirty-three orders, of which eighteen or nineteen are still living and fourteen are extinct. Thus about forty-four per cent of the major groups have failed to survive. The known fauna may be grouped into about 257 families, of which 139 or fifty-four per cent became extinct and about 118 or forty-six per cent have survived. Dividing the mammals further by genera, 2,864 are thought to have existed at one time, but 1,932 or sixty-seven per cent have become extinct, with

Kingdom

    Phylum

        Subphylum

            Superclass

                Class

                    Subclass

                        Infraclass

                            Cohort

                                Superorder

                                  Order

                                    Suborder

                                      Infraorder

                                        Superfamily

                                          Family

                                            Subfamily

                                              Tribe

                                                Subtribe

                                                  Genus

                                                    Subgenus

                                                      Species

                                                         Subspecies

FULL HIERARCHY OF CATEGORIES USED IN CLASSIFYING MAMMALS

only about 932 or thirty-three per cent surviving. A comparison of living and extinct forms down to the species level is not practicable, but it is interesting that on a world-wide basis the present-day mammal fauna of approximately 20,000 species and sub-species represents less than one third of the kinds that lived at one time. The process of evolution of new forms is very slow, but the process of extinction can be extremely fast. Several cases of extinction have been witnessed in the last hundred years (some of them accelerated by modern man) and more seem imminent.

The following outline of the major groups (orders and families) lists the mammal fauna of eastern Canada in relation to world fauna (both living and fossil). The families represented within the boundaries covered by this work are prefixed with an asterisk (*); fossil orders are shown by a dagger (†). A rough indication of the number of families and genera is given in parentheses. It should be understood that the numbers are only approximate, as new knowledge is continually adding forms on the one hand and combining forms on the other.

Class

MAMMALIA

Subclass **PROTOTHERIA**

Order MONOTREMATA
(3 living genera)

Family TACHYGLOSSIDAE: Spiny Anteater or Echidnas of Australia, Tasmania, and New Guinea
Family ORNITHORHYNCHIDAE: Platypus of Australia and Tasmania

Subclass **ALLOTHERIA**

† Order MULTITUBERCULATA
(5 families, 35 genera)

† Order TRICONODONTA
(1 family, 8 genera)

Subclass **THERIA**

Infraclass **Pantotheria**

† Order PANTOTHERIA
(4 families, 22 genera)

† Order SYMMETRODONTA
(2 families, 5 genera)

Infraclass **Metatheria**

Order MARSUPIALIA
(5 families, 81 genera extinct; 57 living genera)

*Family DIDELPHIDAE: Opossums of North and South America
Family DASYURIDAE: Various carnivore-like marsupials of Australia
Family NOTORYCTIDAE: Marsupial mole of Australia
Family PERAMELIDAE: Bandicoots of Australia and New Guinea
Family CAENOLESTIDAE: Shrew-like marsupials of South America
Family PHALANGERIDAE: Phalangers of Australia, Tasmania, New Guinea, and New Zealand
Family PHASCOLOMIDAE: Wombats of Australia and Tasmania
Family MACROPODIDAE: Kangaroos and allies of Australia and Tasmania

Infraclass **Eutheria**

Order INSECTIVORA
(12 families, 88 genera extinct; 71 living genera)

Family SOLENODONTIDAE: Solenodons of Cuba and Haiti
Family TENRECIDAE: Tenrecs of Madagascar
Family POTAMOGALIDAE: African water shrews of Africa
Family CHRYSOCHLORIDAE: Golden mole of Africa
Family ERINACEIDAE: Hedgehogs of North Africa, Europe, and Asia
Family MACROSCELIDIDAE: Jumping or Elephant shrews of Africa
*Family SORICIDAE: Shrews of both the Old and New Worlds
*Family TALPIDAE: Moles of North America, Europe, and Asia

Order DERMOPTERA
(1 family, 2 genera extinct; 1 living genus)

Family CYNOCEPHALIDAE: Flying Lemurs or Colugos of Southeast Asia, the East Indies, and the Philippines

Order CHIROPTERA
(2 families, 16 genera extinct; 118 living genera)

Family PTEROPIDAE: Flying foxes or large fruit-eating bats of the tropics and subtropics of the Old World, Australia, and the Pacific Islands
Family RHINOPOMATIDAE: Valve-nosed or mouse-tailed bats of north Africa and south Asia
Family EMBALLONURIDAE: Sac-winged bats of the tropics in the Old and New Worlds
Family NOCTILIONIDAE: Fish-eating bats of Central and South America
Family NYCTERIDAE: Hispid, hollow-faced or long-tailed bats of Africa and the Malaysian region
Family MEGADERMATIDAE: Large-winged bats of Africa, south Asia, and Australia

Family RHINOLOPHIDAE: Crest-nosed bats of the Old World and Australia

Family HIPPOSIDERIDAE: Horseshoe-nosed bats of Africa, south Asia, and Australia

Family PHYLLOSTOMIDAE: Leaf-nosed bats of southern North America, Central and South America

Family DESMODONTIDAE: Vampire bats of Central and South America

Family NATALIDAE: Long-legged or Yellow bats of Central and South America and the West Indies

Family FURIPTERIDAE: Smoky, thumbless, or pig bats of tropical South America

Family THYROPTERIDAE: American disk-winged or sucker-footed bats of Central and South America

Family MYZOPODIDAE: Madagascarian sucker-footed or golden bat of Madagascar

*Family VESPERTILIONIDAE: Common or smooth-faced bats, world-wide

Family MYSTACINIDAE: Moustache-lipped or short-tailed bats of New Zealand

Family MOLOSSIDAE: Free-tailed bats, world-wide in tropics and subtropics or temperate regions.

Order PRIMATES
(7 families, 99 genera extinct; 59 living genera)

Family TUPAIIDAE: Tree 'shrews' of south-east Asia, East Indies, and Philippines

Family LEMURIDAE: Lemurs of Madagascar

Family INDRIDAE: Woolly lemurs of Madagascar

Family DAUBENTONIIDAE: Aye-aye of Madagascar

Family LORISIDAE: Slow loris, pottos, and galagos or bush babies of Africa, south Asia, East Indies to Philippines

Family TARSIIDAE: Tarsiers of the East Indies to Philippines

Family CEBIDAE: New World monkeys of Central and South America

Family CALLITHRICIDAE: Marmosets of Central and South America

Family CERCOPITHECIDAE: Old World monkeys of Africa, Gibraltar, and Asia

Family PONGIDAE: Gorillas, gibbons, and chimpanzees of Africa and Asia

*Family HOMINIDAE: Man, world-wide

† Order TILLODONTIA
(1 family, 4 genera)

† Order TAENIODONTA
(1 family, 7 genera)

Order EDENTATA
(7 families, 113 genera extinct; 19 living genera)

Family MYRMECOPHAGIDAE: Anteaters of Central and South America

Family BRADYPODIDAE: Sloths of Central and South America

Family DASYPODIDAE: Armadillos of South, Central and southern North America

Order PHOLIDOTA
(3 extinct and 1 living genera)

Family MANIDAE: Pangolins or scaly anteaters of Africa and Asia

Order LAGOMORPHA
(1 family, 23 genera extinct; 10 living genera)

Family OCHOTONIDAE: Pikas or coneys of North America, Asia, and Europe
*Family LEPORIDAE: Rabbits and hares of the Old and New Worlds

Order RODENTIA
(10 families, 275 genera extinct; 344 living genera)

Family APLODONTIDAE: Mountain 'beavers' of northwest North America
*Family SCIURIDAE: Squirrels and allies of the Old and New Worlds
Family GEOMYIDAE: Pocket gophers of North and Central America
Family HETEROMYIDAE: Kangaroo rats and pocket mice of North and Central America
*Family CASTORIDAE: Beavers of Europe, Asia, and North America
Family ANOMALURIDAE: Spiny-tailed squirrels of Africa
Family PEDETIDAE: Spring haas of Africa
*Family CRICETIDAE: Common hamster-like mice and rats of the Old and New Worlds
Family LOPHIOMYIDAE: Maned rats of Africa
Family SPALACIDAE: Mole rats of north Africa, Europe, and Asia
Family RHIZOMYIDAE: Bamboo rats of Africa and Asia
*Family MURIDAE: Old World rats and mice, introduced world-wide
Family GLIRIDAE: Common dormice of the Old World
Family PLATACANTHOMYIDAE: Spiny dormice of Asia
Family SELEVINIIDAE: Asian dormice of Asia
*Family ZAPODIDAE: Jumping mice of Europe, Asia, and North America
Family DIPODIDAE: Jerboas of Africa, Europe, and Asia
Family HYSTRICIDAE: Old World porcupines of Africa, Europe, and Asia
*Family ERETHIZONTIDAE: New World porcupines of North and South America
Family CAVIIDAE: Cavies or guinea pigs of South America
Family HYDROCHOERIDAE: Capybaras of Central and South America
Family DINOMYIDAE: Long-tailed or false paca of South America
Family DASYPROCTIDAE: Agoutis and adouris of West Indies, Central and South America
Family CUNICULIDAE: Pacas or labba of Central and South America
Family CHINCHILLIDAE: Chinchillas and viscachas of South America
*Family CAPROMYIDAE: Hutias and nutria of West Indies and South America
Family OCTODONTIDAE: Octodont rats of South America
Family CTENOMYIDAE: Tucu tucus of South America

Family ABROCOMIDAE: Rat chinchillas of South America

Family ECHIMYIDAE: Spiny rats of Central and South America

Family THRYONOMYIDAE: Cane rats of Africa

Family PETROMYIDAE: Rock rats of Africa

Family BATHYERGIDAE: Mole rats of Africa

Family CTENODACTYLIDAE: Gundis or dassie rats of Africa

Order CETACEA
(9 families, 137 genera extinct; 35 living genera)

Family INIIDAE: Freshwater dolphins of Asia and South America

Family PLATANISTIDAE: River dolphins of Asia

*Family ZIPHIIDAE: Beaked whales of all seas

*Family PHYSETERIDAE: Sperm whales of all seas

*Family KOGIIDAE: Pygmy sperm whales of all seas

*Family MONODONTIDAE: Narwhal and beluga of the Arctic and Subarctic seas

*Family DELPHINIDAE: Dolphins and porpoises of all seas

Family ESCHRICHTIIDAE: Gray whale of North Pacific

*Family BALAENOPTERIDAE: Fin whales of all seas

*Family BALAENIDAE: Baleen or right whales of all seas

Order CARNIVORA
(5 families, 239 genera extinct; 98 living genera)

*Family CANIDAE: Dogs, wolves, and foxes, world-wide

*Family URSIDAE: Bears of Europe, Asia, North and South America

*Family PROCYONIDAE: Raccoons, coatis, kinkajous, and relatives of Asia, North and South America

*Family MUSTELIDAE: Weasels, skunks, otters, badgers, and allies of the Old and New Worlds

Family VIVERRIDAE: Civets, mongooses, and allies of Africa, Europe, and Asia

Family HYAENIDAE: Hyenas of Africa and Southwest Asia

*Family FELIDAE: Cats of the Old and New Worlds

Order PINNIPEDIA
(1 family, 22 genera extinct; 16 living genera)

Family OTARIIDAE: Eared seals and sea lions of Antarctica, Australia, North and South America

*Family ODOBENIDAE: Walrus of the Arctic

*Family PHOCIDAE: Hair seals and sea elephants of all seas

† Order CONDYLARTHRA
(6 families, 42 genera)

† Order LITOPTERNA
(2 families, 41 genera)

† Order NOTOUNGULATA
(14 families, 105 genera)

† Order ASTRAPOTHERIA
(2 families, 9 genera)

Order TUBULIDENTATA
(1 genus extinct)

Family ORYCTEROPODIDAE: Aardvarks of Africa

† Order PANTODONTA
(3 families, 9 genera)

† Order DINOCERATA
(1 family, 8 genera)

† Order PYROTHERIA
(1 family, 6 genera)

Order PROBOSCIDEA
(5 families, 22 genera extinct; 2 living genera)

Family ELEPHANTIDAE: Elephants of Africa and Asia

† Order EMBRITHOPODA
(1 family, 1 genus)

Order HYRACOIDEA
(2 families, 10 genera extinct; 3 living genera)

Family PROCAVIIDAE: Dassies or hyraxes of Africa and Asia

Order SIRENIA
(3 families, 14 genera extinct; 2 living genera)

Family DUGONGIDAE: Dugongs of the Red Sea, Indian Ocean, and Western Pacific

Family TRICHECHIDAE: Manatees of the Atlantic Ocean, from Florida south on the west and West Africa
on the east

Order PERISSODACTYLA
(9 families, 152 genera extinct; 6 living genera)

*Family EQUIDAE: Horses of Africa, Asia, and domestication
Family TAPIRIDAE: Tapirs of Asia, Central and South America
Family RHINOCEROTIDAE: Rhinoceroses of Africa and Asia

Order ARTIODACTYLA
(16 families, 333 genera extinct; 86 living genera)

*Family SUIDAE: Pigs of Africa, Asia, Europe, and domestication
Family TAYASSUIDAE: Peccaries of North, Central, and South America
Family HIPPOPOTAMIDAE: Hippopotami of Africa
Family CAMELIDAE: Camels and llamas of Africa, Asia, and South America
Family TRAGULIDAE: Chevrotains of Africa and Asia
*Family CERVIDAE: Deer and relatives of the Old and New Worlds
Family GIRAFFIDAE: Giraffes of Africa
Family ANTILOCAPRIDAE: Pronghorns of North America
*Family BOVIDAE: Cattle, sheep, goats, antelopes, and allies of the Old and New Worlds and domestication

The Mammalian Skeleton

Two common domestic mammals—the rabbit (*fig.* 1) and the cat (*fig.* 2)—have been selected to illustrate skull parts, since one or the other is usually used in high-school or university curricula for dissection and detailed study.

The domestic cat (*fig.* 3) has been selected to illustrate the basic mammal skeleton.

Most of the names listed here of individual bones and parts of the skull and skeleton are omitted from the Glossary.

1. Zygomatic Arch
2. Nasal
3. Frontal
4. Supraorbital Processes (Antorbital and postorbital)
5. Presphenoid
6. Vomer
7. Maxilla
8. Premaxilla
9. Incisor, I^1
10. Incisor, I^2
11. Incisive Foramen
12. Palatine
13. Optic Foramen
14. Orbitosphenoid
15. Lachrymal (Lacrimal)
16. Diastema
17. Zygomatic
18. Pterygoid
19. Premolar Teeth, Lower
20. Incisor, Lower
21. Mandible or Dentary Bone
22. Parietal
23. Interparietal
24. Supraoccipital
25. Alisphenoid
26. Basisphenoid
27. Occipital Condyle
28. Foramen Magnum
29. Basioccipital
30. Exoccipital
31. Jugular Process
32. Mandibular Fossa
33. Molar Teeth, Upper
34. Premolar Teeth, Upper
35. Squamosal
36. External Auditory Meatus
37. Tympanic Bulla (Auditory Bulla)
38. Mastoid Process
39. Mandibular Condyle
40. Molar Teeth, Lower
41. Coronoid Process
42. Angular Process

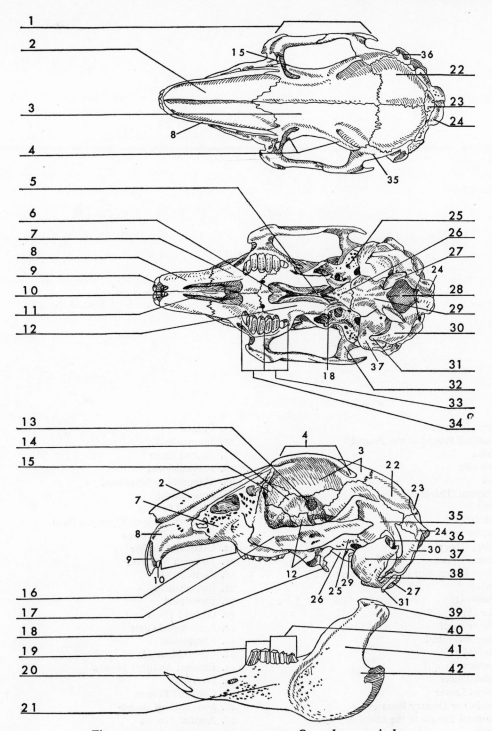

Fig. I –SKULL OF THE DOMESTIC RABBIT, *Oryctolagus cuniculus*

1. Zygomatic Arch
2. Postorbital Process of the Frontal
3. Maxilla
4. Premaxilla
5. Nasal
6. Lachrymal (Lacrimal)
7. Vomer
8. Premolar (P³)
9. Premolar (P²)
10. Canine, Upper
11. Incisors, Upper
12. Incisive Foramen or Palatine Fissure
13. Palatine
14. Premolar (P⁴)
15. Molar (M¹)
16. Malar or Jugal
17. Infraorbital Canal
18. Molar (M₁)
19. Premolars (P₃ & ₄)
20. Canine, Lower
21. Incisors, Lower
22. Mandible or Dentary Bone
23. Postorbital Process of the Malar or Jugal
24. Parietal

25. Frontal
26. Interparietal
27. Sagittal Crest
28. Supraoccipital
29. Temporal or Squamosal
30. Presphenoid
31. Mastoid Process
32. Auditory Bulla or Tympanic Bulla
33. Paroccipital Process
34. Occipital Condyle
35. Foramen Magnum
36. Basioccipital
37. Basisphenoid
38. Exoccipital
39. Glenoid Fossa
40. Lambdoidal Crest
41. Alisphenoid
42. Orbitosphenoid
43. External Auditory Meatus
44. Pterygoid
45. Coronoid Process
46. Mandibular Condyle
47. Angular Process

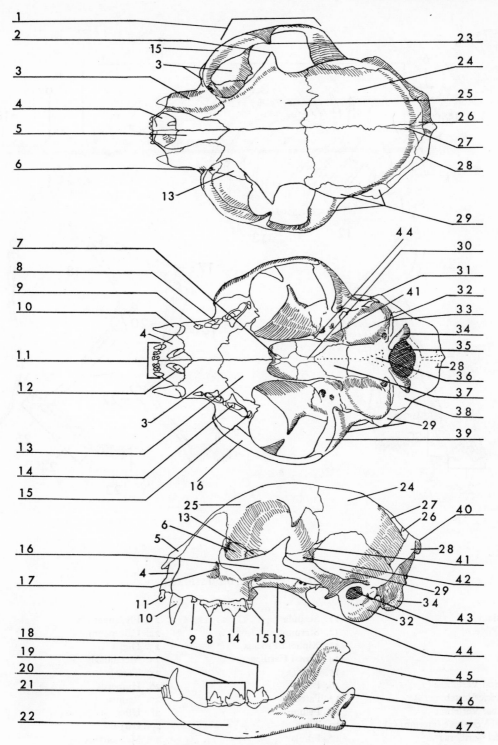

Fig. 2–SKULL OF THE DOMESTIC CAT, *Felis catus*

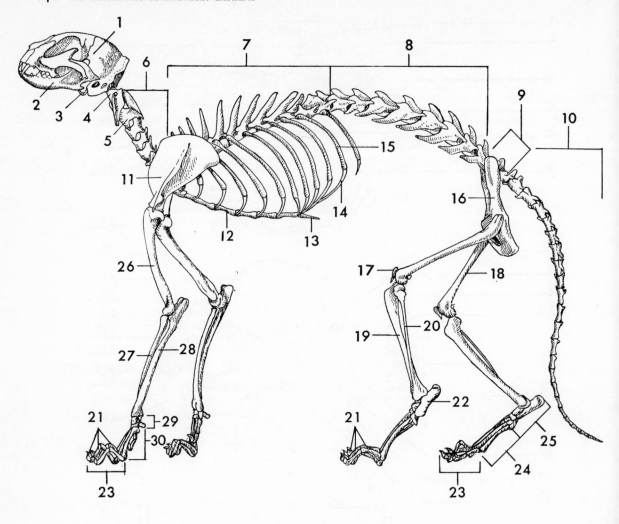

Fig. 3–SKELETON OF THE DOMESTIC CAT

1. Cranium
2. Mandible
3. Hyoids
4. Atlas
5. Axis
6. Cervical Vertebrae (7)
7. Thoracic Vertebrae (8)
8. Lumbar Vertebrae
9. Sacral Vertebrae (sacrum) (3)
10. Caudal Vertebrae

11. Scapula
12. Sternum
13. Xiphoid Process
14. Costal Cartilage
15. Ribs (13)
16. Pelvis
17. Patella
18. Femur
19. Tibia
20. Fibula

21. Phalanges
22. Calcaneum
23. Digits
24. Metatarsals
25. Tarsals
26. Humerus
27. Radius
28. Ulna
29. Carpals
30. Metacarpals

The Region of Eastern Canada

The numerous ecological conditions that exist within the boundaries of eastern Canada are much too complex to receive an adequate description in this work. The basic distribution patterns of mammals are correlated with the flora and other ecological conditions such as soils, topography, moisture levels, temperature, and other climatic factors, and are affected by various interrelations with other species within the fauna.

The biotic or life-zone areas of eastern Canada—imposed by the correlation of flora and fauna—are more or less stratified from north to south, ranging from treeless arctic tundra or barren grounds along the northernmost boundaries through a taiga that merges into a broad zone of coniferous trees, known as the boreal forest or Hudsonian life-zone. Progressing further south into the Great Lakes - St Lawrence watershed, an increasing content of broadleaf or hardwood trees forms a mixed-forest area that is sometimes called the Great Lakes - St Lawrence forest region or the Canadian biotic area; this covers most of the rocky outcrop region of the Canadian Shield. South of the Canadian Shield, deeper soils are more suitable for agriculture and the original forest has been greatly modified or removed to make way for farming and urban development. Further south there is a narrow belt extending along the north shore of Lake Erie representing the Carolinian life-zone in which a wide variety of hardwood forest trees predominates.

The distribution of some species is closely correlated with the basic ecological conditions prevailing within these biotic areas. Species that are characteristic of the eastern-Canadian Arctic include the Ungava varying lemming (*Dicrostonyx hudsonius*), the Arctic hare (*Lepus arcticus*), the Arctic fox (*Alopex lagopus*), and various marine forms including the walrus (*Odobenus rosmarus*) and certain seals and whales.

At the other geographical extreme the following species do not occur beyond the Carolinian biotic area: the little short-tailed shrew (*Cryptotis parva*), the eastern mole (*Scalopus aquaticus*), and the pine mouse (*Microtus pinetorum*), though this mouse has been found near the southern boundary of Quebec.

Between the Arctic and Carolinian life-zones the distribution patterns are quite variable, with some mammal species ranging across both the northern and southern zones.

Key to the Orders of Eastern-Canadian Recent Mammals

1 Limbs modified as flippers.
  2 Tail modified as a horizontal fluke; hind limbs absent.   CETACEA p. 340
  2′ Tail not modified as a horizontal fluke; hind limbs present   PINNIPEDIA p. 288

1′ Limbs not modified as flippers: 3
  3 Fore-limbs modified as wings.   CHIROPTERA p. 59
  3′ Fore-limbs not modified as wings: 4

    4 Feet modified as cloven hooves (even-toed).   ARTIODACTYLA p. 315
    4′ Feet not modified as above: 5

     5 Feet modified as single-hoofed toe (odd-toed).   PERISSODACTYLA p. 312
     5′ Feet not modified as above; toes with claws: 6

      6 Only two pairs of large incisor teeth visible in the front of the mouth: 7

       7 A pair of small incisor teeth located immediately behind the large incisors; rostrum with lattice-like fenestrations on each side.   LAGOMORPHA p. 83
       7′ No small incisors behind the pair of front incisors; a wide diastema separates the incisors from the cheek teeth.   RODENTIA p. 103

      6′ Incisor teeth not as above: 8
       8 Eyes minute or rudimentary, rostrum elongated and usually pointed; neither canines nor incisors conspicuously developed; molars with distinct w-shaped pattern.   INSECTIVORA p. 30

       8′ Eyes not rudimentary, snout normal. Canine teeth distinctly large and well developed: 9

        9 Incisor teeth $\frac{5}{4}$; angle of jaw deflected inward; tail and ears without hair; innermost hind toe thumb-like without claw; marsupium present in females.   MARSUPIALIA p. 27

        9′ Incisor teeth $\frac{3}{3}$ or less; condyle of mandible a transverse half rod, articulating with a deep glenoid fossa; ears and tail well furred.   CARNIVORA p. 194

Order
Marsupialia

This primitive order is widely represented in Australasia where it has evolved with a great number of forms (six families), ranging from small mole-, shrew-, and rodent-like forms through bandicoots, phalangers, carnivore-like marsupials and wombats to kangaroos and their relatives. Elsewhere this order occurs only in the Americas where it is represented by two additional families. The family *Caenolistidae* includes only three genera and seven species of shrew-like marsupials (sometimes called rat opossums)—all restricted to western South America. All other New World members of the order belong to the family *Didelphidae* and are referred to collectively as American opossums. In most species the female has an external abdominal pouch for carrying the young, though in some species the pouch is rudimentary or even absent. The young are born in an incomplete state of development. Although there is extreme variation in the conformation of the skulls of the many kinds of marsupials, all marsupials share one common character: a strong inward deflection of the angle of the lower jaw that distinguishes them from all other mammals except a few rodents that have developed a similar character.

Family **DIDELPHIDAE**

American Opossums – *Opossums d'Amérique*

Living representatives of the family *Didelphidae* include twelve genera and about sixty-five species, all restricted to the Americas, but only one genus —*Didelphis*—extends north of Mexico. This genus ranges from about 47° south latitude in Argentina northward to the southern part of eastern Canada where *D. marsupialis*, the only species to reach North America, is found.

Genus **DIDELPHIS** Linnaeus

Common Opossums – *Opossums communs*

Dental Formula   I $\frac{5-5}{4-4}$ C $\frac{1-1}{1-1}$ P $\frac{3-3}{3-3}$ M $\frac{4-4}{4-4}$ = 50

Didelphis marsupialis Linnaeus – Common Opossum – *Opossum commun*

The opossum is perhaps the most unusual mammalian visitor to take up residence in Canada. Characterized by its long, naked prehensile tail, its black leathery ears, hind feet with opposable thumbs (similar in shape and function to the human hand), and its rather slow awkward gait, the opossum is easily identified. It is about the size of a domestic cat. The fur has a white base with varying amounts of dark-tipped guard hairs that result in considerable variation in coloration of individual

Fig. 4 – COMMON OPOSSUM – *Didelphis marsupialis*

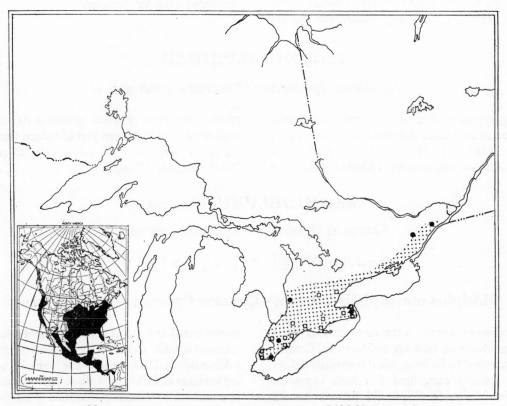

Map I – DISTRIBUTION OF THE COMMON OPOSSUM – *Didelphis marsupialis*

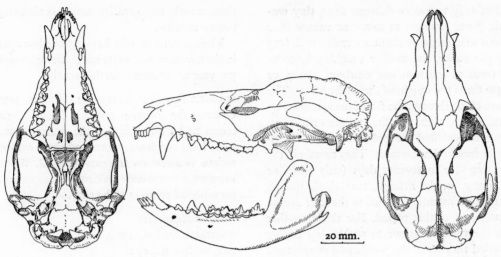

Fig 5 – SKULL OF *Didelphis marsupialis* (ROM 21738♂)

animals, from a light greyish through a brownish colour-phase to a quite dark, almost black pelage. The female possesses a fur-lined abdominal pouch (*marsupium*) in which there are twelve or thirteen teats. The males have a terminally bifurcate (forked) penis which is located posterior to the scrotum. The skull is characterized by a unique shape, a great number of teeth (fifty), a small brain case, and an inward inflection of the angle of the lower jaw.

SIZE Total length 650–850 mm.; tail 220–400; hind foot 60–80. Skull: length 115–130, width 60–70. Weight 3–14 lb.

DISTRIBUTION AND VARIATION The opossum ranges through the eastern half of the United States, south into Mexico and South America. Since 1850 it has appeared in southern Ontario sporadically; detailed records show that it invaded this area on at least four occasions (about 1850–60, 1890–1910, 1930–5, and 1947 to the present). The most recent invasion seems to have been heavier and more extensive than the other ones. While this opossum is most common in the area immediately adjacent to Lake Erie, there has been a recent extension of range into southeastern Ontario across the St Lawrence River. *Didelphis marsupialis virginiana* is the form reaching eastern Canada.

HABITAT The opossum is most common along wooded streams and around lakes and swamps, but it can also be found in agricultural areas near by.

HABITS Perhaps best known for its habit of 'playing possum' or feigning death when attacked, the opossum is prominent in the folklore of the southern United States. Like most mammals it is nocturnal and rarely ventures forth during the day. At this time it is usually alone and is confined to its den in a tree, log, stump, rock pile, or hole in the ground. In escaping enemies and seeking food it demonstrates an excellent climbing ability, making good use of its long prehensile tail and of its opposable thumb on the hind foot which it uses for grasping.

The menu of the opossum is highly variable. Almost anything is acceptable, and any animal, whether living or dead, is relished when available. The opossum occasionally raids poultry houses where either birds or eggs are sought, but vegetable matter of all description is also taken as food.

Opossums are 'born young': after a gestation

period of only twelve to thirteen days, tiny embryonic young emerge, as many as twenty in a litter and weighing only about 2.5 grains each (175 young per ounce, the mother weighing 8,000 to 9,000 times as much as one newborn young, or over 400 times the weight of the entire litter). The newborn climb through the fur of the abdomen up into the pouch where the first twelve or thirteen (rarely fourteen) find a nipple and attach themselves for further development. They remain in the pouch sixty-five to seventy days (only seven or eight young, on the average, surviving), though they are not constantly attached to the teats during the latter part of this period. For about another month the young continue to suckle, but during this period they leave the pouch and supplement their diet. They become independent at about

three months and sexually mature at about eight to twelve months.

The opossum usually has only one litter per year in the northern part of its range, though two litters per year are common further south.

REMARKS Reaching its northern limit in Southern Ontario, the common opossum (*D. m. virginiana*) seems to be increasing at the present time, but most local specimens examined show evidence of serious frostbite on the ears and tail. Whether it becomes a permanent resident or disappears again for a period remains to be seen.

Selected References

HARTMAN, CARL G., 1920, 1952.
LAY, DANIEL W., 1942.
PETERSON, RANDOLPH L. and S. C. DOWNING, 1956.

Order

Insectivora

The members of this old and primitive order, which are found over much of the earth's surface, have diversified habits and habitats. Many forms are fossorial, some are terrestrial, and some aquatic.

All are essentially insect eaters, small in size, and usually have molariform teeth distinctly w-shaped. There are eight living families, only two of which are found in eastern Canada.

KEY TO EASTERN-CANADIAN FAMILIES OF *Insectivora*

1 Size small (less than 30 gr.); forefeet normal, less than 10 mm. wide; ear conch present; skull small (less than 30 mm. long) without either complete zygomatic arch or auditory bullae.

SORICIDAE p. 31

1′ Size larger (more than 30 gr.); forefeet broad, more than 10 mm. wide; ear conch absent; skull larger (more than 30 mm. long) with complete zygomatic arch and auditory bullae.   TALPIDAE p. 52

Family **SORICIDAE**

Shrews – *Musaraignes*

This group includes very small insect-eating mammals of primitive origin. They resemble mice superficially, except that their nose is long and pointed and their teeth are entirely different. The skull is quite fragile and lacks a complete zygomatic arch; the auditory bullae common to most mammals are also absent. There are five toes on both front and hind feet. Most species, the males particularly, have a raised elongated skin gland on the middle of each flank. Four different genera occur in eastern Canada.

KEY TO THE EASTERN-CANADIAN GENERA OF *Soricidae*

1 Tail long, more than half the length of head and body; skull smooth and delicate with long pointed rostrum, 11 mm. wide or less; five unicuspid teeth in each side of upper jaw (one or two may be quite small): 2

    2 Four unicuspid teeth plainly visible; the fifth tooth (the most posterior) small and sometimes inconspicuous when viewed from the side.   SOREX p. 32

    2′ Three unicuspid teeth conspicuous; the third and fifth quite small and usually inconspicuous when viewed from the side.   MICROSOREX p. 44

1′ Tail short, less than half the length of head and body; skull either more than 11 mm. wide with five upper unicuspid teeth or smaller with only four unicuspid teeth: 3

    3 Size large (12–23 gr.; total length 98–136 mm.); skull more than 11 mm. wide with two large unicuspid teeth in front, two smaller ones behind, and a fifth quite small and inconspicuous.   BLARINA p. 47

    3′ Size small (4–7 gr.; total length 69–85 mm.); skull less than 9 mm. wide with only four unicuspid teeth (three conspicuous, the fourth and posterior one quite small).   CRYPTOTIS p. 50

Genus **SOREX** Linnaeus

Long-tailed Shrews – *Musaraignes longicaudes*

Dental Formula   I $\frac{3-3}{1-1}$ C $\frac{1-1}{1-1}$ P $\frac{3-3}{1-1}$ M $\frac{3-3}{3-3}$ = 32

KEY TO THE EASTERN-CANADIAN SPECIES OF *Sorex*

1 Size large, total length more than 135 mm.; feet with fringe of stiff hairs along outer sides; skull more than 21 mm. long and 10 mm. wide, with fourth unicuspid tooth larger than the third.
SOREX PALUSTRIS p. 42

1′ Size smaller, total length less than 135 mm.; feet without stiff hairs on outer sides; skull less than 21 mm. long and 10 mm. wide: 2

2 Adult pelage strongly tricoloured; a wide dark band along the back, brown on the sides, and greyish underneath; skull 19·0–20·6 mm. long and 9·1–10·1 mm. wide, with the fourth unicuspid tooth smaller than the third (a more or less graduated reduction in size from the second to the fifth unicuspid).
SOREX ARCTICUS p. 38

2′ Adult pelage not strongly tricoloured as above; skull not as above: 3

3 Posterior border of infraorbital foramen posterior to plane of space between M^1 and M^2. Skull long and narrow with depressed rostrum; unicuspid teeth relatively narrow, with the third and fourth almost equal in size; tail relatively long (47–62 mm.); pelage greyish and only slightly paler below than above: 4

4 Total length more than 115 mm.; hind foot 13 mm. or more; skull length 17 mm. or more; pelage dark dull greyish.
SOREX DISPAR p. 41

4′ Total length less than 115 mm.; hind foot less than 13 mm.; skull length less than 17 mm.; pelage pale greyish.
SOREX GASPENSIS p. 40

3′ Posterior border of infraorbital foramen even with, or anterior to, plane of space between M^1 and M^2; pelage less greyish (more brownish); tail medium length (33–48 mm.): 5

5 Pelage above and below quite similar in colour; skull 18 mm. or more long and 8·5 mm. or more wide; fourth unicuspid tooth smaller than third; third unicuspid only slightly smaller than second.
SOREX FUMEUS p. 36

5′ Pelage below noticeably paler than above; skull less than 18 mm. long and 8·5 mm. wide; third and fourth unicuspid teeth subequal in size and distinctly smaller than first and second.
SOREX CINEREUS p. 34

Fig. 6 – LONG-TAILED SHREWS

Top to bottom: PYGMY SHREW – *Microsorex hoyi*; COMMON SHREW – *Sorex cinereus*; SMOKY SHREW – *Sorex fumeus*; ARCTIC SHREW – *Sorex arcticus*; GASPÉ SHREW – *Sorex gaspensis*; WATER SHREW – *Sorex palustris*

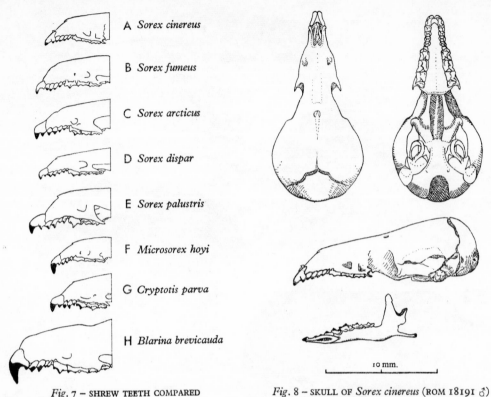

A *Sorex cinereus*

B *Sorex fumeus*

C *Sorex arcticus*

D *Sorex dispar*

E *Sorex palustris*

F *Microsorex hoyi*

G *Cryptotis parva*

H *Blarina brevicauda*

10 mm.

Fig. 7 – SHREW TEETH COMPARED

Fig. 8 – SKULL OF *Sorex cinereus* (ROM 18191 ♂)

Sorex cinereus Kerr – Common Shrew or Mask Shrew – *Musaraigne cendrée*

The common shrew is the most widespread shrew in eastern Canada. Measuring less than 4 in. long, including the tail, this tiny animal is a bundle of energy and a voracious feeder, often consuming more than its own body weight in twenty-four hours. The fur is soft and brownish in colour above, although full adults often develop a darker band along the back; the underparts are greyish or buffy. The winter pelage is darker above and paler below. The tail is brownish or fuscous above and buffy below. The ears are inconspicuous, barely protruding above the fur. The feet and eyes are quite small. The common shrew has a gland on each side that gives off a musky odour.

Usually positive identification cannot be made without examining the teeth. The number and relative sizes of the upper unicuspid teeth (between the large anterior incisor and the molars) serve as the best features for identifying this and similar species of shrews. In the case of the common shrew, the first four unicuspids are approximately similar in size, although the third and fourth, which are about the same size, are slightly smaller than the first and second. This characteristic easily separates the common shrew from the pygmy shrew (*Microsorex*), which it most nearly resembles superficially, and distinguishes it from the smoky shrew to which it sometimes appears similar—although the smoky shrew usually displays a different colour, especially on the underparts, and is larger in size on the average.

SIZE Total length 80–115 (av. 100) mm.; tail 33–47 (av. 36); hind foot 10–13 (av. 12). Skull: length 16–17.5, width 7.4–8.4. Weight 3.5–5.6 (av. 4) gr.

DISTRIBUTION AND VARIATION The common shrew ranges throughout all of eastern Canada with the exception of Newfoundland and the northern extremity of the Ungava peninsula. In September 1958, ten males and twelve females were released four miles east of St George's, Nfld. By 1959 a total of 130 specimens had been captured at the release site, including eleven of the original stock (which came from the Green River watershed of northwestern New Brunswick). This species shows little geographic variation, although in addition to

Sorex cinereus cinereus, which occurs in all except the extreme eastern parts of the species range in eastern Canada, two other races have been described. The name *S. c. acadicus* has been applied to the form occurring in Nova Scotia, New Brunswick, Prince Edward Island, and the eastern part of Quebec south of the St Lawrence River. Compared with *S. c. cinereus*, it has a longer tail and a larger skull; the brain case is larger and the maxillary toothrow is longer and less arched. Compared with *S. c. miscix*, described from Black Bay, Strait of Belle Isle, Labrador, *S. c. acadicus* is darker in both winter and summer pelage, the rostrum is heavier and less tapering, and the cranium is less rounded laterally.

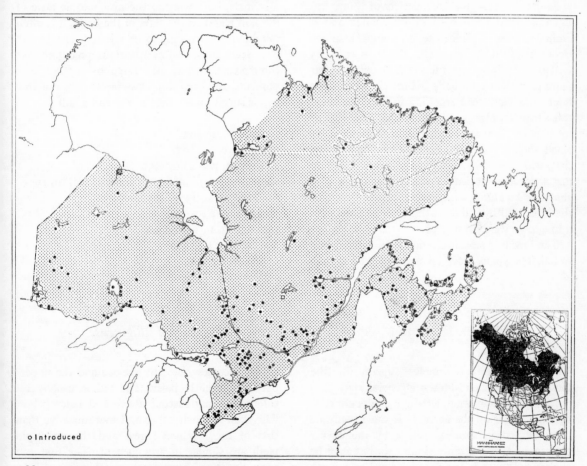

o Introduced

Map 2 – DISTRIBUTION OF THE COMMON SHREW – *Sorex cinereus* – AND TYPE LOCALITIES OF (1) *S. c. cinereus* Kerr; (2) *S. c. miscix* Bangs; (3) *S.c. acadicus* Gilpin

HABITAT The common shrew is rather ubiquitous and may be encountered in all main types of habitat.

HABITS The common shrew is an erratic, high-strung, energetic mammal. Its breathing rate has been recorded at 850 times per minute, with a heart beat of 800 per minute. The eyes are quite small and poorly developed and probably function only for perceiving certain light intensities. The voice is a high-pitched squeak. This shrew moves about in an erratic fashion, with its long, pointed nose constantly twitching and occasionally sniffling or snorting.

Food consists primarily of insects and other invertebrates, although a wide variety of things are eaten, including the flesh of vertebrates and a limited amount of plant material. Common shrews frequently feed on trappers' catches in traps as well as on their caches of food. They normally eat more than their own body weight in twenty-four hours and have been recorded to consume three times their own weight in this period. They appear to 'blunder' into food rather than seek it out by smell, though controlled experiments have shown that, with remarkable acuteness, they will dig up insect cocoons buried in sand; they were also shown to be able to differentiate between cocoons that were healthy and those that were infected with a fungus or were parasitized.

The breeding season extends from early spring to fall. The young reach breeding age in less than one year. Several litters of up to eleven young (the average is about seven or eight) may be produced each season. The gestation period is about eighteen days. The tiny naked young develop rather rapidly; they become well furred in about ten days and leave the globular nest of fine or shredded plant material in about three weeks, fully independent.

Active at all hours and in all seasons, the common shrew is frequently encountered scurrying around above ground, although it spends most of the time below the ground surface where it utilizes runways, both its own and those of other small animals.

REMARKS The common shrew is eaten by many mammals, but owing to the disagreeable taste of the skin gland on the sides of the body, it is often caught and killed only to be rejected. Hawks and owls seem to be the most serious predators, but common shrews are also eaten by reptiles, amphibians, and even fish. Only rarely does this tiny shrew survive more than a year and a half.

Selected References
BLOSSOM, P. M., 1932.
HAMILTON, W. J., JR., 1930.
HAMILTON, W. J., JR. and W. J. HAMILTON III, 1955.
HOLLING, C. S., 1955, 1958.
JACKSON, C. F., 1939a.
JACKSON, H. H. T., 1928.
MACLEOD, C. F., 1960.
MOORE, J. C., 1949.

Sorex fumeus Miller – Smoky Shrew – *Musaraigne fuligineuse*

The smoky shrew resembles superficially the masked or common shrew in general size, proportions, and coloration, although adults are consistently larger on the average. It can usually be distinguished in summer pelage by the darker underparts that are quite similar to, but may be slightly lighter than, the deep brownish or greyish brown of the remainder of the body. In winter the pelage becomes distinctly greyish and the underparts are slightly paler. The tail is usually bicoloured, being fuscous above and paler below. The skull is much larger and more massive than that of the common shrew and the unicuspid teeth are similar in arrangement. The first and second unicuspids are nearly equal in size and the third and fourth are smaller; the third is larger

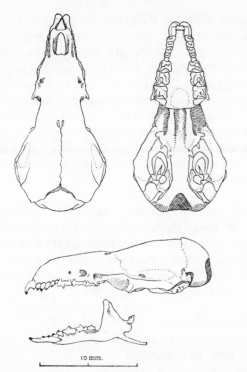

Fig. 9 – SKULL OF *Sorex fumeus* (ROM 16646 ♂)

than the fourth. All the teeth are more massive than those of the common shrew, particularly the third and fourth unicuspids, and they lack the pig-

mented ridge extending from the apex toward the palate as in *Sorex cinereus cinereus*. The skull is flatter throughout compared with that of *S. arcticus*, with a much shallower brain case, and it is relatively narrower and less angular.

SIZE Total length 110–128 (av. 117) mm.; tail 37–48 (av. 45); hind foot 12–15 (av. 13). Skull: length 18.0–19.2, width 8.5–9.3. Weight 6–12 gr.

DISTRIBUTION AND VARIATION The smoky shrew is a distinctly eastern form and reaches both its northern and western as well as its eastern limits in eastern Canada. It occurs throughout the Maritime Provinces and in Quebec from about a line joining the Saguenay River and Lake St John across the Ontario border near Lake Abitibi and west to the north shore of Lake Superior at Schreiber. In Ontario its most northern record is Fraserdale in Cochrane District. It has not been recorded from the most western counties of southern Ontario (Lambton, Kent, Essex), nor from the area immediately north of the western portion of Lake Erie (Elgin, Norfolk, and Haldiman Counties).

Although showing little marked geographic variation, this species has been divided into two races. *Sorex fumeus fumeus* occurs in the area west of the

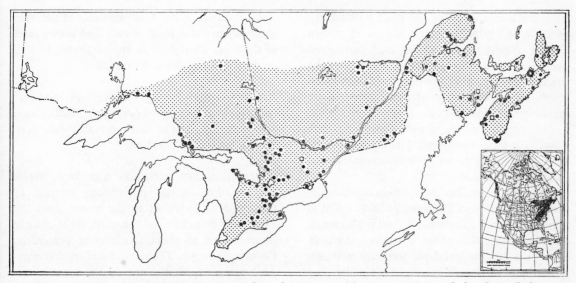

Map 3 – DISTRIBUTION OF THE SMOKY SHREW – *Sorex fumeus* – AND (1) TYPE LOCALITY OF *S. f. umbrosus* Jackson

longitude somewhere near the mouth of the Saguenay River, Que. The name *S. f. umbrosus* has been applied to the smoky shrew found east of this point: it averages slightly larger and in summer is more greyish brown (less reddish brown) on the upper parts than *S. f. fumeus*.

HABITAT The smoky shrew appears to be more exacting in its habitat requirements than the common shrew. Shady, damp, wooded areas seem to constitute the basic habitat requirements. It has been found to be most common in areas of deep moss or leaf mould around rotting logs, stumps, or rocks.

HABITS As far as is known, the habits of the smoky shrew approximate those of the common shrew in general, allowing for the restricted habitat requirements. There are probably only two litters produced each season, with four to seven being the usual number in each litter (three to ten have been reported). Breeding begins in late March in the season following birth, and the gestation period lasts about twenty days. Adults are thought to die by August of their second season—they rarely live longer than eighteen months. During the breeding season the tails of both sexes become swollen and increase to about twice normal size. Earthworms and insect larva seem to be among the favourite foods; insect remains appeared in eighty per cent of 168 stomachs analysed from New York state, while vegetable matter was found in about fifteen per cent.

REMARKS The populations seem to be quite sporadic; smoky shrews are abundant in one restricted locality one year and rare or absent the next, with similar variations from one locality to another in the same year. Much remains to be learned about the basic biology of this species.

Selected References
HAMILTON, W. J., JR., 1930, 1940d.
JACKSON, H. H. T., 1928.

Sorex arcticus Kerr – Arctic or Saddle-back Shrew – *Musaraigne arctique*

This northern shrew has the most striking appearance of any of the native shrews of eastern Canada. Adults show a well-defined tricoloured pattern. A broad band of almost black extends the length of the back; the sides are a rich cinnamon brown to wood brown; and the underparts are greyish with a tinge of buff.

The subadult pelage is pale above and dark below. The tail is bicoloured, dark above and pale below. The young do not show the distinct dorsal band or 'saddle back'.

The arctic shrew has the approximate proportions of the common and smoky shrew but it is much larger on the average. Its skull is also larger and deeper than that of the common and smoky shrew; the first two unicuspid teeth are relatively heavier, and the fourth unicuspid is smaller than the third.

Adult males show a conspicuous raised skin gland (about 7 mm. long) on each flank during most of the year. This gland is apparently not as well developed in females and subadults.

SIZE Total length 110–130 (av. 122) mm; tail 36–47 (av. 43); hind foot 13–16 (av. 14.3). Skull: length 19.0–20.3 (av. 19.5), width 9.1–10.1 (av. 9.4). Weight 7.0–12.8 (av. 11) gr.

DISTRIBUTION AND VARIATION The arctic shrew has a rather curious distribution pattern. In Ontario it is restricted to the north, from the Minnesota boundary and the north shore of Lake Superior east to about the level of Fraserdale, Cochrane District. The name *Sorex arcticus arcticus* has been applied to the Arctic shrew in this area, although animals from areas adjacent to the

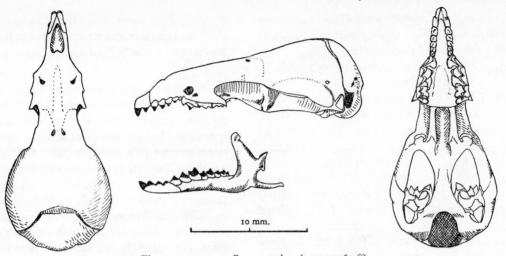

Fig. 10 – SKULL OF *Sorex arcticus* (ROM 19169 ♀)

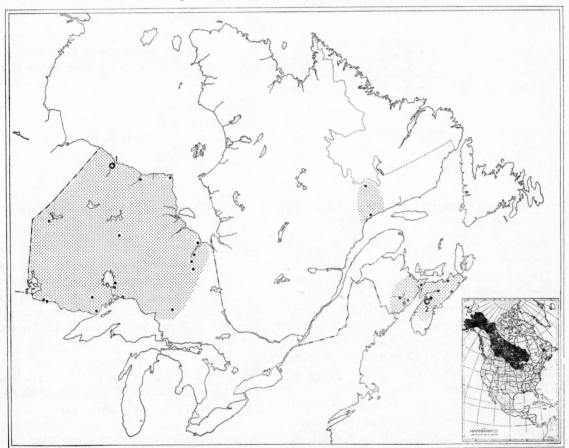

Map 4 – DISTRIBUTION OF THE ARCTIC SHREW – *Sorex arcticus* – AND TYPE LOCALITIES OF
(1) *S. a. arcticus* Kerr; (2) *S. a. maritimensis* R. W. Smith

Minnesota boundary have some of the characteristics of *S. a. laricorum*, which differs principally in having a flatter and shallower brain case.

Apparently the arctic shrew has been taken in only one locality in Quebec—the north shore of the Gulf of St Lawrence along the west bank of the Moisie River. This is about 800 miles east of the nearest-known occurrence of this shrew in Ontario, and a little over 300 miles north of the nearest specimen known from southern New Brunswick. Undoubtedly more extensive collecting will shorten if not bridge these gaps, but until more material becomes available, the affinities of this isolated population must remain in question.

The curious occurrence of this species in Nova Scotia and New Brunswick, quite apart from the main range, poses an interesting zoogeographical problem.

The south-eastern population has been described as a distinct race, *S. a. maritimensis*, which is characterized by its light colour, a short and blunt rostrum, and a more rounded but shallow brain case.

HABITAT Relatively little is known about the specific habitat of the arctic shrew. In general it seems to prefer fairly open areas around treed swamps, marshes, and other moist situations, but it usually avoids open leatherleaf-sphagnum bogs.

HABITS In general it is assumed that the habits of the arctic shrew are similar to those of the common and smoky shrews. Detailed studies of this species are lacking. Pregnant females have been taken in mid-July and late July, and lactating females in late July in northern Ontario, and from April 27th to June 22nd in Wisconsin; records of pregnant females in Nova Scotia include May 3rd and July 10th. The number of young noted to date in eastern Canada has been either five or six per litter, although eight and nine have been recorded elsewhere.

REMARKS This species offers a challenging opportunity to provide much-needed data on many aspects of its distribution, life history, and ecology.

Selected References
JACKSON, C. F., 1938.
JACKSON, H. H. T., 1925, 1928, 1961.
SMITH, R. W., 1939a.

Sorex gaspensis Anthony and Goodwin – Gaspé Shrew – *Musaraigne de Gaspé*

Known only from the Shickshock Mountain region of the Gaspé Peninsula, Que., and near Mount Carleton, N.B., this species probably occupies the smallest total range of any mammal in eastern Canada. Its nearest relative, *Sorex dispar*, also occupies a restrictive (though much larger) range south of the American border in Maine and near the Canadian–New Hampshire border south through eastern New York and New Jersey to Tennessee and North Carolina.

The Gaspé shrew is roughly the same size and has about the same proportions as the common shrew except for its longer tail, but it differs in having a distinctly greyish or slate-coloured pelage, which is darker above and lighter below. The skull, which is similar to that of the common shrew but is relatively longer and thinner, differs in that the posterior border of the infraorbital foramen lies behind the plane of the interspace between the second and third molar teeth. This shrew closely resembles *S. dispar*, but it is usually smaller and lighter in colour.

SIZE Total length 95–118 mm.; tail 47–55; hind foot 11.0–12.5. Skull: length 15.8–16.3, width 7.3–7.9. Weight approximately 3.5–5.0 gr.

DISTRIBUTION Specimens have been taken only from Mount Albert, on the north slope of the Shickshock Mountains on the Gaspé Peninsula,

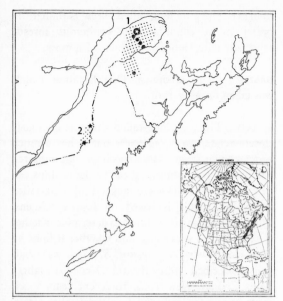

Map 5 – DISTRIBUTION OF THE GASPÉ SHREW – *Sorex gaspensis* – AND THE GRAY LONG-TAILED SHREW – *Sorex dispar.* (1) TYPE LOCALITY OF *S. gaspensis* Anthony and Goodwin; (2) CANADIAN RECORDS OF *Sorex dispar.*

and from the Cascopedia Valley north as far as Big Barry Mountain on the south slope of the Shickshocks; a single specimen was taken near Mount Carleton, N.B., in 1961 and was reported in 1963. The Gaspé shrew would appear to be a surviving relic species isolated for the most part on mountain ranges.

HABITAT Apparently this species prefers streamside habitats similar to those of the water shrew, *Sorex palustris.*

HABITS Very little is known about the Gaspé shrew. The stomach contents of two animals taken in 1953 at Mount Albert were as follows: one contained twenty per cent beetle remains plus plant matter and the other thirty per cent spider remains plus plant matter. The habitat of the Gaspé shrew suggests that some of its habits may be similar to those of the water shrew.

REMARKS The Gaspé shrew is one of the least-known mammals in eastern Canada. It would be highly interesting to learn more about this species and to determine what factors limit its distribution and spread.

Selected References

ANTHONY, H. E. and G. G. GOODWIN, 1924.
GOODWIN, G. G., 1924, 1929.
HALL, E. R. and K. R. KELSON, 1959.
HAMILTON, W. J., JR. and W. J. HAMILTON III, 1955.
JACKSON, H. H. T., 1928.
PETERSON, RICHARD S. and ADAM SYMANSKY, 1963.

Sorex dispar Batchelder – Gray Long-tailed Shrew – *Musaraigne longicaude*

The unusually long tail in proportion to the body serves as the best means of distinguishing this species. It is similar to *Sorex gaspensis* but appears on the average to be larger and darker. The winter pelage is slate-coloured both above and below. The tail is distinctly bicoloured, brownish above and pale below. The skull is long, narrow, and flattened, and is larger than that of *S. cinereus* or *S. gaspensis*, slightly smaller than that of *S. fumeus*, and much smaller than that of *S. palustris*. The posterior border of the infraorbital foramen is situated posterior to the plane of the space between M^1 and M^2.

SIZE Total length 113–130 mm.; tail 49–62; hind foot 13–15. Skull: length 17.3–18.2, width 8.0–8.1. Weight 5–6 gr.

DISTRIBUTION The first known specimens of this long-tailed shrew in Canada were taken as recently as 1955 near Lac du Portage, ten miles southeast of Armstrong, Que., near the Maine border; and south of Cartierville, Que., just a few yards north of the New Hampshire border. Several earlier attempts to locate the long-tailed shrew in nearby areas failed. A better understanding of the habits of this species may make it possible to trace its range more accurately in Canada.

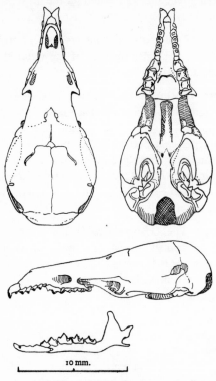

Fig. 11 – SKULL OF *Sorex dispar* (ROM 27936 ♀)

HABITAT The gray long-tailed shrew is thought to prefer moist conditions in coniferous forests, especially talus slopes overgrown with moss.

HABITS Largely unknown. One lactating female was taken on May 18th.

REMARKS The gray long-tailed shrew is obviously closely related to *S. gaspensis* but it has a much wider known range. More specimens are required before a thorough study of their relationships can be carried out. The known range of this long-tailed shrew in Canada is based on four specimens. Further collecting is required to determine whether it exists over a wider area and whether it links up more closely with *S. gaspensis. S. dispar* was originally described from Beedes (Keene Heights), Essex County, New York. In recent years specimens have been collected in several other states, and these have extended its known range considerably.

Selected References
JACKSON, H. H. T., 1928.
HALL, E. R. and K. R. KELSON, 1959.

Sorex palustris Richardson – Water Shrew – *Musaraigne palustre*

The largest of the long-tailed group of shrews in eastern Canada, this species is characterized by a fringe of stiff hairs along the margins of both front and hind feet (they are more conspicuous on the latter) that facilitate swimming for the water-shrew's semi-aquatic existence. The toes are partially webbed. This species not only swims and dives with great agility, but it is also capable of walking on the surface of the water for short distances when the surface is glossy smooth. Apparently the fibrillae or stiff hairs on the feet serve to trap a globule of air that assists in this feat.

The pelage is quite dark above—almost black in some forms—and varies from silver white to buffy grey below.

The skull—the largest of the skulls of *Sorex* inhabiting eastern Canada—is smooth, weak, and fragile, and is characterized by a fourth unicuspid that is larger than the third.

SIZE Total length 140–164 mm.; tail 63–75; hind foot 18–21. Skull: length 21–23, width 10–11. Weight 10–18 gr.

DISTRIBUTION AND VARIATION The water shrew occurs throughout most of the whole of eastern Canada except Newfoundland. (It has not been recorded from Prince Edward Island, Anticosti Island, or the northern portion of the Ungava Peninsula, although extensive trapping in these areas

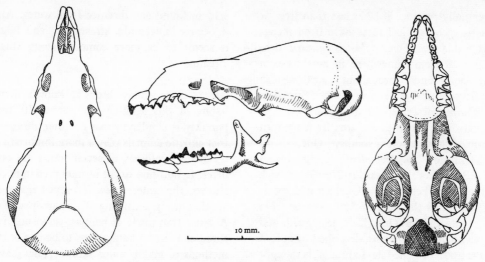

Fig. 12 – SKULL OF *Sorex palustris* (ROM 22134 ♂)

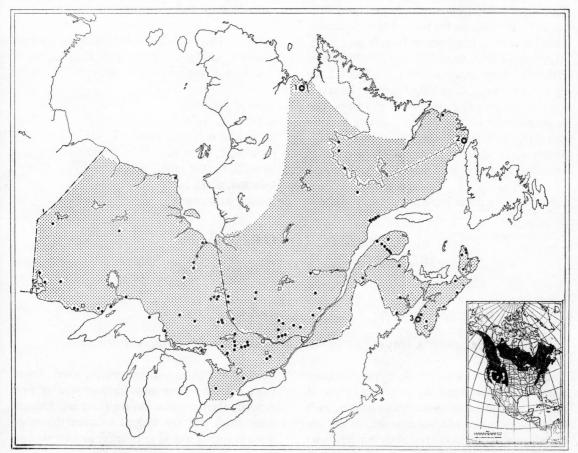

Map 6 – DISTRIBUTION OF THE WATER SHREW – *Sorex palustris* – AND TYPE LOCALITIES OF
(1) *S. p. turneri* Johnson; (2) *S. p. labradorensis* Burt; (3) *S. p. gloveralleni* Jackson

may eventually produce it.) No less than five, or perhaps six, geographical races have been recognized from this area. *Sorex palustris palustris*, described in 1828 from somewhere in northwestern Canada, is found throughout northwestern Ontario from central James Bay to Lake Superior. *S. p. albibarbis*, described from Grafton County, New Hampshire, occupies the area from western New Brunswick west across southern Quebec and southern Ontario. *S. p. gloveralleni*, described from Digby, N.S., occurs also in eastern New Brunswick and in the Gaspé Peninsula of Quebec; and specimens taken across the Gulf of St Lawrence from Godbout to Seal River, Que., have been attributed to this race. *S. p. labradorensis*, described from Red Bay on the Strait of Belle Isle, Labrador, is thought to occur across southern Labrador and adjacent Quebec. *S. p. turneri* was recently described from Fort Chimo, Que., on the basis of two specimens. No other records from eastern Canada are known. *S. p. hydrobadistes*, described from Clark County, Wisconsin, may occur in either the Rainy Lake region or the area east of Lake Superior; however, more specimens and further study will be needed to ascertain the identity of water shrews in these areas. Needless to say, the entire species needs further study based on a more adequate series of specimens from across its range.

HABITAT As its name implies, the water shrew is seldom found any distance from water. Although it occurs in lakeside, streamside, and bog areas, it seems to be more common along small cool streams.

HABITS Surprisingly little is known about the habits of this semi-aquatic shrew. Its food apparently is similar to that of other shrews except that aquatic animals play a more important role in its diet. Usually six or seven young are born per litter. In addition to the normal predators of other shrews, the water shrew is preyed upon by still another group consisting of various species of fish. A water trap made of pails or cans sunk into the shore of a stream bank seems to be one of the best methods of taking water shrews. They have even been caught in submerged minnow traps—an indication of their diving activity.

REMARKS This distinctive shrew should be the subject of much further study from a taxonomic as well as an ecological point of view.

Selected References
BURT, W. H., 1938.
HAMILTON, W. J., JR., 1930.
JACKSON, C. F., 1938.
JACKSON, H. H. T., 1928, 1961.
JOHNSON, D. H., 1951.
MOORE, W. H., 1910.

Genus **MICROSOREX** Coues

Pygmy Shrews – *Musaraignes pygmées*

Dental Formula $\quad$ I $\frac{3-3}{1-1}$ $\quad$ C $\frac{1-1}{1-1}$ $\quad$ P $\frac{3-3}{1-1}$ $\quad$ M $\frac{3-3}{3-3}$ = 32

Microsorex hoyi (Baird) – Pygmy Shrew – *Musaraigne pygmée*

This shrew, the smallest of the North American mammals, may not weigh any more than a ten-cent piece when fully mature. Superficially it looks much like a common shrew (*Sorex cinereus*). Its feet are slightly smaller and its tail is slightly thinner, however. For positive identification one must resort to checking the unicuspid teeth which, when viewed from the side, show only three instead of five. Actually there are five, but the third and fifth are quite small and are wedged between the other teeth in such a way as to be quite inconspicuous.

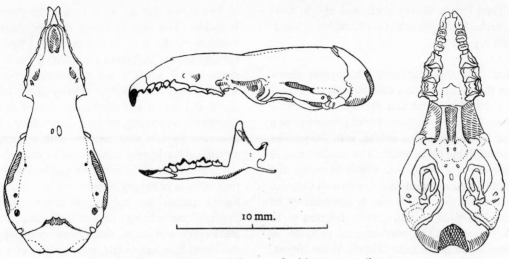

Fig. 13 – SKULL OF *Microsorex hoyi* (ROM 21771 ♂)

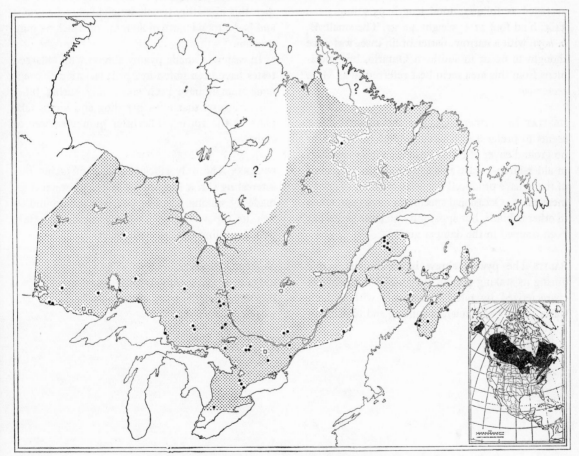

Map 7 – DISTRIBUTION OF THE PYGMY SHREW – *Microsorex hoyi*

SIZE Total length 78–105 mm.; tail 28–38; hind foot 9–12. Skull: length 14–16, width 6.3–7.2. Weight 2.3–7.3 gr.

DISTRIBUTION AND VARIATION The pygmy shrew occurs throughout eastern Canada with the exception of Newfoundland and perhaps the extreme northern Ungava Peninsula. There appears to be a general north-south cline in size, with the smaller specimens living in the south. The smallest race is *Microsorex hoyi thompsoni*, which occupies the Maritime Provinces westward to southern Ontario. The central region in this area is inhabited by an intermediate-sized animal, usually referred to as *M. h. intervectus*. The northernmost race, *M. h. alnorum*, found in northern Ontario, is the largest. A series of sixty-six adults from northern Ontario averaged as follows: total length 95.5 mm.; tail 34.4; hind foot 11.4; weight 4.8 gr. The small *M. h. hoyi*, with a narrow, flatter brain case, was once thought to occur in southern Ontario, but specimens from this area seem best referred to as *M. h. thompsoni*.

HABITAT In northern Ontario the pygmy shrew seems to prefer a dry, open habitat with little or no ground cover of brush or litter. Grass clearings in alder-birch-poplar associations, or in variations of them, have produced the great majority of specimens taken. Occasional specimens have been taken in other habitats, but apparently no large series has been trapped in the damper areas.

HABITS The pygmy shrew is continually active during its waking period. Its general behaviour is characterized by rapid movements with sudden starts and stops, a constant sniffing and twisting of its long thin snout, and by the short, sharp squeaks it makes. The pygmy shrew may be active or asleep at any hour of the day or night, although it appears to take little time for sleep. When it does sleep, it curls up in much the same manner as a sleeping dog. The constant activity of the pygmy shrew requires a remarkable amount of food to sustain it—almost any moving object is seized and devoured by this tiny creature with a voracious appetite. One pygmy shrew kept in captivity for ten days consumed the following within that period: the carcasses of twenty cinereus shrews, one white-footed mouse, one red-backed mouse, and one pygmy shrew, making a total of 107.5 grams. It also ate twenty houseflies, twenty-two grasshoppers, two crane flies, one beetle, and the liver of a meadow mouse during the same period. After such a diet, this immature female weighed only 3.4 grams and had a total length of 89 mm., of which 35 mm. was tail.

In eastern Canada pygmy shrews with enlarged testes have been noted in April; lactating or pregnant animals have been taken only during June. This suggests that most breeding and births take place in the spring. The litter numbers three to eight.

REMARKS The only efficient means of taking this interesting shrew has proved to be by a water trap, made by sinking a can or pail into the ground so that its top is flush with the ground, and then partially filling the can with water.

Selected References
HALL, E. R. and K. R. KELSON, 1959.
JACKSON, H. H. T., 1928, 1961.
PRINCE, L. A., 1941.

Genus **BLARINA** Gray

Big Short-tailed Shrews – *Grandes musaraignes à queue courte*

Dental Formula $\quad$ I $\frac{3-3}{1-1}$ $\quad$ C $\frac{1-1}{1-1}$ $\quad$ P $\frac{3-3}{1-1}$ $\quad$ M $\frac{3-3}{3-3} = 32$

Blarina brevicauda (Say) – Big Short-tailed Shrew – *Grande musaraigne*

The largest of the native shrews of eastern Canada is easily recognized by its short tail and large size. The big short-tailed shrew has most of the characteristics common to all shrews, and these, together with its dark soft fur and poorly developed eyes, distinguish it from rodents of the same size. The skull is the largest and most massive of the shrews of eastern Canada and has well-developed crests and ridges; it tends to become more angular with advancing age, and the tip of the rostrum becomes thicker and the first incisors are forced downward. The male skull is slightly larger on the average than the female. The unicuspid teeth are in two pairs, the front two being larger; the fifth unicuspid is small and inconspicuous. Well-developed skin glands on the flanks, especially in the males, emit a strong, pungent odour that apparently makes big short-tailed shrews unpalatable to many predators, although hawks, owls, and fishers are known to take them in large numbers.

A unique feature of this mammal is the submaxillary glands that emit a poison at the base of the lower incisor teeth. While apparently not toxic enough to endanger humans or other large animals, this poison, which is roughly comparable to that of reptiles, quickly immobilizes small animals when they are bitten. Animals up to the size of small rabbits are known to have been attacked and killed by *Blarina*.

SIZE Total length 98–136 mm.; tail 20–30; hind foot 13–18. Skull: length 20.5–25.0, width 11.3–13.3. Weight 12–27 gr.

DISTRIBUTION AND VARIATION The big short-tailed shrew is common and widespread south of a line joining the Gaspé Peninsula, Lake St John, Lake Nipigon, and Lake of the Woods. This boundary is penetrated northward along the Moose River drainage up to the river's mouth at James Bay. Unfortunately the overall trends in geographic variation are poorly understood as yet. The following forms are thought to occur in eastern Canada. *Blarina brevicauda talpoides* was described

Fig. 14 – BIG SHORT-TAILED SHREW – *Blarina brevicauda*

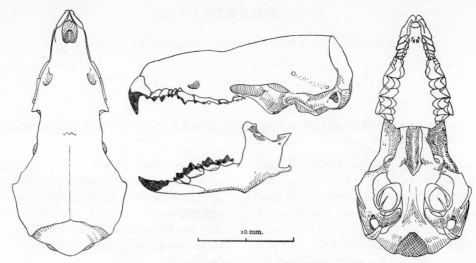

10 mm.

Fig. 15 – SKULL OF *Blarina brevicauda* (ROM 24225 ♀)

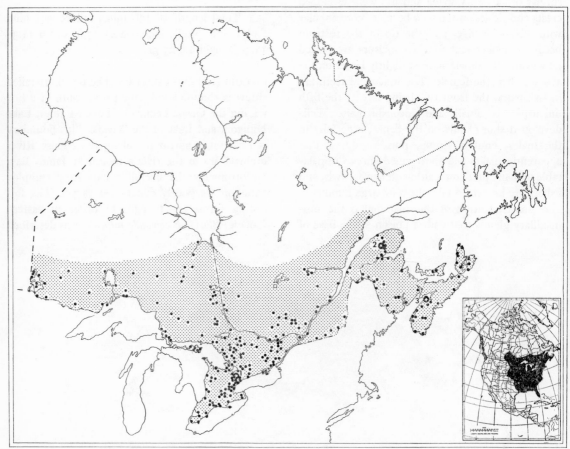

Map 8 – DISTRIBUTION OF THE BIG SHORT-TAILED SHREW – *Blarina brevicauda* – AND TYPE LOCALITIES OF
(1) *B. b. talpoides* (Gapper); (2) *B. b. angusta* Anderson; (3) *B. b. pallida* Smith

in 1830 from a site supposedly between Lake Simcoe and York (Toronto); it occurs throughout Ontario and Quebec north of the St Lawrence. *B. b. hooperi,* described from Vermont, is thought to occupy western Quebec south of the St Lawrence, while the name *B. b. angusta* has been applied to specimens from the Gaspé Peninsula and northern New Brunswick. *Blarina* from Nova Scotia and Prince Edward Island have been described as *B. b. pallida.* Only a thorough-going revisionary study will clarify the true relationships of these forms.

HABITAT The big short-tailed shrew may be found in a wide variety of habitats, although it is more common in heavy forests with deep litter that is not too dry. It sometimes occurs in unusually high numbers—the forest floor is occasionally riddled with its runways.

HABITS The fact that the *Blarina,* unlike most shrews, burrows out its own runway system in the forest floor or in bog vegetation has caused some authors to give it the name 'mole shrew'. The large populations are made possible by several annual litters of three to ten young (the average is five to seven). Breeding activity reaches its first peak about late March or early April, with matings lasting about five minutes on the average. A pair have been observed to mate twenty or more times in one day. The early litters, maturing at a little over one month, may breed and bring forth young (gestation is twenty to twenty-two days) in their first year. At birth the young are about 25 mm. long and weigh slightly more than one gram; they are hairless, pink, and have their eyes closed. In about ten days they become fully furred and are about half grown in two weeks. At eighteen to twenty days the young leave the nest, and they are essentially mature at three months. *Blarina* may live as

long as three years; however, relatively few are thought to live longer than eighteen months. There are two moults annually, one in the spring and the other in the autumn.

Like other shrews, *Blarina* carry on an accelerated existence all year long beneath the forest floor or snow. In addition to a wide variety of insects (approximately one half of their diet) and other invertebrates (about twenty-three per cent of their diet), *Blarina* feed on the flesh of vertebrates as well as plant material (about ten to twenty-five per cent). *Blarina* regularly eat about half their own weight daily and they are sometimes known to eat more than their weight in twenty-four hours. Unlike most shrews, *Blarina* will store food for future use. Recent studies have recorded a number of external and internal parasites.

REMARKS *Blarina* populations occasionally reach remarkably high proportions in certain areas, although no overall cyclic pattern has been demonstrated. Population densities are thought to exceed 250 *Blarina* per acre in areas of high density. At more normal population levels, the home range of one shrew may vary from half an acre to two acres. The collective destruction of insects and mice by *Blarina* reaches rather staggering proportions, and for this reason they are of direct economic importance to man.

Selected References
HAMILTON, W. J., JR., 1929, 1930, 1931a, 1940c.
HOLLING, C. S., 1955, 1958.
JACKSON, H. H. T., 1961.
JAMESON, E. W., JR., 1950.
KLUGH, A. B., 1921.
LAWRENCE, BARBARA, 1946.
PEARSON, O. P., 1942, 1944, 1945.
SMITH, R. W., 1940.

Genus **CRYPTOTIS** Pomel

Little Short-tailed Shrews – *Petites musaraignes à queue courte*

Dental Formula   I $\frac{3-3}{1-1}$ C $\frac{1-1}{1-1}$ P $\frac{2-2}{1-1}$ M $\frac{3-3}{3-3}$ = 30

Cryptotis parva (Say) – Little Short-tailed Shrew – *Petite musaraigne*

The little short-tailed shrew or least shrew has a very restricted range in Canada. It is readily recognized by its short tail and small size. It is dark brown above and ashy grey below. The skull differs from that of all other shrews by having only thirty instead of thirty-two teeth.

SIZE Total length 68–85 mm.; tail 13–17; hind foot 9–11. Skull: length 16.2–17.1, width 7.6–8.3. Weight 4.0–6.5 gr.

DISTRIBUTION This southern shrew has been taken in Canada only along the north shore of Lake Erie at Long Point, Ont. *Cryptotis parva parva* is the form occurring in Canada.

HABITAT Open dry grassy areas. The sandy shore of Lake Erie is the best-known habitat of this shrew in Canada.

HABITS Not much is known about the little short-tailed shrew, particularly in its northernmost range. The breeding season starts in March. The gestation period is sixteen days, and up to four or five litters per season have been reported. The young—three to nine per litter (the average is five or six)—weigh only about three-tenths of a gram each at birth. The newborn are hairless, pink, and have their eyes closed; pubescent hair appears after three or four days, and the eyes open at about ten days. The young develop quite rapidly and are weaned in about twenty-one to twenty-four days; they reach full size at one month.

The little short-tailed shrew utilizes the runways of other small mammals in its search for insects, worms, grubs, and other invertebrates. It is known to enter a beehive occasionally and even to build a nest there, where it secures an abundant supply of food. It has also been observed to attack, kill, and eat frogs and small mammals. It appears to be more sociable and gregarious than most other shrews—as many as eight have been found together under one log or stone. Owls have been known to take large numbers of this species in areas where conventional trapping methods have produced only a few, if any, specimens. The little short-tailed shrew is also eaten by other birds of prey, and by snakes and mammals.

REMARKS The little short-tailed shrew is considered difficult to trap in numbers, even in spite of relatively high populations which have been indicated by large numbers of skulls found in owl pellets. So few specimens have been taken in Canada that little is known about its local ecological requirements.

Selected References

HAMILTON, W. R., JR., 1944.

HATT, R. T., 1938.

JACKSON, H. H. T., 1961.

SNYDER, L. L., 1929a.

Fig. 16 – LITTLE SHORT-TAILED SHREW – *Cryptotis parva*

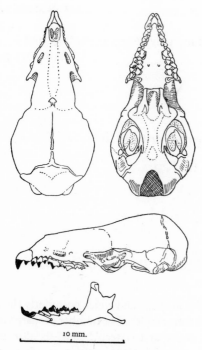

Fig. 17 – SKULL OF *Cryptotis parva*
(ROM 22881 ♂)

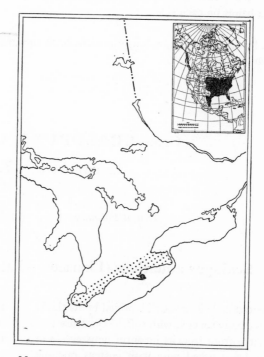

Map 9 – DISTRIBUTION OF THE LITTLE SHORT-TAILED
SHREW – *Cryptotis parva*

Family **TALPIDAE**

Moles – *Taupes*

The highly specialized burrowing insectivores are grouped together in the family *Talpidae*. The front feet are modified for digging and the entire front limbs are enlarged and powerful. To support these large muscular limbs, the sternum has a well-developed crest or keel. All moles have short dense fur, no external ear conch, and the eyes are much reduced. The zygomatic arches of the skull are present but they are weakly developed.

KEY TO THE EASTERN-CANADIAN GENERA OF *Talpidae*

1 Tail long, more than 50 mm.; end of snout has 22 small, slender, fleshy, finger-like tentacles around its edge; nostrils open toward front; skull long, with long thin rostrum and 44 teeth; upper incisors project forward and are easily seen from dorsal view of skull; bony palate terminates anterior to last molars. CONDYLURA p. 56

1′ Tail short, less than 50 mm.; end of snout without tentacles; skull relatively broader; upper incisors do not project forward; bony palate terminates posterior to the last molars: 2

2 Tail conspicuously hairy (24–30 mm. long); nostrils open forward; skull has 44 teeth (11 above and below on each side). PARASCALOPS p. 54

2′ Tail naked (21–38 mm. long); nostrils open upward; skull has only 36 teeth (10 above and 8 below on each side). SCALOPUS p. 52

Genus **SCALOPUS** E. Geoffroy-Saint Hilaire

Eastern Moles – *Taupes de l'est*

Dental Formula $I \frac{3-3}{2-2}$ $C \frac{1-1}{0-0}$ $P \frac{3-3}{3-3}$ $M \frac{3-3}{3-3} = 36$

Scalopus aquaticus (Linnaeus) – Eastern Mole – *Taupe à queue glabre*

The eastern mole is quickly identified by its thick, heavy-set body covered with soft, silky, dense fur, by its large front feet, its inconspicuous eyes and ears, its long, naked nose with nostrils opening upward, and its short, naked tail. The skull is triangular in shape and wider posteriorly than that of other native moles. The number of sharp teeth—twenty above and sixteen below—is also unique among moles. The bony palate extends posterior to the last molars.

Fig. 18 – EASTERN MOLE – *Scalopus aquaticus*

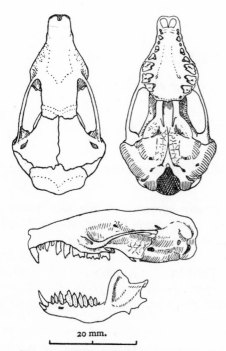

Fig. 19 – SKULL OF *Scalopus aquaticus*
(ROM 30.1.15.6 ♂)

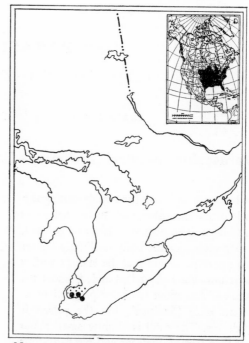

Map 10 – DISTRIBUTION OF THE EASTERN MOLE –
Scalopus aquaticus

SIZE Total length 175–206 mm.; tail 28–38; hind foot 22–26. Skull: length 37–40, width 19–20.7. Weight 75–120 gr.

DISTRIBUTION In Canada the eastern mole, *S. a. machrinus*, occurs only in Essex County, Ont. It is the largest race of the species and was originally described from Lexington, Fayette County, Kentucky.

HABITAT Sandy or sandy-loam soil suitable for underground burrowing.

HABITS The eastern mole spends all its life underground and seldom comes out on the surface. It is active at any time of the day or night or at any season of the year. It makes conspicuous tunnels just below the surface of the ground, forming pushed-up ridges, as well as deeper tunnels eight to twenty-four inches below the surface. Earthworms, insects, their larvae and pupae, and other invertebrates constitute about eighty-five per cent of this mole's diet, while vegetative matter makes up the rest. Its breeding habits are similar to those of the hairy-tailed mole; breeding begins in March. The gestation period is about forty-five days. The potential life-span is thought to be five or six years, but it probably averages only three or four. Although it bears the name *S. aquaticus*, the eastern mole is not an aquatic form. In fact it is much less aquatic than the star-nosed mole, *Condylura cristata*.

REMARKS This species becomes a serious pest when it invades golf-course greens and the lawns and gardens, truck gardens, or nurseries within its range. Control measures require a poisoning program or special mole traps.

Selected References
ARLTON, A. V., 1936.
HISAW, F. L., 1923a and b.
JACKSON, H. H. T., 1915, 1961.
SILVER, J. and A. W. MOORE, 1941.

Genus **PARASCALOPS** True

Hairy-tailed Moles – *Taupes à queue chevelue*

Dental Formula $I \frac{3-3}{3-3}$ $C \frac{1-1}{1-1}$ $P \frac{4-4}{4-4}$ $M \frac{3-3}{3-3} = 44$

Parascalops breweri (Bachman) – Hairy-tailed Mole – *Taupe à queue velue*

A short hairy tail and dark fur readily distinguish this mole from the other two moles native to eastern Canada. The nose is naked and pointed. The under-surface of the body is slightly lighter than the upper parts and may be stained with a tinge of yellow. The hairy-tailed mole is about the same size and has about the same proportions as the eastern mole (*Scalopus*), but the pelage is usually darker. The skull is slightly smaller and narrower than that of *Scalopus* and has forty-four instead of thirty-six teeth. As special mole traps are usually necessary to take this species efficiently, knowledge of its distribution and habits is quite sketchy for eastern Canada.

SIZE Total length 150–170 mm.; tail 24–30; hind foot 17–21. Skull: length 31–34, width 13.9–15.0. Weight 40–65 gr. Males are slightly larger than females.

DISTRIBUTION The known range of the hairy-tailed mole in eastern Canada is restricted to south

Fig. 20 — HAIRY-TAILED MOLE — *Parascalops breweri*

of a line south of Lake Nipissing in Ontario, due east across southern Quebec to Quebec City, and apparently extending into southern New Brunswick. (The only record available for New Brunswick is a report from Charlotte County in 1884.)

HABITAT Well-drained light soil suitable for burrowing. Heavy clay and gravel are usually avoided, and so are moist areas.

HABITS Maturity is reached in one year. Mating occurs in March and April. After a gestation period of about one month, a litter of four or five young is born in April or May in a nest of dry vegetation located about a foot or more beneath the ground surface. They weigh one third of an ounce and are blind, naked, and helpless. They develop rapidly and are able to shift for themselves at about one month.

During the summer the hairy-tailed mole makes a network of tunnels (which are much less conspicuous than those of the eastern mole) just below the surface of the ground where it feeds on earthworms, insects and their larvae, and other invertebrates. It occasionally leaves a tunnel at night but it is seldom seen by most people. As winter

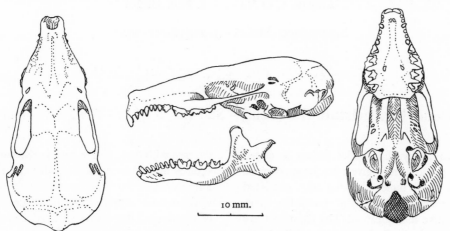

10 mm.

Fig. 21 — SKULL OF *Parascalops breweri* (ROM 17516 ♂)

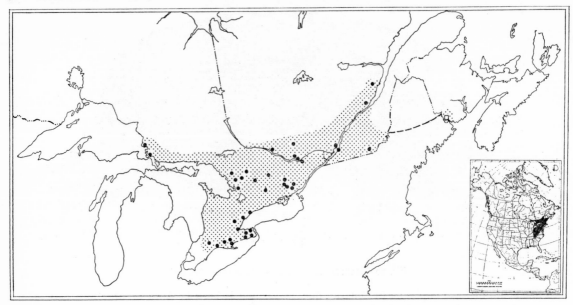

Map 11 – DISTRIBUTION OF THE HAIRY-TAILED MOLE – *Parascalops breweri*

approaches, it retreats to deeper tunnels which it clears by pushing up small mounds of earth, about three inches high and six inches wide, at intervals. The hairy-tailed mole becomes a serious pest when it invades golf greens or lawns. A voracious feeder, it is known to consume more than three times its own weight in twenty-four hours.

REMARKS The hairy-tailed mole is endemic to northeastern North America. About the northern third of its range is confined to eastern Canada.
Selected References
EADIE, W. R., 1947.
JACKSON, H. H. T., 1915.
MORRIS, R. F., 1948.

Genus **CONDYLURA** Illiger

Star-nosed Moles – *Condylures étoilés*

Dental Formula $\quad$ I $\frac{3-3}{3-3}$ $\quad$ C $\frac{1-1}{1-1}$ $\quad$ P $\frac{4-4}{4-4}$ $\quad$ M $\frac{3-3}{3-3} = 44$

Condylura cristata (Linnaeus) – Star-nosed Mole – *Condylure étoilé*

Twenty-two fleshy, finger-like feelers arranged around the tip of the nose give a unique appearance and a name to this mole. The long tail, constricted at the base and swollen with stored fat, gives further positive identification. The front feet are not as large as those of other moles, and the body, covered with dark, coarse hair, is also smaller. The skull is more delicate and slender and tapers to a long thin rostrum. The front incisors project forward and are clearly visible from the dorsal view of the skull. Like the hairy-tailed mole, the star-nosed mole has forty-four teeth.

Fig. 22 – STAR-NOSED MOLE – *Condylura cristata*

SIZE Total length 170–207 mm.; tail 60–87; hind foot 26–30. Skull: length 33.5–35.2, width 13–14.2. Weight 34–77 gr.

DISTRIBUTION AND VARIATION The star-nosed mole extends much further north than any other mole—well up both sides of James Bay and eastern Hudson Bay to Little Whale River, to southern Labrador in the east and northwest to Big Trout Lake in the Patricia portion of Kenora District, Ont. It is a distinctly eastern species—about half its range is in eastern Canada. *Condylura cristata cristata* is the form occurring throughout eastern Canada, except in Nova Scotia where the race *C. c. nigra* occurs. *C. c. nigra* differs from *C. c. cristata* by being slightly larger and darker (its winter pelage is black instead of brown above and darker grey, less brown, below) and by having a slightly larger and wider skull.

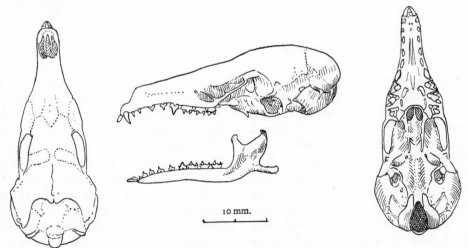

10 mm.

Fig. 23 – SKULL OF *Condylura cristata* (ROM 31.9.11.592 ♂)

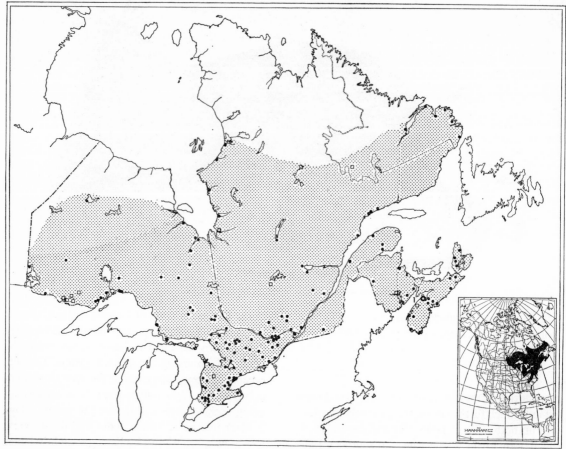

Map 12 – DISTRIBUTION OF THE STAR-NOSED MOLE – *Condylura cristata* – AND (1) TYPE LOCALITY OF
C. c. nigra Smith

HABITAT Moist areas—including swamps, bogs, and wet meadows—shunned by other moles.

HABITS The star-nosed mole frequently enters the water, where it forages for food. It is an excellent swimmer both under water and on the surface, and has been known to swim about under a layer of ice. Its underground tunnels—which may proceed directly into water—are usually wider than high and located deeper than those of other moles. Mounds of earth from its deep tunnels are about the only evidence of the star-nosed mole's presence. It spends much more time above ground than other moles and can be taken in numbers with an ordinary mouse-trap. It is not so well modified for burrowing as other moles and can tunnel at the rate of only about eight feet per hour in normal soil.

Breeding starts in March and the gestation period lasts forty-five days. Three to seven (an average of six) young per litter are born from mid-April to June. They are about 70 to 75 mm. long (tail about 25 mm.), pink, and virtually hairless; the nose tentacles are well formed. The young remain in the nest about one month.

Less than a quarter of the diet of full-grown star-nosed moles includes the same bill of fare as that of other moles, while aquatic organisms, including even small fish, make up the remainder. The fleshy rays of the nose, except the two median upper ones which are held rigidly forward, are in constant motion when this mole is searching for food.

Populations as high as thirty per acre have been recorded, although about ten per acre is thought to be a normal high population.

REMARKS The star-nosed mole occurs on Cape Breton Island, N.S., but it apparently failed to reach Prince Edward Island, Anticosti Island,

(Que.), and Newfoundland. It has pushed a surprising distance northward in Quebec and Labrador.

An ordinary snap-back trap placed in a narrow ditch will frequently catch this mole.

Selected References
HAMILTON, W. J., JR., 1931b.
JACKSON, H. H. T., 1915, 1961.
SMITH, R. W., 1940.

Order

Chiroptera

The development of 'hand wings' (Chiroptera), which enable bats to fly, is the chief distinguishing characteristic of this order. With this modification for flight, several features of the anatomy of bats are affected. The pectoral muscles are greatly enlarged; a keel on the sternum supports their attachments. The hind limbs are weakly formed and are directed backward and upward rather than down.

All bats are primarily nocturnal, although their eyesight is poor. However, the auditory sense is highly developed so that bats are able to guide themselves in total darkness by a system of sonar based on an ultrasonic cry—produced by a specialized larynx—which they emit at regular intervals, usually between twenty and sixty times per second. The pulse rate of the cry is varied at will, becoming more frequent on the approach of an obstacle or flying prey. Each pulse usually lasts less than 1/100th of a second (or 10 milliseconds); its frequency varies from about 20 to 100 kilocycles

in bats studied thus far. These pulses bounce back from objects in the flight path of the bat and are picked up by its sensitive ears in time to warn it of an obstruction, or of the presence of prey. Much research has been done on the ultrasonic cries and the process of acoustic orientation of bats. Recent advances in this new field, commonly called echolocation, have been ably reviewed by D. R. Griffin in *Listening in the Dark* (Yale University Press, 1958).

Little is known about the breeding habits of most bats. The actual fertilization of the ovum of hibernating bats takes place after a delay of six to eight months from the time of mating.

Selected References
ALLEN, G. M., 1939b.
GRIFFIN, D. R., 1958.
GRIFFIN, D. R., F. A. WEBSTER and C. R. MICHAEL, 1960.
MILLER, G. S., 1897b.

Family **VESPERTILIONIDAE**

Common Bats – *Chauves-souris*

All bats found in eastern Canada belong to this family. Some are migratory, others hibernate locally; some species are solitary while others are gregarious. The primary migratory species are solitary and have a well-furred interfemoral membrane. Females of local migratory bats are significantly larger on the average than males—the length of the female forearm gives a good index to their larger size. This appears to be correlated with the fact that the solitary species have larger litters and tend to carry them longer than the gregarious species, which leave their young at the roost when they become a burden in flight.

All members of this family are insectivorous and for the most part capture their food in flight, although some species are known to pick up insects from the ground or from trees. During hunting or orientation these bats emit pulses of ultrasonic sound at intervals of 50 to 100 milliseconds on a frequency of 25 to 100 kilocycles. When a bat is cruising in the clear, high above the ground, its pulse rate may be as low as 4 per second, but when it is flying at about twenty to forty feet above ground its pulse rate is speeded up to about 10 per second. When a flying insect is detected, the pulse rate is progressively speeded up on about the same frequency (usually below 50 kilocycles) and the flight is reorientated toward the prey. When the bat is within a few centimetres of its prey, the pulse duration shortens to about 0.5 milliseconds and the interval between pulses reduces to 5 or 6 milliseconds while the frequency drops to 25 or 30 kilocycles to produce a rapid buzz, just above the upper limits of human hearing. In areas of high insect population, ten or fifteen insects per minute may be captured in this manner. A bat was observed in a laboratory experiment to capture two flying insects in less than half a second.

One species, *Myotis sodalis*, has been taken south of Lake Erie and more recently near Watertown, New York, by Mr M. Brock Fenton, but it has not yet been recorded in Canada; it is included in the keys to provide a means of identification, since it may eventually be discovered in eastern Canada.

KEY TO THE EASTERN-CANADIAN GENERA OF *Vespertilionidae*

1 Dorsal surface of interfemoral membrane densely furred; ears relatively short and rounded; dentition with either 36 or 32 teeth with only one upper incisor on each side: 2

    2 Dentition with one upper incisor on each side and two premolars above and below (total 32); skull high, short, and broad with wide rostrum; dorsal coloration reddish- or greyish-brown with white-tipped hairs; metacarpals of third, fourth, and fifth fingers successively much shortened.   LASIURUS p. 78

    2′ Dentition with two upper incisors on each side and two premolars above and three below (total 36); skull relatively long and low with tapered rostrum; dorsal coloration blackish with white-tipped hairs; metacarpals of third, fourth, and fifth fingers subequal in length.
          LASIONYCTERIS p. 70

1′ Dorsal surface of interfemoral membrane not densely furred; ears not short and rounded; dentition not as above: 3

3 Dentition with only 30 teeth (one upper incisor, one premolar above and two below); tragus short, rounded, blunt, with end curved forward; usually less than half the height of ear from notch; forearm 33–38 mm. NYCTICEIUS p. 77

3′ Dentition with more than 30 teeth (two upper incisors) :4

    4 Dentition with 32 teeth (one premolar above and two below); forearm more than 40 mm.; tragus relatively broad; dorsal coloration brownish. EPTESICUS p. 74

    4′ Dentition with more than 32 teeth; forearm less than 40 mm.: 5

        5 Dentition with 34 teeth (two premolars above and below); dorsal coloration yellowish brown to golden brown; fur tricoloured; tragus height less than one-half the height of the ear from notch. PIPISTRELLUS p. 72

        5′ Dentition with 38 teeth (three premolars above and below); dorsal coloration brownish; fur not tricoloured (except in *Myotis sodalis*★); tragus long and slender, usually more than half the height of the ear from notch. MYOTIS p. 62

★ Not recorded from eastern Canada.

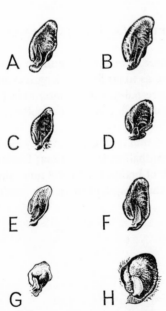

Fig. 24 – BAT EARS COMPARED

A – *Myotis lucifugus*	E – *Pipistrellus subflavus*
B – *Myotis keenii*	F – *Eptesicus fuscus*
C – *Myotis subulatus*	G – *Lasiurus borealis*
D – *Lasionycteris noctivagans*	H – *Lasiurus cinereus*

Genus **MYOTIS** Kaup

Mouse-eared Bats – *Chauves-souris communes*

Dental Formula $\text{I} \frac{2-2}{3-3}$ $\text{C} \frac{1-1}{1-1}$ $\text{P} \frac{3-3}{3-3}$ $\text{M} \frac{3-3}{3-3} = 38$

KEY TO THE EASTERN-CANADIAN SPECIES OF *Myotis*

1 Forearm less than 33 mm.; foot small, 7 mm. or less; length of third metacarpal less than length of forearm; face usually black; fur on back with long shiny tips, giving a burnished appearance; skull 13–14 mm. long and 8.0–8.6 mm. wide, with flattened brain case and gradually rising profile.
MYOTIS SUBULATUS p. 68

1' Forearm more than 33 mm.; foot more than 7 mm.; skull with more arched and rounded brain case: 2

2 Dorsal fur with tricoloured pattern (basally black, greyish in the middle, and cinnamon at tips), giving a cinnamon-brown appearance; texture of fur loose; foot relatively small; calcar with well-developed keel; skull with narrow brain case (6.6–7.2 mm.) and narrow interorbital width (3.5–3.9 mm.).
MYOTIS SODALIS
Not recorded from eastern Canada.

2' Dorsal fur without tricoloured pattern; foot larger; calcar without well-developed keel: 3

3 Ear relatively long, 16 mm. or more, extending beyond tip of nose when laid forward in fresh specimen; foot about half as long as tibia; forearm length averaging 35.5 mm. (34–38 mm.); skull narrow; width of brain case 6.8–7.6 mm.; interorbital width 3.4–4.0 mm.; greatest width of palate less than length of tooth row (canine-molars).
MYOTIS KEENII p. 66

3' Ears relatively short, less than 16 mm., not extending beyond tip of nose when laid forward in fresh specimen; foot more than half as long as tibia; forearm length averaging 37.6 mm. (36–40 mm.); skull broad; width of brain case 7.1–7.8 mm.; interorbital width 4.0–4.5 mm.; greatest width of palate greater than length of tooth row (canine-molars).
MYOTIS LUCIFUGUS p. 63

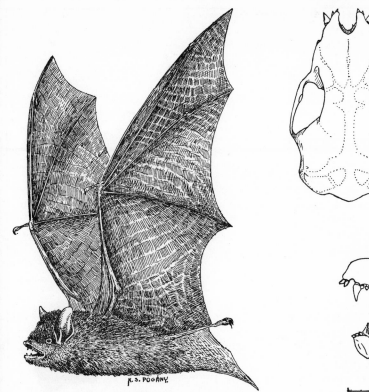

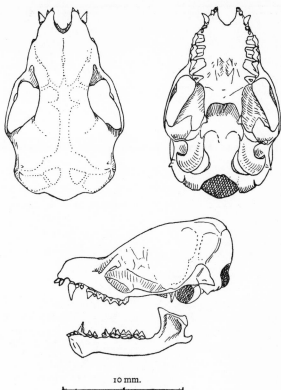

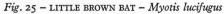

10 mm.

Fig. 25 – LITTLE BROWN BAT – *Myotis lucifugus*   *Fig.* 26 – SKULL OF *Myotis lucifugus* (ROM 10563 ♂)

Myotis lucifugus (LeConte) – Little Brown Bat – *Chauve-souris brune*

The most common of the bats of eastern Canada, the little brown bat is of medium size and is olive brown, reddish brown, or yellowish brown, with a darker area on the shoulder. The underparts are washed with buffy tones. The ears, wings, and interfemoral membranes are dark brown (sometimes almost black) and completely or nearly devoid of hair. In living or freshly killed specimens the ear may reach, but not extend beyond, the end of the nose. The tragus of the ear is long and tapered (it is usually less than 9 mm.). The skull, with thirty-eight teeth, differs from that of other native *Myotis* in being relatively broader. The interorbital width is 4 mm. or more, while in other species of *Myotis* the width is less. It is frequently difficult to distinguish this species externally from *Myotis keenii*.

However, the longer forearm and the shorter ear and tragus help identification.

SIZE Total length 80–97 mm.; tail 31–45; hind foot 8–11; ear from notch 13–16; forearm 36–40 (av. 37.6). Skull: length 14.1–15.4, width 8.2–9.6. Weight 6–13 gr.

DISTRIBUTION The little brown bat is widely spread, though seldom abundant, across eastern Canada as far north as the south end of James Bay and southern Labrador. As this bat is sparsely distributed and difficult to collect, it is quite probable that it extends well north of its present known range. *Myotis lucifugus lucifugus* is the race occurring in eastern Canada.

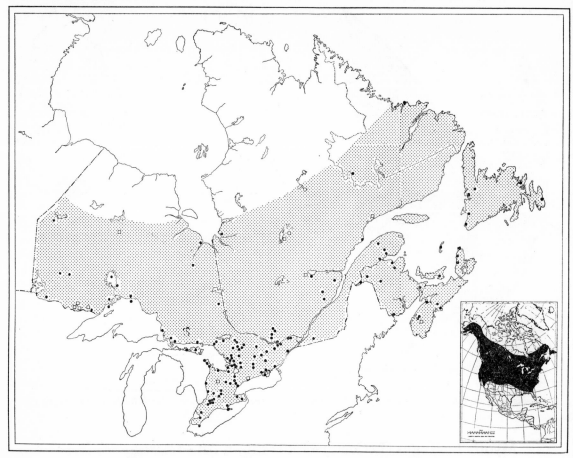

Map 13 – DISTRIBUTION OF THE LITTLE BROWN BAT – *Myotis lucifugus*

HABITAT The little brown bat roosts and hibernates in caves, buildings, and, in the summer, in a wide variety of other sheltered places. Hibernating sites must remain above freezing but below 10° C. and have a relatively high humidity.

HABITS This bat begins its search for food as dusk approaches and returns to its roost—where it hangs head down to sleep all day—some time before dawn. Strictly an insect-eater, it catches its food on the wing, flying about through wooded areas or over fields, lakes, and streams.

Little brown bats are very efficient hunters, sometimes catching ten to fifteen insects per minute by means of echo-location; recent studies have shown estimates of about one gram of insects per hour of active feeding. They have been known to make 540 to 3,120 dives per hour at insects or on pursuit manoeuvres, or an average of 1,665 dives per hour of active feeding. Laboratory studies show that an insect is detected (by echo-location at half a metre or 23 to 83 cm.), located, and intercepted in flight within about half a second. Swooping low over bodies of water seems to be one of these bats' favourite methods of hunting, although they may be seen darting back and forth almost any place. Their characteristic flight appears erratic and almost feeble, but it averages about fifteen wing strokes per second. The ultrasonic pulses used for echo-location have an average frequency of 78 kilocycles at the beginning, 48 kilocycles in the middle, and 39 kilocycles at the end. Each pulse has an average duration of 2.3 milliseconds.

Mating usually takes place in the fall (September and October). The spermatozoa are stored in the uterus until spring—usually late April or early May—when ovulation takes place; females are known to give birth to young after five months' separation from males. A single offspring (there are rarely twins) is born in June or July after from fifty to sixty days' gestation. A newborn little brown bat may weigh almost a third as much as the mother (1.5–2.3 grams). It clings to the fur of the mother for the first three or four days as she flies about. After that it may be left at the roost during the night. The females tend to congregate in groups to form nursing centres until the young are weaned, while the males may be dispersed in solitary sites.

The young grow at a rapid rate, reaching adult weight in three or four weeks; they become sexually mature at about eight months.

With the lowering temperatures of late fall, the little brown bat (along with other hibernating bats) seeks out a protected locality that remains at just a few degrees above freezing, and spends the winter there. At rest in this location, the bat's body temperature fluctuates with the air temperature. It cannot sustain flight when its temperature is below 33° C., and it cannot move about when its body temperature is below the 25–30° C. range. Hibernating bats occasionally fly to a new location within a cave, sometimes to seek water. Apparently a drop in temperature to the freezing point usually, but not always, arouses a sleeping bat in time for it to search for a more favourable temperature. Like many other bats, the little brown bat has a well-developed homing instinct when it is taken some distance away from its home roost—distances up to 180 miles have been recorded. Even blindfolded little brown bats have made their way home when released five miles away.

Banded bats of this species have lived as long as twenty-one years and several have been recaptured after nine to nineteen years. There is one record of a twelve-year-old female's giving birth to young.

REMARKS The preference of colonies of little brown bats for buildings—often people's homes—makes them a troublesome pest. They are associated with several old wives' tales—that they bite babies, that they get caught in women's hair, or carry human parasites—that have no basis in fact. However, they are understandably obnoxious to humans for the noise they make scratching around their roosts and for the odour that is given off by the accumulation of their droppings. Once little brown bats are established in a building, it is difficult to keep them from returning from their nightly flight in search of food unless all openings large enough to allow passage are sealed off. The use of chemicals such as moth balls or naphthalene flakes will make their favourite roosts uninhabitable—though sometimes only temporarily, for they may return when the fumes dissipate.

This species is known to have contracted rabies in North America, but so far no positive records of rabies-infected little brown bats are known from eastern Canada.

Perhaps it is worth remembering that in spite of the unpopular characteristics of little brown bats, they consume a large number of insects.

Selected References

ALLIN, A. E., 1942.

DYMOND, J. R., 1936.

GOULD, E., 1955, 1959.

GRIFFIN, D. R., 1940, 1958.

GRIFFIN, DONALD R., FREDERICK A. WEBSTER and CHARLES R. MICHAEL, 1960.

HALL, JOHN S., ROGER J. CLOUTIER and DONALD R. GRIFFIN, 1957.

HITCHCOCK, H. B., 1940, 1949.

HITCHCOCK, H. B. and K. REYNOLDS, 1942.

HOCK, R. J., 1951.

MILLER, G. S., JR., 1897a, 1897b.

MILLER, G. S., JR., and G. M. ALLEN, 1928.

SMITH, R. W., 1940.

WIMSATT, W. A., 1942, 1944a, 1944b, 1945.

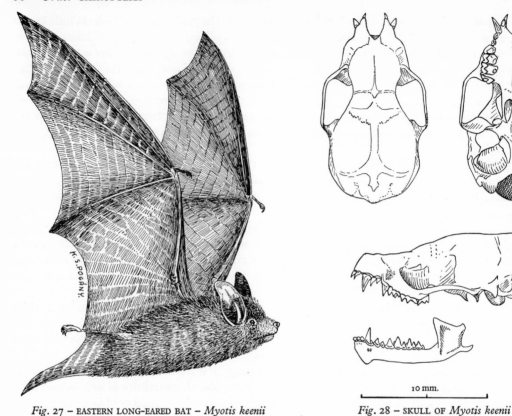

Fig. 27 – EASTERN LONG-EARED BAT – *Myotis keenii*

Fig. 28 – SKULL OF *Myotis keenii*
(ROM 16333 ♀)

10 mm.

vreitland brun

Myotis keenii (Merriam) – Eastern Long-eared Bat, Keen Bat – *Chauve-souris de Keen*

Except for its relatively larger ear, the Keen bat is very similar in appearance to the little brown bat. In colour the pelage is duller on the average, especially the underparts. The brown tips are usually shorter and expose more of the slate colour of the base of the fur. In living or freshly killed specimens the ear extends three or four millimetres beyond the end of the nose when it is pulled forward, while the ear of the little brown bat does not exceed the end of the nose. The tragus of the ear of the Keen bat is also slightly longer than that of the little brown bat and more pointed (length 10–12 mm.). The skull differs in being narrower and relatively longer. The interorbital width is less than 4 mm. and the greatest width of the palate is less than the length of the toothrow (canine-molars). The forearm also averages less.

SIZE Total length 78–95 mm.; tail 34–42; hind foot 8–10; ear from notch 15–19.5; forearm 34–38 (av. 35.5). Skull: length 14.2–15.5, width 8.4–9.2. Weight 6–9 gr.

DISTRIBUTION Keen bats range along the southern portion of eastern Canada and north to a line extending from Newfoundland along the northern side of the Gulf of St Lawrence through Lake St John, Gouin Reservoir, Lake Abitibi, Lake Nipigon, and Red Lake near the Manitoba border.

HABITAT Similar to that of the little brown bat, but the Keen bat tends to be more common in heavily forested areas. It occurs less frequently in buildings, apparently preferring abandoned mines and small caves where it seems to like cool, moist sites away from strong draughts. It is regularly found

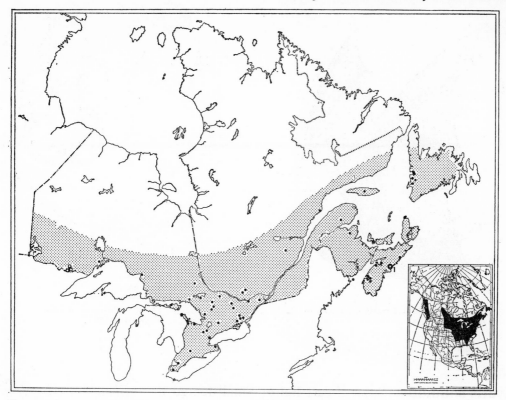

Map 14 – DISTRIBUTION OF THE EASTERN LONG-EARED BAT – *Myotis keenii* AND (I) TYPE LOCALITY OF *M. k. septentrionalis* (Trouessart)

clinging to moist walls, and is sometimes covered with droplets of water.

HABITS Comparatively little is known about this rather uncommon bat. In all probability the habits of the Keen bat are quite similar to those of the little brown bat, but specific details are lacking. Studies of the Keen bat's high-frequency pulses used in echo-location indicate that they are of shorter duration (0.9 milliseconds) than those of *M. lucifugus* (2.3 milliseconds) and of a higher frequency—an average of 95 kilocycles at the beginning, 57 kilocycles in the middle, and 46 kilocycles at the end (*M. lucifugus* 78, 48 and 39 kc.).

One bat of this species was recaptured nineteen years after banding.

REMARKS The lack of suitable hibernating sites may well be the limiting factor controlling the population level of the Keen bat in eastern Canada. Certainly there is much to be learned about this interesting species.

Selected References
ALLEN, G. M., 1939b.
ALLIN, A. E., 1942.
CAHN, A. R., 1937.
CAMERON, A. W., 1951a.
GRIFFIN, DONALD R., 1958.
HALL, JOHN R., ROGER J. CLOUTIERS, and DONALD R. GRIFFIN, 1957.
HITCHCOCK, H. B., 1940, 1949.
MACLEOD, C. F. and A. W. CAMERON, 1961.
MILLER, G. S., JR., 1897b.
MILLER, G. S., JR. and G. M. ALLEN, 1928.
RYSGAARD, G. N., 1942.

Fig. 29 – LEAST BAT – *Myotis subulatus*

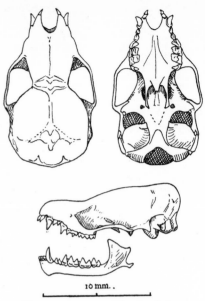

10 mm.

Fig. 30 – SKULL OF *Myotis subulatus*
(ROM 16336 ♂)

Myotis subulatus (Say) – Least Bat or Small-footed Bat – *Chauve-souris pygmée*

This species is the smallest of the local *Myotis*. It has a blackish mask across the face. The ears and wing membranes are black and the fur is relatively long and tends to be yellowish brown, with long shiny tips that give it a burnished appearance. A keeled calcar, a short forearm, a short third metacarpal measuring less than the length of the forearm, and a small delicate skull with flattened brain case and thirty-eight teeth are further identifying characteristics.

SIZE Total length 73–82 mm.; tail 30–35; hind foot 6.5–7.0; ear from notch 12.2–15.0; forearm 30–32 (av. 31.3). Skull: length 13–14, width 8.0–8.6. Weight 3–8 gr.

DISTRIBUTION AND VARIATION Until recently, the known records in Canada of the least bat, all of the race *Myotis subulatus leibii*, were restricted to the southern part of Ontario and the adjacent part of Quebec. However, Mr F. N. Cowell, naturalist at the Lake Superior Provincial Park, Ont., discovered a *M. s. leibii* hanging on the exterior of a cabin at Agawa Bay, at the east end of Lake Superior, on September 21st, 1964; the specimen was submitted to the author for confirmation of identification. This record of occurrence lies some 325 miles north-west of the previous known range for the species. The range extends south to West Virginia, South Carolina, and Tennessee.

HABITAT. The least bat is primarily a cave-dweller, and may migrate from cave to cave even during the winter months. Little else is known about its habitat. For hibernation it seems to prefer colder, drier, and more draughty sites than other *Myotis*. In summer it has been taken in buildings not far away from its hibernating caves.

HABITS Unlike most *Myotis* that hang with their

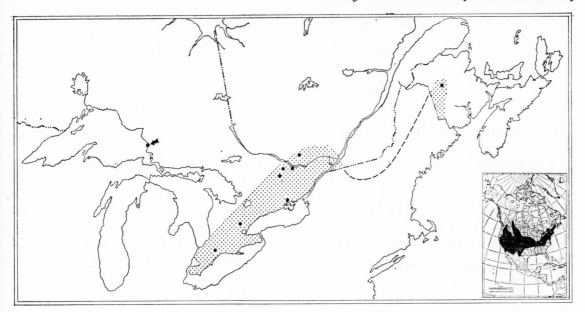

Map 15 – DISTRIBUTION OF THE LEAST BAT – *Myotis subulatus*

wings folded tightly against the body, the least bat usually hangs with its wings partly outstretched.

Under laboratory conditions for feeding on the wing, the least bat was estimated to capture about ten mosquitoes per minute, or one every six seconds.

The least bat does not usually enter hibernating caves until about a month after *M. lucifugus*—that is, toward the end of November—and frequently leaves during warm spells, perhaps to take up residence in another cave. Studies indicate that males and females normally hibernate together in approximately even numbers. In one summer record for Ontario, a least bat selected a well-ventilated site that was cooler than most sites selected by *M. lucifugus*.

A single offspring is thought to be born about May or June.

Recaptures of *M. s. leibii* in Ontario have been made at least five years after banding. Further studies may show that this species has an expected longevity approaching that of the much better-known *M. lucifugus*.

REMARKS This interesting little-known bat deserves much further study.

Selected References

GRIFFIN, D. R., 1958.

GRIFFIN, D. R., F. A. WEBSTER, and C. R. MICHAEL, 1960.

HITCHCOCK, H. B., 1941, 1945, 1949.

MILLER, G. S., JR., 1897b.

MILLER, G. S., JR. and G. M. ALLEN, 1928.

MOHR, C. E., 1936.

Genus **LASIONYCTERIS** Peters

Silver-haired Bats – *Chauves-souris argentées*

Dental Formula $I \frac{2-2}{3-3}$ $C \frac{1-1}{1-1}$ $P \frac{2-2}{3-3}$ $M \frac{3-3}{3-3} = 36$

Lasionycteris noctivagans (LeConte) – Silver-haired Bat – *Chauve-souris argentée*

The silver-haired bat is a striking blackish-brown colour and its hairs are tipped with silvery white. The basal half of the interfemoral membrane is furred. It is medium in size and has broad rounded ears with a short, blunt tragus (6–8 mm. long). The skull is quite distinctive and has thirty-six teeth.

SIZE Total length 90–115 mm.; tail 35–50; hind foot 8–12; ear from notch 14.5–17.0; forearm 37.1–42.0 (av. 39.6). Skull: length 16–17, width 9.5–10.3. Weight 6–12 gr. Females are larger than males on the average.

DISTRIBUTION Present in eastern Canada only during the summer, the silver-haired bat is widely distributed, but it is always relatively scarce, and known records may fail to indicate its true range. Only the one species occurs in all of Canada and the United States. The winter is thought to be spent in the southernmost portion of the United States where hibernation is not necessary, although this has not been definitely established. Few bats of this species seem to have been banded and no returns are available to establish where those of eastern Canada spend the winter.

HABITAT Forested areas along streams and lakes seem to be the preferred habitat of the silver-haired bat, which is one of the three species of 'Tree Bats'. (The other two are the red and the hoary bat.) It is rarely found either in caves or buildings in eastern Canada, although recently isolated silver-haired bats have been found in caves in Minnesota, West Virginia, and Virginia.

HABITS The silver-haired bat is solitary and migratory. A single bat or family group usually hangs in trees, under bark or in hollows, during the day. At night it ventures forth later than most bats and forages for food with a rather distinctive fluttering flight consisting of abrupt twists or darts and short glides. Preliminary studies of the high-frequency sound used for echo-location by this species indicates that there is a fairly close similarity to that of the little brown bat, *Myotis lucifugus*. One or usually two young are born during June or July. They cling to the mother until they are about three weeks old, at which time they begin to fly.

During the fall (about mid-September) silver-haired bats have been observed to congregate along the northern shore of Lake Erie where they apparently follow the migratory routes of birds as they cross the lake, particularly at Long Point and Point Pelee. The bats continued flying until about $1\frac{1}{2}$ hours after dawn.

Normally the silver-haired bat disappears from eastern Canada by October (our last date record is September 26th from Norfolk County, Ont., except for one specimen found at Rondeau Provincial Park clinging to a stone pillar during the daylight of December 16, 1959) and returns in the spring (we have one May record from York County, Ont., and several for mid-June in southern Ontario).

REMARKS The solitary habits of this species make it a difficult one to observe and it has escaped comprehensive study. Our knowledge of it is therefore unusually meagre, in spite of the fact that it is a fairly common bat across central North America. A single specimen was found hibernating in a cave in Minnesota on January 23rd, 1952. Perhaps this is the first authentic record of such an occurrence and it points to the need for more study.

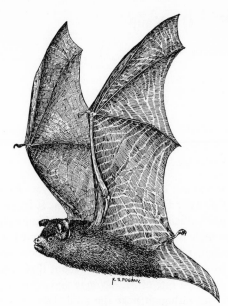

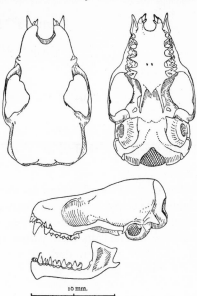

Fig. 31 – SILVER-HAIRED BAT –
Lasionycteris noctivagans

Fig. 32 – SKULL OF *Lasionycteris noctivagans*
(ROM 22947 ♀)

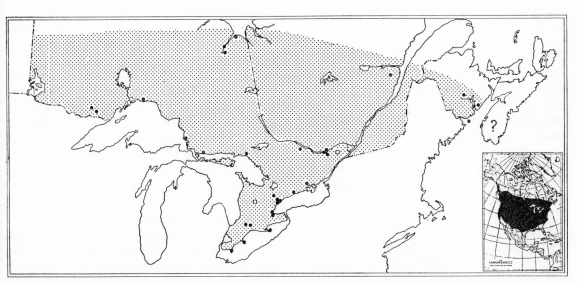

Map 16 – DISTRIBUTION OF THE SILVER-HAIRED BAT – *Lasionycteris noctivagans*

Selected References

ALLEN, G. M., 1939b.
BEER, J. R., 1956.

GRIFFIN, D. R., 1958.
MILLER, G. S., JR., 1897b, 1907.
SAUNDERS, W. E., 1930.

Genus **PIPISTRELLUS** Kaup

Pipistrelles – *Pipistrelles de l'Est*

Dental Formula $\quad I\frac{2-2}{3-3} \quad C\frac{1-1}{1-1} \quad P\frac{2-2}{2-2} \quad M\frac{3-3}{3-3} = 34$

Pipistrellus subflavus (Cuvier) – Eastern Pipistrelle – *Pipistrelle de l'Est*

The smallest of the bats of eastern Canada, the pipistrelle may be easily identified not only by its size but by a yellowish to dark-brown pelage above that is paler below. The hairs when parted show a distinctive tricolour pattern: dark at the base, light in the middle, and dark at the tips. The tragus is short (6.4–6.8 mm.), blunt, and bent forward at the tip. The skull is unique among the bats of eastern Canada in having thirty-four teeth.

SIZE Total length 77–89 mm.; tail 37–42; hind foot 7.8–9.0; ear from notch 13.5–14.5; forearm 31.5–35.3 (av. 33.3). Skull: length 12.2–13.3, width 6.6–8.2. Weight 3.5–7.0 gr.

DISTRIBUTION AND VARIATION In eastern Canada *Pipistrellus subflavus obscurus* has been taken only in Nova Scotia and south-eastern Ontario and the adjacent part of Quebec. Apparently it has not been taken in Ontario in the western Lake Erie district or anywhere in Michigan, northern Indiana, or northeastern Illinois, though there are records from Wisconsin, Iowa, southeastern Minnesota, and central Illinois which have been identified as the race *P. s. subflavus*.

HABITAT The preference of the eastern pipistrelle for hibernating in caves may be one of the factors limiting distribution and abundance. It selects warmer draught-free situations within the cave and rarely associates closely with other species of bats. It seldom if ever roosts in buildings or trees in eastern Canada. It is often found covered with droplets of condensation. Perhaps a high relative humidity is one of the key requirements.

HABITS An early-evening erratic flyer, the eastern pipistrelle feeds on flying insects. It is one of the more efficient bats at insect-catching—estimates as high as 3.3 grams of insects per hour have been taken, which would account for about half this bat's body weight or more (about three times the estimated rate of *M. lucifugus* and young *Eptesicus fuscus*, although near the adult rate of the latter species). Two pipistrelle specimens could not be induced to feed on the wing under laboratory conditions in which some *Myotis* became quite efficient. The pulses of high-frequency sound used for echo-location by the eastern pipistrelle have about the same average duration as those of *M. lucifugus*, but the pipistrelle utilizes less spread in average frequency, which is 75 kilocycles at the beginning, 54 kilocycles in the middle, and 45 kilocycles at the end.

Mating takes place about November. Two offspring are the usual rule (occasionally there are one or three), and they are born in June or July. The young cling to the mother in flight for the first week or two. They reach adult size at about four weeks. Records to date do not include specimens taken during the months of August, September, October, or November. Of the colonies hibernating in Ontario and Quebec, about ninety per cent are males. Recent studies have shown that the winter sex ratio changes from north to south to about the level of Georgia before a fifty-fifty ratio is encountered (eighty per cent male in West Virginia, seventy-one per cent male in Missouri and northeastern Alabama). The pipistrelle apparently goes into hibernation earlier and remains longer than most hibernating bats. It

Fig. 33 – EASTERN PIPISTRELLE –
Pipistrellus subflavus

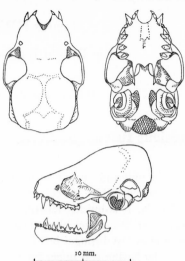

10 mm.

Fig. 34 – SKULL OF *Pipistrellus
subflavus* (ROM 21809 ♂)

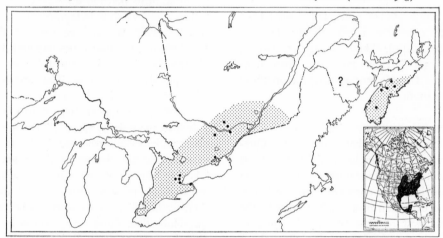

Map 17 – DISTRIBUTION OF THE EASTERN PIPISTRELLE – *Pipistrellus subflavus*

rarely clusters in large numbers: it is more frequently encountered singly or in groups of less than five or six. Pipistrelles transported from their home cave have been known to return from distances of up to eighty miles. Banding suggests that some live at least seven years.

REMARKS This species is reported to be able to fly directly from the surface of water when knocked into it uninjured.

Selected References
ALLEN, G. M., 1939.

BLEAKNEY, J. SHERMAN, 1965.
DAVIS, W. H., 1959.
DOWNING, S. C., 1938.
GOULD, E., 1955.
GRIFFIN, D. R., 1958.
HITCHCOCK, H. B., 1949.
HITCHCOCK, H. B. and K. REYNOLDS, 1940.
MILLER, G. S., JR., 1897b.
RYSGAARD, G. N., 1942.
SAUNDERS, W. E., 1920.
WIMSATT, W. A., 1945.

Genus **EPTESICUS** Rafinesque

Big Brown Bats – *Grandes chauves-souris brunes*

Dental Formula $I \frac{2-2}{3-3}$ $C \frac{1-1}{1-1}$ $P \frac{1-1}{2-2}$ $M \frac{3-3}{3-3} = 32$

Eptesicus fuscus (Beauvois) – Big Brown Bat – *Grande chauve-souris brune*

This is a large, uniformly pale-brown to dark-brown bat that is one of the more common species in eastern Canada. It is quickly identified by its broad, rounded ears and rather blunt tragus. The skull is large and can be distinguished from others of similar size by having two upper incisors and one premolar.

SIZE Total length 96–118 mm.; tail 34–50; hind foot 10–14; ear from notch 16–20; forearm 40.1–50.2 (av. 44.5). Skull: length 18.1–20.6, width 11.5–13.4. Weight 11–19 gr. Specimens from northern Ontario average larger than those from further south.

DISTRIBUTION AND VARIATION This is one of the more common bats in southern Ontario and Quebec, though even there its limit of distribution is poorly known. Records for central Quebec and the maritime provinces are apparently not available, with the one exception of a single record in the extreme southwest of New Brunswick. *Eptesicus fuscus fuscus* is the form occurring throughout most of the known range, although a few specimens from west of Lake Nipigon, Ont., approach *E. f. pallidus* in being paler with almost whitish underparts.

HABITAT This wide-ranging species utilizes buildings more regularly than most bats of eastern Canada, and it is the only one that normally hibernates therein. It is also the most tolerant of cold, dryness, and air movements—frequently it may be found in situations that are a few degrees below freezing. The big brown bat utilizes most available caves for hibernation; and in summer it roosts under the bark or in the hollow of trees as well as in buildings, mines, and caves.

HABITS The big brown bat is a strong flyer that goes into hibernation late and comes out early. It occasionally becomes active during the mid-winter. This activity might be caused either by a warming of its place of hibernation, which would waken it, or by a drop in temperature to well below freezing, which would force it to seek a new roost. Big brown bats sometimes congregate in tight clusters for hibernation, and this assists in maintaining body temperatures. They are more solitary when roosting during the summer.

Usually two young are born during June or early July (average weight, 2.5 gr.). They are weaned at about three weeks, reach adult size in about two months, and may live up to nine years or longer. The big brown bat seems to have a high water-intake requirement. Captured animals drink freely; their feeding in the wild seems to be preceded by quenching their thirst—they do this by flying low over the water to drink. It is reasonable to assume that this species is able to withstand dry situations because of its high intake of water.

Feeding on flying insects, which it locates by echo-location, the big brown bat has been estimated to catch from 1 to 2.7 grams of insects per hour during active feeding. One observation indicated that during active feeding the big brown bat makes an average of 1,283 pursuit-dives at insects per hour (480 to 1,800). It operates on a lower average frequency in echo-location than the well-studied little brown bat, *Myotis lucifugus*: its beginning frequency is about 50 kilocycles, falling to a middle frequency of 39 kilocycles and to 25

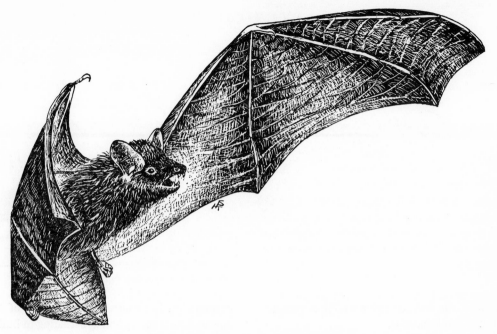

Fig. 35 – BIG BROWN BAT – *Eptesicus fuscus*

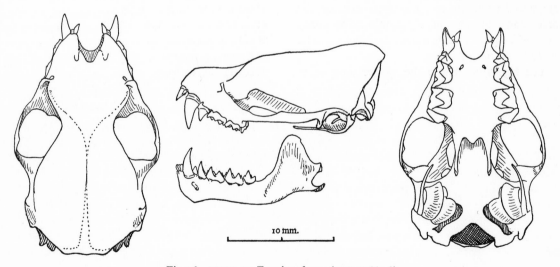

10 mm.

Fig. 36 – SKULL OF *Eptesicus fuscus* (ROM 20664 ♀)

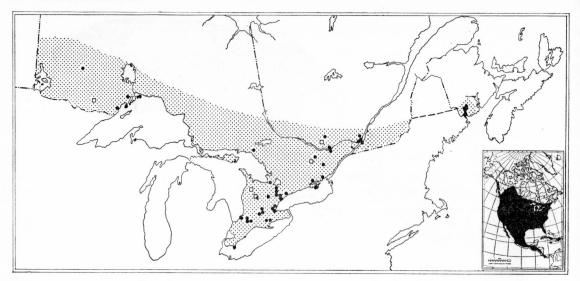

Map 18 – DISTRIBUTION OF THE BIG BROWN BAT – *Eptesicus fuscus*

kilocycles at the end. Its pulse duration averages longer at 2.7 milliseconds.

This species exhibits a rather well-developed homing ability, with even the young being able to return home quite quickly from distances of up to ten miles or further. Adults have returned to their home roost when taken as far as ninety-five miles away.

REMARKS In Ontario in 1961 there occurred the first known instance of a person's being bitten by a rabies-positive bat, which was reported to be an *Eptesicus fuscus*.

The big brown bat is the species most often encountered in eastern Canada because of its predilection for roosting and hibernating in buildings.

Selected References
ALLEN, G. M., 1933.
ALLIN, A. E., 1942.
BANFIELD, A. W. F., 1948.
GOULD, E., 1955, 1959.
GRIFFIN, D. R., 1958.
HALL, J. S. and W. H. DAVIS, 1958.
HAMILTON, W. J., JR., 1933a.
HITCHCOCK, H. B., 1949.
KLUGH, A. BOOKER, 1924.
REYNOLDS, K., 1942.
WIMSATT, W. A., 1945.

Genus **NYCTICEIUS** Rafinesque

Evening Bats – *Chauves-souris vespérale*

Dental Formula $\mathrm{I}\frac{1-1}{3-3}$ $\mathrm{C}\frac{1-1}{1-1}$ $\mathrm{P}\frac{1-1}{2-2}$ $\mathrm{M}\frac{3-3}{3-3} = 30$

Nycticeius humeralis Rafinesque – Evening Bat – *Chauve-souris vespérale*

This bat has been recorded in Canada only once. It superficially resembles a miniature big brown bat: its ears are rounded and it has a short, blunt tragus. However, it is darker brown above and has buffy underparts and the ears and membranes are almost black. It can also be distinguished from the big brown bat by its shorter forearm and from the genus *Myotis* by its rounded ear and short tragus. The skull is quite distinctive because of the reduced number of teeth—only thirty: twelve above and eighteen below.

SIZE Total length 86–103 mm.; tail 33–40; hind foot 6–9; forearm 33.8–37.3 (av. 36.3); ear from notch 9–14. Skull: length 14.1–14.6, width 9.6–10.2. Weight 6–12 gr.

DISTRIBUTION A single specimen of *Nycticeius*

humeralis humeralis—taken by W. E. Saunders at Point Pelee, Lake Erie, Ont., on May 16th, 1911—is the only known record for this species in Canada. It is now in the collection of the Royal Ontario Museum.

HABITAT Unknown for Canada.

HABITS This species roosts in trees, crevices, and houses. It is a slow, deliberate flyer. Almost nothing is known about its habits in Canada.

REMARKS The single record of this species may well be an accidental occurrence only.

Selected References
HALL, E. R. and K. R. KELSON, 1959.
MILLER, G. S., JR., 1897b.

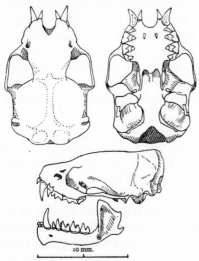

Fig. 37 – SKULL OF *Nycticeius humeralis*
(ROM 17923 ♀)

Map 19 – DISTRIBUTION OF THE EVENING BAT –
Nycticeius humeralis

Genus **LASIURUS** Gray

Hairy-tailed Bats – *Chauves-souris à queue velue*

Dental Formula $I \frac{1-1}{3-3}$ $C \frac{1-1}{1-1}$ $P \frac{2-2}{2-2}$ $M \frac{3-3}{3-3} = 32$

KEY TO THE EASTERN-CANADIAN SPECIES OF *Lasiurus*

1 Forearm more than 50 mm.; a distinctive yellow band below the throat; basic dorsal colour cinnamon brown; skull more than 17 mm. long and 11.5 mm. side.   LASIURUS CINEREUS p. 81

1′ Forearm less than 42 mm.; throat without yellow band; basic dorsal colour brick red or yellowish red; skull less than 15 mm. long and 11 mm. wide.   LASIURUS BOREALIS p. 78

Lasiurus borealis (Müller) – Red Bat – *Chauve-souris rousse*

The body colour of the male of this species is brick red, while the female is paler—a more yellowish red. This sexual difference in colour is more pronounced in the younger bats. The pelage has a distinctive pattern: the individual hairs are black at the base, with a band of golden yellow in the middle and a narrow band of red toward the end, which may show a short tip of white. The interfemoral membrane is completely furred above. The wing membranes are black, or nearly so. The female has four mammae. The forearm is less than 42 mm. in length. There are thirty-two teeth (fourteen above, eighteen below). The first upper premolar is quite small. The skull is smaller than that of *Lasiurus cinereus* and rather heavily built; it is distinctly short and deep.

SIZE Total length 93–117 mm.; tail 40–55; hind foot 8–11; forearm 36.6–42.0 (av. 39); ear from notch 10–13. Skull: length 13.0–14.4, width 9.0–10.4. Weight 6.5–13.5 gr. Females average larger than males and the limited sample examined indicates that they have significantly longer forearms.

DISTRIBUTION *Lasiurus borealis borealis* has been taken only along the southern region of Nova

Scotia, in New Brunswick, southern Quebec, and Ontario. Apparently only two Nova Scotia records are known, both of which were taken on ships at sea. In western Ontario the most northerly record is Favorable Lake, Kenora District, but in all probability the red bat ranges further north: specimens have been taken as far north as Southampton Island in the northern part of Hudson Bay. No specimens have been taken in eastern Canada in winter because red bats normally migrate south for the winter. Until recently it was thought that they did not hibernate at all; however, hibernating records are now available from West Virginia, Missouri, southern Indiana, and southern Illinois.

HABITAT The red bat is primarily an animal of the forest, particularly near water. There are no records of this species' occurring in caves or buildings in eastern Canada.

HABITS Migrating into eastern Canada only during the summer, the solitary red bat usually spends the day hanging in a tree. It is fairly agile, a strong and fast flier, and can manoeuvre quite well through dense vegetation. It is known to be able to alight on

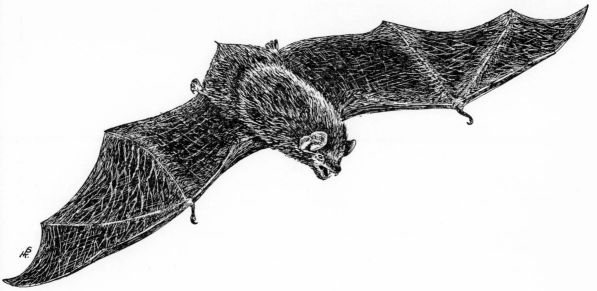

Fig. 38 – RED BAT – *Lasiurus borealis*

foliage to pick off insects (most other bats feed only 'on the wing'). It frequently flies in the late afternoon, particularly on cloudy days.

Mating is thought to take place on the wing, at least on some occasions, and the mating has been observed during August and September. One to four offspring (usually two or three) are born in late May or early June and weigh about half a gram each. Newborn young have relatively large 'thumbs' and claws on the hind feet that aid in clinging to the mother during flight. In addition they have well-developed teeth with hooked points that slope backward in the mouth and allow them to become securely fastened to the mother's nipple. They cling to the mother in flight until their combined weight exceeds hers and forces her to abandon them before each nightly foray. The young begin to fly at about five or six weeks.

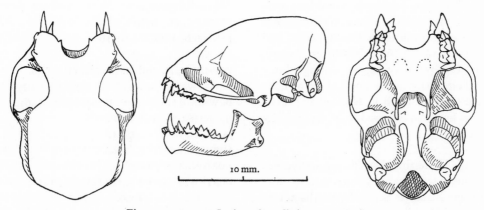

10 mm.

Fig. 39 – SKULL OF *Lasiurus borealis* (ROM 21718 ♂)

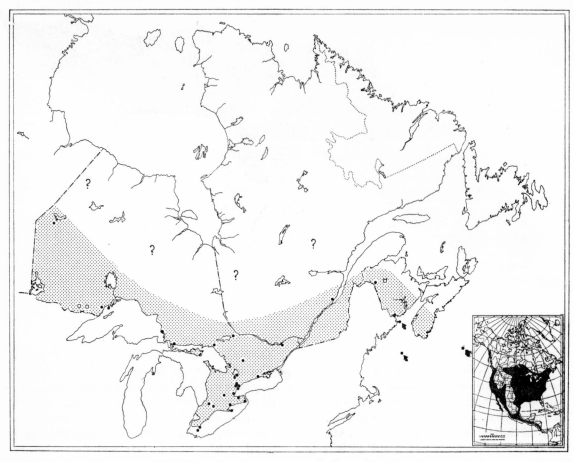

Map 20 – DISTRIBUTION OF THE RED BAT – *Lasiurus borealis*

May 31st is the earliest date that a red bat specimen has been taken for the collection of the Royal Ontario Museum (from Essex County, Ont.) and October 27th the latest (from Middlesex County, Ont.). Red bats regularly migrate through Long Point and Point Pelee on the north shore of Lake Erie where they are taken in bird-banding nets. This species has been observed to be captured by birds of prey.

REMARKS It is interesting that this species reaches ships well out to sea. The red bat has made its way to such remote islands as Bermuda, Southampton, Galápagos, and Hawaii.

Selected References
ALLEN, G. M., 1939b.
BANFIELD, A. W. F., 1961b.
BROWN, N. R., 1953.
COPELAND, M. and M. L. CHURCH, 1906.
DAVIS, WAYNE N. and W. Z. LIDICKER, 1956.
DOWNING, S. C. and D. H. BALDWIN, 1961.
HAGMEIER, E. M., 1957b.
JACKSON, H. H. T., 1961.
MYERS, RICHARD F., 1960.
NORTON, A. H., 1930b.
QUAY, W. B. and J. S. MILLER, JR., 1955.
SAUNDERS, W. E., 1930.
VAN DEUSEN, H. M., 1961.

Fig. 40 – HOARY BAT – *Lasiurus cinereus*

Lasiurus cinereus (Beauvois) – Hoary Bat – *Chauve-souris cendrée*

The hoary bat is the largest and most striking in appearance of all *Vespertilionid* bats of North America—it has a wing span of 14 inches or more. It is quickly identified by a distinctive yellow band around the throat, by its large size, by a furred interfemoral membrane, and by its multibanded white-tipped fur. The hairs are dark brown or blackish at the base with a band of golden yellow, a dark brown or blackish subterminal band, and a terminal tip of white. The skull is similar to that of *Lasiurus borealis* but it is larger. Compared with the only other skull of similar size, *Eptesicus fuscus*, the skull of the hoary bat is shorter but it has a larger brain case; the dental formulae also distinguish these two species easily.

SIZE Total length 130–150 mm.; tail 52–64; hind foot 10–14; ear from notch 17–19; forearm 48.0–56.3 (av. 54). Skull: length 17.0–18.2, width 11.8–12.8 Weight 25–35 gr.

M.E.C.—8

DISTRIBUTION AND VARIATION *L. c. cinereus* is the only race that occurs throughout most of North America south of the tree line. This large, solitary bat has rarely been taken, so that its true northern limits of distribution are unknown. However it *has* been taken north of Lake of the Woods and along the north shore of Lake Superior in Ontario. And on one occasion a single specimen was taken on Southampton Island, far beyond the tree-line, at the north end of Hudson Bay.

HABITAT Like the red bat, the hoary bat prefers forested areas, particularly coniferous regions.

HABITS Mating is thought to take place about September and October. Usually two offspring (occasionally one to four) are born in June and weigh about five grams each. The eyes are closed for the first ten days or so; the young continue to cling to the mother for about three weeks after

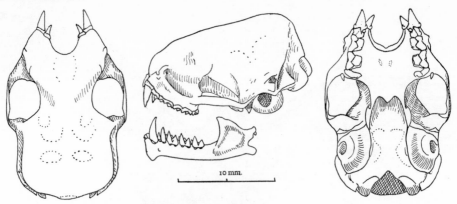

Fig. 41 – SKULL OF *Lasiurus cinereus* (ROM 35.7.29.7 ♂)

birth, by which time they may weigh ten grams each. The hoary bat does not leave its secluded roost until quite late in the evening and so escapes the notice of most observers. It usually flies strongly and in a direct line, and because of its long, narrow wings and large size it is impressive to anyone fortunate enough to see it in flight.

One captive male was kept alive for six weeks, during which time it learned to feed on mealworms and other insects offered by hand. It seized and then spat out all house-flies offered, however, and would not accept dead insects. It became quite tractable and could be easily handled. It drank water by taking two or three laps with its tongue and then raising its head in birdlike fashion to swallow.

The hoary bat migrates southward in winter and returns in the spring. The earliest specimen in the collections of the Royal Ontario Museum is one taken by the author on June 15th, 1947, on St Ignace Island, Lake Superior, Ont. The hoary bat has been observed in York County, Ont., as late as October 23rd.

It was formerly thought that the hoary bat rarely entered caves. However, recent reports show that it enters caves during the summer in Missouri;

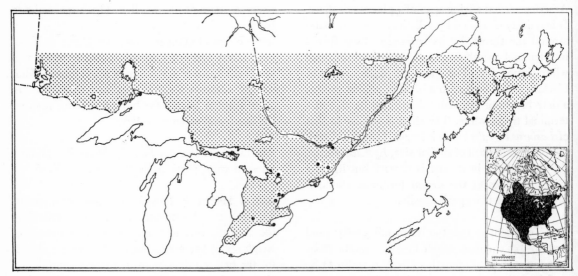

Map 21 – DISTRIBUTION OF THE HOARY BAT – *Lasiurus cinereus*

remains have been taken from caves in Indiana and Minnesota.

REMARKS There is a record of the hoary bat's having preyed upon the *Pipistrellus* in New York State, indicating that it does at times become carnivorous and attack other bats, and perhaps other vertebrates. Much is yet to be learned of this big, colourful bat.

Selected References

ALLEN, H., 1893.

ANDERSON, R. M., 1947.

BEER, JAMES R., 1954

BISHOP, S. C., 1947.

MILLER, G. S., JR., 1897b.

MURPHY, R. C. and J. T. NICHOLS, 1913.

MYERS, RICHARD F., 1960.

POOLE, E. L., 1932.

PROVOST, E. E. and C. M. KIRKPATRICK, 1952.

SAUNDERS, W. E., 1930.

Order
Lagomorpha

The name of this order is derived from the Greek *lago* (hare) and *morpha* (form). It includes two living families: *Leporidae*, the rabbits and hares, well represented in eastern Canada, and *Ochotonidae*, the pikas of the mountains of western North America. The Order *Lagomorpha* is distinctive because its members have two pairs of upper incisors, one directly behind the other. The front incisors, both above and below, have a longitudinal groove on the anterior surfaces. The fibula is fused to the tibia and articulates with the calcaneum.

Family **LEPORIDAE**

Rabbits and Hares – *Lapins et Lièvres*

The hind feet are much larger than the front and the hind legs much longer than the front. All feet are furred on the entire sole. The tail is short and the ears are long. The skull is quite distinctive: it has well-developed supraorbital processes and open lattice-like fenestrae on each side of the rostrum. The width between the lower toothrows is much less than between the upper. Chewing is therefore accomplished by a lateral motion of the lower jaws in order to allow the upper and lower cheek-teeth to occlude. As in the case of rodents, the incisor teeth continue to grow throughout life, and are normally worn away by chewing. If for some reason the incisors fail to occlude, growth may continue to unusual lengths.

Although the terms 'hare' and 'rabbit' are often used indiscriminately, the genus *Lepus* applies to the hare alone. Thus restricted, hares do not usually provide dens or well-prepared nests as the young are quite precocious: they are born fully furred with eyes open and are able to move about shortly after birth. By contrast the young of true rabbits (genera *Oryctolagus* and *Sylvilagus*) are usually born in nests or dens and are altricial—i.e. they are born almost devoid of hair, the eyes are closed, and they must remain in the nest for several days.

Lagomorphs have a habit of passing food twice through the body by ingesting their own faecal pellets. Microbial digestion in the caecum permits a further utilization of the remaining food value left in the droppings.

KEY TO THE EASTERN-CANADIAN GENERA OF *Leporidae*

1 Interparietal fused with parietals; hind foot usually more than 120 mm. long.   LEPUS p. 85

1' Interparietal not fused with parietals: 2

   2 Tip of posterior extension of the supraorbital process is fused to or is nearly in contact with the frontals; hind foot 110 mm. or less; ear from notch 66 mm. or less; skull less than 82 mm. long; posterior edge of palate lies at about the level of, or in front of, a line drawn between the third and fourth molariform teeth.   SYLVILAGUS p. 96

   2' Tip of posterior extension of supraorbital process free; posterior edge of palate usually lies behind the level of a line drawn between the third and fourth molariform teeth; size and colour variable (domestic rabbits).   ORYCTOLAGUS p. 102

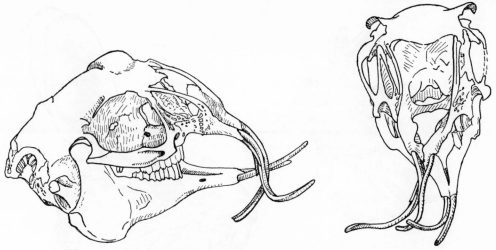

Fig. 42 – UNUSUAL GROWTH OF INCISOR TEETH OF AN ARCTIC HARE (ROM 12852)

Genus **LEPUS** Linnaeus

Hares – *Lièvres*

Dental Formula $I\frac{2-2}{1-1}$ $C\frac{0-0}{0-0}$ $P\frac{3-3}{2-2}$ $M\frac{3-3}{3-3} = 28$

KEY TO THE EASTERN-CANADIAN SPECIES OF *Lepus*

1 Ears less than 85 mm. long (measured from notch); skull usually without well-developed anterior projections on the supraorbital processes: 2

  2 Skull less than 90 mm. long and 44 mm. wide; upper incisors normally recurved.

                                            LEPUS AMERICANUS p. 87

  2′ Skull more than 90 mm. long and 44 mm. wide; upper incisors project noticeably forward (little recurved).

                                             LEPUS ARCTICUS p. 89

1′ Ears more than 85 mm. long (measured from notch); skull with well-developed anterior projections on supraorbital processes: 3

  3 Pelage in winter usually white; body-build light; skull less massive with narrow and shallow rostrum; nasals short, the greatest extent usually being less than 42 mm.   LEPUS TOWNSENDII p. 92

  3′ Pelage not white in winter; body-build heavy; skull massive with broad and deep rostrum; greatest extent of nasals usually more than 42 mm.   LEPUS EUROPAEUS p. 95

Fig. 43 – VARYING HARE – *Lepus americanus*

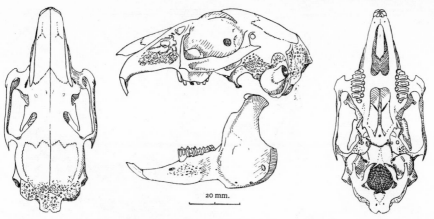

Fig. 44 – SKULL OF *Lepus americanus* (ROM 19810 ♀)

Lepus americanus Erxleben – Varying Hare, Snowshoe Hare – *Lièvre d'Amérique*

This is the most widespread and common lagomorph in eastern Canada. Its change of colour from brownish in summer to white in winter and its violent cyclic fluctuation in numbers have made this species well known. The well-furred hind feet of the varying hare, which give it one of its names, is a useful adaptation for the deep snows of the boreal forests. This hare differs from the Arctic hare in that the base of the white fur is dark or slate-coloured rather than completely white. There are two complete moults annually, one in spring and the other in late autumn. The skull is smaller than that of any other local species of *Lepus* and it is easily distinguished from that of the cottontails by the form of the supraorbital process, and by the absence of a distinct interparietal bone which also distinguishes it from the skull of the domestic rabbit, *Oryctolagus*.

SIZE Total length 380–506 mm.; tail 25–45; hind foot 121–150; ear from notch 62–68. Skull: length 74.9–85.2, width 37–42. Weight 3–5 lb.

DISTRIBUTION AND VARIATION The varying hare is found in all of eastern Canada north to the treeline. The species has been divided as follows in this area: *Lepus americanus americanus*, described from Hudson Bay, occupies all the north regions of Ontario; *L. a. phaeonotus* occurs in the Rainy River region of Ontario; *L. a. virginianus* in southern Ontario and Quebec; and *L. a. struthopus*, described from Nova Scotia, occurs in the Gaspé region of Quebec, the Maritime Provinces, and has been introduced into Newfoundland, where it is now widespread, and to Anticosti Island, Que. *L. a. virginianus* is the largest, most richly coloured form. *L. a. americanus* is smaller, duller, and less rusty in colour, and the skull is smaller with a short rostrum that is broad at its base. *L. a. struthopus* is similar in colour to *L. a. virginianus* but is duller and the skull is smaller. *L. a. phaeonotus* is almost the same size as *L. a. americanus* but is paler and more buffy coloured in summer pelage.

HABITAT. The varying hare is primarily an animal of the boreal forests, but along the southern periphery of its range it is usually concentrated in cedar or spruce swamps. Mixed forests with conifers and escape cover such as thick brush deadfalls and low shrubs provide the preferred habitat of this species.

HABITS During the day the varying hare remains relatively inactive in the shelter of forest cover. It becomes active in the evening as it seeks its food, which consists of a wide variety of herbs, shrubs, and other vegetable matter. In years of high popu-

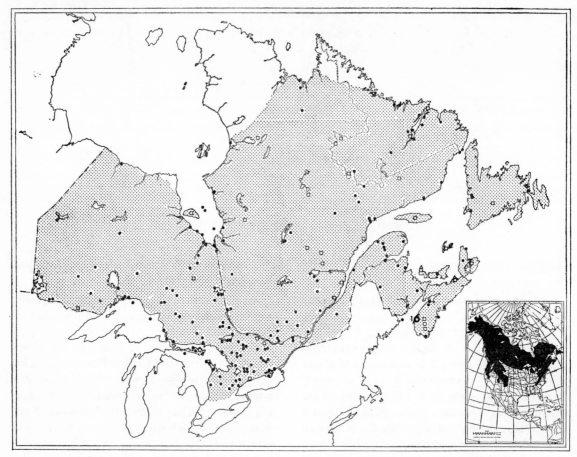

Map 22 – DISTRIBUTION OF THE VARYING HARE – *Lepus americanus* – AND (1) TYPE LOCALITY OF *L. a. phaeonotus* Allen

lation, varying hares may strip most of the forest vegetation to a height of two feet or more above the snowline. They tend to remain in a fairly discreet home range of about four or five acres and usually return to it quite quickly whenever they are chased away by a predator.

Breeding starts in March. After a gestation period of thirty-six days, two to four young are born, with births reaching a peak in May. Two litters may occur in one season. The young weigh seventy or eighty grams (about 2½ oz.) at birth and are fully furred, their eyes are open, and they are able to scurry about almost at once. They start to nibble at green vegetation when they are about a week or ten days old, and they are weaned at about four to eight weeks, at which time they have attained almost adult size.

Unlike the cottontail or true rabbit, the varying hare does not use nests or dens. It makes a shallow depression in the earth, snow, or vegetation that is commonly referred to as a 'form'. Occasionally it may retreat into a hollow log or into the den left by another mammal.

The varying hare, like most other lagomorphs, is normally silent except when captured, at which time it utters a low, piercing squeal. The mother communicates with her young by means of grunts or guttural calls.

The varying hare is subject to regular cycles of pronounced abundance and scarcity. A sharp buildup of population occurs within only one or two years, followed by a sudden and even quicker decline to a very low level. Peaks of abundance occur about nine or ten years apart.

REMARKS The varying hare is one of the more important foods of many boreal fur-bearers.

When they are abundant, varying hares may do extensive damage to reforested areas.

In spite of considerable research on the population dynamics of this species, many questions remain unanswered concerning the factors that contribute to the violent and regular increases and decreases in its numbers.

Selected References

ALDOUS, C. M., 1936, 1937.
BIRD, RALPH D., 1955.
DODDS, DONALD G., 1962.
GRANGE, WALLACE B., 1932a, 1932b.
MACLULICH, D. A., 1937.
SEVERAID, JOYE HAROLD, 1942, 1945.

Lepus arcticus Ross – Arctic Hare – *Lièvre arctique*

In winter only the eyes and black-edged ears of this large white rabbit contrast with the snow. The fur is quite long, dense, and soft and provides an excellent insulation against the rigorous arctic climate. It is white all the way to the base, which distinguishes it from the fur of the varying hare. In summer the less dense coat is greyish brown above and white below, but the dorsal pelage is still characterized by a white base. As with most arctic mammals, the ears of the arctic hare are relatively shorter than those of the southern species such as the jack rabbit and the European hare. The skull is characterized by its large size and by its protruding upper incisors which are less recurved than any other representative of the genus.

The juvenile pelage differs from the summer pelage of the adult by having considerably more black coloration. The guard hairs are entirely black and short over the forehead and black and long with white tips over the upper portion of the body. Most of the underparts are white, and there is a pale buff tone on the cheeks. The upperparts are a blackish grey and are noticeably darker than those of the adult. The tips of the ears are black and the tail and posterior margin of the ears, as well as a spot on the lower lip, are white.

SIZE Total length 480–663 mm.; tail 34–73; hind foot 150–174; ears from notch 70–84. Skull: length 94.1–99.9, width 47.7–49.8. Weight 6–15 lb.

DISTRIBUTION AND VARIATION *Lepus arcticus labradorius* occurs from the Great Whale River north through the Ungava Peninsula and north Labrador. *L. a. bangsii*, which is slightly larger than *L. a. labradorius*, occupies the east coast of central and southern Labrador and Newfoundland.

HABITAT Open upland tundra and rocky slopes are the usual homes of the arctic hare; the latter are preferred. Apparently it rarely ventures into wooded or lowland areas.

HABITS More gregarious, perhaps, than most other hares, arctic hares are often seen in groups of from ten to sixty or more, especially in areas where the wind has swept the snow free in winter. They sometimes dig long tunnels through the snow, but usually they utilize only a depression in the snow or the lee of a rock for shelter. Surrounded by snow, they are exceedingly well camouflaged. A peculiar habit of walking upright on their hind feet has been noted by several observers. When frightened on a slope, they almost invariably run uphill. The young—four to eight per litter—are born in late June or July.

Willow shoots appear to be the primary food: apparently their availability governs the local distribution of the arctic hare.

Whenever it sees a human, from August through January, this hare 'freezes' and sits motionless until

Fig. 45 – ARCTIC HARE – *Lepus arcticus*

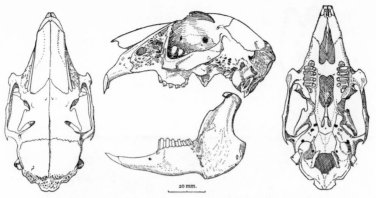

Fig. 46 – SKULL OF *Lepus arcticus* (ROM 27.12.13.29)

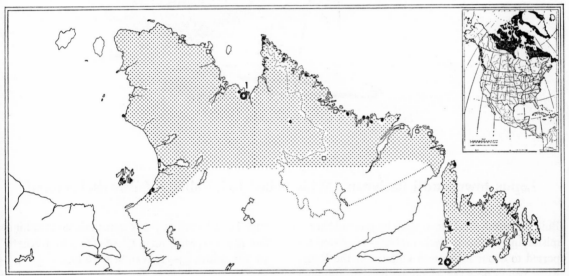

Map 23 – DISTRIBUTION OF THE ARCTIC HARE – *Lepus arcticus* – AND TYPE LOCALITIES OF
(1) *L. a. labradorius* Miller; (2) *L. a. bangsii* Rhoads

it is approached quite closely, whereas during the remainder of the year it bounds away at the slightest suggestion of danger, usually retreating to high ground where it watches alertly for further danger. Wolves, foxes, and snowy owls are its most common predators.

REMARKS The arctic hare is quite important in the economy of Eskimos and northern Indians, for it provides both food and skins for blankets and clothing. The fur is also marketed. Unfortunately

our knowledge of this species is seriously inadequate. Detailed field studies are much needed for a better understanding of the role of this hare in its arctic environment.

Selected References
HALL, E. R., 1951b.
HOWELL, A. H., 1936.
MANNING, T. H., 1943.
SOPER, J. DEWEY, 1944.

Fig. 47 – WHITE-TAILED JACK RABBIT – *Lepus townsendii*

Lepus townsendii Bachman – White-tailed Jack Rabbit – *Lièvre de Townsend*

Built for speed, this long-legged, long-eared hare—misleadingly named 'jack rabbit'—has been reported to occur in western Ontario in the Rainy River region near the Manitoba border, although as yet no specimens from that area have reached museums. At this latitude the jack rabbit turns white in winter, whereas further south, across the central plains of North America, it does not. In summer the pelage is greyish brown above with a darker stripe down the top of the white tail. The underparts are white and the ears have black tips that remain black even during the winter.

The skull has well-developed anterior projections on the supraorbital processes and is distinguished from that of *L. europaeus* by its lighter build, particularly with respect to the rostrum, which is narrower shallower, and has shorter nasals.

SIZE Total length 565–655 mm.; tail 66–112; hinp foot 145–172; ear from notch 96–113. Skull: length 90–103, width 43–51. Weight 5–10 lb.

DISTRIBUTION AND VARIATION The first Ontario specimen of *Lepus townsendii campanius* was not obtained until September 1965, though it commonly occurs in adjacent Manitoba and Minnesota. A population was reported to be present on Sable Island (ten miles north of Rainy River, Ont.) prior to 1929. The Ontario specimen (ROM 36019) was taken three miles north of Sleeman, Blue Township, Rainy River District.

HABITAT Open fields or prairies.

HABITS The jack rabbit usually mates in April. Three to six young are born after about thirty-six to forty-three days' gestation. Living on grass and

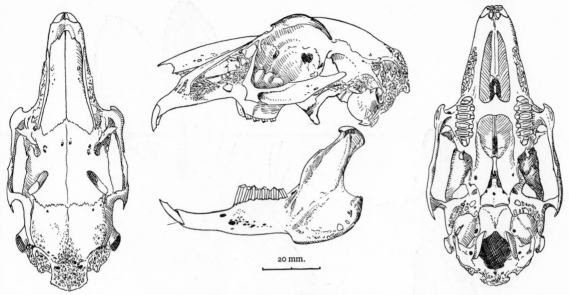

Fig. 48 – SKULL OF *Lepus townsendii* (ROM 20797 ♀)

20 mm.

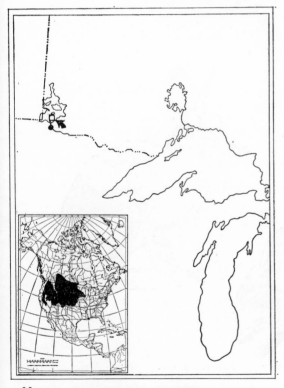

Map 24 – DISTRIBUTION OF THE WHITE-TAILED JACK
RABBIT – *Lepus townsendii*

herbs of the open country, this hare depends on either camouflage or speed to escape from enemies —it has been recorded at speeds above thirty-five miles per hour. It commonly makes bounding leaps of ten to fifteen feet.

The jack rabbit is most active at dawn and dusk, although it may move about at any time of the night and (less frequently) during the day. It is a solitary species, rarely congregating in large numbers.

REMARKS The jack rabbit is thought to have become established east of the original true prairie (in Minnesota and Wisconsin) as a result of repeated introductions, although the areas immediately adjacent to the prairies may have been invaded naturally as a result of man's clearing the forest and thereby providing a suitable habitat. Further study is required to clarify the present status of this species in Ontario.

Selected References
JACKSON, H. H. T., 1961.
SNYDER, L. L., 1938.

Fig. 49 – EUROPEAN HARE – *Lepus europaeus*

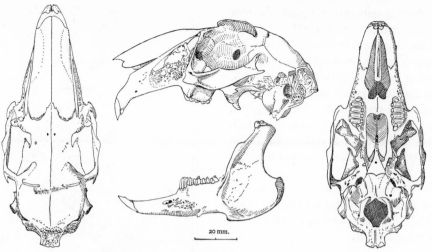

Fig. 50 – SKULL OF *Lepus europaeus* (ROM 22648 ♂)

Lepus europaeus Pallas – European Hare – *Lièvre d'Europe*

In 1912 nine European hares—*Lepus europaeus hybridus*, probably from eastern Germany—were released near Brantford, Ont. They have since spread throughout a wide area in southern Ontario. They are larger than native rabbits of this area and have long ears (averaging 123 mm. from the crown) with black tips. The upper parts of the pelage are yellowish to greyish brown and the underparts are pure white. The sides of the head and the rump are greyish, sometimes appearing almost blue-grey. The relatively short tail is black above and white below. Except for the black on the tip of the tail and a slightly heavier build, this species resembles the white-tailed jack rabbit, and it is commonly referred to as a jack rabbit in Ontario. The skull differs from that of *Lepus townsendii* in being more massive—particularly the rostrum, which is both wider and deeper and has longer and wider nasals.

SIZE Total length 600–750 (av. 680) mm.; tail 72–110 (av. 95); hind foot 142–161 (av. 151); ear from notch 94–102 (av. 98). Skull: length 96–104 (av. 100), width 44–51 (av. 47.3). Weight 7–12 (av. 9) lb.

DISTRIBUTION AND VARIATION At present the range includes all of southern Ontario south of the Canadian Shield, though there are isolated records

further north. Introductions were made in the Fort William–Port Arthur region in 1942, 1943, and 1945, but apparently they failed to survive beyond 1950.

HABITAT The European hare seems to prefer a less open habitat than the jack rabbit of the west, *Lepus townsendii*, and survives well in agricultural areas where open fields and pastures are bordered by hedgerows and woodlots. It is therefore ecologically separated from the cottontail and snowshoe hare.

HABITS Like the western jack rabbit, this species does not seek shelter in burrows or covered dens but instead merely crouches down in a furrow or a clump of vegetation during the day and depends on its keen senses and speed to escape its enemies. It is more active at night when it seeks out tender vegetation for food. It has been estimated that two or three adults will consume as much vegetation as one sheep.

Breeding begins in February or March and the litter size varies from two to eight (usually three to five). Studies in Europe indicate that the gestation period of this hare is forty-two to forty-four days. The young are precocious and are soon dispersed over a moderately wide area where the mother leaves each offspring stationed in a particular spot and then makes her rounds to nurse them in turn. The time of weaning is not specifically known, but sexual maturity is reached in about eight months— there is therefore no breeding in the year of birth.

Both sexes make low grunts and the doe uses a 'guttural' call to her young. It has been suggested that the grinding of teeth may signify an alarm call. As with other lagomorphs, a shrill, penetrating scream is uttered when this hare is hurt or terrified.

REMARKS The European hare has become an important game animal in southern Ontario. There seems to be little if any competition with the native species for food and cover.

Selected References
ALLIN, A. E., 1950.
PETERSON, RANDOLPH L. and J. K. REYNOLDS, 1954.
REYNOLDS, J. K., 1955.

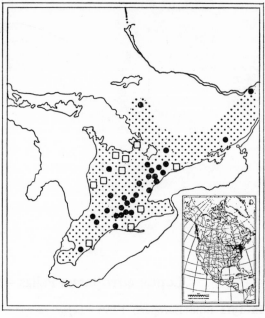

Map 25 – DISTRIBUTION OF THE EUROPEAN HARE –
Lepus europaeus

Genus **SYLVILAGUS** Gray

Cottontails – *Lapins à queue blanche*

Dental Formula $I \frac{2-2}{1-1}$ $C \frac{0-0}{0-0}$ $P \frac{3-3}{2-2}$ $M \frac{3-3}{3-3} = 28$

KEY TO THE EASTERN-CANADIAN SPECIES OF *Sylvilagus*

1 Anterior projection of supraorbital process well developed; auditory bullae relatively large; a white spot usually present on forehead; ears medium sized without a well-defined black spot between; body size medium.   SYLVILAGUS FLORIDANUS p. 97

1' Anterior projection of supraorbital process absent or greatly reduced: forehead without a white spot; ears relatively small and relatively wider with a distinct black spot between; body size relatively small.   SYLVILAGUS TRANSITIONALIS p. 100

Sylvilagus floridanus (Allen) – Cottontail – *Lapin à queue blanche*

The cottontail is one of the smaller rabbits that inhabit eastern Canada. The pelage in summer is a dark buffy brown with tippings of greyish and black; it is only slightly paler or greyer in winter. There are two moults annually, spring and fall. There is a rich, reddish-brown patch on the neck behind the ear. The underparts are white except for a buffy spot under the neck. On the forehead there is usually a white spot which, together with the absence of a distinct black spot between the ears, distinguishes this species from *S. transitionalis*, the New England cottontail. The cottontail (*S. floridanus*) can also be distinguished by its relatively short ears and tail. The skull is characterized by its small size and by the fusion of the posterior projection of the supraorbital process with the frontal bones. Compared with *S. transitionalis*, the auditory bullae are relatively larger and the anterior projection of the supraorbital process is well developed instead of being reduced or absent.

SIZE Total length 375–490 mm.; tail 39–70; hind foot 80–108; ear from notch 53–66. Skull: length 72–82, width 34–40. Weight 2.0–4.5 lb. Females average about two-per-cent larger than males.

DISTRIBUTION AND VARIATION *S. floridanus mearnsii* is the form occurring in eastern Canada – in the more southern agricultural areas of Ontario, and in the Mont Tremblant (Lac Monroe) and Montreal areas and adjacent regions south of the St Lawrence River where it may be confused with *S. transitionalis*, a slightly smaller but fairly similar species.

HABITAT Hedgerows, woodlots, and ravines in agricultural and suburban areas. Escape cover such as brush piles, tall grass, or dense shrubbery is an essential requirement.

HABITS Unlike the hares, this species uses nests, hollow logs, brush piles, and a variety of other covers for nests or homes. The female may even dig a shallow burrow in which to bring forth her young—usually four to seven. Breeding starts about February and the first litter usually appears in mid-March after a gestation period of twenty-eight to thirty-two days. The nest is lined with dry grass and a layer of the mother's own fur. The young, weighing about two to five grams each, are born blind, naked, and helpless. They are concealed in the nest for about two weeks, during which time the mother visits them regularly to nurse them. They are weaned after about four or five weeks when they emerge from the nest, having grown to about the size of a chipmunk. The mother may breed soon after the birth of the young and produce a second or even a third litter before winter.

The cottontail normally restricts its movements to a fairly well-defined home range or territory: whenever it is flushed away it soon circles back to its familiar surroundings. Recent studies have found the home range of the cottontail to be as small as half an acre and as large as forty acres, but it usually averages between two and fourteen acres.

Food consists of a wide variety of vegetable matter. In summer the diet is chiefly green herbage, including grasses, weeds, and the leaves of small shrubs. In urban areas the cottontail thrives on occasional forays into vegetable and flower gardens; it frequently does considerable damage to nurseries, field crops, and truck gardens. The staple food in winter is made up of buds, tender twigs, and bark.

The cottontail may be active at any hour of the day or night, but there are two peak periods of activity: one at daybreak and the other at dusk. It is a solitary species, rarely encountered in groups. Normally there is little vocalization outside the nest. This rabbit communicates by thumping the hind feet and by making low grunts or guttural calls. When captured or injured, a loud, piercing, human-sounding scream may be uttered.

The potential life-span is about seven or eight years, although the average probably does not exceed two years.

Fig. 51 – COTTONTAIL – *Sylvilagus floridanus*

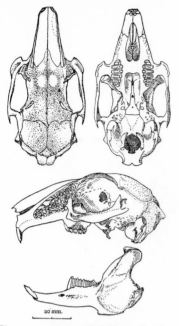

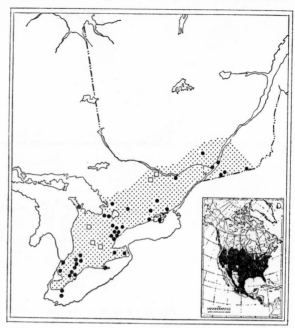

Fig. 52 – SKULL OF *Sylvilagus floridanus*
(ROM 20330 ♀)

Map 26 – DISTRIBUTION OF THE COTTONTAIL –
Sylvilagus floridanus

REMARKS The cottontail is favoured game for many hunters and its meat is tasty. It is an important link in the food chain from plants to carnivores.

There appear to be fairly regular cyclic fluctuations in population numbers at about ten-year intervals, although this has not been as dramatically demonstrated for the cottontail as for the snowshoe hare.

Care should be exercised in handling any sickly, or abnormal-appearing rabbit. Most lagomorphs, as well as some rodents, are subject to a disease known as 'Tularemia' or 'rabbit fever' caused by the bacterium *Pasteurella tularensis*. This disease resembles plague and is readily transmitted to humans. It is usually quite serious and sometimes even fatal if not properly diagnosed in its early stages. Transmission of the bacteria may be made through any small abrasion in the skin as a result of handling infected rabbits, although the disease may also be contracted from the bites of flies, ticks, and fleas, or of other parasites that have previously fed on an infected animal. The incubation period in humans is three or four days. Symptoms include a pimple-like swelling where the organism has entered the skin and an inflammation and enlargement of the lymph nodes, accompanied by an undulant fever with chills, weakness, and prostration.

Selected References
DALKE, PAUL D., 1942.
DALKE, PAUL D. and PALMER R. SIME, 1941.
HAMILTON, W. J., JR., 1940b.
HAUGEN, ARNOLD O., 1942a, 1942b.
TODD, JOHN B., 1927.

Fig. 53 – NEW ENGLAND COTTONTAIL – *Sylvilagus transitionalis*

Sylvilagus transitionalis (Bangs) – New England Cottontail – *Lapin de Nouvelle-Angleterre*

Superficially this species resembles the common cottontail, *Sylvilagus floridanus*, although it is smaller in size on the average; and it has no white spot on the forehead but has a distinct black spot between the ears. The ears are relatively smaller (shorter and wider) and more densely furred on the inside than those of *S. floridanus* and have a distinct narrow band of black or dark brown along the anterior outer edge that does not blend gradually into the rest of the ear. The upper pelage, especially along the flank, is buffy coloured. The skull may be distinguished by the relatively smaller auditory bullae and by the absence of, or a great reduction in, the anterior projection of the supra-orbital process, while the posterior projection narrows and lies close to, but is not usually fused with, the frontal bone.

SIZE Total length 355–450 mm.; tail 35–57; hind foot 81–110; ear from notch 48–60. Skull: length 66–76, width 34–37. Weight 2.0–3.5 lb.

DISTRIBUTION The New England cottontail, a monotypic species, ranges from northeastern Alabama along the Allegheny Mountains through central New Hampshire and northern Vermont to southwestern Maine. It probably crosses over the border into southern Quebec from northeastern New York, but no specimens have as yet been authoritatively identified from eastern Canada.

HABITAT The New England cottontail is primarily a forest dweller.

HABITS Essentially similar to those of the common cottontail, *S. floridanus*. However, it has been suggested that the New England cottontail may be more nocturnal in its activities.

REMARKS A study needs to be made of the lagomorphs along the border in southern Quebec to determine the northern limits of distribution of this unique species. In much of its range in New

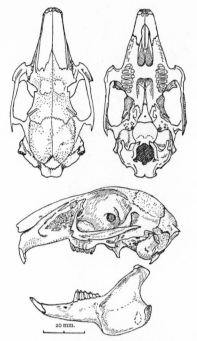

Fig. 54 – SKULL OF *Sylvilagus transitionalis*
(ROM 16758 ♀)

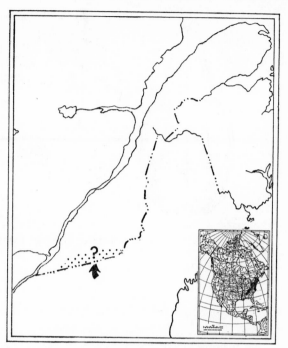

Map 27 – DISTRIBUTION OF THE NEW ENGLAND
COTTONTAIL – *Sylvilagus transitionalis*

England there have been introductions of various races of *S. floridanus*. It is felt by some that the *S. transitionalis* populations have become reduced as a result of competition between the two species and because of land-use practices that open up forested areas and tip the balance in favour of the habitat conditions of *S. floridanus*.

Selected References

DALKE, PAUL D. and PALMER R. SIME, 1941.
FAY, F. H. and E. H. CHANDLER, 1955.
HAMILTON, W. J., 1943.

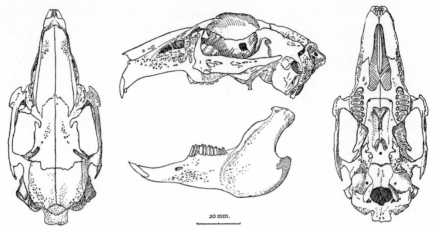

20 mm.

Fig. 55 – SKULL OF DOMESTIC RABBIT – *Oryctolagus cuniculus*

Genus **ORYCTOLAGUS** Lilljeborg

Domestic Rabbits – *Lapins de garennes*

Dental Formula $I \frac{2-2}{1-1}$ $C \frac{0-0}{0-0}$ $P \frac{3-3}{2-2}$ $M \frac{3-3}{3-3} = 28$

Oryctolagus cuniculus (Linnaeus) – Domestic Rabbit – *Lapin de garenne*

Many strains, breeds, or varieties of domestic rabbits have been developed under selective breeding. In many of these strains there is little superficial resemblance to the native *Oryctolagus cuniculus* of central Europe where the original stocks were started. Size and colour have been modified widely; however, certain cranial characters have persisted that allow the domestic rabbit to be distinguished from the five living lagomorphs in eastern Canada. As in *Sylvilagus*, the interparietal is not fused closely with the parietal except perhaps in extremely old rabbits. *Oryctolagus* can be distinguished from *Sylvilagus* by the free and flaring posterior extensions of the supraorbital process and by the position of the posterior edge of the palate which usually lies behind the level of the third and fourth molariform teeth.

Occasionally escaped domestic rabbits live feral (in the wild) for a period, but apparently they cannot survive the winter period in eastern Canada.

The native wild form living in Europe has a gestation period of twenty-eight days and a litter size of three to seven. Does may breed within twelve hours after parturition; lactation continues for about three weeks. The young reach sexual maturity at three or four months but continue to grow for about nine months before reaching full adult size.

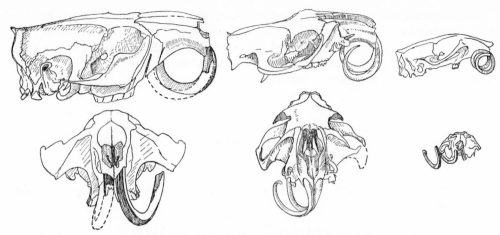

Fig. 56 – EXAMPLES OF TOOTH MALOCCLUSIONS
Left – BEAVER (ROM 11693); *Centre* – WOODCHUCK (ROM 27550); *Right* – NORWAY RAT (ROM 10144)

Order
Rodentia

The Order *Rodentia* (from the Latin *rodere*—to gnaw) contains more living species than all other mammals combined: over 2,800 (not including geographic races or subspecies) are known. Rodents occur on all major land masses of the world except Antarctica. Members of this order have become adapted for living in almost every conceivable major ecological situation and demonstrate well the principle of adaptive radiation. Some are fossorial, others are cursorial, ambulatory, semi-aquatic, arboreal, or gliders (volant). None has become marine or has developed the power of flight. In spite of these widely diverging adaptations, the order has remained remarkably homogeneous in its morphological characters. For example, representatives of the order have only one pair of curved, chisel-shaped incisors in the upper and lower jaw; no canine teeth; a wide diastema or vacant space between the incisors and the cheek teeth; and premolar teeth that are reduced in number or absent.

The incisor teeth continue to grow throughout the life of the rodent and are not rooted. The front surface of the incisors has a layer of usually orange-coloured enamel that is much harder than the rest of the tooth which consists of a softer dentine. As the dentine wears away rapidly, the leading edge of the enamel of each incisor remains sharp and chisel-like. Occasionally malformation or accident accounts for a non-occluding tooth which, in the absence of constant wear, can grow into a full circle or a corkscrew spiral. In some species the cheek teeth (premolars and molars) are also rootless and continue to grow throughout the life of the animal, while in other species the molariform teeth are rooted and cease to grow after having erupted fully.

The Order *Rodentia* may be conveniently divided into three living suborders:

(1) *Sciuromorpha*, in which the infraorbital canal does not transmit any part of the medial masseter muscle, is represented in eastern Canada by the families *Sciuridae* and *Castoridae*.

(2) *Myomorpha*, in which the infraorbital canal is usually greatly reduced in size (except in the family *Zapodidae*) but transmits at least a reduced median masseter muscle, is represented in eastern

Canada by the families *Cricetidae*, *Zapodidae*, and *Muridae* (an introduced group).

(3) *Hystricomorpha*, in which the infraorbital foramen or canal is greatly enlarged and through which the medial masseter muscle is transmitted, is represented in eastern Canada by the family *Erethizontidae*. A member of the family *Capromyidae* of South America, the nutria, has been imported by fur farmers.

KEY TO THE EASTERN-CANADIAN FAMILIES OF *Rodentia*

1 Infraorbital foramen conspicuously large: 2

    2 Weight more than 5 lb.; skull more than 90 mm. long; infraorbital foramen larger than the foramen magnum: 3

        3 Hair on body mixed with long sharp quills; posterior margin of bony palate extends almost to the level of the space between the third and fourth molariform teeth; nasals relatively short, broad, and elevated.   ERETHIZONTIDAE p. 188

        3′ Hair on body not mixed with quills; tail long, round, and relatively naked; posterior margin of palate extends to about the level of the posterior margin of the last molariform tooth; nasals relatively long, narrow, and not elevated. (Introduced.)   CAPROMYIDAE p. 192

    2′ Weight less than 30 gr.; tail longer than head and body; hind feet much larger than front feet; hair on belly completely white to base; infraorbital foramen large but smaller than foramen magnum.   ZAPODIDAE p. 181

1′ Infraorbital foramen not conspicuously large: 4

    4 Tail broad and flat; hind feet webbed; skull massive (more than 100 mm. long) but with relatively narrow interorbital width with no well-developed postorbital process.   CASTORIDAE p. 133

    4′ Tail not broad and flat; skull size variable: 5

        5 Tail bushy, with length of hair at the middle of the tail length longer than the width of the fleshy portion at that point; postorbital processes well developed (interorbital space wide); molars with an internal heel from which two or three ridges pass to the outside margin of the tooth.   SCIURIDAE p. 105

        5′ Tail not bushy; postorbital process lacking; interorbital space relatively narrow: 6

            6 Tail nearly naked, the annulations clearly visible; upper molars with tubercles in three longitudinal rows.   MURIDAE p. 173

            6′ Tail haired (usually with short, fine hair) with annulations nearly or completely invisible; upper molars with tubercles arranged in two longitudinal rows or with a complicated enamel pattern of prismatic triangles.   CRICETIDAE p. 138

Suborder
Sciuromorpha

Family SCIURIDAE
Squirrels – *Ecureuils*

The family *Sciuridae* includes such familiar species as the tree squirrel, the ground squirrel, the flying squirrel, the chipmunk, the woodchuck or marmot, and the prairie dog. Eastern Canada has a particularly good representation of species, including all the above except the prairie dog. All species have well-developed postorbital processes and four toes on the front feet and five on the hind.

All have moderate-to-long tails that are well furred (some are quite bushy), and most have internal cheek pouches that they utilize for carrying food. All species of this family except the flying squirrels are active during the daylight hours; and all are active the year round except the woodchuck, the ground squirrel, and the chipmunk which hibernate.

KEY TO THE EASTERN-CANADIAN GENERA OF *Sciuridae*

1 Membrane present between foreleg and hind leg as a modification for gliding; dorsal contour of the skull (viewed from the side) consists of a straight line from tip of nasals to orbits and a strongly arched cranium to the occiput; large auditory bullae and basioccipital region project noticeably below the plane of the palate; 5 upper cheek teeth present.   GLAUCOMYS p. 126

1' No membrane present between foreleg and hind leg; dorsal contour of skull not arched as above; upper cheek teeth number 4 or 5: 2

2 Infraorbital foramen pierces the zygomatic plate with no infraorbital canal; multiple dorsal stripes present on back; size small (under 300 mm. in total length): 3

3 Dorsal stripes (five dark and four light coloured) of approximately equal width; tail usually more than 40 per cent of the total length (185–225 mm.); 5 upper cheek teeth usually present on each side, the first premolar small and peglike.   EUTAMIAS p. 124

3' Dorsal stripes with two wide greyish ones on either side of the narrow median dark one and three lateral stripes, two dark and one light, all ending high on the rump; tail usually less than 40 per cent of the total length (225–265 mm.); 4 upper cheek teeth present on each side.   TAMIAS p. 121

2' Infraorbital foramen modified as a canal. No multiple dorsal stripes present along the back: 4

4 Zygomatic width more than 45 mm.; dorsal contour of skull almost straight (viewed from the side); incisor teeth usually pale yellowish orange; weight 5 to 10 lb.

MARMOTA p. 115

4′ Zygomatic width less than 45 mm.; weight less than 5 lb.: 5

5 Zygomatic arches converging anteriorly to a relatively long tapering rostrum; dorsal contour of skull a shallow arch; skull relatively narrow; usually 5 cheek teeth present on each side (P³ well developed); tail relatively short, with relatively short (not bushy) hairs; ears relatively small and not well furred or tufted.

CITELLUS p. 118

5′ Zygomatic arches nearly parallel along sides; rostrum relatively short; cheek teeth commonly number 4 or 5 (P³ small or absent); tail long and bushy; ears well furred, occasionally tufted: 6

6 Total length of head, body, and tail less than 350 mm.; weight less than 250 gr.; baculum absent; a yellowish or reddish dorsal stripe is present in winter and a dark stripe is present on each flank in summer; skull less than 50 mm. long and 30 mm. wide.

TAMIASCIURUS p. 112

6′ Total length of head, body, and tail more than 400 mm.; weight more than 330 gr.; skull length more than 55 mm. long and 30 mm. wide; baculum present; no dorsal or lateral stripes.

SCIURUS p . 106

Genus **SCIURUS** Linnaeus

Tree Squirrels – *Ecureuils*

Dental Formula   I $\frac{1-1}{1-1}$ C $\frac{0-0}{0-0}$ P $\frac{1-1}{1-1}$ or $\frac{2-2}{1-1}$ M $\frac{3-3}{3-3}$ = 20 or 22

KEY TO THE EASTERN-CANADIAN SPECIES OF *Sciurus*

1 Tips of tail hairs and tufts behind the ears fulvous (reddish orange); belly usually pale to bright fulvous. Skull usually with only one premolar above and below; dentition heavy with last molar noticeably smaller than preceding one. Restricted in eastern Canada to an introduced population on Pelee Island, Lake Erie, Ont.

SCIURUS NIGER p. 110

1′ Tips of tail hairs, of tufts behind the ears (in winter), and of eye-rings (in summer) usually whitish (in grey colour-phase); general coloration usually either grey or black with much individual variation. Skull usually with two premolars above (the anterior one a small, simple peg); dentition lighter with last molar about equal in size or larger than the preceding one. Widely introduced in city parks beyond its normal range.

SCIURUS CAROLINENSIS p. 108

Fig. 57 – EASTERN GRAY SQUIRREL – *Sciurus carolinensis*

Sciurus carolinensis Gmelin – Eastern Gray Squirrel – *Ecureuil gris*

This squirrel comes in two basic colour-phases, grey and black. The black phase is quite common in eastern Canada, but as one progresses southward the ratio becomes more predominantly grey; occasionally squirrels with a black body and a rusty-reddish tail are seen. A common animal in city parks, the eastern gray squirrel flourishes in the heart of large metropolitan areas. Except for the fox squirrel, present in Canada only on Pelee Island, Ont., this is the largest common squirrel in eastern Canada.

A white eye-ring and white-tipped hairs on the bushy tail help to identify the summer pelage of the grey phase. In winter pelage the whitish eye-ring is usually not distinct, but a white tuft develops behind the ears.

The very small anterior upper premolar (P^3) and the relatively large last molar distinguish the skull from that of *Sciurus niger*, the fox squirrel; the skull of *S. carolinensis* is much larger than that of *Tamiasciurus*, the red squirrel. Unlike chipmunks, tree squirrels have no well-developed internal cheek pouches.

SIZE Total length 450–540 mm.; tail 200–252; hind foot 60–75; ear from notch 25–35. Skull: length 59.4–66.5, width 31.8–36.0. Weight 340–680 gr. (0.75–1.5 lb.).

DISTRIBUTION AND VARIATION Two races occur in eastern Canada. The primitive range of the eastern race, *S. c. pennsylvanicus*, once included only southern Ontario, but introductions have established this species in isolated areas in southern Quebec, southern New Brunswick, and Nova Scotia. It is also known as *S. c. leucotis*, which was originally described from somewhere between Toronto and Lake Simcoe. *S. c. hypophaeus* is the name of the western race, found in western Ontario along the Minnesota border.

HABITAT Hardwood forests, although this species thrive well in the average city park and in wooded ravines.

HABITS The eastern gray squirrel is a very agile and graceful arboreal species that is perhaps more familiar to city dwellers than any other native small mammal. It becomes quite tame and many will take food at close range.

This squirrel eats nuts, seeds, bugs, fungi, and birds' eggs. (It has a remarkable skill in distinguishing between good and bad nuts.) It often buries excess food, much of which may not be recovered. Nests may be either hollows in trees or leaf-nests lodged in branches.

After a gestation period of forty to forty-four days, three to five young are born in March or April, usually in hollow trees. The newborn are naked and blind and weigh about fifteen grams. The eyes remain shut for at least a month, after which the young begin to make excursions outside the nest, but they do not venture far until they are about six weeks old. At two months the young are about half the size of the adults and are fully furred and have bushy tails. A second litter per season is common.

In captivity eastern gray squirrels are known to live up to fifteen years, but the average life-span in the wild is probably no more than five or six years.

REMARKS In rural areas the eastern gray squirrel is considered a prize small game animal. Although it is an attractive inhabitant of public parks, it becomes a serious pest whenever it makes its home in an attic, where it is always an unwelcome guest, often damaging electrical circuits.

This squirrel has been introduced in Great Britain (where it is known as the American Grey Squirrel), where it has become a serious pest.

Selected References
BANGS, OUTRAM, 1896d.
BROWN, LOUIS G. and LEE E. YEAGER, 1945.
JACKSON, H. H. T., 1961.
MIDDLETON, A. D., 1930.

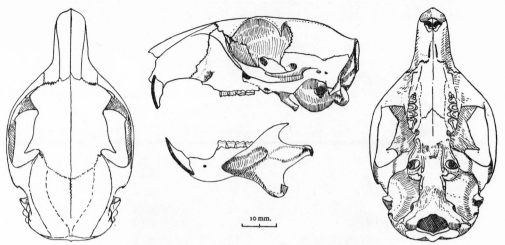

Fig. 58 – SKULL OF *Sciurus carolinensis* (ROM 22586 ♂)

10 mm.

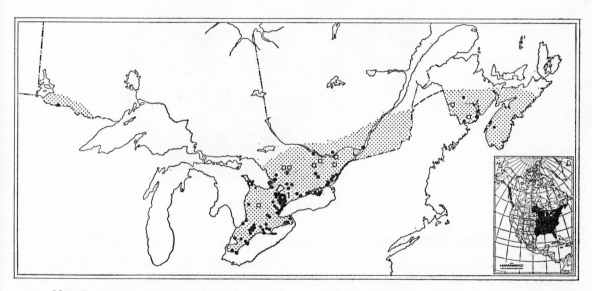

Map 28 – DISTRIBUTION OF THE EASTERN GRAY SQUIRREL – *Sciurus carolinensis* – AND (1) TYPE LOCALITY OF
S. c. leucotis (Gapper) (=*S. c. pennsylvanicus* Ord)

Fig. 59 – EASTERN FOX SQUIRREL – *Sciurus niger*

Sciurus niger Linnaeus – Eastern Fox Squirrel – *Ecureuil fauve*

The largest of the tree squirrels of eastern Canada was introduced from Ohio to Pelee Island, Ont., in Lake Erie, where it has become well established. Other efforts to introduce it on the adjacent mainland have apparently failed. The eastern fox squirrel is a striking species, characterized by a fulvous or rusty-brown coloration mixed with greyish on the upper parts, fulvous or buffy shades on the belly, and pure fulvous on the tips of the long tail hairs and on the tufts behind the ears. The ears tend to be broader and more rounded than those of the eastern gray squirrel, and the inside of the ears is fulvous or orange-coloured rather than dusky brown. Identifying features of the skull are the absence of the third premolar and the heavy dentition; the last molar is smaller than the preceding one.

SIZE Total length 500–565 mm.; tail 217–265; hind foot 62–80; ear from notch 20–35. Skull: length 62.4–70.0, width 35.0–40.1. Weight 544–1,360 gr. (1.2–3.0 lb.).

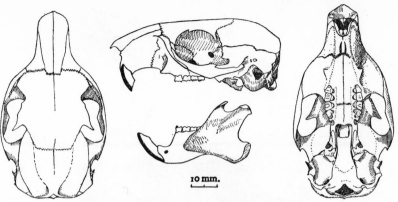

Fig. 60 – SKULL OF *Sciurus niger* (ROM 19518 ♀)

DISTRIBUTION AND VARIATION The only known established population in Canada occurs on Pelee Island, Lake Erie, Ont. The original introduction from Ohio was *Sciurus niger rufiventer*. This species ranges up to the Ontario-Minnesota boundary; it has apparently not been recorded on the Ontario side.

HABITAT Wooded streams and small hardwood woodlots.

HABITS Although similar to the eastern gray squirrel in its habits, the fox squirrel spends more time on the ground and apparently tends to bury more food caches. The food of the two species is similar, although 'corn-on-the-cob' is highly relished by the fox squirrel.

Compared with the eastern gray squirrel, the fox squirrel tends to be even more diurnal; it is most active between 8 a.m. and 4 p.m.

Breeding starts at one year. Yearlings are thought to produce only one litter while older females commonly produce two. The first mating occurs during January or February and the second about May or June. The gestation period is forty-four days. Litter sizes average three to five, although as many as seven have been reported. The development of the young is similar to that of the gray squirrel, *S. carolinensis*.

The potential life-span has been estimated to be fifteen years, but the average is only four or five under natural conditions.

REMARKS The Pelee Island population has apparently thrived well and has produced good small game hunting. In agricultural areas this squirrel frequently does considerable damage to corn—particularly when it is in the 'milk' stage—as well as to other grain or legume crops.

The meat of this large squirrel is delicious when it is properly prepared.

Selected References
ALLEN, DURWARD L., 1944.
BROWN, L. G. and L. E. YEAGER, 1945.
HICKS, ELLIS A., 1949.
OSGOOD, W. H., 1907.

Map 29 – DISTRIBUTION OF THE EASTERN FOX SQUIRREL – *Sciurus niger* (*Introduced*)

Fig. 61 – RED SQUIRREL – *Tamiasciurus hudsonicus*

Genus **TAMIASCIURUS** Trouessart

Red Squirrels – *Ecureuils roux*

Dental Formula $\mathrm{I}\frac{1-1}{1-1}$ $\mathrm{C}\frac{0-0}{0-0}$ $\mathrm{P}\frac{1-1}{1-1}$ or $\frac{2-2}{1-1}$ $\mathrm{M}\frac{3-3}{3-3} = 20$ or 22

Tamiasciurus hudsonicus (Erxleben) – Red Squirrel – *Ecureuil roux*

This noisy little squirrel is found throughout the entire forested area of eastern Canada. Its loud, long, rachet-like call is usually heard before the animal is seen. In summer a black stripe on its side separates the rusty-olive colour of the upper part from the whitish belly. The tail, which differs little with the seasons, is usually bright yellowish, orange, or rusty or deep red, depending on the locality, with lighter-coloured tips that vary from white to pale orange. In winter pelage the bright tail colour is extended as a stripe of varying width all along the back; the black side stripe is lost and the feet change from a bright reddish to grey, and the small ear tufts become more conspicuous. As winter progresses the upper pelage begins to fade, with the dorsal stripe becoming more yellowish and the dark olive sides becoming greyer.

The skull normally has only twenty teeth, although occasionally two very small upper premolars occur. The dental formula, together

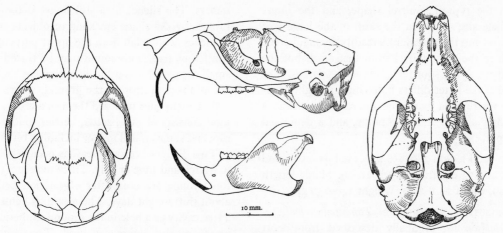

Fig. 62 – SKULL OF *Tamiasciurus hudsonicus* (ROM 12978)

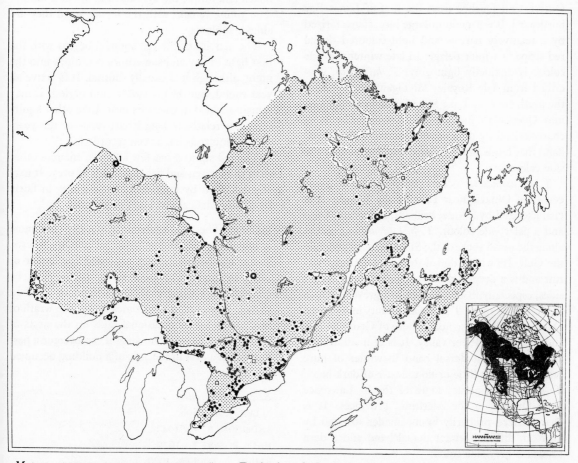

Map 30 – DISTRIBUTION OF THE RED SQUIRREL – *Tamiasciurus hudsonicus* – AND TYPE LOCALITIES OF (1) *T. h. hudsonicus* (Erxleben); (2) *T. h. regalis* A. H. Howell; (3) *T. h. ungavensis* Anderson (= *T. h. regalis*); (4) *T. h. laurentianus* Anderson

with the typical squirrel shape, and the intermediate size (between the skull of the large tree squirrel and the chipmunk), readily distinguish the skull of the red squirrel from that of all but the northern flying squirrel, *Glaucomys sabrinus*. The skull of the latter differs in having a straight, shallow rostrum, a narrower interorbital width, a strongly arched cranial contour, and a depressed occiput.

SIZE Total length 280–350 mm.; tail 95–150; hind foot 40–57; ear from notch 18–26. Skull: length 42–49, width 24.1–28.2. Weight 140–250 gr.

DISTRIBUTION AND VARIATION *Tamiasciurus hudsonicus hudsonicus*, originally described from Fort Severn, Ont., occupies the northern portions of Ontario and Quebec from the foot of James Bay northward. It is a medium-large race, characterized by a relatively narrow and light-coloured dorsal red stripe in winter pelage. In late winter the side colour is distinctly light grey. *T. h. regalis*, described from Isle Royale, Michigan, occurs along the north shore of Lake Superior and extends east into Quebec to include *T. h. ungavensis*. It is characterized by dark olive sides and a dorsal red band that tends to be diffused and blends into the side colour.

T. h. minnesota occurs only in the extreme corner of Ontario near Lake of the Woods. It is characterized by a wide, brilliant, red winter band and a paler side colour. *T. h. laurentianus* occurs along the north shore of the St Lawrence River and the Gulf. Its winter dorsal stripe is relatively narrow and is a deeper, duller colour on the average; sides, especially in late winter, are greyer than in the following races. *T. h. loquax* occurs in southern Ontario, north to the north shore of Georgian Bay and the Ottawa River valley. It is of medium size and has a bright dorsal band in winter of pure orange red with little or no mixture of dark hairs. *T. h. gymnicus* occurs south of the St Lawrence from Quebec to the Maritime Provinces. It is characterized primarily by its smaller size and by a broad, diffused winter dorsal band and a dark brownish-grey side colour.

HABITAT Boreal coniferous forests.

HABITS The silence of a still forest is frequently broken by the sharp crackling of objects striking branches as they fall from the upper parts of a tall coniferous tree. This sound may be traced to the small red squirrel as it busily cuts green cones and allows them to drop to the ground, where it will collect them later to hoard them in a cache. Other food consists of nuts, seeds, berries, buds, fungi, sap, and some animal matter including birds' eggs.

Two distinct breeding seasons occur: February to March and June or July. Three to seven (usually four) young are born after a gestation period of about thirty-eight days. The nest may be in either a tree cavity or a hole in the ground. Spherical tree nests are also sometimes used. The young are naked and blind; the eyes open in about a month. The young remain with the female until they are almost adult size.

The activity of the red squirrel begins with the first light of day and sometimes continues into the night, although it is usually diurnal. It is active all year round, but during severe cold periods it may remain bedded down in its nest. Like other squirrels, it is relatively long-lived: nine- or ten-year-old red squirrels have been recorded.

The red squirrel has few effective enemies other than the marten and fisher or birds of prey. It may also be taken by large fish as it engages in fairly frequent swims across lakes or streams.

REMARKS The red squirrel is usually the most omnipresent mammal in eastern-Canadian forests. It has not been seriously exploited for its fur or meat by man. This squirrel is believed to be effective as a planter of forest trees in its food caches. However, it sometimes incurs the wrath of bird lovers for its occasional raids on the nests of birds, and in more urban areas it can become a pest if it builds a nest in the attic of a building occupied by humans.

Selected References
ALLEN, J. A., 1898.
ANDERSON, R. M., 1942a.
HATT, ROBERT T., 1929.
KLUGH, A. BOOKER, 1927.
LAYNE, JAMES N., 1952, 1954.

Fig. 63 – WOODCHUCK – *Marmota monax*

Genus **MARMOTA** Blumenbach

Woodchucks – *Marmottes*

Dental Formula $I \frac{1-1}{1-1}$ $C \frac{0-0}{0-0}$ $P \frac{2-2}{1-1}$ $M \frac{3-3}{3-3} = 22$

Marmota monax (Linnaeus) – Woodchuck – *Marmotte commune*

This heavy-set rodent, frequently referred to as a ground hog or marmot, is the largest member of the squirrel family in eastern Canada. It is a familiar sight in rural agricultural areas where it is regarded either as a serious pest when it moves into gardens or as a game animal for small-bore rifle hunting.

The brownish pelage above usually has a grizzled appearance caused by alternating bands of colour on the guard hairs, which are black at the base and have bands of buff, black, light buff, and

black tips. The under-fur is tipped with a yellowish straw colour. The underparts and legs are a reddish brown and the feet are black. There is one annual moult beginning in June or July.

The ears are small and the tail is relatively short. The front feet have only four well-developed toes with digging claws, but the fifth is present as a pollex with a small claw or nail located high up on the foot. There are five toes on the hind feet. The skull is readily distinguished by its large size and by being broad and flattened, with prominent post-orbital processes and very pale-coloured enamel on the leading edges of the incisor teeth.

SIZE Total length 500–657 mm.; tail 110–155; hind foot 74–92; ear from notch 25–40. Skull: length 73–102, width 50–69. Weight 4–12 lb.

DISTRIBUTION AND VARIATION The woodchuck occurs throughout Ontario except for the treeless triangle across the coast from Hudson Bay to James Bay. It is absent from the northernmost sections of Quebec and Labrador. In the rest of eastern Canada it has not been recorded from Anticosti Island, Prince Edward Island, Cape Breton Island, or Newfoundland. Most of the northern regions are occupied by *Marmota monax canadensis*, a relatively small and pale-reddish form. The east coast of Labrador and eastern Quebec is occupied by the larger, darker *M. m. ignava*, which has a broad short skull. *M. m. rufescens*, which occurs across southern Ontario and adjacent Quebec, is approximately the same size as *M. m. ignava*, but it is paler and has a longer and narrower skull. Woodchuck specimens from the Gaspé Peninsula of Quebec have been described as *M. m. johnsoni*, although they may prove to be a melanistic variety of *M. m. canadensis*.

HABITAT Fields, pastures, fence-rows, ravines, woodlots, semi-open forests, and rock slopes.

HABITS The daylight hours of the woodchuck are spent feeding, sunning on a rock, a branch, or some other vantage point, or enlarging its burrow system. Breeding starts soon after it comes out of hibernation, usually in March. After a gestation period of thirty-one to thirty-two days, a litter (usually two to six) is born in April or May. The kits are about 100–110 mm. long, with tails of 15 or 16 mm.; they weigh from twenty-five to thirty grams and are blind and naked. At four weeks the kits have doubled their length and increased their weight by five or six times. In June or July, at five or six weeks, they are weaned. At about eight weeks they may weigh two pounds and soon fatten up for hibernation. Normally only one litter per year is produced. Sexual maturity is reached at one year, but the woodchuck continues to grow for two years before reaching maximum weight.

Food consists of fresh green vegetation, including clover and alfalfa; woodchucks may also consume garden vegetables as well as wild plants.

The burrow system usually has more than one entrance and the hibernating chamber is usually located below frost level, although the nesting material used to line it may be sufficient to keep the chamber from freezing at a slightly higher level. After becoming enormously fat in late September or early October, the woodchuck retires to its chamber even though really cold weather has not set in and food may be still plentiful. Contrary to popular opinion, hibernation is not continuous, for the woodchuck may become active during mid-winter. It enters its deep sleep rather slowly and gradually, taking from three days to a month to attain a torpid condition, when its body temperature drops from a normal 98.9° F. to as low as 37.4° F. and the heart-beat drops from about eighty beats per minute to only four or five. The stored fat seems to be primarily for insulation and is not actually utilized until the animal becomes active in the spring when food supplies are limited. Most woodchucks come out of hibernation in March (not February 2nd), at which time there may be little or no green foods and the weather may be extremely cold and the ground still covered with snow.

The life-span has been known to extend to ten years. However, it probably does not average more than about three years.

REMARKS The woodchuck's ability to hibernate has been the subject of considerable research. As the largest of the true hibernators of eastern Canada, it has become the subject of medical research in an effort to discover what factor or factors control the hibernating phenomenon. The findings of these studies might have an application to humans, particularly with respect to the lowering of body temperatures and the reduction of the speed of the heart-beat in facilitating certain types of heart surgery.

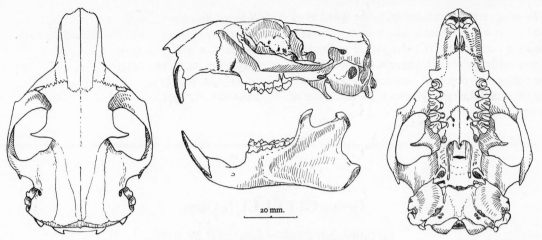

Fig. 64 – SKULL OF *Marmota monax* (ROM 20978 ♀)

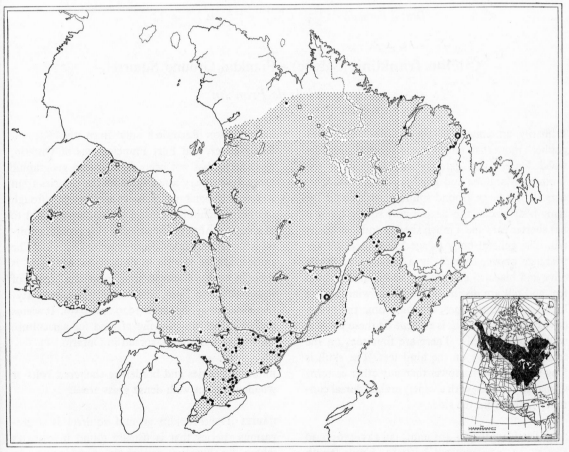

Map 31 – DISTRIBUTION OF THE WOODCHUCK – *Marmota monax* – AND TYPE LOCALITIES OF
(1) *M. m. canadensis* (Erxleben); (2) *M. m. johnsoni* Anderson; (3) *M. m. ignava* (Bangs)

In urban and agricultural areas the woodchuck can be a serious pest, but in wilder areas it provides food for carnivores. Its burrows are utilized by several other species of mammals. The woodchuck has become the object of considerable sport hunting for small-bore rifle shooters. Its fur is not of commercial quality.

Selected References

BENEDICT, FRANCIS G. and ROBERT C. LEE, 1938.
GRIZZELL, ROY A., JR., 1955.
HAMILTON, W. J., JR., 1934.
HOWELL, A. H., 1915.
LANDIS, C. S., 1951.

Genus **CITELLUS** Oken

Ground Squirrels – *Ecureuils de terre*

Dental Formula $\text{I} \frac{1-1}{1-1} \quad \text{C} \frac{0-0}{0-0} \quad \text{P} \frac{2-2}{1-1} \quad \text{M} \frac{3-3}{3-3} = 22$

Citellus franklinii (Sabine) – Franklin Ground Squirrel –

Spermophile de Franklin

Primarily an animal of the prairies, this 'grey gopher', more than most ground squirrels, invades wooded areas and extends into Ontario at the southern-Manitoba and northern-Minnesota borders. It is a large ground squirrel, with about the same body size as the eastern gray squirrel, but it has shorter ears and a much shorter and less bushy tail. The general body pelage has a speckled appearance above, created by a banding of tawny olive and blackish colours on the hairs. The hind feet and tail are distinctly greyish in winter but a little less so in summer, at which time the tawny olive colour of the back is evident on these parts as well as on the belly. There are four toes on the front feet and five on the hind feet. The skull is long and narrow, narrower than any other eastern-Canadian sciurids, with a widely arched dorsal contour viewed from the side.

SIZE Total length 360–401 mm.; tail 125–156; hind foot 51–57; ear from notch 10–12. Skull: length 50.0–56.1, width 30–32. Weight 300–710 gr.

DISTRIBUTION Recorded only from the Kenora, Rainy River, and Fort Francis areas of Ontario, this species has not been divided into geographic races. Its primary range includes the prairies from western Indiana to Kansas northward through southern Manitoba, central Saskatchewan, and to east central Alberta. Apparently this ground squirrel is a relatively recent immigrant to Ontario. (The earliest-known record in Ontario is 1925.) It is thought to have spread from near the Town of Rainy River to Emo, some twenty-five or thirty-five miles away, between 1929 and 1936. It seems probable that the clearing of land for agriculture allowed this animal to spread in Ontario.

HABITAT Prairies and bordering sheltered belts or wooded regions with dense grass areas.

HABITS The Franklin ground squirrel is a gregarious species that is usually found in colonies where its burrows are made conspicuous by mounds of earth at the entrance. Active during the

Fig. 65 – FRANKLIN GROUND SQUIRREL – *Citellus franklinii*

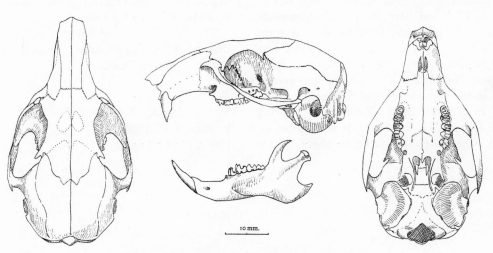

10 mm.

Fig. 66 – SKULL OF *Citellus franklinii* (ROM 21046 ♂)

day, its whistled twitter may announce its presence before it is seen. This species tends to be relatively shy and wary compared with other ground squirrels. It climbs trees quite readily.

The young—five to ten (usually six or seven) per litter—are born in May or June after a gestation period of about twenty-eight days. They are naked and blind at birth but develop rapidly, becoming active and venturing out of the burrow in about a month or six weeks. The eyes open at about twenty-seven days. Ten mammae are present—four pectoral, two abdominal, and four inguinal.

Food consists of about two-thirds vegetable matter, including many seeds, agricultural crops and their seeds, as well as leaves and berries and the seeds of wild plants. The remaining third is made up of animal matter that includes insects and other invertebrates and even frogs, small mammals, birds, and eggs.

The Franklin ground squirrel enters hibernation about October and comes out in late March or early April.

REMARKS This is the only ground squirrel known to occur regularly in eastern Canada, and it is limited to a small range.

The thirteen-lined ground squirrel, *Citellus tridecemlineatus tridecemlineatus*, occurs across the Detroit River in Michigan and on the west side of Lake St Clair and near the Ontario-Minnesota boundary. No specimens have yet been taken on the Canadian side; however, one animal was photographed in July 1959 in Sibley Provincial Park near Port Arthur, Ont. (It was seen several times in the summer of 1959, but not at all in 1960.) In all probability it will eventually be added to the eastern-Canadian fauna. It is some ten or eleven inches long and dark brown above, with a

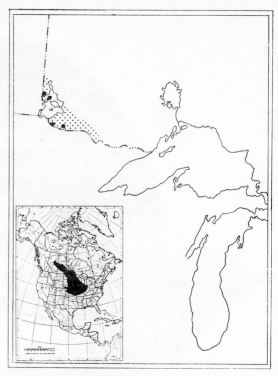

Map 32 – DISTRIBUTION OF THE FRANKLIN GROUND SQUIRREL – *Citellus franklinii*

striking pattern of thirteen long stripes of yellowish buff; over the back, every other stripe becomes a series of yellowish-buff spots. It is so distinctly different from the Franklin ground squirrel that it can be recognized at once.

The Franklin ground squirrel has been condemned as a serious predator of duck nests in the prairie regions of Canada.

Selected References
BAILEY, VERNON, 1893.
HOWELL, A. H., 1938.
SOWLS, LYLE K., 1948.

Fig. 67 – EASTERN CHIPMUNK – *Tamias striatus*

Genus **TAMIAS** Illiger

Eastern Chipmunks – *Suisses*

Dental Formula   I $\frac{1-1}{1-1}$ C $\frac{0-0}{0-0}$ P $\frac{1-1}{1-1}$ M $\frac{3-3}{3-3}$ = 20

Tamias striatus (Linnaeus) – Eastern Chipmunk – *Suisse*

This colourful chipmunk is one of the more familiar of the small mammals of eastern Canada. The upper part of the body is marked with a narrow, dark-brown, median stripe bordered on each side by a broad greyish stripe that is followed by two dark-brown stripes separated by a pale-buff one. All stripes end at the rump which is a bright reddish brown. The tail is less than forty per cent of the total length. Large internal cheek pouches enable this chipmunk to stuff its face with a great quantity of food that it stores in its private cache. The skull can be distinguished from other skulls of similar size by the presence of only one premolar on each side (i.e. four cheek teeth on each side). The conformation of the infraorbital foramen distinguishes the chipmunk from other sciurids. The colour of the enamel of the incisor teeth is pale orange (compared with the dark-orange enamel of *Eutamias minimus*). Eight mammae are present: two pectoral, four abdominal, and two inguinal.

SIZE Total length 225–273 mm.; tail 65–115; hind foot 32–40; ear from notch 16–20. Skull: length 37–42, width 21–24. Weight 75–115 gr.

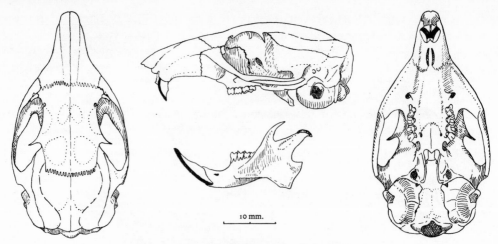

Fig. 68 – SKULL OF *Tamias striatus* (ROM 18782 ♂)

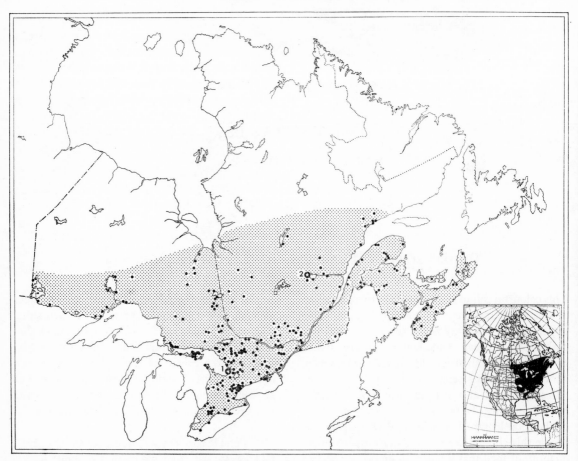

Map 33 – DISTRIBUTION OF THE EASTERN CHIPMUNK – *Tamias striatus* – AND TYPE LOCALITIES OF (1) *T. s. lysteri* Richardson); (2) *T. s. quebecensis* Cameron

DISTRIBUTION AND VARIATION Three races of the eastern chipmunk occur in eastern Canada: *Tamias striatus griseus* is found north and west of Lake Superior; *T. s. quebecensis* north and east of Lake Superior; and *T. s. lysteri* in southern Ontario, southern Quebec, and the Maritime Provinces. The species is absent from Anticosti Island and Newfoundland. The largest race is *T. s. griseus*, which has an admixture of buff in the grey dorsal stripes. *T. s. quebecensis* is slightly smaller and the dorsal stripes are greyer in colour. In *T. s. lysteri*, the smallest race, a buffy coloration predominates.

HABITAT Hardwood forests and well-drained areas providing shelter. The eastern chipmunk uses brush piles, rock piles, old buildings, and even refuse dumps as den sites. By comparison the least chipmunk, *Eutamias minimus*, prefers coniferous areas, although the two frequently range through the same parts.

HABITS Although capable of climbing fairly well, this chipmunk prefers to stay close to the ground most of the time. Nests are usually underground. The burrows commonly go straight down from a fairly level surface and then extend laterally.

Breeding starts in late March or early in April, and two to seven (an average of four to five) young are born one month later. A second breeding may take place toward the end of June or throughout July. The young, weighing about three or four grams, are born blind and naked. The striped coat begins to show in about eight days, and the eyes are open about one month after birth when the young first venture from the nest.

During the coldest weather the eastern chipmunk regularly hibernates, although hibernation seems quite intermittent, as this animal is occasionally active in mid-winter. By the middle of March full activity begins, and it continues until about the middle or end of November.

A wide variety of food is eaten, including nuts, seeds, berries, insects and other invertebrates, and even small birds and birds' eggs. The loud 'chip' of this chipmunk, repeated at regular intervals, is one of the more familiar calls of the forest. The eastern chipmunk is known to have lived up to eight years in captivity, but it probably does not average more than three years in the wild.

REMARKS The eastern chipmunk is rarely regarded as a pest and is usually enjoyed by everyone who meets it. In many areas it becomes quite tame and can be encouraged to take food from the hand. It makes an interesting pet when it is captured before maturity.

Selected References
ALLEN, ELSA G., 1938.
CAMERON, A. W., 1950a.
HOWELL, A. H., 1929.
KLUGH, A. BROOKER, 1923.
PANUSKA, JOSEPH A. and NELSON J. WADE, 1956, 1957.
YERGER, RALPH W., 1955.

Fig. 69 – WESTERN CHIPMUNK – *Eutamias minimus*

Genus **EUTAMIAS** Trouessart

Western Chipmunks – *Suisses de l'ouest*

Dental Formula $I \frac{1-1}{1-1}$ $C \frac{0-0}{0-0}$ $P \frac{2-2}{1-1}$ $M \frac{3-3}{3-3} = 22$

Eutamias minimus (Bachman) – Least or Western Chipmunk – *Tamia mineur*

This is undoubtedly one of the most appealing small mammals. It is considerably smaller than the eastern chipmunk and is readily distinguished by three dark and two light stripes on the sides of the face and by five dark and four light stripes of approximately equal width extending from the head to the base of the tail. The tail is more than forty per cent of the total length. The skull is the smallest of the sciurids of eastern Canada and has an evenly arched dorsal contour. A second small peg-like upper premolar (P^3) is usually present.

The enamel of the incisors is dark orange (compared with the paler orange colour of *Tamias striatus*). The conformation of the infraorbital foramen distinguishes the skull of the least chipmunk from that of the flying squirrel which has the same dental formula. There are eight mammae, as in *T. striatus*.

SIZE Total length 185–225 mm.; tail 80–100; hind foot 28–35; ear from notch 13–18. Skull: length 31–34, width 17.5–18.8. Weight 35–53 gr.

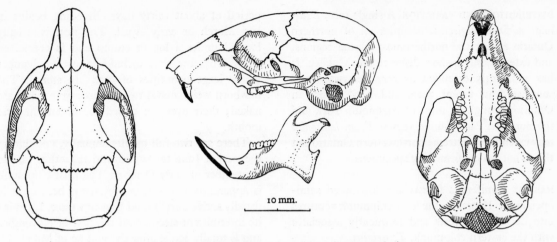

Fig. 70 – SKULL OF *Eutamias minimus* (ROM 10056 ♂)

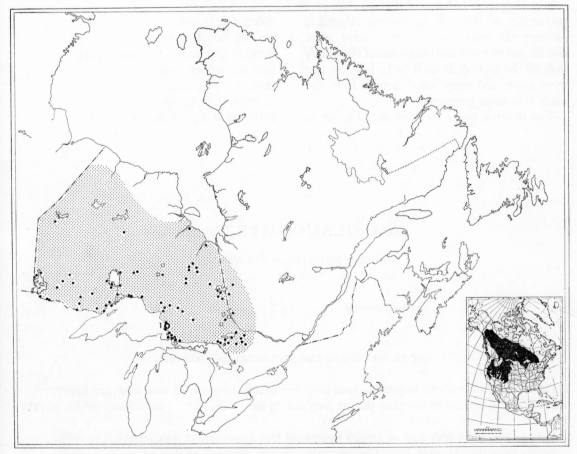

Map 34 – DISTRIBUTION OF THE WESTERN CHIPMUNK – *Eutamias minimus* – AND (1) TYPE LOCALITY OF
E. m. neglectus (Allen)

DISTRIBUTION AND VARIATION A single race, *Eutamias minimus neglectus*, occupies all of northern Ontario except the northernmost coastal regions, and extends only a short distance into Quebec. It has apparently extended its range eastward and southward in recent years and now occurs in Ontario throughout most of Algonquin Park and the northern Parry Sound region. *E. m. hudsonius* may extend into extreme northwestern Ontario but this is not yet confirmed by specimens.

HABITAT Coniferous forests and associated semi-open areas. However, the least chipmunk ventures into deciduous forests and frequently associates with the eastern chipmunk, *T. striatus*.

HABITS In general the habits of the least chipmunk are similar to those of the eastern chipmunk, although the least seems to be a more adept climber and ventures into trees, some of them quite high off the ground. It tends to be less shy, and more active and noisy when disturbed. It also tends to be more gregarious.

Two to seven young are born after a gestation period of about thirty days. Breeding begins in late March or early April. The nest is usually located under a log or stump and is connected with a burrow that includes a cache chamber where large quantities of food are stored. The newborn weigh about two or three grams and are naked; their eyes are closed for about the first month.

There are two full moults annually, one during the period June to August and the other in late September or early October. The least chipmunk is apparently not a deep hibernator because it is usually active during mild days in winter. It begins its intermittent sleep about the first of November and is totally active after the middle of March.

Selected References

ALDOUS, SHALER E., 1941.
ANDERSON, R. M. and A. L. RAND, 1944.
CRIDDLE, STUART, 1943.
HOWELL, A. H., 1929.
JACKSON, H. H. T., 1957.
PETERSON, R. L., 1953b.

Genus **GLAUCOMYS** Thomas

Flying Squirrels – *Polatouches*

Dental Formula $\quad$ I $\frac{1-1}{1-1}$ $\quad$ C $\frac{0-0}{0-0}$ $\quad$ P $\frac{2-2}{1-1}$ $\quad$ M $\frac{3-3}{3-3} = 22$

KEY TO THE EASTERN-CANADIAN SPECIES OF *Glaucomys*

1 Fur on belly white all the way to its base; hind foot usually less than 33 mm. long; tail usually less than 110 mm.; skull less than 36 mm. long and 22 mm. wide. $\quad$ GLAUCOMYS VOLANS p. 128

1' Fur on belly white with slate or greyish base; hind foot more than 33 mm. long; tail vertebrae usually more than 110 mm. long; skull more than 36 mm. long and 22 mm. wide.

GLAUCOMYS SABRINUS p. 129

Fig. 71 – EASTERN FLYING SQUIRREL – *Glaucomys volans*

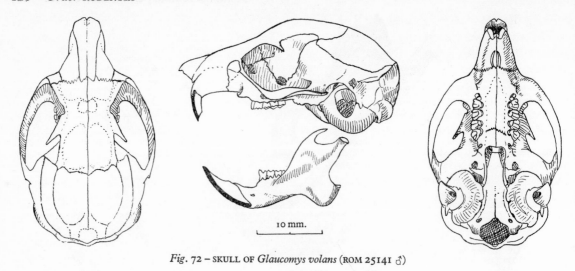

Fig. 72 – SKULL OF *Glaucomys volans* (ROM 25141 ♂)

Glaucomys volans (Linnaeus) – Eastern Flying Squirrel – *Petit polatouche*

The smallest of the flying squirrels of eastern Canada, this species can easily be recognized by the pure white fur of the underparts which is white all the way to the base (compare the dusky base of the northern flying squirrel). A loose fold of skin extends along the side of the body from the wrist of the front foot to the hind foot. Spur-like cartilaginous supports extend from the wrist along the edge of the skin fold, increasing the width of the gliding surface when the legs are outstretched. The fur of the tail is flattened; this adds to the squirrel's buoyancy and allows the tail to act both as a rudder and as a horizontal stabilizer in guiding the animal during a glide.

The eyes, which are conspicuously large and black, are well adapted for night vision. The eyelids are black.

The *Glaucomys* skull has a straight shallow rostrum and a distinctively rounded dorsal and posterior contour that distinguish it from other *Sciuridae*. The skull of *Glaucomys volans* is distinctly smaller than that of *G. sabrinus*. There are eight mammae: two pectoral, four abdominal, and two inguinal.

SIZE Total length 230–257 mm.; tail 85–110; hind foot 26–33; ear from notch 13–18. Skull: length 33.1–36.0, width 19.6–21.6. Weight 52–69 gr.

DISTRIBUTION AND VARIATION Only the race *G. volans volans* is found in eastern Canada. It is restricted to southern Ontario, primarily to those regions south of the Canadian Shield.

HABITAT Hardwood forests.

HABITS The aerial antics of the eastern flying squirrel are well known. On a perch high up in a tree it will sway from side to side (this may be a range-finding technique) and then leap out into space with legs outstretched. Glides of up to 150 feet are known. In a long glide it manipulates its tail to alter the direction of flight. As the point of landing is neared, the tail is raised and the glide plane is elevated to allow the fully outstretched under-surface of the body to act as an air brake and to slow the flight to a stall just before landing. Once it alights, this squirrel may climb back to a higher altitude and repeat the manoeuvre. Unfortunately for the average observer, most of these flying activities take place at night, when the only indication of them is a sharp 'thump' on the roof of a tent or a cottage.

Usually a woodpecker hole or a rotted knot-hole in a standing tree is selected as a home site, but occasionally the eastern flying squirrel builds a home in the attic of a building and provides an eerie mystery with the pattering of its small feet and an occasional loud thump. It occasionally builds in a tree a leaf-nest similar to that of the gray and fox squirrel.

Breeding starts about late February or March. (A second mating may take place in June or July.) After a gestation period of about forty days, two to six young are born—tiny, naked, and blind; they weigh about three or four grams each. The young become well furred in about three weeks; their eyes are open in about four weeks, and they are weaned at about five or six weeks. At about eight weeks they begin to glide.

Food consists of seeds, nuts, buds, tree blossoms, fruits, insects, and sometimes eggs and young birds.

These flying squirrels are quite sociable and gregarious, with several congregating in one den tree. They are known to live up to thirteen years in captivity.

REMARKS A flying squirrel makes a most interesting pet and is quite tractable when captured young. It can be trained to glide from a perch to an open hand on call or to curl up contentedly in one's pocket. It even seems to enjoy being thrown between two

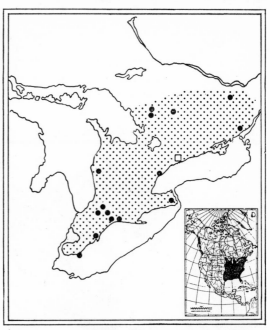

Map 35 – DISTRIBUTION OF THE EASTERN FLYING SQUIRREL – *Glaucomys volans*

persons like a ball. Unfortunately its nocturnal habits make it reluctant to be disturbed in the daytime, which it spends curled up in a nest with its tail over its eyes. An otherwise perfectly tame pet may show its displeasure at being wakened during the day by nipping the finger of the intruder.

Selected References
HATT, ROBERT T., 1931.
HOWELL, A. H., 1918.
SOLLBERGER, DWIGHT E., 1940, 1943.

Glaucomys sabrinus (Shaw) – Northern Flying Squirrel – *Grand polatouche*

This species differs from the eastern flying squirrel in being larger and in having a dusky or slate-coloured base to the whitish fur of the underparts. The larger size is also reflected in a longer tail and hind foot. Like the eastern flying squirrel, it has conspicuously large, black eyes. There are eight

mammae, as in *Glaucomys volans*. The northernmost races are decidedly larger than the southern. The skull can be distinguished from *G. volans* by its larger size, which in some of the northern races approaches the size of the skull of a small red squirrel, *Tamiasciurus*.

M.E.C — 11

Fig. 73 – NORTHERN FLYING SQUIRREL – *Glaucomys sabrinus*

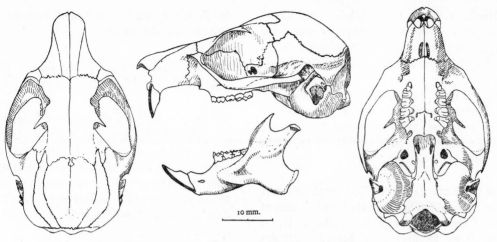

Fig. 74 – SKULL OF *Glaucomys sabrinus* (ROM 13067 ♀)

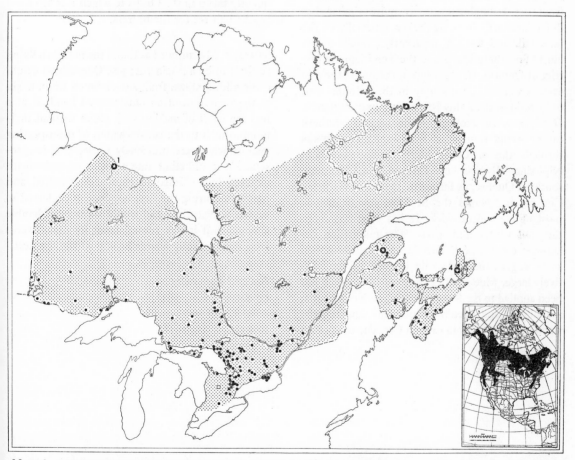

Map 36 – DISTRIBUTION OF THE NORTHERN FLYING SQUIRREL – *Glaucomys sabrinus* – AND TYPE LOCALITIES OF (1) *G. s. sabrinus* (Shaw); (2) *G. s. makkovikensis* (Sornborger); (3) *G. s. goodwini* Anderson; (4) *G. s. gouldi* Anderson

SIZE Northern races: *G. s. sabrinus* and *G. s. makkovikensis*. Total length 285–347 mm.; tail 125–157; hind foot 37–45; ear from notch 18–25. Skull: length 39–42, width 23–26. Weight 100–200 gr.

Southern races: *G. s. canescens*, *G. s. macrotis*, *G. s. goodwini*, and *G. s. gouldi*. Total length 260–295 mm.; tail 110–137; hind foot 34–40; ear from notch 16–25. Skull: length 36–39, width 22–24. Weight 75–150 gr.

DISTRIBUTION AND VARIATION The northern flying squirrel is found in almost all the wooded areas of eastern Canada except Newfoundland. *G. s. sabrinus* (type locality: Fort Severn) occupies northern Ontario. *G. s. makkovikensis*, described from the Labrador coast, is quite similar but differs primarily in being darker, especially on the face, tail, and feet. It apparently extends across most of northern Quebec to the Temiskaming district of Ontario. *G. s. canescens*, the palest form in eastern Canada, occurs only in the extreme west of Ontario in the Rainy River-Fort Francis region. *G. s. macrotis*, another of the smaller southern races, occurs southward from southern Algoma through the southern Sudbury and northern Nipissing districts of Ontario, east through southern Quebec, as far north as central Gatineau County, and across the St Lawrence to include most of New Brunswick. It has relatively large ears and whiter underparts. The population occupying the Gaspé Peninsula has been described as *G. s. goodwini*, primarily because of the relatively large, wide skull. The name *G. s. gouldi* has been applied to the form occurring in Nova Scotia, including Cape Breton Island; this squirrel, the smallest of the races in eastern Canada, also occurs in Prince Edward Island and perhaps southeastern New Brunswick.

HABITAT Coniferous and mixed forests. Areas of high moisture and fallen mossy logs are preferred.

HABITS The habits of the northern flying squirrel are primarily the same as those of the eastern flying squirrel, *G. volans*. It apparently spends more time on the ground, however. Mating takes place between late March and late May, and two to five young are born in May and June after forty days' gestation. Newborn young weigh five or six grams.

In the northern regions this species is frequently taken in steel traps to which it is attracted by the bait set for fur-bearers.

REMARKS The author has found the northern flying squirrel to be a fascinating pet. One animal would come gliding down from a doorway or window-sill at the invitation of an outstretched hand. It also had the habit of making such glides without invitation, much to the consternation of unsuspecting visitors who were previously unaware of its presence. It would climb into a pocket or underneath clothing and seemed to enjoy being petted and handled. During the day, however, it preferred to be left undisturbed and would show considerable annoyance if it was roused from its nest. Excess food was carefully hoarded away within the nest.

Selected References
COVENTRY, A. F., 1932.
COWAN, IAN MCT., 1936.
HOWELL, A. H., 1918.

Family **CASTORIDAE**

Beavers – *Castors*

This family contains only one genus, *Castor*, and four living species. Only one species is found in Canada

Genus **CASTOR** Linnaeus

Beavers – *Castors*

Dental Formula $\text{I } \frac{1-1}{1-1} \quad \text{C } \frac{0-0}{0-0} \quad \text{P } \frac{1-1}{1-1} \quad \text{M } \frac{3-3}{3-3} = 20$

Castor canadensis Kuhl – Beaver – *Castor*

The vital role played by the beaver in the early exploration and development of Canada has made it an emblem of the country. As Canada's largest and most distinctive rodent, it is perhaps more famous than any other native mammal. It is easily identified by its broad, flat tail, by its large, powerful incisor teeth, its large size, and rich brown coloration. The hind feet are webbed and the second hind toe has a split nail that acts as a comb for grooming the fur. It has four mammae, all of which are in the pectoral region.

SIZE Total length 875–1250 mm.; tail 230–440; hind foot 160–180. Skull: length 119–145, width 80–105. Weight 30–80 lb.

DISTRIBUTION AND VARIATION The beaver is found in most of the wooded areas of eastern Canada where a suitable habitat persists. It has been extirpated along the southern agricultural regions where its habitat has been destroyed.

In spite of the beaver's long familiarity and economic importance, knowledge of the nature of its geographic variation is still meagre. The first-known form was described as *Castor canadensis*

canadensis from Hudson Bay. Subsequently the following have been named: *C. c. caecator*, restricted to Newfoundland; *C. c. michiganensis*, a dark form occurring in the upper Great Lakes area, presumably only in the southern Algoma region of eastern Canada; *C. c. labradorensis*, an intermediate form described from eastern Labrador (Hamilton and Paradise Rivers); and *C. c. acadicus*, described from New Brunswick and thought to represent the original beaver of the St Lawrence valley, although subsequent introductions of animals from outside the valley have now obscured the identity of the beavers in that region.

HABITAT Wooded waterways, including lakes and streams where aspen and/or other suitable foods are present.

HABITS The engineering feats regularly performed by the beaver have gained it world-wide fame. In order to maintain a fairly constant water level around its lodge or bank den, a dam is constructed across a stream. It is made of brush, and sticks of cut limbs and tree trunks interwoven with mud and other objects. Saplings, which form the

Fig. 75 – BEAVER – *Castor canadensis*

skeleton foundation of the dam, are secured in the bed of the stream (their butts upstream) with amazing skill and purpose. When the desired water level is reached, the dam is constantly maintained by further additions of mud and sticks, etc. Damage to a dam is quickly detected, and repairs are usually made without delay, although most dam work takes place at night with all but the smallest members of one or more families participating.

The home of the beaver may vary from a simple burrow in the shore or bank of a pond, lake, or stream, to an elaborate structure called a lodge, house, or hut. The lodge may be situated on the shore or a few feet away, or it may be completely isolated as an island. The most common and best-known lodge is the island type which is conical in shape, varying in diameter from about six to forty feet and in height from three to ten feet. It has to be high enough to provide for a resting chamber above the level of high water and it must be

situated in water deep enough to avoid freezing at the entrance. It has to be built on a fairly firm foundation, and may frequently be situated on a submerged island or around a small island of shrubs, stumps, or growing trees. All types of lodges are characterized by one or more underwater entrances.

The basic structure is made of sticks or branches and mud and begins as a mere pile which is built up gradually to the desired size. The inside is then fashioned, beginning with a tunnel near the bottom which is burrowed into the centre of the lodge. Projecting or obstructing sticks are gnawed away and finally a chamber is enlarged in the interior, a few inches above the water level, which forms the resting or sleeping quarters. This chamber is usually lined with either shredded wood or grass. Two levels may be created, the lower one providing an entrance vestibule where the beaver may feed or simply dry off before ascending to the resting chamber. Usually more than one entrance

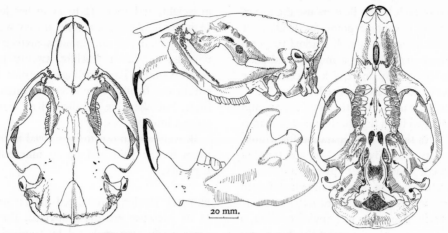

Fig. 76 – SKULL OF *Castor canadensis* (ROM 19985 ♀)

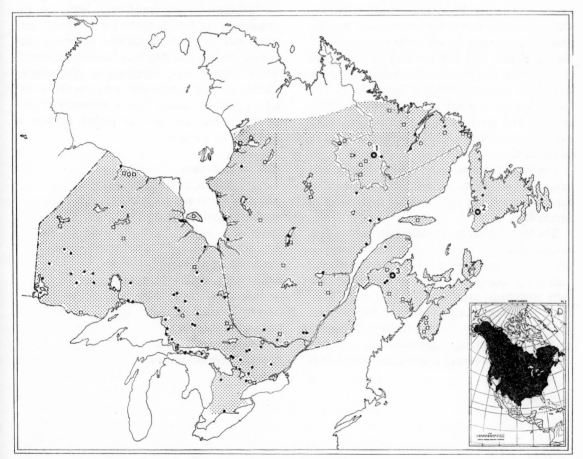

Map 37 – DISTRIBUTION OF THE BEAVER – *Castor canadensis* – AND TYPE LOCALITIES OF (1) *C. c. labradorensis* V. Bailey and Doutt; (2) *C. c. caecator* Kuhl; (3) *C. c. acadicus* V. Bailey and Doutt

is established in each lodge. Beavers use the top of the structure as a vantage point for feeding or resting—this is indicated by well-marked trails up the side. There may also be a mud-packed slide on one side for an easy and quick descent to the water in case of danger from a predator.

A lodge may be used more than one season, and it may be enlarged from time to time. Fresh mud is usually added in the fall in preparation for winter.

Food consists primarily of the bark and twigs of trees, although many other plants are eaten, especially in summer. In order to obtain sufficient food, the beaver cuts standing trees with its powerful incisor teeth. (Contrary to popular opinion, a beaver is not always able to predict the direction a tree will fall when cut. Frequently a tangle of several cut trees results, of which no tree is usable.) Once down, the tree is cut into sections and the smaller cuts are taken away to be eaten or stored for future use near the entrance to the lodge. (Occasionally narrow water channels are dug out to facilitate the transporting of cut sections.) The larger, heavier sections may be stripped where they fall and the bark eaten on the spot. Small peeled sticks may be added either to the house or to the dam.

The beaver becomes quite vulnerable to animal predators (wolves, bears, and others) when it is forced to travel any great distance from water to secure food.

The breeding habits are still poorly known. It is thought that the beaver breeds first when it is about twenty-one months old (during winter), and that the young (called kits) are born about 120 days afterwards, usually in April, May, or June. They are covered with a dense, soft fur and their eyes are open at birth. Litters usually number three to four on the average (the maximum is eight). Each kit is half-a-pound to one-and-a-half pounds

in weight, and about 12 to 15 inches long with a $3\frac{1}{2}$-inch tail. After six months it may weigh ten to fifteen pounds; at nine months, sixteen to twenty pounds; and as a yearling, twenty to twenty-seven pounds. The yearlings continue to remain within the family lodge after the birth of a new litter, but they are usually driven out before a second litter arrives.

Beavers are known to have lived at least eleven years in the wild and up to nineteen years in captivity.

REMARKS Having a restricted habitat where signs of its presence are quite obvious, the beaver is quite easily over-exploited by trappers. Government control has been recently imposed by the establishment of registered trap lines, by the maintenance of flexible quotas for the annual harvests, and by the reintroduction of beaver into suitable areas where they have been exterminated. These controls have combined to give eastern Canada a sound conservation program and a sustained yield of valuable furs. A summary of production during the ten-year period 1950–60 is presented in Table I.

Selected References
BAILEY, VERNON, 1913, 1927a, 1927b.
BAILEY, VERNON and J. K. DOUTT, 1942.
BANGS, OUTRAM, 1913.
CAHN, A. R., 1930.
CONIBEAR, FRANK and J. L. BLUNDELL, 1949.
COURTNEY, T. J., 1947.
DUGMORE, A. RADCLYFFE, 1914.
JOHNSON, CHARLES EUGENE, 1927.
MARTIN, HORACE T., 1892.
MILLS, ENOS A., 1913.
MORGAN, LEWIS H., 1868.
WARREN, EDWARD R., 1927.

Table I

Production of Beaver Pelts in Eastern Canada, 1950–60

	ALL CANADA	EASTERN CANADA	ONTARIO	QUEBEC	NEW BRUNSWICK	NOVA SCOTIA	PRINCE EDWARD I.	NEW-FOUNDLAND
TOTAL PELTS 1950–60	2,768,228	1,613,615	1,155,473	338,428	*53,629	37,837	**19	***27,829
Average Annual Production	276,823	161,362	115,547	33,843	7,661	3,784	3.8	3,092
Minimum Annual Production	180,817 (1950–1)	112,865 (1950–1)	87,608 (1950–1)	18,665 (1952–3)	5,970 (1954–5)	114 (1950–1)	1 (1951–2 & 1955–6)	260 (1954–5)
Maximum Annual Production	344,766 (1959–60)	202,764 (1957–8)	141,263 (1957–8)	51,942 (1958–9)	11,981 (1953–4)	7,659 (1951–2)	7 (1952–3 & 1957–8)	8,156 (1957–8)
TOTAL VALUE 1950–60	$36,373,880	$22,743,509	$15,044,475	$5,998,112	$599,754	$554,153	$118	$360,031
Average Annual Value	$3,637,388	$2,274,350	$1,504,478	$599,811	$85,679	$55,415	$23.60	$40,003
Minimum Annual Value	$2,561,786 (1953–4)	$1,575,081 (1953–4)	$1,016,734 (1953–4)	$343,422 (1953–4)	$71,214 (1954–5)	$2,390 (1950–1)	$5.00 (1951–2)	$3,724 (1958–9)
Maximum Annual Value	$4,767,232 (1954–5)	$2,975,929 (1954–5)	$2,070,177 (1950–1)	$819,778 (1950–60)	$96,885 (1955–6)	$126,586 (1951–2)	$51.00 (1957–8)	$110,185 (1955–6)
Average Value per Pelt	$13.16	$14.10	$13.10	$17.73	$11.18	$14.66	$6.22	$12.94
Minimum Average Value per Pelt	$10.20 (1958–9)	$10.70 (1953–4)	$9.65 (1953–4)	$13.00 (1958–9)	$8.00 (1953–4)	$10.72 (1953–4)	$3.00 (1956–7)	$7.00 (1958–9)
Maximum Average Value per Pelt	$23.58 (1950–1)	$25.40 (1950–1)	$23.63 (1950–1)	$31.00 (1950–1)	$15.00 (1955–6)	$20.96 (1951–2)	$12.00 (1955–6)	$23.00 (1950–1)

* Seven years only, 1953–60.   ** Five years only.   *** Nine years only, 1951–60.

Suborder
Myomorpha

Family **CRICETIDAE**
Native Mice and Rats – *Souris et Rats*

The family name is derived from the Latin *cricetus* meaning hamster. The family includes a wide assemblage of rodents differing in structure as well as in habits and habitat requirements. It may be conveniently divided into two subfamilies. *Cricetinae* is characterized by rodents that have upper molars with two longitudinal rows of tubercles, skulls with weak depressed zygomatic arches, large, conspicuous ears, and long tails. This subfamily is represented in eastern Canada by the genus *Peromyscus*—the deer mouse and the white-footed mouse. The subfamily *Microtinae* is characterized by rodents with complicated patterns of tooth enamel that form numerous triangles or transverse folds. With the exception of the muskrat, with its long, laterally compressed tail, members of this subfamily are vole-like with short tails. All have relatively short inconspicuous ears. Microtines constitute the majority of the rodents of eastern Canada, both in terms of number of species and total numbers.

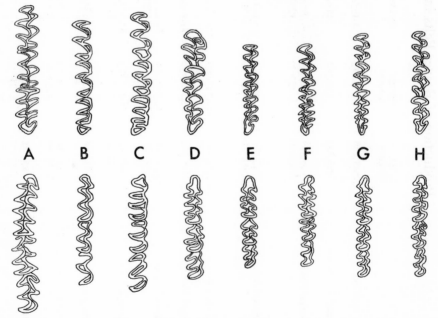

Fig. 77 – TOOTH ENAMEL PATTERNS OF MICROTINE RODENTS (*upper right dentition above, lower right below, anterior facing up*)

A – *Dicrostonyx hudsonius* (ROM 25240); B – *Synaptomys cooperi* (ROM 29241); C – *Synaptomys borealis* (ROM 262230); D – *Phenacomys ungava* (ROM 24425); E – *Clethrionomys gapperi* (ROM 10506); F – *Microtus pennsylvanicus* (ROM 21201); G – *Microtus chrotorrhinus* (ROM 24360); H – *Microtus pinetorum* (ROM 15647)

KEY TO THE EASTERN-CANADIAN GENERA OF *Cricetidae*

1 Total length more than 450 mm.; tail 200 mm. or more. Skull more than 60 mm. long and 35 mm. wide.

ONDATRA p. 169

1' Total length less than 450 mm.; tail less than 200 mm. Skull less than 60 mm. long and 35 mm. wide: 2

  2 Ears prominent and conspicuous above fur; underparts and feet white and upper parts brown or grey; tail relatively long; upper molar teeth with tubercles arranged in two longitudinal rows.

PEROMYSCUS p. 140

  2' Ears relatively small and inconspicuous; underparts and feet not white; tail relatively short; upper molars with prismatic triangles: 3

    3 Skull more than 18 mm. wide; cheek-teeth complex with many loops; body robust; tail short; pelage white in winter.

DICROSTONYX p. 147

    3' Skull less than 18 mm. wide; pelage not white in winter: 4

      4 Upper incisors grooved; tail less than 25 mm.; enamel pattern with deep re-entrant angles on the inner side of the lower molars and on the outer side of the upper molars.

SYNAPTOMYS p. 150

      4' Upper incisors not grooved; re-entrant angles of upper molars not restricted to one side: 5

        5 Cheek-teeth rooted in adults: 6

          6 Posterior palate terminating as a simple transverse shelf; lower molars with inner re-entrant angles, little if any deeper than the outer re-entrant angles; adults with band of red or blackish fur along back.

CLETHRIONOMYS p. 155

          6' Posterior palate terminating with a median spinous process (not as above); lower molars with the inner re-entrant angle much deeper than the outer; nose yellowish; feet light-coloured (whitish to pinkish).

PHENACOMYS p. 158

        5' Cheek teeth not rooted in adults. Ears short and rounded but not hidden in fur; colour of back about the same as sides; feet usually greyish or darker, particularly in sub-adults.

MICROTUS p. 161

Genus **PEROMYSCUS** Gloger

Deer Mice and White-footed Mice – *Souris sylvestres et Souris à pattes blanches*

Dental Formula I $\frac{1-1}{1-1}$ C $\frac{0-0}{0-0}$ P $\frac{0-0}{0-0}$ M $\frac{3-3}{3-3}$ = 16

KEY TO THE EASTERN-CANADIAN SPECIES OF *Peromyscus*

1 Fur on throat and forearms pure white; tail indistinctly bicoloured, sparsely furred with little if any pencilling on the tip; incisive foramina constricted anteriorly, forming a slight angle near the junction of the premaxilla and maxilla; molars relatively small and uniform in width.

PEROMYSCUS LEUCOPUS p. 144

1' Fur on throat and forearms white with slate- or greyish-coloured base; tail usually distinctly bi-coloured, more furred and with a longer distinct pencil of hairs on the tip; incisive foramina with evenly arched or nearly parallel lateral sides (usually not forming an angle); molars relatively large and not uniform in width, the first being the widest and the last the narrowest.

PEROMYSCUS MANICULATUS p. 140

Peromyscus maniculatus (Wagner) – Deer Mouse – *Souris sylvestre*

This is perhaps the most ubiquitous native mouse in North America. In eastern Canada it has been divided into no less than eight geographic races that show a wide range of variation. A closely related species, *Peromyscus leucopus*, is less extensive in distribution but is sometimes more difficult to distinguish from various races of *P. maniculatus* than are the various races of the latter from one another. In general, *P. maniculatus* has a distinctly bicoloured tail that has more fur and a distinct pencil of hairs projecting beyond the tip; the white underfur has a slate-coloured base that extends well up the throat, whereas the tail of *P. leucopus* is less distinctly bicoloured, is scantily furred, has a short pencil (if any) on the tip, and the throat and under-surface of the legs are pure white, without the slate-coloured base. In all species the young are duller and greyer than the adults. Other characteristics are useful in distinguishing the various races in eastern Canada (see below); however, positive identification should be sought from a specialist familiar with the variations that occur within this group. A careful study of a large number of specimens is required in order to assess the range of apparent variations that may be due to sex, age, season, or random individual variations as opposed to geographic or subspecific variations.

SIZE See below.

DISTRIBUTION AND VARIATION This species occurs throughout most of eastern Canada except in the Cape Henrietta Maria region of Ontario (at the junction of Hudson and James Bays), the Ungava Peninsula of Quebec, and Newfoundland. The following forms occur in eastern Canada:

Peromyscus maniculatus maniculatus. Total length 172–201 mm.; tail 79–108; hind foot 19–23; ear from notch 17–21. Skull: length 23.7–26.1, width 11.4–13.3. Weight 16–32 gr. This name has been applied to the form occurring across northern Quebec and northern Ontario. The type locality is the Labrador coast.

P. m. gracilis. Total length 165–206 mm.; tail 80–114; hind foot 19–22; ear from notch 16–23 (av. 17–19). Skull: length 24.3–27.8, width 12.4–13.9. Weight 12–31 gr. This is a long-tailed

Fig. 78 – PRAIRIE DEER MOUSE – *Peromyscus maniculatus bairdii*

Fig. 79 – WOODLAND DEER MOUSE – *Peromyscus maniculatus gracilis*

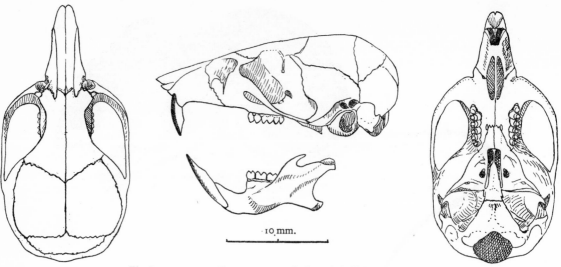

Fig. 80 – SKULL OF *Peromyscus maniculatus bairdii* (ROM 18597 ♂)

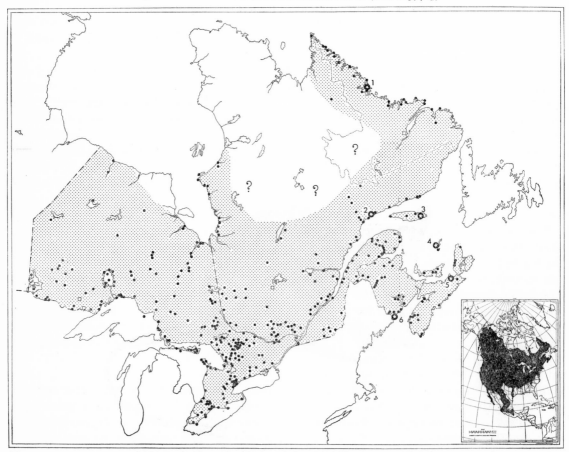

Map 38 – DISTRIBUTION OF THE DEER MOUSE – *Peromyscus maniculatus* – AND TYPE LOCALITIES OF (1) *P. m. maniculatus* (Wagner); (2) *P. m. plumbeus* C. F. Jackson; (3) *P. m. anticostiensis* Moulthrop; (4) *P. m. eremus* Osgood; (5) *P. m. abietorum* (Bangs); (6) *P. m. argentatus* Copeland and Church

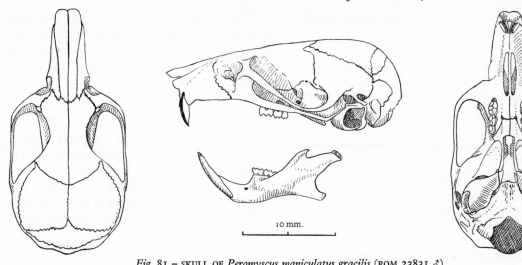

Fig. 81 – SKULL OF *Peromyscus maniculatus gracilis* (ROM 23831 ♂)

form. It occurs in southern Ontario and southern Quebec and is usually found in forested areas. The type locality is Michigan.

P. m. abietorum. Total length 171–200 mm.; tail 82–103; hind foot 20–22; ear from notch 16–19. Skull: as in *P. m. gracilis.* Similar to *P. m. gracilis* but paler and greyer, this form occurs in the Gaspé Peninsula of Quebec and the Maritime Provinces.

P. m. argentatus. Total length 171–194 mm.; tail 82–93; hind foot 20–22; ear from notch 16–19. Skull: as in *P. m. maniculatus.* This form is restricted to Grand Manan Island, N.B. It is greyish, with a slightly shorter tail than *P. m. abietorum.*

P. m. eremus. Total length 172–189 mm.; tail 78–90; hind foot 20–21; ear from notch 16–19. Skull: as in *P. m. abietorum.* This is another insular race restricted to the Magdalen Islands, Quebec. Its colour is intermediate, between that of *P. m. abietorum* and *P. m. maniculatus;* it has a shorter tail than the former and is slightly smaller than the latter.

P. m. anticostiensis. Total length 175–190 mm.; tail 88–95; hind foot 19–21. Skull: length 24–26, width 12–14. This race is also an insular form, restricted to Anticosti Island, Que. It is dark greyish brown with a pronounced brown dorsal stripe approaching black.

P. m. plumbeus. Total length 176–181 mm.; tail 88.0–91.2; hind foot 19–22. Skull: length 24.0–25.1, width 12–13. This race has been described from the north shore of the Gulf of St Lawrence in Saguenay County, Que. It is reputed to be a dark form without a pronounced dorsal stripe and with the ventral pelage light plumbeous or cinereous rather than white. Its range is unknown beyond the region of the type locality. This race may prove to be based on subadult specimens of either *P. m. maniculatus* or *P. m. gracilis* or on an intergrade between the two.

P. m. bairdii. Total length 119–156 mm.; tail 47–69; hind foot 16–18; ear from notch 11–14. Skull: length 22.2–24.8, width 11.1–12.9. Weight 10–24 gr. This race is characterized by its short tail, small ears, and usually greyish-brown coloration with no bright fulvous shades. It is restricted to southern Ontario and is found in open grassland areas where it usually selects fairly dry situations. Following the grassy areas rather rigidly, this race frequently interdigitates its distribution with that of *P. m. gracilis,* but there is no real evidence of intergradation with it.

HABITAT As indicated above, this species occurs in a wide range of habitats, although certain races show a well-marked preference for specific habitats. *P. m. bairdii,* for example, prefers open grassland and *P. m. gracilis* wooded areas. In general the genus *Peromyscus* enters buildings more readily than any other native mouse.

HABITS Deer mice are primarily nocturnal and begin activity in the evening twilight. All races seem to prefer some degree of cover or shelter and avoid as far as possible prolonged trips across bare, exposed sites.

Breeding starts in early spring, with about four to six (two to eight) young being born in early March after a gestation period of about twenty-five to twenty-seven days. The blind, naked young remain in the nest for about three weeks. The eyes open in about two weeks and the young are weaned at about thirty days. Breeding continues until October, with several litters being produced each year (up to four or five). However, there appears to be a decline in breeding during the months of July and August, after which a new peak of activity arises. Occasionally litters are produced during the winter. Young females may start to breed at five to eight weeks of age.

Internal cheek pouches are used in gathering and transporting seeds to a cache for future use. Insects, other invertebrates, and vegetative matter are also eaten.

This species has survived as long as nine years in captivity, although it is probable that it does not live more than two or three years in the wild. It is more tractable than *P. leucopus* and adapts well in laboratory colonies.

REMARKS The deer mouse is always a threat to owners of cottages, which it commonly invades. When left for the winter season, bedding and any available food provide for its needs.

The deer mouse probably shares with the meadow mouse the distinction of providing more pounds of protein for predators than any other rodent in eastern Canada.

Selected References

BLAIR, W. FRANK, 1942.
DICE, LEE R., 1932b, 1933, 1936, 1937a.
HOWARD, WALTER E., 1949.
JACKSON, C. F., 1939b.
MANVILLE, RICHARD H., 1949.
MOODY, PAUL A., 1941.
MOULTHROP, PHILIP N., 1937.
OSGOOD, WILFRED H., 1909.
SVIHLA, ARTHUR, 1932, 1935.

Peromyscus leucopus (Rafinesque) – White-footed Mouse – *Souris à pattes blanches*

This species closely resembles the deer mouse, *P. maniculatus*. White fur without a slate-coloured base on the throat and forearms and an indistinctly bicoloured tail and a dusky upper lip are the most distinctive characteristics for identifying *P. leucopus*. The molar teeth tend to be relatively smaller and more uniform in width than those of *P. maniculatus*. The shape of the incisive foramina (see Key) also assists in identifying this species. The young are duller and greyer than the adults.

SIZE Total length 145–198 mm.; tail 60–105; hind foot 18–23; ear from notch 15–19. Skull: length 24.0–27.4, width 12.1–14.1. Weight 12–31 gr.

DISTRIBUTION AND VARIATION *Peromyscus leucopus noveboracensis* occurs in Ontario south of Lake Nipissing and in Quebec along the lower Ottawa River valley and south of the St Lawrence along the southern Canada-U.S. boundary. This species apparently has not been taken in New Brunswick,

Fig. 82 – WHITE-FOOTED MOUSE – *Peromyscus leucopus*

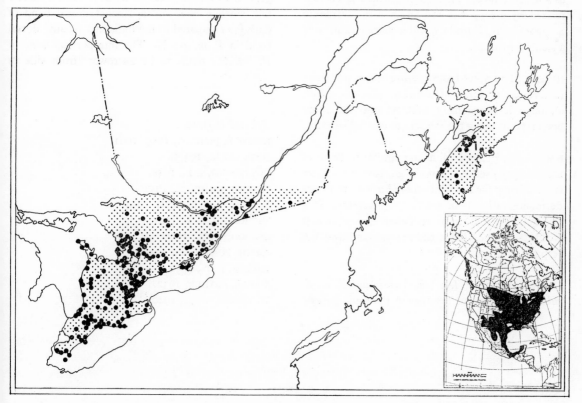

Map 39 – DISTRIBUTION OF THE WHITE-FOOTED MOUSE – *Peromyscus leucopus* – AND (1) TYPE LOCALITY OF
P. l. caudatus Smith

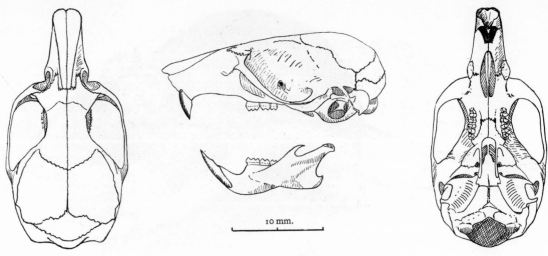

Fig. 83 – SKULL OF Peromyscus leucopus (ROM 23138 ♂)

but it occurs in southern and central Nova Scotia as a distinct race, *P. l. caudatus*, which is characterized by a long tail and larger ears (averaging 88.7 mm. and 17.7 mm.), and a shorter skull with a slender rostrum.

HABITAT The white-footed mouse occurs primarily in forested or other areas with sufficient cover, although it occasionally wanders out into more open regions along the borders of wooded areas.

HABITS The general habits are similar to those of the deer mouse, *P. maniculatus*. However, there is a tendency for the white-footed mouse to prefer deciduous rather than coniferous vegetation. It is also quite different in its behaviour in captivity: it is always more excitable and nervous and does not respond to handling.

REMARKS Where *P. l. noveboracensis* and *P. maniculatus gracilis* occur together in the same general region, they may be difficult to distinguish. In general *P. l. noveboracensis* tends to have a shorter tail, smaller ears, and a distinct dorsal band of dark fur compared to the indistinct (if any) dorsal band in *P. m. gracilis*. The interparietal bone of *P. leucopus* tends to be narrower (from side to side).

Selected References

BENDELL, JAMES F., 1959, 1961.

DICE, LEE R., 1937b.

GOTTSHANG, J. L., 1956.

HOOPER, EMMET T., 1958.

HORNER, B. ELIZABETH, 1954.

NICHOLSON, A. J., 1941.

OSGOOD, W. H., 1909.

SMITH, RONALD W., 1939b.

SNYDER, D. P., 1956.

SVIHLA, ARTHUR, 1932.

WHITAKER, W. L., 1940.

Fig. 84 – UNGAVA VARYING LEMMING – *Dicrostonyx hudsonius*

Genus **DICROSTONYX** Gloger

Varying Lemmings – *Lemmings variés*

Dental Formula I $\frac{1-1}{1-1}$ C $\frac{0-0}{0-0}$ P $\frac{0-0}{0-0}$ M $\frac{3-3}{3-3}$ = 16

Dicrostonyx hudsonius (Pallas) – Ungava Varying Lemming – *Lemming d'Ungava*

This species is a robust, heavy-set rodent with very short ears and tail. In winter it is white and in summer it is brownish to greyish above with a very narrow dark grey dorsal stripe, and buffy grey below with a buffy or rusty throat. The young are similar but darker (more brownish, approaching deep olive grey) and have a more distinct narrow blackish median dorsal stripe. Winter-born animals in captivity may be either white or coloured.

The forefeet have a very small thumb with a rudimentary nail and larger third and fourth claws that develop a bulbous portion in winter. This partially split or bifid tip gives the appearance of a double claw. As the lower portion of the claw grows larger and vertically deeper it finally exceeds the size of the upper portion from which it is separated by a deep lateral groove (see *fig.* 86). With the approach of spring this lower portion drops off and the claw returns to a normal appearance for the summer months. Young born in winter develop bifid claws when they are about twenty-five days old; the bulbous toe-pads are evident when they are only ten to fourteen days old.

Cranially this species is distinguished from *Dicrostonyx groenlandicus* (occurring in western and northern Canada) by the first and second upper molariform teeth, which lack a posterior internal vestigial angle, and by the third last molar which is usually without an anterior inner fold. The skull is wider and more robust than that of all other microtines in eastern Canada except the muskrat.

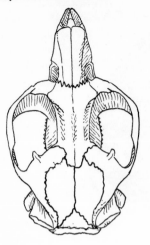
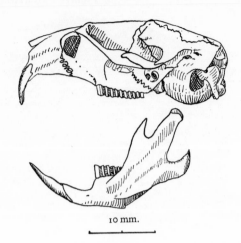
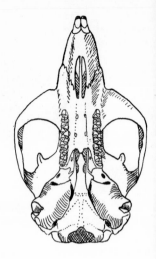

10 mm.

Fig. 85 – SKULL OF *Dicrostonyx hudsonius* (ROM 25240)

A

B

Fig. 86 – FEET OF *Dicrostonyx hudsonius* (A – *Summer*; B – *Winter*)

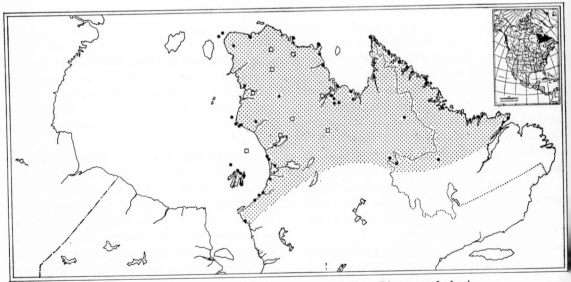

Map 40 – DISTRIBUTION OF THE UNGAVA VARYING LEMMING – *Dicrostonyx hudsonius*

SIZE Total length 125–166 (av. 148) mm.; tail 15–22 (av. 20); hind foot 18–24 (av. 22); ear from notch 5–9. Skull: length 28–32 (av. 29.1), width 18.2–21.5 (av. 20.5). Weight 25–65 gr.

DISTRIBUTION The Ungava lemming is one of the few distinct species wholly confined to eastern Canada. It occupies the tundra regions of Quebec and Labrador and adjacent small islands in the Northwest Territories. An early report (1896) that it extended south of the tundra in Labrador, along the George River to Lake Michikamau, has apparently not been confirmed by recent specimens.

HABITAT Open tundra and rocky hillsides.

HABITS Little is known about this species, but no doubt it is similar to *D. groenlandicus*, on which the following data is based. After a gestation period of about twenty days, one to eight (average of three or four) blind and naked young are born weighing about 3.8 grams (average 2.7–4.8 grams). At four days the back is covered with short, stiff hairs; the incisor teeth become prominent at five days; by six days the young are able to crawl on all four feet;

and a complete covering of hair is reached by eight days, after which the external ears are open and become functionally efficient at eleven days. The eyes are open at twelve days after which the young begin to wander out of the nest; and by fourteen days they begin to eat vegetation. At about eighteen to twenty days they are weaned, and by twenty-five to thirty days the females become sexually mature but still retain immature pelage and weigh from 16 to 35 grams.

REMARKS The Ungava lemming is subject to rather violent fluctuations in population densities that vitally affect many Arctic predators such as the Arctic fox and snowy owl which depend on it as a source of food. This lemming should be the subject of serious study.

Selected References

ALLEN, G. M., 1919.
ANDERSON, R. M. and A. L. RAND, 1945.
DEGERBOL, MAGNUS and U. MØHL-HANSEN, 1943.
DOUTT, J. K., 1954.
HARPER, FRANCIS, 1961.
LOW, A. P., 1896.

Genus **SYNAPTOMYS** Baird

Lemming Mice or Bog Lemmings – *Campagnol-lemmings*

Dental Formula $I \frac{1-1}{1-1}$ $C \frac{0-0}{0-0}$ $P \frac{0-0}{0-0}$ $M \frac{3-3}{3-3} = 16$

KEY TO THE EASTERN-CANADIAN SPECIES OF *Synaptomys*

1 Lower molars with triangles formed on the outer sides; incisors relatively heavy, deeply orange-coloured, and with a shallow groove located near the outside edge; posterior edge of palate without a spinous projection.   SYNAPTOMYS COOPERI p. 150

1' Lower molars without triangles formed on the outer sides; incisors relatively light, pale-coloured, and with a groove located more medially; posterior edge of palate with a spinous projection.   SYNAPTOMYS BOREALIS p. 152

Fig. 87 – SOUTHERN LEMMING MOUSE – *Synaptomys cooperi*

Synaptomys cooperi Baird – Southern Lemming Mouse or Bog Lemming –

Campagnol-lemming de Cooper

This is a sturdy little mouse with a short tail (only about as long as its hind foot) and small grooves along the outer edge of the upper incisors. The skull is rather robust and has a short, depressed rostrum; the brain case has parallel sides. Apparently six is a normal number of mammae in this species, although reports of from four to eight may be found in the literature. The pelage is quite long and thick and has a grizzled grey appearance above. The underparts are tipped with silver. There are four toes on the front feet and five on the back. The ears are relatively small and almost hidden in the long fur. The southern bog lemming is quite similar externally to the northern lemming mouse, *Synaptomys borealis*, but it differs in having heavier incisors that are deeper in colour, with the groove more laterally situated; a posterior palate without a spinous projection; and lower cheek teeth in which triangles are present on the outer sides.

SIZE Total length 99–134 mm.; tail 15–24; hind foot 16–20; ear from notch 10–15. Skull: length 24–27, width 14.0–16.8. Weight 14–40 gr.

DISTRIBUTION Only one race, *Synaptomys cooperi cooperi*, occurs in eastern Canada. Its range is largely contiguous to that of *S. borealis* except in the region south of the St Lawrence River, where both species occur.

HABITAT This species is largely restricted to low, damp bogs or meadows, particularly in the southern parts of its range. Further north, specimens have been taken in higher and drier situations, but usually in areas of deep litter.

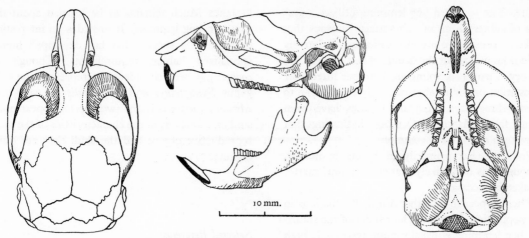

10 mm.

Fig. 88 – SKULL OF *Synaptomys cooperi* (ROM 23951 ♀)

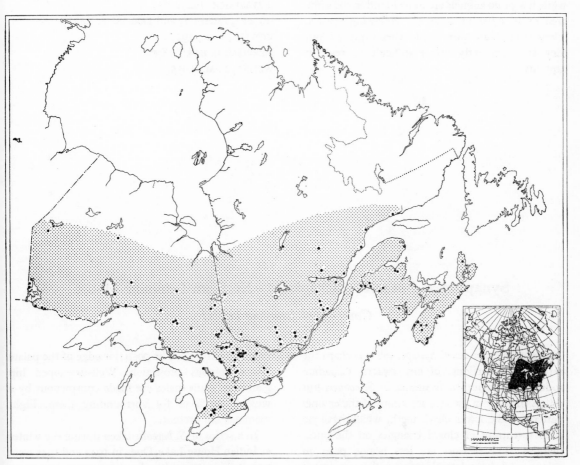

Map 41 – DISTRIBUTION OF THE SOUTHERN LEMMING MOUSE – *Synaptomys cooperi*

HABITS The southern bog lemming utilizes a system of subterranean or sub-surface runways that make its presence quite inconspicuous. Relatively little is known about the details of this species' life history. Two to six young are born per litter after a gestation period of approximately twenty-one to twenty-three days. Pregnant females have been found from March to October, indicating that more than one litter is common.

Food consists primarily of vegetable matter, although it is quite likely that some animal matter is taken on occasion.

There appear to be rather drastic fluctuations in the population duration. The habitat of the southern bog lemming is usually quite restricted; high populations are evident in an area one season, while few or no animals are to be found in the same area or in adjacent areas the following season. These animals are quite docile when captured, but they are apparently rather difficult to rear in captivity.

REMARKS Much remains to be learned about the southern bog lemming. It provides an interesting example of a species that has developed highly specialized habitat requirements. Though *S. cooperi* has been considered to represent the subgenus *Synaptomys* and *S. borealis* the subgenus *Mictomys*, externally the two species appear quite similar. However, in the characteristics of the male reproductive organs and the skull they are quite distinct.

Selected References

HOFFMEISTER, DONALD F. and JOHN E. WARNOCK, 1947.
HOOPER, EMMET T. and BARBARA S. HART, 1962.
HOWELL, A. B., 1927.
MERRIAM, C. HART, 1896.
WETZEL, R. M., 1955.

Synaptomys borealis (Richardson) – Northern Lemming Mouse –

Campagnol-lemming boréal

This northern species of *Synaptomys* is perhaps the rarest, in collections, of any eastern Canadian rodent. It is superficially similar to *S. cooperi* but differs strongly in the conformations of the enamel pattern of the lower cheek teeth, which have no deep re-entrant or closed triangles on the outer margins. The incisors are less heavy, paler in colour, and have lateral grooves that are more medially situated. The posterior edge of the palate has a spinous projection. Well-developed hip glands on adult males are made conspicuous by a whitish patch of fur surrounding them. Eight mammae are present.

In a series of *S. borealis* taken during the winter at Indian House Lake, Que., in 1944 and 1945 were two striking examples of an unusual enlargement

Fig. 89 – FEET OF NORTHERN LEMMING MOUSE –
Synaptomys borealis
A – *October* 12; B – *December* 2; C – *January* 26;
D – *April* 14; E – *June* 15

of the two middle claws (see *fig.* 89). Specimens taken on October 12 and December 2 appeared normal. The specimens taken on January 26 and April 14 showed an extreme enlargement of the nails or claws to approximately twice normal size, but an additional specimen secured on June 15 appeared normal. While suggesting the well-known enlargement of the same claws in *Dicrostonyx*, the condition observed in *S. borealis* was merely an enlargement of the claw proper and showed no tendency to develop a bifid condition similar to that of *Dicrostonyx*. Attempts to determine whether this enlargement was abnormal or whether it was a normal development in winter failed because no other specimens were found that had been taken during the period from January to May. No similar enlargement has been observed on any *S. cooperi* checked to date.*

The above-mentioned series of specimens are now in the Museum of Comparative Zoology, Harvard University.

SIZE Total length 110–150 mm.; tail 19–27; hind foot 17–22; ear from notch 11–16. Skull: length 22–27, width 13.5–18.5. Weight 18–60 gr.

DISTRIBUTION AND VARIATION At least four names are available for the few known specimens from eastern Canada. In all probability this number will be reduced when sufficient specimens are available to make a more complete assessment of the normal range of variations in the entire area. *S. b. smithi* is currently thought to include all specimens from Ontario, *S. b. innuitus* occupies northern Quebec, *S. b. medioximus* most of Labrador, and *S. b. sphagnicola* south of the St Lawrence River, in Quebec, New Brunswick, and Nova Scotia.

HABITAT The rare occurrence of the northern lemming mouse has prevented an accurate appraisal of its habitat requirements. A series of six taken in 1953 south of Leaf Bay in the Finger Lake region

* Acknowledgement is made to Dr Charles P. Lyman, Museum of Comparative Zoology, Harvard University, who first noted the enlarged claws of *Synaptomys borealis* and kindly turned over to the author his data on attempts to locate other similar examples.

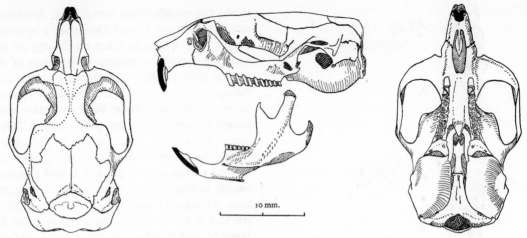

Fig. 90 – SKULL OF *Synaptomys borealis* (ROM 26230 ♂)

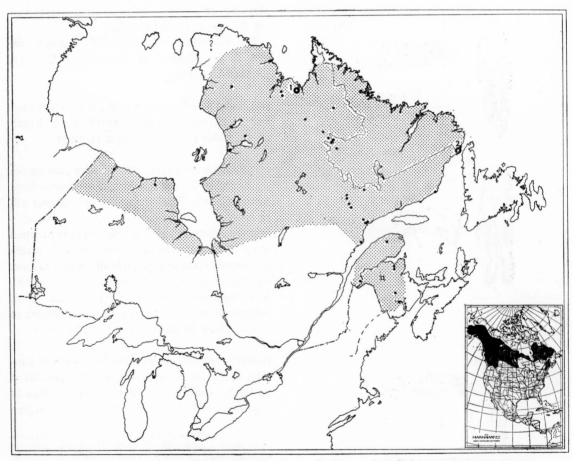

Map 42 – DISTRIBUTION OF THE NORTHERN LEMMING MOUSE – *Synaptomys borealis* – AND TYPE LOCALITIES OF
(1) *S. b. innuitus* (True); (2) *S. b. medioximus* Bangs

(65 miles west of Fort Chimo, Que.) were all found in a habitat that was dry and partly wooded—not a low and moist bog situation, the typical habitat in the southern part of the range.

HABITS Virtually nothing is known about the habits of this species, although it may be assumed that they are similar to those of *S. cooperi*.

The Royal Ontario Museum has two June records of pregnant females with four embryos each; an additional female with seven has been reported for the same month.

REMARKS Taxonomic revisions of the northern lemming mouse have been based on inadequate specimens. In general, size differences have been considered important; however, recent collections indicate considerable variation in size within local populations. A detailed revision is required to assess properly the geographic variation of the northern lemming mouse within eastern Canada and throughout its whole range. Additional specimens caught in mid-winter would reveal the normal condition of the front claws.

Selected References

ANDERSON, R. M. and A. L. RAND, 1943a.
CROSS, E. C., 1938.
DOWNING, S. C., 1940.
HARPER, FRANCIS, 1961.
HOOPER, EMMET T. and BARBARA S. HART, 1962.
HOWELL, A. B., 1927.

Genus **CLETHRIONOMYS** Tilesius

Red-backed Mice – *Campagnols à dos roux*

Dental Formula $\text{I}\frac{1-1}{1-1}$ $\text{C}\frac{0-0}{0-0}$ $\text{P}\frac{0-0}{0-0}$ $\text{M}\frac{3-3}{3-3} = 16$

Clethrionomys gapperi (Vigors) – Red-backed Mouse – *Campagnol à dos roux de Gapper*

In typical pelage this species has a striking dorsal band of reddish, bright chestnut, hazel, or yellowish brown. The sides are usually greyish with a slight wash of yellowish. The underparts are whitish, silvery, or washed with buff. In one colour phase the reddish dorsal band is replaced by a brownish or almost blackish colour. This 'dark' or 'fusco-dorsalis' phase occurs throughout the range of the species, although it is apparently clinal, becoming increasingly common in the more northern latitudes. The skull may be distinguished by the posterior border of the palate, which is straight and ends abruptly in a thin bony shelf without a median projection. The cheek teeth are rooted but are not noticeably so until the animal becomes a full adult.

SIZE Total length 116–158 mm.; tail 31–50; hind foot 17–21; ear from notch 13–17. Skull: length 22.5–25.4, width 12.1–13.8. Weight 16–37. gr.

DISTRIBUTION AND VARIATION The red-backed mouse occurs throughout eastern Canada except in the southernmost part and in the Hudson–James Bay triangle of northern Ontario, the Ungava peninsula and Anticosti Island in Quebec, and Newfoundland. Unfortunately the true geographic variation within this species is still only poorly understood and should be thoroughly revised. The following names are in current usage in eastern Canada: *Clethrionomys gapperi gapperi* in southern Ontario and southern Quebec north of the St Lawrence; *C. g. ochraceus* in southern Quebec south

Fig. 91 – RED-BACKED MOUSE – *Clethrionomys gapperi*

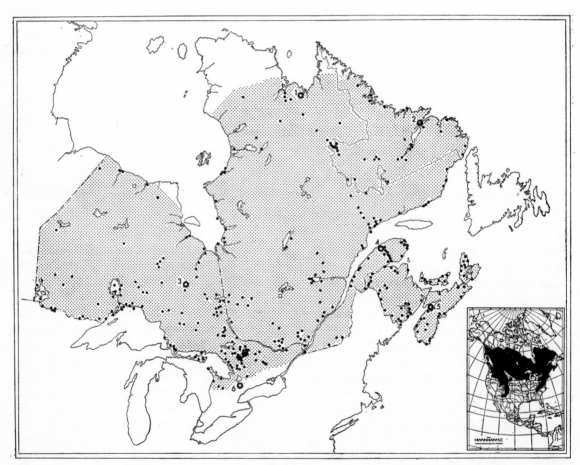

Map 43 – DISTRIBUTION OF THE RED-BACKED MOUSE – *Clethrionomys gapperi* – AND TYPE LOCALITIES OF (1) *C. g. ungava* (Bailey); (2) *C. g. proteus* (Bangs); (3) *C. g. hudsonius* Anderson; (4) *C. g. gaspeanus* Anderson (5) *C. g. pallescens* Hall and Cockrum; (6) *C. g. gapperi* (Vigors)

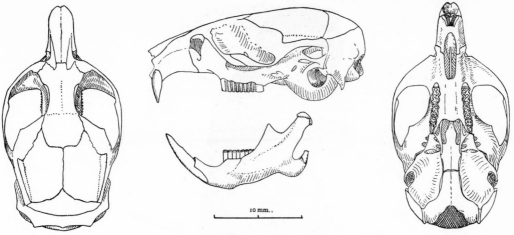

Fig. 92 – SKULL OF *Clethrionomys gapperi* (ROM 10506 ♀)

of the St Lawrence and in New Brunswick and Prince Edward Island; *C. g. pallescens* in Nova Scotia; *C. g. gaspeanus* in the Gaspé Peninsula, Que.; *C. g. proteus* in Labrador and in adjacent Quebec along the Gulf of St Lawrence; *C. g. ungava* in the northern Ungava portion of Quebec; *C. g. hudsonius* in the James Bay watershed; and *C. g. loringi* in the Lake-of-the-Woods region of Ontario.

HABITAT The red-backed mouse inhabits forested areas, especially those near water and with deep litter such as decaying logs, stumps, and brush.

HABITS Nocturnally active, this species seldom makes well-marked runways and so leaves little evidence of its presence. Three to eight (an average of four) young are born after a gestation period of seventeen to nineteen days. Breeding activity usually lasts from April to October, with two or more litters being born each season. The blind, naked, pink young, weighing 1.8–2.0 grams at birth, develop the first evidence of hair at about three or four days and are fairly well furred at seven to nine days. The incisor teeth erupt at about six to nine days. The young crawl about at ten days. The eyes are open after about eleven to sixteen days and solid food is eaten in about thirteen to sixteen days. They may be weaned at fifteen to twenty days. The juvenile pelage lasts about a month after birth and the moult to adult pelage is complete at about three months. Seeds and other vegetative matter and insects and other invertebrates are eaten, but little else is known about the food habits of this species.

REMARKS A preliminary examination of a large series of skulls of *Clethrionomys* has suggested that the average life span of the red-backed mouse is quite low. Comparisons with two laboratory specimens of known age (255 days) indicated that only a surprisingly low percentage of specimens in the collection of the Royal Ontario Museum had reached a comparable age.

Selected References

ANDERSON, R. M., 1940, 1943C.
BAILEY, VERNON, 1897.
BLAIR, W. FRANK, 1941.
GABBUTT, PETER D., 1961.
HALL, E. R. and E. L. COCKRUM, 1953.
HOOPER, EMMET T. and BARBARA S. HART, 1962.
MANVILLE, RICHARD M., 1949.
SMITH, RONALD W., 1940.
SVIHLA, ARTHUR, 1930.

Fig. 93 – EASTERN PHENACOMYS – *Phenacomys ungava*

Genus **PHENACOMYS** Merriam

Phenacomys

Dental Formula   I $\frac{1-1}{1-1}$ C $\frac{0-0}{0-0}$ P $\frac{0-0}{0-0}$ M $\frac{3-3}{3-3}$ = 16

Phenacomys ungava Merriam – Eastern Phenacomys – *Phenacomys d'Ungava*

The adult eastern phenacomys is characterized by a yellowish nose, a relatively small size, a short tail (less than 45 mm.), a brownish pelage, and by light-coloured feet (usually pinkish). The juveniles are generally darker and more plumbeous and may lack the suffusion of yellow on the nose. The skull is typically microtine in shape, but the cheek teeth of the lower jaws have deep re-entrant angles that extend more than halfway across the tooth (see *fig.* 77). The cheek teeth are rooted in the adults; the rooted condition is evident above the alveoli of the jaw after about eight to ten months.

SIZE Total length 125–160 mm.; tail 30–40; hind foot 17–19; ear from notch 12–16. Skull: length 24.0–27.2, width 13.3–15.9. Weight 27–41 gr.

DISTRIBUTION AND VARIATION The phenacomys has not been taken south of a boundary formed by the French River, Lake Nipissing, and the Ottawa and St Lawrence Rivers. This species occurs in the remainder of Ontario, Quebec, and Labrador, except perhaps for the northernmost section of the Ungava Peninsula. Known specimens from the Labrador coast have been referred to as

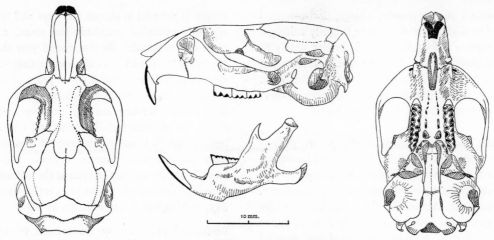

Fig. 94 – SKULL OF *Phenacomys ungava* (ROM 24425 ♂)

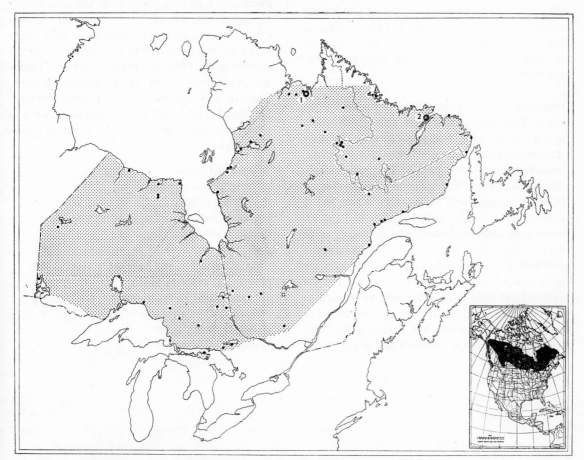

Map 44 – DISTRIBUTION OF THE EASTERN PHENACOMYS – *Phenacomys ungava* – AND TYPE LOCALITIES OF
(1) *P. u. ungava* Merriam; (2) *P. u. crassus* Bangs

Phenacomys ungava crassus, a large, dull-coloured race. The slightly smaller, more brightly coloured *P. u. ungava* is found west of Labrador nearly to the Manitoba border. A single specimen from the Kenora (Ont.) region apparently approaches *P. u. soperi*, while specimens from northwestern Ontario compare favourably with *P. u. mackenzii*.

HABITAT The basic habitat of the eastern phenacomys seems to consist of relatively dry situations with a heather-like cover such as blueberry, willow, chokecherry, bush honeysuckle, soapberry, bearberry, or kalmia. In the southern latitudes most specimens have been taken in dry, sandy, or rocky jack-pine associations containing ground cover of one or more of the above. Further north they have been taken in stunted willow associations within the tundra proper and in a wide variety of habitats along the edge of the tree line; however, in each situation heather-like vegetation was available.

HABITS After a gestation period of twenty-one to twenty-four days, two to eight young (sub-adults average about four, adults about six) are born weighing from 2.0 to 2.7 grams with a crown-rump measurement of about 30 mm. They are pinkish, blind, and hairless. Within one day the skin begins to show pigment and by six days a fine fur is evident. By nine days the young are well furred, movements are co-ordinated, and the incisor teeth have erupted through the gums. The young are able to walk by eleven days and after the eyes are open on the fourteenth day they begin to leave the nest and eat solid food. They may be weaned as early as seventeen days. The females may breed as early as four to six weeks, but males apparently do not breed until they are almost a year old. An adult

weight is reached in almost 100 days and the teeth are fully extended (exposing the roots) at about eight to ten months. By the second year the teeth are badly worn and it would appear that very few eastern phenacomys reach three years of age.

Food consists primarily of the leaves, stems, and bark of heather-like shrubs. Sections averaging about two or three inches are cut and taken to the nest, which is usually quite simple and does not have an elaborate runway system. Frequently fresh-cut sections may be seen at the entrance to a den. The eastern phenacomys is active during the day, although it is more active at night.

REMARKS Until recently the eastern phenacomys was considered extremely rare, but studies have discovered high local populations and have greatly expanded our knowledge of this little-known species. The eastern phenacomys is mild mannered and relatively easy to keep under laboratory conditions. No births occurred as a result of breeding in captivity at the Royal Ontario Museum, Toronto, although several matings were observed. Successful births did occur, however, when a colony was maintained in the far north, at Churchill, Man.

Selected References
ANDERSON, R. M., 1942b.
FOSTER, J. BRISTOL, 1961.
FOSTER, J. BRISTOL and R. L. PETERSON, 1961.
GABBUTT, PETER D., 1961.
HALL, E. R. and E. L. COCKRUM, 1953.
HOOPER, EMMET T. and BARBARA S. HART, 1962.
HOWELL, A. BRAZIER, 1926.
MILLER, GERRIT S., JR., 1897c.
PETERSON, R. L., 1956a.
SAUNDERS, W. E., 1927.
SNYDER, L. L., 1929b.

Genus **MICROTUS** Schrank

Voles – *Campagnols*

Dental Formula I $\frac{1-1}{1-1}$ C $\frac{0-0}{0-0}$ P $\frac{0-0}{0-0}$ M $\frac{3-3}{3-3}$ = 16

KEY TO THE EASTERN-CANADIAN SPECIES OF *Microtus*

1 Tail less than 30 mm.; fur of fine texture and uniform chestnut brown or auburn in colour; last upper molar with two deep re-entrant angles on outer side. MICROTUS PINETORUM p. 167

1' Tail more than 30 mm.; fur coarser in texture and grizzled greyish brown; last upper molar with more than two deep re-entrant angles on outer side: 2

 2 Pelage of nose or face yellow or orange; last upper molar with four deep re-entrant angles on outer side. MICROTUS CHROTORRHINUS p. 164

 2' Pelage of nose or face not yellow or orange; last upper molar with three deep re-entrant angles on outer side. MICROTUS PENNSYLVANICUS p. 161

Microtus pennsylvanicus (Ord) – Meadow Vole – *Campagnol des champs*

The meadow vole is one of the most evenly widespread species in eastern Canada. It is fairly uniform in colour: dark brown or greyish brown above and below, though slightly paler below. The ears are relatively short and are partially hidden in the long fur. The tail, though relatively short, is longer and the feet are usually darker than those of the other genera of microtines. The meadow vole lacks the yellowish nose of *Microtus chrotorrhinus* and *Phenacomys ungava* and has a longer tail than *M. pinetorum* and *Synaptomys*. The ears are relatively smaller than those of *Clethrionomys* and there is no dark dorsal band along the back.

The skull has a palate with a median projection on the posterior border. The least interorbital width is less than four millimetres. The anterior palatine foramina is more than five millimetres. The last upper molar has three deep re-entrant angles on the outer side; the re-entrant angles on the inner side may be three or four, with the variation in the posterior loop. *M. pinetorum* normally

has two and *M. chrotorrhinus* has four re-entrant angles on both the inner and outer sides.

SIZE Total length 120–188 mm.; tail 38–65; hind foot 18–25; ear from notch 11–16. Skull: length 25.5–29.0, width 14–16. Weight 20–68 gr.

DISTRIBUTION AND VARIATION This wide-ranging species is in need of a thorough study to determine more accurately the geographic variation across its range. At present, six geographic races are regarded as being present in eastern Canada:

Microtus pennsylvanicus acadicus occurs in Nova Scotia, Prince Edward Island, Grand Manan Island, and possibly southeastern New Brunswick. It is characterized by a pale pelage with a yellowish or clay-coloured tinge in both winter and summer coats.

M. p. pennsylvanicus occurs in northern New Brunswick, the southern half of Quebec (including the range of *M. p. fontigenus*), and in southern

Fig. 95 – MEADOW VOLE – *Microtus pennsylvanicus*

Ontario north to the north shore of Georgian Bay and west to Lake Superior. It is a dark race, with a brownish tinge in the pelage.

M. p. enixus occurs across the Ungava Peninsula from Hamilton Inlet and Hebron, Labrador, to James Bay. Compared with *M. p. pennsylvanicus*, it has a darker summer pelage and is characterized by a flat, slightly arched skull. It has a relatively long tail (averaging 30.9 per cent of the total length).

M. p. labradorius is found in northern Ungava from Port Burwell on the Hudson Strait to the Great Whale River on the east side of Hudson Bay. It differs from *M. p. pennsylvanicus* primarily in its skull characters; its upper incisors project more forward and it has shorter, less projecting nasals.

M. p. terraenovae is restricted to Newfoundland. It is a light-coloured race without any rufous tinge on the underparts and it has a buffy nose patch.

M. p. drummondi, described from Alberta, is thought to extend eastward across northern Ontario to James Bay. In Alberta it is a relatively small form, but Ontario specimens average much larger. A more thorough study is needed to clarify the status of this race.

HABITAT Grassy areas, both moist and upland, are the preferred habitat, although meadow voles range into other areas occasionally, especially insular populations, which may be found in all available types of habitat.

HABITS This is one of the most prolific species of mammals in eastern Canada, although it is subject to violent fluctuations in numbers. Peak populations occur about every four years on the average, but the year of highest population varies from region to region.

One to nine blind, naked, pink young, weighing about three grams each, are born after a gestation period of twenty-one days. The growth of hair is evident within three days. The incisor teeth erupt and crawling begins at one week. The eyes are opened in eight to ten days and solid food may be eaten as early as eleven days. Meadow voles may be weaned as early as two weeks of age. Several litters are produced in a year—as many as seventeen have been born in a laboratory in one year, but this number is probably unlikely in the wild. Young females breed as early as twenty-five days and young males as early as forty-five days. The

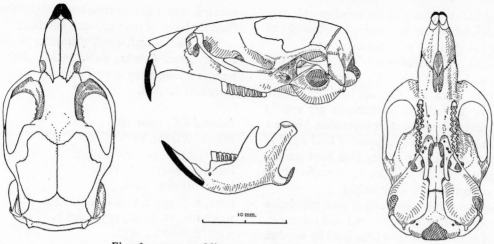

Fig. 96 – SKULL OF *Microtus pennsylvanicus* (ROM 21201 ♀)

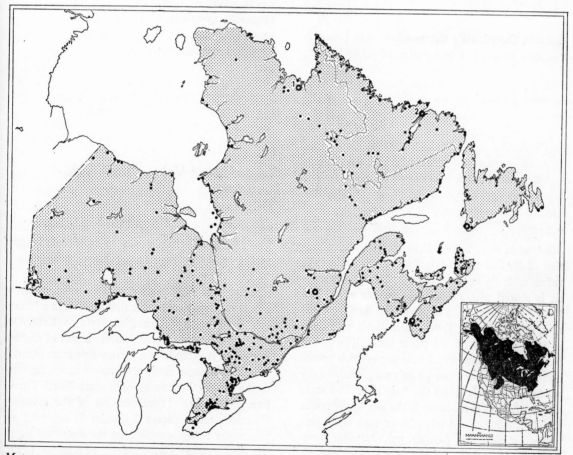

Map 45 – DISTRIBUTION OF THE MEADOW VOLE – *Microtus pennsylvanicus* – AND TYPE LOCALITIES OF (1) *M. p. labradorius* Bailey; (2) *M. p. enixus* Bangs; (3) *M. p. terraenovae* (Bangs); (4) *M. p. fontigenus* Bangs (5) *M. p. acadicus* Bangs

potential life expectancy of the meadow vole may be as high as three to five years; it is thought to average less than one year, however.

The bulk of the meadow vole's food consists of grasses and sedges, although other material is occasionally eaten. Runways are used both above and below ground; surface runways are usually under a cover of grass or other vegetation. Meadow voles are known to eat an amount of food equal to their own weight in a twenty-four hour period, although their daily food intake averages about sixty per cent of their body weight.

Spring thaws following years of peak population may uncover very elaborate and extensive networks of runways that have been used by meadow voles under the snow.

REMARKS Occasionally the meadow vole becomes a serious menace to forestry plantations and young orchards where it may completely girdle the bark from the bases of trees and thus kill them.

This species undoubtedly provides more food for predators (hawks, owls, snakes, foxes, and weasels among many others) than any other rodent in eastern Canada.

Selected References

BAILEY, VERNON, 1900.

BANGS, O., 1894a, 1896a, 1896c.

CAMERON, AUSTIN W., 1959.

DAVIS, DAVID E., 1936.

HALL, E. R. and E. L. COCKRUM, 1952.

HAMILTON, W. J., JR., 1937a and b.

HATT, ROBERT T., 1930.

HOOPER, EMMET T. and BARBARA S. HART, 1962.

LANTZ, DAVID E., 1907.

PETERSON, RANDOLPH L., 1947.

RAND, L., 1944a.

SNYDER, DANA P., 1954.

Microtus chrotorrhinus (Miller) – Yellow-nosed Vole or Rock Vole – *Campagnol des rochers*

Externally the yellow-nosed vole differs from other *Microtus* in eastern Canada in the striking coloration of its face which is yellowish to dull orange rufous from the eyes to the nose. This characteristic is shared with *Phenacomys ungava* which has lighter-coloured feet, a richer brown dorsal coloration, and distinctive lower cheek teeth with deep re-entrant angles on the inner sides. The upper parts of the yellow-nosed vole are greyish brown and the underparts are plumbeous, occasionally washed with whitish on the hair tips. The most diagnostic cranial character is the last upper molar which has five closed triangles or four re-entrant angles on each side (see *fig.* 77). *Microtus pennsylvanicus* has three on the outer side and *M. pinetorum* has two.

SIZE Total length 132–183 mm.; tail 34–54; hind foot 18–22; ear from notch 12–18. Skull: length 26.8–27.5, width 14.5–15.5. Weight 30.0–47.8 gr.

DISTRIBUTION AND VARIATION This species has a purely eastern distribution that extends in a broad belt from northwestern Minnesota to Labrador north of the St Lawrence River. South of the St Lawrence it extends in a narrow belt from central Gaspé southwest along the mountainous regions to the Smoky Mountains of western North Carolina and eastern Tennessee. All of the eastern-Canadian range except Labrador is regarded at present as being occupied by the nominate race, *M. chrotorrhinus chrotorrhinus*. Specimens taken along the Labrador coast have been described as

Fig. 97 – YELLOW-NOSED VOLE OR ROCK VOLE – *Microtus chrotorrhinus*

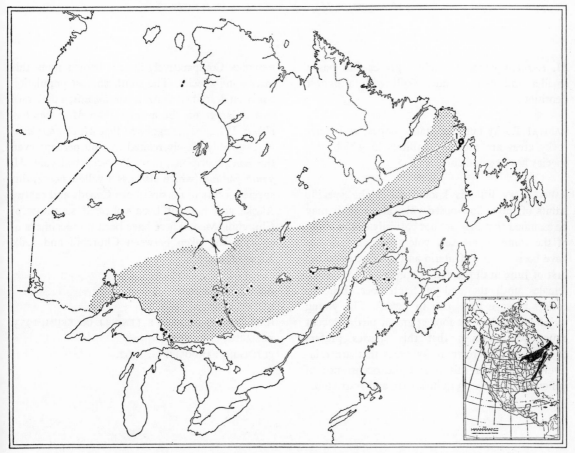

Map 46 – DISTRIBUTION OF THE YELLOW-NOSED VOLE OR ROCK VOLE – *Microtus chrotorrhinus* – AND (I) TYPE LOCALITY OF *M. c. ravus* Bangs

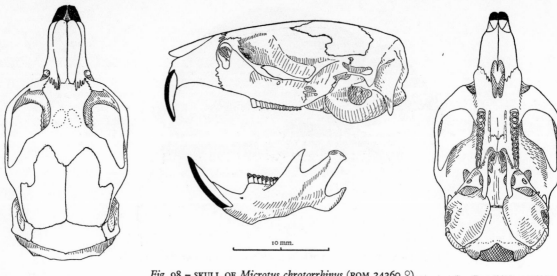

Fig. 98 – SKULL OF *Microtus chrotorrhinus* (ROM 24360 ♀)

M. c. ravus which is slightly greyer and has a smaller and more slender skull with a lighter dentition.

HABITAT Rocky outcrops, talus slopes, and other rocky areas are the only habitats in which this species has been taken.

HABITS Very little is known about the specific habits of the yellow-nosed vole, although it may be assumed that they are not basically unlike those of the common meadow vole. Pregnant females have been taken in Ontario and Quebec from the first of June until the end of August and lactating females until the end of September. Embryo counts average four (two to seven). The young weigh about three or four grams at birth. Recent experience indicates that this species prefers covered or overgrown rocky areas that are relatively moist. For this reason the occurrence of yellow-nosed voles is quite spotty and restricted.

REMARKS Comparatively little is known about this interesting species. The southernmost population has been described as *M. c. carolinensis*, a dark race that is larger on the average than *M. c. chrotorrhinus*. It has been suggested that *M. chrotorrhinus* is reasonably closely related to, and perhaps even the same species as, the yellow-cheeked vole, *M. xanthognathus* (which also has a yellow nose); this species occurs in northwestern Canada and central Alaska and has not been collected southeast of Churchill, Man. There have been no specimens of either form taken between Churchill and Lake Nipigon, Ont.

Selected References

BAILEY, VERNON, 1900.
HALL, E. RAYMOND and E. LENDELL COCKRUM, 1953.
KOMAREK, E. V., 1932.
PETERSON, RANDOLPH L., 1962.

Fig. 99 – PINE MOUSE – *Microtus pinetorum*

Microtus pinetorum (Le Conte) – Pine Mouse or Pine Vole – *Campagnol sylvestre*

The pine mouse is characterized by very fine long fur that is rich chestnut brown or auburn colour above and lightly washed with buff below, and by relatively short ears and a short tail. The skull is broad but typically microtine in shape; it can be distinguished by the last upper molar which has only two deep re-entrant angles on each side, whereas *Microtus pennsylvanicus* has three on the outside and *M. chrotorrhinus* has four. The least interorbital width is more than four millimetres; the upper incisors are not grooved and the palate does not end abruptly in a thin, bony shelf.

Much of the recent literature has treated this species under *Pitymys pinetorum*. However, more recent studies indicate that *Pitymys* is a valid sub-genus of *Microtus*.

SIZE Total length 110–132 mm.; tail 16–25; hind foot 15–18; ear from notch 7–9. Skull: length 21.7–25.4, width 13.1–15.8. Weight 19–35 gr.

DISTRIBUTION AND VARIATION *M. p. scalopsoides* is found in eastern Canada and it has a very limited distribution. It occurs in the so-called Carolinian zone, a narrow strip north of Lake Erie in Ontario, and in a limited area along the southern Quebec-United States border where it was discovered for the first time in 1956 on Mt Pinnacle in Missisquoi County, Que.

HABITAT The burrowing habits of this species limit its distribution to areas with a good ground cover of grass, leaves, or forest litter that is usually associated with hardwood forests rather than areas of pine. In fact the pine mouse is seldom encountered in pure pine forests.

HABITS Most of the life of pine mice is spent in a subterranean network of runways, some made by the animals themselves and some appropriated from other burrowing species. Surface runways under a cover of grass, leaves, or forest litter are also used.

The gestation period is assumed to be about twenty-one days, after which two to seven (the average is three or four) young, weighing about 2.2 grams, are born blind and naked. The eyes are opened at about nine to twelve days, and young

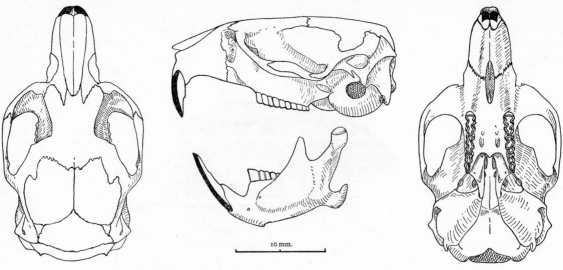

Fig. 100 – SKULL OF *Microtus pinetorum* (ROM 15647 ♀)

may be weaned as early as seventeen days. The sub-adults are darker and greyer than the adults.

Food consists primarily of vegetable matter; sections of roots and tubers are stored in underground caches.

REMARKS The single Quebec specimen taken in 1956 extends the known range of the pine mouse in the eastern part of its range. Further work should be carried out to determine whether this specimen was taken from an isolated population or whether there is a general continuity of distribution into Quebec from New York or Vermont.

Selected References

BAILEY, VERNON, 1900.

BENTON, ALLEN H., 1955.

HALL, E. R. and E. LENDELL COCKRUM, 1953.

HAMILTON, W. J., JR., 1938.

HOOPER, EMMET T. and BARBARA S. HART, 1962.

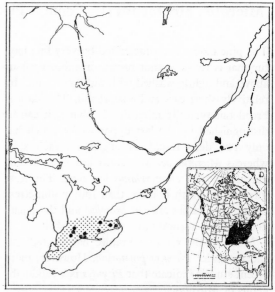

Map 47 – DISTRIBUTION OF THE PINE MOUSE – *Microtus pinetorum*

Fig. 101 – COMMON MUSKRAT – *Ondatra zibethicus*

Genus **ONDATRA** Link

Common Muskrats – *Rats musqués*

Dental Formula   I $\frac{1-1}{1-1}$ C $\frac{0-0}{0-0}$ P $\frac{0-0}{0-0}$ M $\frac{3-3}{3-3}$ = 16

Ondatra zibethicus (Linnaeus) – Common Muskrat – *Rat musqué*

The largest of the family *Cricetidae*, the muskrat is easily recognized not only by its size but by its tail, which is laterally compressed and is scaly with sparse hairs, and by its large hind feet which are webbed between the toes and have a fringe of stiff hairs on the outer sides. The skull is typically microtine in shape with sixteen teeth and an infra-orbital foramen of less than five millimetres in greatest diameter; it lacks a broad supraorbital process that is characteristic of woodchucks and other *Sciuridae*. The muskrat has five toes on both front and back feet.

SIZE Total length 477–636 mm.; tail 200–276; hind foot 73–92; ear from notch 20–25. Skull: length 61.2–69.0, width 36.9–43.7. Weight 810–1,580 gr.

DISTRIBUTION AND VARIATION The common muskrat is found throughout eastern Canada. *Ondatra zibethicus obscurus*, a relatively small and dark race, occurs in Newfoundland. The mainland species is divided into three races: *O. z. zibethicus* which occupies the whole central portion of eastern Canada except Labrador and the adjacent part of

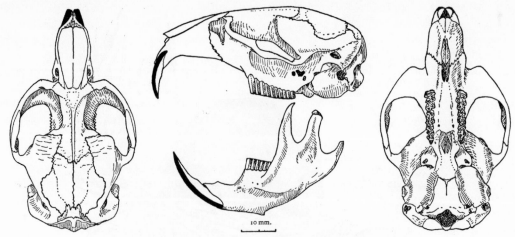

10 mm.

Fig. 102 – SKULL OF *Ondatra zibethicus* (ROM 19067 ♀)

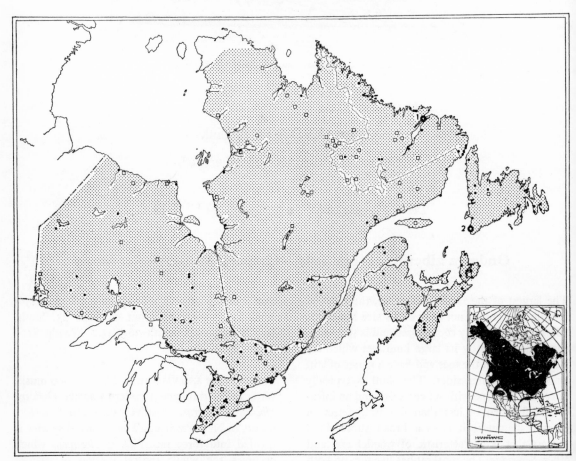

Map 48 – DISTRIBUTION OF THE COMMON MUSKRAT – *Ondatra zibethicus* – AND TYPE LOCALITIES OF (1) *O. z. aquilonius* (Bangs); (2) *O. z. obscurus* (Bangs)

Quebec where *O. z. aquilonius*, a slightly smaller and possibly darker race, occurs; and *O. z. albus*, another slightly smaller but possibly paler race which is found in northwestern Ontario. A thorough study is required to refine our knowledge of the geographic variations within this species.

HABITAT Marshes, ponds, lakes, and streams, especially those with aquatic vegetation.

HABITS The common muskrat spends its life in or near water. Its marsh home is typically a cone of reed or some other aquatic plant that protrudes above the surrounding water. An underwater entrance leads to a dry nest or feeding platform above the water level. A home on a stream, lake, or pond is made by digging a tunnel-like den in a bank, the entrance to which is below or just above the water level.

The breeding season starts in April. After a gestation period of about twenty-seven to thirty days a litter of one to eleven (the average is about six) blind, nearly naked young are born, weighing an average of about 21 grams each. The eyes open at about two weeks, at which time the young start to swim and dive and feed on green vegetation. They are weaned at about one month. They apparently do not breed until the following spring. Adults may have as many as three litters per season.

The food consists primarily of the roots and stems of aquatic vegetation, although considerable animal matter is also eaten. I have observed muskrats living in large lakes feeding on fresh-water clams or mussels. They would swim out into the lake, dive down, and return to their feeding area with a clam in their mouth. Grasping the clam with the front foot, they would easily force it open with their teeth and proceed to eat the insides. Accumulations of more than a bushel of shucked clam shells formed a mound near the feeding site.

While most activities are carried on at night, the muskrat is perhaps more diurnal than other microtine rodents. Activity continues at a fairly high level all year long.

With the fall season there is an increased amount of activity. New houses are built and sub-adults wander about, sometimes a considerable distance overland, presumably in search of a new territory in which to establish their own home sites.

REMARKS Hawks, owls, mink and other carnivores prey on muskrats, but in a good habitat neither these predators nor heavy trapping appear to affect population numbers seriously.

Although a single muskrat pelt is not particularly valuable, the muskrat ranks high in total value to eastern-Canadian trappers by virtue of the large numbers in which it is trapped. (For a ten-year summary of muskrat-pelt production, see Table 2.) Properly prepared, the flesh of the muskrat is quite palatable; it has been marketed in the United States as 'marsh rabbit'. The muskrat has played an important role in the economy of eastern-Canadian Indians and early white settlers by providing both food and skins for clothing and commerce. Modern methods of furriers account for a long list of trade names for muskrat fur that cover a wide variety of colours and appearances. Hudson seal is only one of the many names applied to the fur of this species when it is converted into a coat of fashion.

Selected References

BANGS, O., 1894b.

CAMERON, AUSTIN W., 1959.

ELTON, C. and M. NICHOLSON, 1942a.

ERRINGTON, PAUL L., 1937a, 1937b, 1940, 1941, 1943, 1948, 1951.

HOLLISTER, N., 1911.

JOHNSON, CHARLES E., 1925.

WRAGG, L. E., 1954.

Table 2

Production of Muskrat Pelts in Eastern Canada, 1950–60

	ALL CANADA	EASTERN CANADA	ONTARIO	QUEBEC	NEW BRUNSWICK	NOVA SCOTIA	PRINCE EDWARD I.	NEW-FOUNDLAND
TOTAL PELTS 1950	33,424,219	8,757,554	6,375,630	1,612,574	*227,947	373,463	8,721	**159,219
Average Annual Production	3,342,422	875,755	637,563	161,257	28,493	37,346	872	17,691
Minimum Annual Production	1,562,617 (1959–60)	674,099 (1959–60)	415,621 (1959–60)	122,709 (1954–5)	16,060 (1959–60)	19,278 (1959–60)	12 (1959–60)	8,617 (1957–8)
Maximum Annual Production	5,619,277 (1954–5)	1,124,248 (1952–3)	841,135 (1954–5)	206,195 (1959–60)	55,231 (1951–2)	57,220 (1953–4)	1,649 (1952–3)	28,809 (1951–2)
TOTAL VALUE 1950–60	$38,047,075	$11,859,751	$8,275,730	$2,526,679	$334,909	$583,360	$11,201	$118,872
Average Annual Value	$3,804,708	$1,185,075	$827,573	$252,668	$41,863	$58,336	$1,120	$13,208
Minimum Annual Value	$1,303,661 (1959–60)	$583,129 (1957–8)	$336,653 (1959–60)	$136,205 (1957–8)	$14,333 (1957–8)	$21,205 (1959–60)	$18 (1959–60)	$4,309 (1957–8)
Maximum Annual Value	$6,518,993 (1954–5)	$2,223,492 (1950–1)	$1,700,045 (1950–1)	$424,523 (1950–1)	$96,654 (1951–2)	$100,485 (1952–3)	$2,513 (1952–3)	$41,124 (1951–2)
Average Value per Pelt	$1.13	$1.35	$1.29	$1.56	$1.46	$1.56	$1.28	$0.74
Minimum Average Value per Pelt	$0.83 (1959–60)	$0.81 (1957–8)	$0.81 (1959–60)	$1.00 (1957–8)	$0.80 (1957–8)	$1.00 (1958–9)	$0.69 (1957–8)	$0.50 (1956–60)
Maximum Average Value per Pelt	$2.25 (1950–1)	$2.54 (1950–1)	$2.59 (1950–1)	$2.35 (1950–1)	$1.75 (1951–2)	$2.75 (1950–1)	$1.96 (1950–1)	$1.43 (1951–2)

* Eight years only, 1951–5 and 1957–60.   ** Nine years only, 1951–60.

Family **MURIDAE**

Old World Rats and Mice – *Rats et Souris d'Ancien Monde*

KEY TO THE EASTERN-CANADIAN GENERA OF *Muridae*

1 Total length less than 250 mm.; tail length less than 110 mm.; skull length less than 35 mm.; first upper molar longer than the lengths of both second and third combined.   MUS p. 178

1′ Total length more than 250 mm.; tail length more than 110 mm.; skull length greater than 35 mm.; first upper molar less than the lengths of both the second and third combined.   RATTUS p. 173

Muridae is from the Latin word for 'mouse-like'. This family includes many Old World rats and mice of which several have been universally distributed by introduction. It differs from the *Cricetidae* in having molar teeth that are always bunodont and brachydont and in having three longitudinal rows of cusps in the upper molars and two rows in the lower.

The hard palate in this family extends posteriorly well beyond the last molar, and the palatine slits extend posteriorly beyond the anterior border of the first molar.

The tail is relatively long and sparsely haired with well-defined annulations.

Eastern-Canadian forms have resulted from introductions.

Genus **RATTUS** Fischer

Old World Rats – *Rats d'Ancien Monde*

Dental Formula $\text{I}\frac{1-1}{1-1}$ $\text{C}\frac{0-0}{0-0}$ $\text{P}\frac{0-0}{0-0}$ $\text{M}\frac{3-3}{3-3}=16$

KEY TO THE EASTERN-CANADIAN SPECIES OF *Rattus*

1 Tail longer than head and body; ear usually more than 20 mm. measured from notch; first upper molar with distinct outer notch on the anterior row of tubercles.   RATTUS RATTUS p. 177

1′ Tail length less than length of head and body; ear usually less than 20 mm. measured from notch; first upper molar without a distinct outer notch on the anterior row of tubercles.

RATTUS NORVEGICUS p. 174

Fig. 103 – NORWAY RAT – *Rattus norvegicus*

Rattus norvegicus (Berkenhout) – Norway Rat – *Rat surmulot*

The Norway or brown rat was originally a native of Europe but it has now spread to most of the temperate and tropical climates in the world (it seldom remains established far from human habitations, however). Norway rat is its common name, but it has been widespread for centuries; in fact it was originally described in 1769 from England, not Norway.

This large rat is greyish brown above and a bit paler below and has a scaly, sparsely haired tail that measures less than the length of the head and body combined. The cheek teeth have three longitudinal rows of small rounded tubercles or cusps. The first molar lacks the distinct notch or indentation on the outer side of the anterior row of tubercles (see *fig.* 105) that is present in *Rattus rattus*. There are twelve mammae, six on each side. The ears are usually less than 20 mm. measured from the notch, and they are covered with fine, short hair, whereas in *Rattus rattus* the ears are larger, more than 20 mm. long, and devoid of hair.

SIZE Total length 315–460 mm.; tail 122–215; hind foot 30–45; ear from notch 15–20. Skull: length 41.0–51.5, width 20.6–25.2. Weight 195–485 gr.

DISTRIBUTION AND VARIATION The northern limits of occurrence of *Rattus norvegicus* in eastern Canada are generally around the northernmost railway depots. While this species is occasionally transported still further north, it has apparently failed to persist there as a permanent population. It is constantly being transported and reintroduced across the land.

HABITAT The habitations of man, where the Norway rat seeks food and warm shelter from the freezing temperatures of winter. It may move out into an open area in spring and back into a building in winter.

HABITS This prolific mammal may produce from six to twenty-two young per litter and have as many as twelve litters per year, but it normally produces from three to seven (gestation period, twenty-one to twenty-two days). The young begin to breed at three or four months. Typical nesting places are old dumps, stored grain, warehouses, and buildings under which the Norway rat is able to burrow and where a food supply is readily available.

The Norway rat is among the most completely

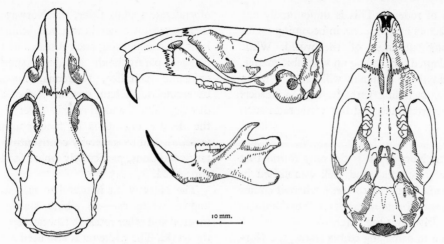

Fig. 104 – SKULL OF *Rattus norvegicus* (ROM 18485 ♂)

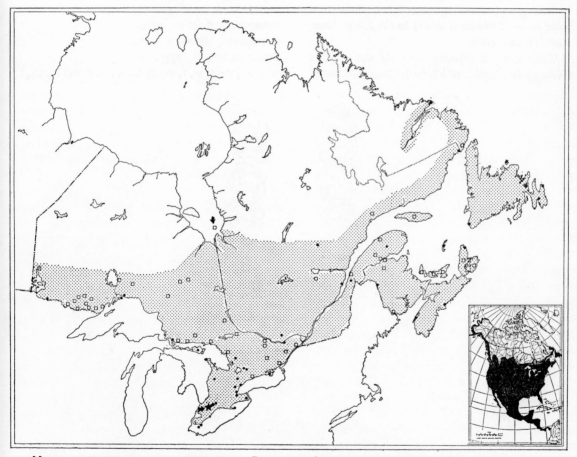

Map 49 – DISTRIBUTION OF THE NORWAY RAT – *Rattus norvegicus* – AND THE BLACK RAT – *Rattus rattus**

omnivorous of rodents. This is undoubtedly one of the key factors in its success in becoming established throughout most of the world. While primarily adapted for feeding on vegetable matter, it will eat anything a human will eat plus many other things, including garbage, carrion, insects and other invertebrates, and live vertebrates such as baby chicks.

REMARKS The Norway rat is the only *Rattus* that has become widespread and well established in eastern Canada. In northern areas, where it comes into contact with *Rattus rattus*, it tends to dominate and usually drives out the latter.

In addition to damaging edible stores, the Norway rat causes almost as much loss by chewing fabrics or containers and other materials, or merely by soiling and rendering unsaleable or unusable a wide range of products stored in the home, barn, store, or warehouse.

While not the primary host for the rat flea (*Xenopsylla cheopis*), which is the principal vector of endemic typhus fever, the Norway rat nevertheless creates other health and sanitation problems by transmitting such diseases as trichinosis, mange, paratyphoid, glanders, spotted fever, epidemic jaundice, tularemia, rat-bite fever, tuberculosis, cholera, dysentery, foot and mouth disease, rabies, and Haverhill fever; by carrying the disease organisms of food poisoning (*Salmonella*); and by generally contributing to unsanitary conditions, particularly where food stores are concerned.

The Norway rat is useful to man as the well-known white rat—an albino strain—found in medical and other research laboratories throughout the world. The white rat is also used as a pet.

Selected references

ANDERSON, R. M., 1947.
CAMERON, AUSTIN W., 1959.
DONALDSON, HENRY H., 1924.
GREEN, EUNICE C., 1935.
SILVER, JAMES, W. E. CROUCH and M. C. BETTS, 1942.

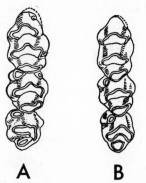

A   **B**

Fig. 105 – UPPER CHEEK TEETH OF *Rattus*
A – *R. norvegicus*; B – *R. rattus*

Rattus rattus (Linnaeus) – Roof Rat and Black Rat – *Rat des toits et Rat noir*

Two races of *Rattus rattus* are known to have been introduced into eastern Canada, but apparently neither has become established for more than a brief period. This species has a longer tail than the Norway rat (usually equal to, or exceeding, the length of head and body). The ears also tend to be longer (over 20 mm.), and they are naked instead of being covered with fine short hair.

The first upper molar has a distinct notch on the outer side of the first row of tubercles and in general the dentition is lighter than that of the Norway rat.

The roof rat, *Rattus rattus alexandrinus*, is characterized by its long tail, which is usually quite a bit longer than the head and body. The coloration may be similar to that of the Norway rat or it may tend to be lighter or greyer.

The black rat, *Rattus rattus rattus*, tends (as its name indicates) to be black or dark grey—darker than the normal colour of either the Norway or roof rat—and it has a shorter tail than the roof rat.

SIZE Total length 325–455 mm.; tail 160–255; hind foot 30–40; ear from notch 20–25. Skull: length 39.0–45.4, width 18.1–21.6. Weight 115–350 gr.

DISTRIBUTION AND VARIATION *Rattus rattus* tends to be common aboard ships, and most records in eastern Canada tend to be from seaports. On one occasion both *R. r. alexandrinus*, the roof rat, and *R. r. rattus*, the black rat, were inadvertently introduced at Strathroy, Ont.; specimens were collected from there and deposited in the Royal Ontario Museum. *Rattus rattus rattus* was originally described from Sweden and *R. r. alexandrinus* from Egypt.

HABITAT This species adapts to conditions similar to those described for the Norway rat, although in general it seems to live more successfully in warmer climates. Where it is found along with the Norway rat, *Rattus rattus* tends to take advantage of its superior climbing ability and move into roofs, attics, upper floors, and even into trees, leaving the ground floor for its more aggressive relative.

HABITS Except for its skill in climbing, the general habits of the species are quite similar to those of the Norway rat. *Rattus rattus* tends to be less prolific, however, and produces fewer and smaller litters.

REMARKS The black rat has been responsible for untold misery and death through its spread of the infectious agents of plague and typhus fever. The epidemic or European typhus fever is transmitted by a rat-borne louse and the endemic or murine typhus fever by rat fleas. (The Norway rat does not normally harbour these parasites.) It is fortunate that *Rattus rattus* has been unable to become established in eastern Canada—perhaps because of the presence of the more aggressive Norway rat.

Modern control methods have greatly reduced the influx of rats from ships, but constant vigilance is required.

Selected References
HAMILTON, WILLIAM J., JR., 1943.
See also references cited under *Rattus norvegicus*.

Fig. 106 – HOUSE MOUSE – *Mus musculus*

Genus MUS Linnaeus

House Mice – *Souris communes*

Dental Formula $I\frac{1-1}{1-1}$ $C\frac{0-0}{0-0}$ $P\frac{0-0}{0-0}$ $M\frac{3-3}{3-3} = 16$

Mus musculus Linnaeus – House Mouse – *Souris commune*

This species is basically a smaller version of the Old World rats (genus *Rattus*). It is brown or greyish brown above and usually slightly lighter coloured, with a yellowish tinge, below. Occasionally the underparts of the house mouse may be quite light, approaching the coloration of the genus *Peromyscus*. The tail is long and sparsely haired. The female has ten mammae, more than any other mouse in eastern Canada. The skull has all the family characteristics, including cheek teeth with three longitudinal rows of rounded tubercles or cusps. The first upper molar is longer than both the second and third combined.

SIZE Total length 140–200 mm.; tail 65–105; hind foot 15–21; ear from notch 11–18. Skull: length 20.1–22.9, width 10.2–12.1. Weight 12–24 gr.

DISTRIBUTION AND VARIATION Like the Norway rat, the house mouse, *M. m. domesticus*, is res-
tricted largely to centres of human habitation; its northernmost limit of regular occurrence is quite similar to that of the Norway rat, although it seems to persist more successfully in northern isolated communities. No doubt its smaller size gives it greater scope for living more intimately with humans without detection or eradication; at the same time it is better able to maintain itself on limited food supplies. The form that has been introduced into eastern Canada was originally described from Dublin, Ireland.

HABITAT In winter, buildings providing warmth and food form the basic habitat. In summer the house mouse may move into nearby fields, especially where grain or other food is available.

The house mouse is particularly well adapted to a wide range of habitat conditions. This has allowed it to survive successfully in most areas of the world to which it has been transported.

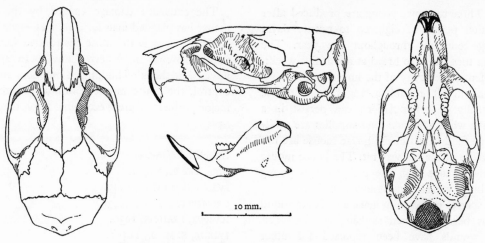

Fig. 107 – SKULL OF *Mus musculus* (ROM 36.11.23.5 ♂)

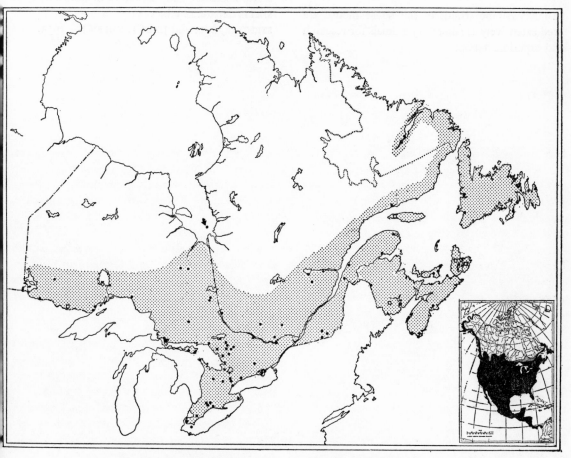

Map 50 – DISTRIBUTION OF THE HOUSE MOUSE – *Mus musculus*

HABITS Three to twelve young are produced after a gestation period of eighteen to twenty days; breeding continues throughout the year. The young in turn begin to breed at about five weeks. The potential longevity of the house mouse is six years, although it probably averages less than two.

Unusually high populations can persist in a small area when adequate food supplies are available. The food habits of the house mouse are not unlike those of the Norway rat. The house mouse is unable to cope with live prey such as young chicks, but it will eat almost anything else.

This species is known to make a chirping sound that has been described as 'singing'; however, similar sounds have been reported for other species of mice.

REMARKS Albino strains of the house mouse are bred extensively as laboratory animals for research and experimentation.

The extensive damage caused by the house mouse has plagued man for centuries—next to the Norway rat, it is the most destructive species of small mammal in eastern Canada. In spite of modern methods of building, sanitation, and pest control, the house mouse continues to present a major problem of great economic importance.

Selected References
DICE, LEE R., 1932a.
EVANS, FRANCIS C., 1949.
GRUNEBERG, HANS, 1943.
HARPER, FRANCIS, 1930.
LAURIE, E. M. O., 1946b.
SCHWARZ, ERNST, 1945.
SCHWARZ, ERNST and HENRIETTA K. SCHWARZ, 1943.
SNELL, GEORGE D. ed., 1943.
STRECKER, R. L. and JOHN T. EMLEN JR., 1953.

Family **ZAPODIDAE**

Jumping Mice – *Souris sauteuses*

The tail and hind legs of this family are greatly elongated. Internal cheek-pouches are present. Upper incisors are narrow and grooved in front. The crown surface of the molars has a complex folded pattern. The skull has a large infraorbital foramen. The zygomatic plate is nearly horizontal and is always narrower than, and completely beneath, the infraorbital foramen. The jumping gait, consisting of bounds of up to three feet or more, is unique among eastern-Canadian mammals.

KEY TO THE EASTERN-CANADIAN SPECIES OF *Zapodidae*

1 Tip of tail white; three upper cheek teeth present on each side (there is no fourth upper premolar). NAPAEOZAPUS p. 185

1' Tip of tail not white; four upper cheek teeth present on each side (a small fourth upper premolar is present). ZAPUS p. 181

Genus **ZAPUS** Coues

Meadow Jumping Mice – *Souris sauteuses des champs*

Dental Formula $I \frac{1-1}{1-1}$ $C \frac{0-0}{0-0}$ $P \frac{1-1}{0-0}$ $M \frac{3-3}{3-3} = 18$

Zapus hudsonius (Zimmermann) – Meadow Jumping Mouse – *Souris sauteuse des champs*

The long bicoloured tail of the meadow jumping mouse has no white tip. It averages shorter (it is about sixty per cent of the total length) than the tail of the woodland jumping mouse, *Napaeozapus insignis*. The meadow jumping mouse is quickly identified by its large hind foot, its pure white underparts and yellowish-olive sides, and by a dark band down the back. The skull shows the family characteristics and can be distinguished from that of the woodland jumping mouse by the presence of a small upper premolar to give a total of eighteen teeth.

SIZE Total length 182–227 mm.; tail 105–142; hind foot 26–32; ear from notch 12–17. Skull: length 20.6–23.3, width 10.0–11.4. Weight 10.0–22.5 gr.

DISTRIBUTION AND VARIATION The meadow jumping mouse occurs throughout the main portion of eastern Canada, excep in the northernmost parts

Fig. 108 – MEADOW JUMPING MOUSE – *Zapus hudsonius*

of the Ungava Peninsula and Labrador. The nominate race, *Zapus hudsonius hudsonius*, occurs in western Ontario east to a line extending northward from Lake Superior just east of Lake Nipigon. It is a medium-sized, relatively dark race with a relatively short zygomata, a relatively broad brain case, and relatively long, broad, flat auditory bullae.

Z. h. canadensis occurs east of Lake Nipigon and eastward through the remainder of Ontario and western Quebec to approximately the mouth of the St John River. This race averages lighter than *Z. h. hudsonius* and has fewer black-tipped hairs in the dorsal band and along each side. It has a broader mastoid region and a slightly larger rostrum.

Further eastward, south of the St Lawrence River, *Z. h. acadicus* is found. Compared with *Z. h. canadensis*, this race is slightly larger, with upper parts that are usually less brownish and more ochraceous. The zygomata is relatively narrower.

North of the St Lawrence River, the remainder of Quebec and southern Labrador are occupied by *Z. h. ladas*. This is the darkest of the forms of this species in eastern Canada and it has relatively short, broad, inflated bullae and short, broad zygomata.

This species is not known from Newfoundland or Anticosti Island.

HABITAT Low, moist meadows are the preferred habitat, although in years of abundance, meadow jumping mice frequently spread out into higher, drier situations. Hibernating sites vary, but they are usually situated in well-drained areas where dens can be constructed two or three feet below the ground surface.

HABITS After a gestation period of approximately eighteen days, two to eight (the average is five or six) blind, naked, helpless young are born, weighing about three-quarters of a gram. Hair becomes apparent at about the ninth day; the incisors erupt at about twelve days but the eyes do not open for about twenty-two to twenty-five days, after which time the young may be weaned. The juvenile pelage is replaced by the adult pelage during the fourth week. Two litters per year are common and perhaps a third is possible. The early-born young may produce a litter before fall.

Meadow jumping mice prepare for hibernation

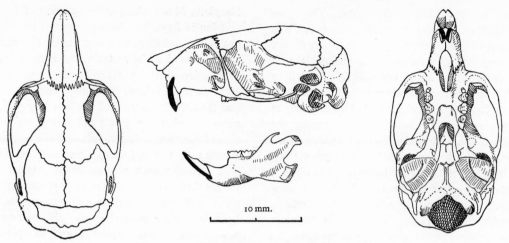

Fig. 109 – SKULL OF *Zapus hudsonius* (ROM 23491 ♀)

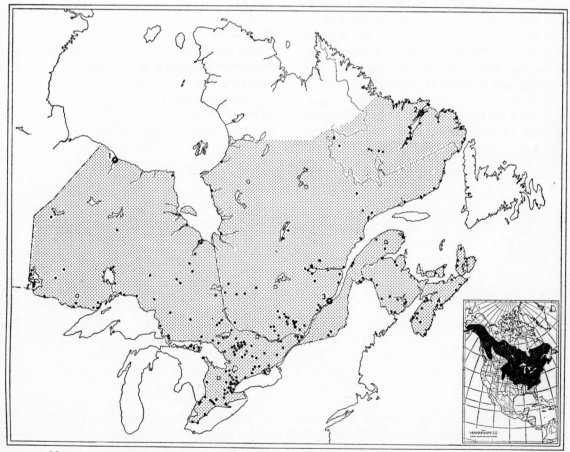

Map 51 – DISTRIBUTION OF THE MEADOW JUMPING MOUSE – *Zapus hudsonius* – AND TYPE LOCALITIES OF
(1) *Z. h. hudsonius* (Zimmermann); (2) *Z. h. ladas* Bangs; (3) *Z. h. canadensis* (Davies); (4) *Z. h. acadicus* (Dawson)

as early as the middle of September. They gradually become torpid and remain more or less in a deep sleep for an unusually long time: they do not come out of hibernation until spring is well advanced (usually about the middle of April or later). The males apparently emerge first and may precede the appearance of females by as much as one to three weeks. Grass seeds are among the primary foods, with fleshy fruits of various plants as well as insects and other invertebrates making up a high percentage of the balance of the diet.

Although primarily nocturnal, the meadow jumping mouse may be active in the daytime, especially during cloudy weather. It becomes almost totally inactive during cold weather. Its normal gait is a series of hops of some two to ten inches, although when it is disturbed, the hops may extend to at least three feet and sometimes to as far as six feet. When it moves about in grassy tunnels or burrows, it progresses on all four feet. It is a poor climber, a reasonably good digger or burrower, and an excellent swimmer.

REMARKS I was rather surprised to find this species in 1948 on the barren tundra region of Cape Henrietta Maria, Ont., at the junction of Hudson and James Bays. The high permafrost level in the ground made hibernating sites scarce. The only site that appeared to be suitable was a line of sandy ridges deposited by older beach levels, now a short distance inland. Trapping began on July 1 and the first *Zapus* was collected on July 5. Specimens taken between July 5 and July 11 showed no sign of breeding activity, although the testicles of a male collected on July 12 were slightly enlarged. The last specimen was taken on August 5—a female that was in an early stage of pregnancy. The short frost-free period in the summer at that latitude would apparently allow only one litter per season and would require *Zapus* to spend an unusually high percentage of its life in hibernation.

Selected References
BANGS, OUTRAM, 1899b.
HAMILTON, WILLIAM J., JR., 1935b.
KRUTZCH, PHILIP N., 1954.
PREBLE, E. A., 1899.
QUIMBY, DON C., 1951.
SHELDON, CAROLYN, 1934, 1938a.

Fig. 110 – WOODLAND JUMPING MOUSE – *Napaeozapus insignis*

Genus **NAPAEOZAPUS** Preble

Woodland Jumping Mice – *Souris sauteuses des bois*

Dental Formula I $\frac{1-1}{1-1}$ C $\frac{0-0}{0-0}$ P $\frac{0-0}{0-0}$ M $\frac{3-3}{3-3}$ = 16

Napaeozapus insignis (Miller) – Woodland Jumping Mouse – *Souris sauteuse des bois*

Pure white underparts, bright, fulvous sides, a dark dorsal band, and a long tail with a white tip are the characteristics that make this species the most strikingly colourful small rodent in eastern Canada. Its proportions are quite similar to those of the meadow jumping mouse, *Zapus hudsonius*, but it differs in being larger on the average and in having a white tip on the tail which averages longer and a richer, more orange colour on the sides or flanks in sharp contrast to the dorsal band and white underparts. The skull differs in not having the small, peg-like upper premolar.

SIZE Total length 220–260 mm.; tail 130–165; hind foot 29–34; ear from notch 14–18. Skull: length 20.0–25.2, width 11.8–13.3. Weight 18–34 gr.

DISTRIBUTION AND VARIATION The genus *Napaeozapus* is restricted to eastern North America, with the largest portion of its range lying in eastern Canada. No less than seven geographic races of *Napaeozapus insignis* have been described, six of which occur in eastern Canada. Of these, some have been based on a series of specimens that does not adequately demonstrate the normal range of

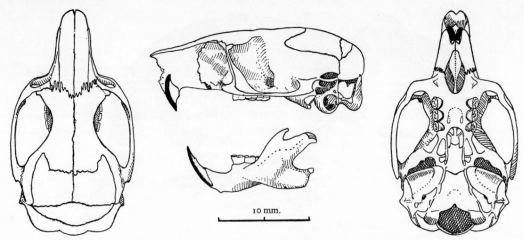

Fig. 111 – SKULL OF *Napaeozapus insignis* (ROM 23538 ♀)

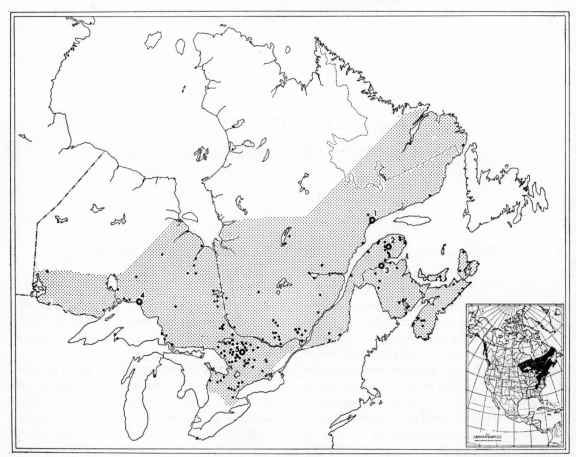

Map 52 – DISTRIBUTION OF THE WOODLAND JUMPING MOUSE – *Napaeozapus insignis* – AND TYPE LOCALITIES OF (1) *N. i. saguenayensis* Anderson; (2) *N. i. gaspensis* Anderson; (3) *N. i. insignis* (Miller); (4) *N. i. abietorum* (Preble); (5) *N. i. algonquinensis* Prince

variation within the species: undoubtedly a thorough study will show that some of these races are invalid. The following races have been recognized: *Napaeozapus insignis insignis* from New Brunswick and Nova Scotia; *N. i. gaspensis* from Gaspé Peninsula, Que.; *N. i. saguenayensis* from the north shore of the Gulf of St Lawrence; *N. i. algonquinensis* from southern Ontario and southern Quebec; *N. i. abietorum* from northern Ontario east of Lake Nipigon and Lake Superior; and *N. i. frutectanus* from Ontario west of Lake Nipigon.

HABITAT Forested areas with available water provide the basic requirements of the woodland jumping mouse, which apparently never ventures out into the open grassy or meadow habitat of the meadow jumping mouse.

HABITS Except for the adaptations of the woodland jumping mouse to its habitat, its habits are basically similar to those of *Zapus* but are as yet much less well known.

The gestation period is from twenty to twenty-three days, with two to eight young being produced in one or (rarely) two litters per year. The young weigh approximately one gram each at birth. The eyes and ears are closed and the body is pinkish. Pigmentation does not appear until about the tenth day after birth at which time it is first revealed on the dorsal regions of the head, body, and tail. The ear unfolds and opens at about this age. Fine fur appears at about twelve days and by seventeen days the back is well furred but the belly is still sparsely furred. The entire body is well furred at twenty-four days. The incisor teeth erupt at about nineteen days and the eyes are opened at about twenty-six days. Solid food is eaten regularly at approximately thirty-four days, at which time weaning is in process. For the first three weeks the mother nurses the young by hunching over them. Afterwards she may lie on her side to accommodate the larger young. Both plant and animal material serve as food; seeds and insect larvae are the most common things eaten.

Nests for rearing the young are usually underground and have an entrance so well concealed that it may even be plugged while the jumping mice are inside.

REMARKS For some unexplained reason this species (along with the meadow jumping mouse) seems to have a predilection for exploring cavities in the ground. A trap made by placing in the soil a pail or can partly filled with water, the top flush with the ground surface, has a strong attraction for jumping mice. The mice are unable to escape and consequently drown. In one experiment, water traps were surrounded with a large number of conventional snap traps which were avoided by jumping mice en route to the water traps where they were caught.

Selected References
ANDERSON, R. M., 1942a.
FOWLE, C. DAVID and R. Y. EDWARDS, 1954.
PREBLE, E. A., 1899.
PREBLE, NORMAN A., 1956.
SHELDON, CAROLYN, 1934, 1938b.
SNYDER, L. L., 1924.

Suborder
Hystricomorpha

Family **ERETHIZONTIDAE**

New World Porcupines – *Porc-épics du Nouveau Monde*

The name *Erethizontidae* derives from the Greek word meaning 'to irritate'. Only one genus of this family of New World porcupines has spread northward into Canada; the other members of the family are found in Central and South America. The infraorbital foramen is large and has a part of the median masseter muscle transmitted through it, a condition that is shared by other members of the suborder. The molar crown pattern is complex. There is only one species occurring in Canada. It is well characterized by the long spines interspersed in its fur.

Genus **ERETHIZON** F. Cuvier

North American Porcupines – *Porc-épics d'Amérique*

$$\textit{Dental Formula} \quad \text{I}\,\tfrac{1-1}{1-1} \quad \text{C}\,\tfrac{0-0}{0-0} \quad \text{P}\,\tfrac{1-1}{1-1} \quad \text{M}\,\tfrac{3-3}{3-3} = 20$$

Erethizon dorsatum (Linnaeus) – Porcupine – *Porc-épic*

The porcupine, with its covering of sharp quills, is undoubtedly the most distinctive rodent in eastern Canada. As many as 30,000 quills have been counted from a single animal. The quills are longest on the back, where they may be as long as four inches, and become denser toward the rear and on the tail. There are no quills on the undersurface of the body. Each quill is yellowish white with a brownish or blackish tip that is covered with tiny barbs. When it penetrates flesh, these barbs make removal difficult and painful. In winter the quills are almost hidden by long, dark, guard hairs, some of which have light-coloured tips. At a distance some animals appear quite black except when the light-coloured quills are raised and exposed. The young tend to be darker than the adults. There are four mammae, two pectoral and two abdominal.

The porcupine is a heavily built mammal with fairly large feet that have four toes on the front and five behind. The tail is thick and heavily armed with quills. The skull is easily distinguished from that of other Canadian rodents by the very large infraorbital foramen on each side of the rostrum, though this characteristic is shared with the introduced coypu, which has a longer rostrum and nasals and a posterior palate that extends back to the level of the posterior edge of the last molars.

SIZE Total length 650–1,030 mm.; tail 150–200; hind foot 75–91; ear from notch 25–42. Skull: length 93–112, width 62.5–78.9. Weight 10–30 lb.

DISTRIBUTION AND VARIATION The porcupine ranges roughly to the limit of trees on the mainland of eastern Canada, but it is quite rare north of the

Fig. 112 – PORCUPINE – *Erethizon dorsatum*

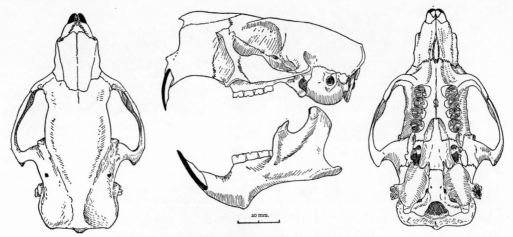

Fig. 113 – SKULL OF *Erethizon dorsatum* (ROM 22460 ♀)

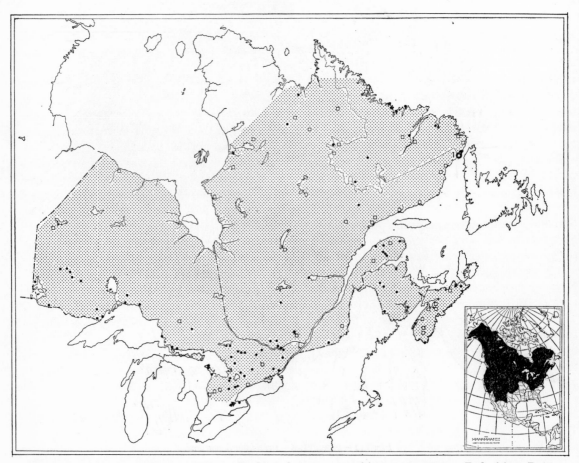

Map 53 – DISTRIBUTION OF THE PORCUPINE – *Erethizon dorsatum* – AND (1) TYPE LOCALITY OF *E. d. picinum* Bangs

Great Lakes–St Lawrence watershed. It is not found on the following islands: Anticosti, Prince Edward, Cape Breton, and Newfoundland.

Erethizon dorsatum picinum, described from L'Anse au Loup, Strait of Belle Isle, Labrador, is thought to occupy Labrador and northeastern Quebec, although the limits of its distribution and its morphological variation are unknown. Compared with *E. d. dorsatum*, which occupies the remainder of the range, *E. d. picinum* is thought to be larger with a slightly shorter tail. It is black and is without white-tipped guard hairs; its skull is larger with a stouter rostrum; its incisors are larger and a dull yellow instead of orange; and it has smaller molariform teeth. A revisionary study based on an adequate sample of material is much needed.

HABITAT Woodlands, especially coniferous forests.

HABITS This large, slow, awkward-appearing rodent is an efficient climber and spends much of its time in tree-tops where it feeds on bark, buds, and leaves. Pines, hemlock, aspens, and sugar maples are among the preferred foods.

Breeding takes place in the fall and is accompanied by an elaborate courtship that includes much vocalization (the predominating sound is a cat-like screech). The mating act is carried on from the posterior-mount position, with the female elevating her tail when receptive. The gestation period requires seven months and a single kit (rarely two) is born any time from April to June. Newborn young are about ten inches long, weigh twelve to twenty ounces, and have their eyes open. The quills are well formed; they are soft at birth but harden quite rapidly, within an hour. Judging by captive animals, the young are weaned at about four months.

Porcupines are basically solitary animals, although during the winter several may den together in hollow logs or trees or subterranean chambers. They are active in all seasons. They become a nuisance around cabins and cottages, chewing sills, doors, tools, or anything with a trace of salt on it, especially during the winter when such places are deserted.

The porcupine's enemies include the bobcat, lynx, fisher, and wolf, which frequently end up with a face full of quills when they attack this formidable rodent. There is a persistent belief among the uninformed that the porcupine can throw its quills at an adversary. During the moult the quills may drop where the animal is threshing about, but direct contact is necessary for the quills to pierce the skin of an intruder and be pulled out. Perhaps the saddest victim is the inexperienced young dog that rushes into a foray with a porcupine and receives the full force of a flashing swipe of a quilled tail.

Most porcupines seem to be heavily parasitized internally.

REMARKS The porcupine has gained few friends because of its habit of chewing its way into summer cottages, outhouses, boats, canoes, and many other possessions of man, and damaging forest trees, especially plantations, and cultivated trees and shrubs. It is even known to gnaw automobile tires and glass bottles. No satisfactory chemical repellent has yet been devised.

Properly prepared, the flesh of the porcupine is edible, although few choose to eat it unless forced to. The quills have long been used by Indian tribes for the ornamentation of clothing and other articles.

Selected References

ANDERSON, R. M. and A. L. RAND, 1943b.

BATCHELDER, CHARLES F., 1930, 1948.

CURTIS, JAMES D. and EDWARD L. KOZICKY, 1944.

PO-CHEDLEY, DONALD S. and ALBERT R. SHADLE, 1955.

SHADLE, ALBERT R., 1950, 1951, 1952, 1955.

SHADLE, ALBERT R. and WILLIAM R. PLOSS, 1943.

SHADLE, ALBERT R., WILLIAM R. PLOSS and EUGENE M. MARKS, 1944.

SHADLE, ALBERT R., MARILYN SMELZER and MARGERY METS, 1946.

SHAPIRO, JACOB, 1949.

SPENCER, DONALD A., 1950.

Family CAPROMYIDAE

This is a group of South American rodents that includes the hutias and the coypu or nutria. The latter has been widely propagated in various parts of the world primarily as a ranch-raised fur-bearer, although it has also been released in certain areas of the southern United States as a means of controlling aquatic vegetation.

Genus MYOCASTOR Kerr

Coypus or Nutrias – *Ragondins ou Nutrias*

Dental Formula I $\frac{1-1}{1-1}$ C $\frac{0-0}{0-0}$ P $\frac{1-1}{1-1}$ M $\frac{3-3}{3-3}$ = 20

Myocastor coypus Molina – Coypu or Nutria – *Nutria*

The nutria is an aquatic form intermediate in size between the muskrat and the beaver, but it differs strongly from both in that the tail is round in cross-section and is sparsely covered with stiff hairs. Four of the five toes on the hind foot are webbed, but the first digit is free for its entire length. There are five unwebbed toes on the front feet all bearing claws, but the pollex or 'thumb' is much shorter than the other digits. The fur consists of two basic types: the long guard hairs are quite stiff and coarse, while the underfur is shorter and quite soft. The pelage colour varies through shades of greyish and brownish; the underparts are similar to the upperparts. The mammary glands are located high up on the flanks or sides of the back; this location permits the young to suckle while the mother maintains a swimming level in the water. The vibrissae are conspicuously long.

The skull is of the same general size and shape as that of the porcupine, but it differs in having a longer, shallower rostrum with longer nasals. The posterior edge of the palate extends to the level of the end of the toothrow, rather than being indented about the depth of one tooth. The upper toothrows are quite close together in front and the teeth are graded in size; the smallest are in front and the largest are behind.

SIZE Total length 800–1,200 mm.; tail 275–400; hind foot 120–140; ear from notch 20–30. Skull: length 95–120, width 60–75. Weight 10–25 lb.

DISTRIBUTION AND VARIATION The nutria is native to southern South America, including Chile, Argentina, Uruguay, Paraguay, and southern Brazil. The form introduced in North America is thought to have originated from Argentina and represents the race *Myocastor coypus bonariensis*. It has been widely introduced to fur farms across eastern Canada from which many have escaped. The Royal Ontario Museum possesses wild-caught specimens from Oxford County, York County, and Thunder Bay District, Ont., and reports from many other sites. There is no positive evidence to date that escaped nutrias have been able to survive a full year in the wild.

HABITAT The nutria prefers an aquatic habitat similar to that of the beaver and the muskrat, but it thrives best where there is a lush growth of aquatic vegetation.

HABITS Breeding takes place throughout the year. Young females first breed at about one year of age and produce about three to five young after about

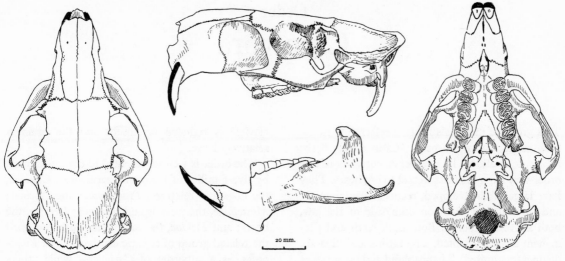

Fig. 114 – SKULL OF COYPU OR NUTRIA – *Myocastor coypus* (ROM 20883 ♀)

100 to 135 days. Older females may produce up to eight young per litter, with a gestation period of from 130 to 150 days. The newborn young weigh about 200 to 250 grams and measure about a foot in length, including a five- or six-inch tail. The eyes are open at birth and the young soon become quite active: they have been known to swim in the first twenty-four hours and may even feed on vegetable matter in this period.

Food consists almost exclusively of vegetable matter, particularly aquatic and semi-aquatic plants. Burrows may be dug into banks and runways may be constructed through dense vegetation. Floating nests not unlike those of the muskrat may be built in suitable marsh areas.

REMARKS   Unfortunately the prospect of great riches from the prolific nutria has been suggested to many people by promoters interested in a profit from the sale of breeding stock. The large market for nutria fur has yet to materialize and many fur farmers are poorer for their attempts to market nutria pelts. According to the statistics provided on fur production in Canada, few nutria pelts reached the market prior to 1956–7, when only 63

pelts were marketed for the whole of Canada (42 from Ontario). Subsequent totals of Canadian production have been as follows: 1957–8, 163 pelts (Ontario 67, Quebec 5); 1958–9, 749 pelts (Ontario 144, Quebec 63); and 1959–60, 2,206 pelts (Ontario 986, Quebec 257). Published records contain no reference to production in other eastern-Canadian provinces.

The establishment of wild populations in areas such as England and the southern United States has been of questionable value. In the southern United States nutria have been successfully used to clear excessive aquatic vegetation from lakes and streams. However, most knowledgeable biologists fear that these animals may eventually prove detrimental to the local fauna and flora. Fortunately the climate would seem to preclude the establishment of wild-nutria populations in eastern Canada.

Selected References
ASHBROOK, FRANK G., 1948.
ATWOOD, EARL L., 1950.
LAURIE, E. M. O., 1946a.
HODGSON, ROBERT G., 1949.
PETERSON, RANDOLPH L., 1957.

Order
Carnivora

This group of mammals is often referred to as the flesh eaters, hence the name (Latin *carnis*, flesh; *vorare*, to swallow). In size, representatives of this order vary from the least weasel to big bears. They have large, well-developed, recurved canine teeth, and three incisor teeth on each side of the jaw, both above and below. Both milk teeth and permanent teeth are rooted. The radius and ulna are distinct (not united). The scaphoid and lunar bones of the wrist are united into one. The condyle of the lower jaw is a transverse rod-like structure. The clavicle is reduced or absent and the brain is relatively large.

The order is well represented in eastern Canada by five families of terrestrial carnivores: *Canidae*, the dogs and relatives; *Procyonidae*, the raccoon; *Mustelidae*, the weasels and relatives; *Ursidae*, the bears; and *Felidae*, the cats. Some authors regard the related group of aquatic carnivores, the *Pinnipedia*, as a suborder of *Carnivora*, while others consider it as a distinct but obviously related order.

KEY TO THE EASTERN-CANADIAN FAMILIES OF *Carnivora*

1 Feet fully digitigrade; tympanic bullae with a longitudinal septum; carnassial teeth well developed; caecum present: 2

    2 Claws elongate and relatively blunt; toes not retractable and not fully concealed in the fur of the foot; rostrum elongated; lower jaws with four premolars and three molars on each side.

            CANIDAE p. 195

    2′ Claws recurved and sharp; toes fully retractable and largely concealed in the fur of the foot; rostrum short; lower jaws with only two premolars and one molar on each side.   FELIDAE p. 275

1′ Feet plantigrade or nearly so; tympanic bullae without a longitudinal septum; carnassial teeth variable in modification; caecum absent: 3

    3 Lower jaw with three molars; alisphenoid canal present; molar teeth not developed as carnassials (crowns flat without cutting edges); size large (more than 41 in. long; weight more than 60 lb.); tail short (less than 14 per cent. of total length).   URSIDAE p. 218

    3′ Lower jaw with two molars; alisphenoid canal absent; carnassial or modified carnassial teeth present; size medium to small (less than 41 in. long; weight less than 60 lb.); tail medium to long (more than 14 per cent. of total length): 4

        4 Molars two over two; carnassial teeth modified for crushing; face with black 'mask' about eyes; tail with conspicuous black rings.   PROCYONIDAE p. 226

        4′ Molars one over two; carnassial teeth developed for cutting; anal musk glands present; no 'mask' of black about eyes; tail without rings.   MUSTELIDAE p. 231

Family **CANIDAE**

Wolves, Coyotes, Dogs and Foxes – *Loups, Coyotes, Chiens et Renards*

Canidae is from the Latin for dog. The members of this family are small-to-large cursorial, digitigrade carnivores. The eyes and ears are relatively large and the ears are usually pointed. The tail is medium to long, often bushy. The feet are rounded and have four functional toes on each foot. The pollex is rudimentary; the third and fourth digits are the longest; and the claws are blunt and non-retractile.

The skull is elongate, the rostrum is narrow, the tympanic bullae are large, and the paroccipital processes are closely appressed and partly fused with them. There is an alisphenoidal canal and the carnassial teeth are well differentiated. The baculum is grooved and the intestine is with caecum.

KEY TO THE EASTERN-CANADIAN GENERA OF *Canidae*

1 Lower jaw with a distinct 'step' or notch; parietal or temporal ridges well developed and widely spaced (not forming a median sagittal crest); colour of upper pelage greyish, formed by white banded hairs with black tips; tail with a mane of stiff black-tipped hair on the dorsal surface.
UROCYON p. 215

1′ Lower jaw without a 'step' or notch; parietal ridges, if present, low and come together to form a sagittal crest; pelage colour variable; tail without a mane of stiff black hair: 2

2 Postorbital processes thickened and convex dorsally. Skull length either over 165 mm. or with a 'brow' developed by an enlargement of the postorbital region of the frontals; colour and size variable (weight usually more than 15 lb.).
CANIS p. 196

2′ Postorbital processes thin and concave dorsally. Skull length less than 165 mm. with no development of a distinct 'brow'; weight less than 15 lb.: 3

3 Ears short and rounded; legs and tail relatively short; winter pelage either white or bluish grey; rostrum relatively short and broad; teeth, especially those of lower jaw, closely spaced.
ALOPEX p. 205

3′ Ears long and pointed; legs and tail relatively long; winter pelage not white or bluish grey; rostrum relatively long and narrow; teeth of lower jaw usually not closely spaced.   VULPES p. 210

Genus **CANIS** Linnaeus

Coyotes, Dogs and Wolves – *Coyotes, Chiens et Loups*

Dental Formula $I \frac{3-3}{3-3}$ $C \frac{1-1}{1-1}$ $P \frac{4-4}{4-4}$ $M \frac{2-2}{3-3} = 42$

KEY TO THE EASTERN-CANADIAN SPECIES OF *Canis*

1 Skull length greater than 205 mm.: 2

  2 Skull without enlarged postorbital and supraorbital region forming a distinct 'brow'.

    3 Rostrum moderately long and heavy (36 to 47 mm. wide, averaging about 41 mm. in southern and central Canada and 45 mm. in the north); skull width more than 122 mm.; nose pad more than one inch in diameter; tail usually held high when running.   CANIS LUPUS p. 200

    3' Rostrum long and thin; skull width less than 122 mm.   (Collie type) CANIS FAMILIARIS p. 203

  2' Skull usually with an enlarged postorbital-supraorbital region forming a distinct 'brow'; rostrum usually short and heavy (frequently wider than 47 mm.); canine and incisor teeth relatively short and heavy.   CANIS FAMILIARIS p. 203

1' Skull length less than 205 mm.: 4

  4 Skull length 180 to 205 mm.

    5 Skull without a distinct 'brow'; rostrum relatively long and thin, averaging 29 mm. wide (26 to 33); canines and incisors relatively long and thin; nose pad one inch or less in diameter; tail usually held low when running.   CANIS LATRANS p. 197

    5' Skull usually with a distinct 'brow'; rostrum usually relatively short and thick (may be foreshortened to an extreme degree); canines and incisors relatively short and heavy.

        CANIS FAMILIARIS p. 203

  4' Skull length less than 180 mm.   CANIS FAMILIARIS p. 203

Canis latrans Say – Brush Wolf or Coyote – *Coyote*

The brush wolf resembles a small, shy German shepherd dog. It has a drooping bushy tail, erect pointed ears, and a pale yellowish-brown or grey coloration. The underfur has a rich tawny or buff tone and the fur is consistently softer in texture than that of the brush wolf's larger relative, the timber wolf, which has an underfur more slate grey in colour.

In general appearance and behaviour the brush wolf is quite different from the timber wolf. The brush wolf is much smaller and has a much thinner, more pointed muzzle. The nose pad is usually one inch or less in diameter. When it runs, the brush wolf usually carries its tail quite low (the timber wolf elevates its tail when running). There are eight or ten mammae.

The skull of the brush wolf is smaller than that of the timber wolf and it has a much narrower rostrum. It can be distinguished from most dog skulls by the lack of a well-developed 'forehead' or 'brow'. Among the thoroughbred breeds of dogs, only the collie has a straighter dorsal contour to the skull. Some mongrel dogs of assorted heritage and hybrid dog-wolf crosses have a skull that may be extremely difficult to distinguish from that of the brush wolf.

SIZE Total length 1,150–1,350 mm.; tail 275–395; hind foot 180–220; ear from notch 95–125. Skull: length 180–205, width 95–110. Weight 25–50 lb.

DISTRIBUTION AND VARIATION Prior to about 1900, the brush wolf, *Canis latrans thamnos*, was restricted in Ontario to a triangle extending northwest from Lake Nipigon to the Manitoba border and south to the Minnesota border. It has since spread quite rapidly to occupy virtually all of Ontario and has extended an unknown distance into western Quebec. Considerable hybridization with domestic dogs is thought to have taken place, particularly in the agricultural areas of southern Ontario.

HABITAT This species is typically an animal of the open country, although *C. l. thamnos* has become well adapted to the more wooded areas of northern Ontario as well as to the agricultural areas of the southern parts of the province, particularly where large woodlots afford sufficient cover.

HABITS The brush wolf is a shy creature and is rarely observed by most people. It has been highly successful in eluding the persistent efforts of man to eliminate it from many areas. Breeding usually takes place in February; after sixty to sixty-three days the litter is born, usually numbering five to seven (up to nineteen have been recorded in western races of coyotes). Sexual maturity is reached in one year. At least one den (sometimes more) is utilized until the young—which differ little from average domestic dog pups—are about eight to ten weeks old. Both male and female hunt for the young and care for them, and in general they show a strong tendency towards monogamy, often apparently mating for life. Brush wolves possess a high order of intelligence. There is considerable co-operation in hunting—occasionally as many as a dozen animals band together in packs, although usually brush wolves do not congregate in more than family groups. Small mammals up to the size of woodchucks and rabbits form the primary diet, although a wide range of other foods is eaten, including deer, birds, eggs, frogs, fish, crayfish, insects, carrion, and various plant species, as well as poultry and other domestic livestock where this is readily available. In the vocal department the brush wolf has produced more nostalgic sounds of the wild than any other predator except perhaps the timber wolf. The habit of howling has apparently been suppressed by animals that live in close proximity to man, but in the wild it is freely indulged in. The known life-span is at least eighteen years, although it probably averages less than nine.

REMARKS For some time the brush wolf has been the centre of much controversy between deer-hunters and farmers who would like to see this

Fig. 115 – BRUSH WOLF *– Canis latrans*

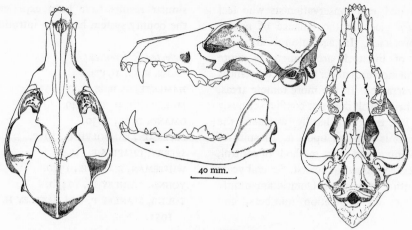

Fig. 116 – SKULL OF *Canis latrans* (ROM 18763 ♀)

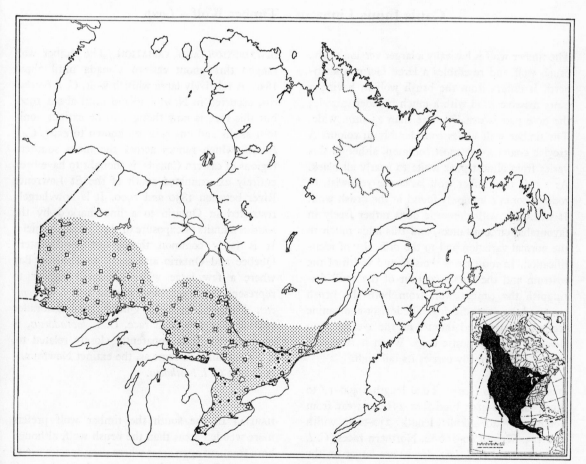

Map 54 – DISTRIBUTION OF THE BRUSH WOLF – *Canis latrans*

wolf exterminated, and conservationists who feel that the wolf's place in the balance of nature should be protected. In agricultural areas its depredations of livestock are sometimes quite serious; control measures under such circumstances are entirely warranted. In the more remote areas, however, the brush wolf does not conflict seriously with man's interests and hardly warrants the harassment that is inflicted upon it. In spite of bounties, poisoning, and other methods of control, this species has continued to persist. Several years of bounty hunting in northern Ontario apparently had little effect on population numbers, and similar results have been experienced wherever the bounty system has been introduced.

Selected References
CROSS, E. C., 1937a.
HAMLETT, GEORGE W. D., 1938.
JACKSON, H. H. T., 1949.
OMAND, D. N., 1950.
PETERSON, RANDOLPH L., 1957.
SPERRY, CHARLES E., 1941.
WHITEMAN, ELDON E., 1940.
YOUNG, STANLEY P., 1941b.
YOUNG, STANLEY P. and HARTLEY H. T. JACKSON, 1951.

Canis lupus Linnaeus – Timber Wolf – *Loup*

The timber wolf is basically a larger version of the brush wolf and resembles a large German shepherd. It differs from the brush wolf in having a more massive head with a much broader muzzle; the nose pad is usually more than 25 mm. wide. The timber wolf varies considerably in colour. A greyish coloration is most common, although this varies from almost pure white to nearly all black. As a rule the timber wolf lacks the yellowish to reddish tones commonly found in the brush wolf. It will cross with domestic dogs rather freely in favourable circumstances, and this adds much to the normal variation and to the difficulty of identification. In most cases the size and width of the rostrum and the dorsal contour of the skull distinguish the timber wolf from both the brush wolf and the domestic dog. The incisor and canine teeth are longer and thinner on the average than those of most domestic dogs. When it runs, the timber wolf normally carries its tail high.

SIZE *Canis lupus lycaon.* Total length 1,490–1,650 mm.; tail 390–480; hind foot 255–290; ear from notch 100–140. Skull: length 230–268, width 120–143. Weight 60–100 lb. Northern races (*C. l. hudsonicus* and *C. l. labradorius*) are larger on the average.

DISTRIBUTION AND VARIATION The timber wolf ranged throughout eastern Canada until about 1850. A relatively large whitish wolf, *C. l. beothucus*, occurred in Newfoundland until about 1900, but this race is now thought to be extinct—only four skulls and one skin are known to exist. *C. l. lycaon*, which ranges across the more southern regions of eastern Canada, is thought to have been entirely exterminated south of the St Lawrence River between 1850 and 1900. It is now largely restricted in Ontario to a line marked by the southern limits of exposure of the Canadian shield. It is fairly common throughout southwestern Quebec and Ontario and north to Hudson Bay where a few large whitish animals appear to represent the larger, more northern *C. l. hudsonicus*. Further north in Quebec and Labrador another larger whitish race, *C. l. labradorius*, is encountered. It is apparently closely related to, if not actually the same as, the extinct Newfoundland race *C. l. beothucus*.

HABITAT In the south the timber wolf prefers more wooded areas than the brush wolf, although both frequent open areas where prey species are to be found. In far northern regions the timber wolf

Fig. 117 – TIMBER WOLF – *Canis lupus*

ranges out on the open tundra and along the barren tide-flats of the coast.

HABITS The timber wolf is a shy, elusive, nocturnal animal, and is seldom seen by the average person. While basically similar to brush wolves in general habits, timber wolves tend to band together in packs in late fall and winter, at which time big game becomes the primary target for food to supplement the diet that is otherwise similar to that of brush wolves. White-tailed deer rank highest in the big-game diet of *C. l. lycaon*, although a number of moose and woodland caribou are also taken. Domestic livestock is eaten when it is available, but timber wolves and livestock are usually not common in the same area. The northern races prey on caribou on the barrens and in the taiga. Hunting circuits are established in a fairly regular pattern and may extend to over a hundred miles in circumference.

Breeding usually starts at two or three years of age and takes place about January or February; four to thirteen (usually four to seven) pups are born after sixty-three days. One or more dens are used. The young begin to leave the den and shift for themselves when they are about two or three months old, but they remain in the family circle for at least a year. The male remains devoted to the family and not only hunts to provide food but may also act as a sentinel, guarding the den from some vantage point. Males are known to expose themselves and to decoy men miles away from the den.

Five distinct vocal sounds of the timber wolf have been described, and each one has a different significance. One of its calls is distinctive—a deep,

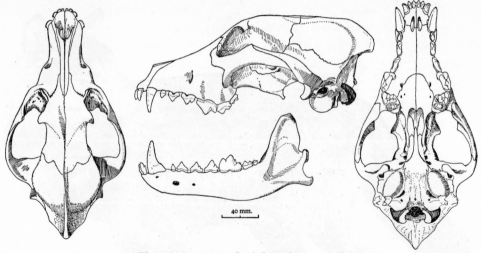

Fig. 118 – SKULL OF *Canis lupus* (ROM 18778)

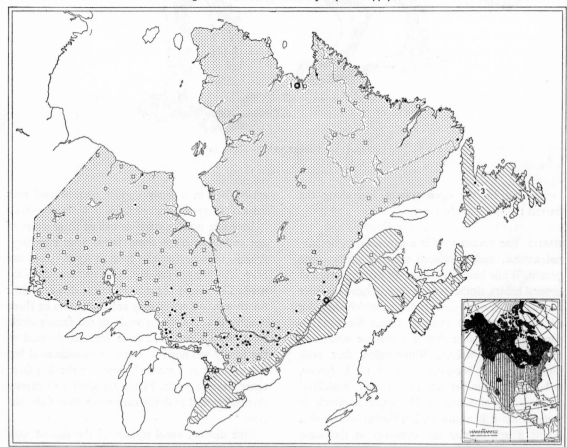

Map 55 – DISTRIBUTION OF THE TIMBER WOLF – *Canis lupus* – AND TYPE LOCALITIES OF (1) *C. l. labradorius* Goldman; (2) *C. l. lycaon* Schreber; (3) *C. l. beothucus* Allen and Barbour

prolonged, loud, throaty howl that 'tingles the spine' of even a seasoned woodsman. It has been described as a call of loneliness and may be given at any time of the year, but it is most frequently heard in the breeding season, at which time it performs the function of a mating call.

A high, soft, plaintive sound is used mostly by the female when her young whelps are playing near the den. It is not unlike the whine of a domestic pup and is thought to indicate solicitude for the offspring. The pitch of this whine is so variable that a ventriloquial effect is produced.

Another sound is a hunting call and consists of a loud, deep, guttural howl. It is thought to be a call for assembling a group and is usually answered by other wolves as the hunt proceeds. It may also be accompanied by one or two loud, dog-like barks.

The fourth sound is the call of the chase, which is uttered during the active pursuit of prey. It is not as throaty or as guttural as the call of the hunt and consists of several short, deep, rapid barking sounds, not unlike those of a pack of hounds on a hot trail.

Finally the fifth sound—the call of the kill—indicates the successful end of the chase. It is basically a deep, ferocious-sounding snarl emitted while the wolf is tearing a carcass.

REMARKS   Many stories have been related of timber wolves' attacking humans, particularly in the early days of the white man's settlement. It would appear that most of these stories were embellished in the telling, for documentary proof of timber wolves' attacks on humans is lacking.

Today they have developed a respect for man. One has little to fear from a normal, healthy wolf, although a danger has developed recently with the spread of rabies in the wild population of mammals.

Like the brush wolf, the timber wolf has been the centre of much controversy because of its predation on deer and moose. In spite of continual harassment by man through bounties and other means, timber-wolf populations have remained fairly stable in the more northern forested areas of eastern Canada. In agricultural areas and in most of the region south of the St Lawrence, it has been almost, if not completely, extirpated.

When sentiment and prejudice are discounted, the fact remains that the timber wolf does sometimes come in direct conflict with the interests of man, and when this is so, sound control measures are justified. On the other hand, the timber wolf plays a vital role in the ecology of the Canadian northland.

Selected References
ALLEN, GLOVER M. and THOMAS BARBOUR, 1937.
ANDERSON, R. M., 1943a.
COMEAU, NOEL M., 1940.
DE VOS, A., 1949.
GOLDMAN, EDWARD A., 1937.
OLSON, SIGURD F., 1938.
OMAND, D. N., 1950.
POCOCK, R. I., 1935.
STENLUND, MILTON H., 1955.
THOMPSON, DANIEL Q., 1952.
YOUNG, STANLEY P., 1941b, 1946.
YOUNG, STANLEY P. and E. A. GOLDMAN, 1944.

Canis familiaris Linnaeus – Domestic Dog – *Chien*

Traditionally the domestic dog is not included in treatises on regional mammalian faunas. However, in the course of identifying mammalian skeletal material from various sources, particularly from archaeological excavations and government bounty claims, the bones of domestic dogs must frequently be distinguished from those of the native wild canids. Purebred strains of the domestic dog usually have sufficiently distinct cranial characteristics to be readily identified.

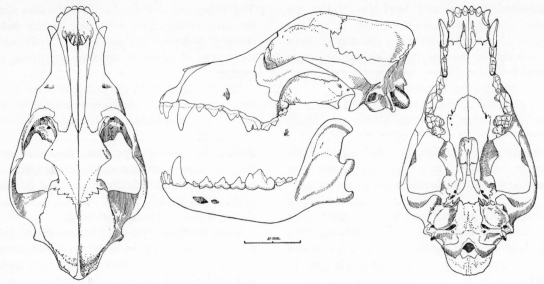

Fig. 119 – SKULL OF DOMESTIC DOG – *Canis familiaris* (ROM 15611 ♀)

Mongrels, however, and cross breeds and back-crosses of domestic dogs of uncertain ancestry display such an endless number of variations of characteristics that it is impossible to select any one character or combination of characters by which they can be distinguished consistently from wild canids. This problem is further complicated by the fact that in certain areas dogs of the approximate sizes of coyotes and wolves interbreed rather freely with their wild relatives to produce dog-wolf hybrids.

Although several attempts have been made by various authors to provide characters, combinations of characters, or indices by which the wild and domestic canids can be segregated, no completely satisfactory key has been devised; indeed, it is apparent that a simple solution should not be expected. However, the following cranial characters will help to identify the majority of specimens encountered.

The conformation of the supraorbital-postorbital or so-called sinus region will serve to distinguish most of the more typical dog skulls (see *fig.* 119). Most domestic dogs can be recognized by the distinct 'brow' or stepped forehead, while timber and brush wolves have a much straighter dorsal profile from the nasal bone to the forehead—they lack the enlarged sinus region. However, purebred collies and their close relatives have an even straighter dorsal profile (viewed from the side) than wolves. On the other hand, most purebred collies have a relatively narrower skull and a longer, narrower rostrum. Hybrids and mongrels with collie ancestry may approach the typical wolf shape, but they usually have shorter and relatively broader canine and incisor teeth; these tooth characteristics apply to many of the other domestic dogs of the coyote-to-timber-wolf size. Also, the rostrum is usually relatively shorter and broader in most other varieties of dogs in this size range when compared with that of the wild canids.

The incisor and canine teeth of the domestic dog erupt in the fourth or fifth month; the premolars in the fifth to the sixth month; the first molars in approximately the fourth month; the second lower molar in the two weeks prior to the fifth month; the second upper molar in the fifth or sixth month; and the third lower molar in the sixth or seventh month.

Genus **ALOPEX** Kaup

Arctic Foxes – *Renards arctiques*

Dental Formula I $\frac{3-3}{3-3}$ C $\frac{1-1}{1-1}$ P $\frac{4-4}{4-4}$ M $\frac{2-2}{3-3}$ = 42

Alopex lagopus (Linnaeus) – Arctic Fox – *Renard arctique*

This small fox is characterized by relatively short rounded ears, a short broad muzzle, and long dense fur in winter. The pads of the feet are completely encased in winter fur to provide excellent insulation against the intense cold of the Arctic. Two basic colour-phases occur. In winter the pelage is either a pure white or a 'blue' phase that is actually a Maltese or light smoky blue-grey. In summer the white-phase foxes become brownish while the blue becomes a darker blue-grey. The colour-phase ratios vary geographically, with the highest percentage of the blue phase occurring on the islands of the eastern Arctic. In eastern Canada the lowest percentage of blue-phase foxes—usually less than one per cent of the population—is found in the western region. On the east coast of Hudson Bay, the percentage rises slightly to 0.6–0.8 per cent, while on the Atlantic side a further increase to an average of one to four per cent has been observed.

The skull of the arctic fox is remarkably similar in basic conformation to that of the genus *Vulpes*, differing primarily in relative proportions. As the rostrum is shorter and broader, with a constriction behind the canine teeth, the skull is relatively shorter and broader than that of *Vulpes*. The teeth, particularly those of the lower jaw, are usually more closely spaced than the teeth of the red fox.

SIZE Total length 800–1,100 mm.; tail 275–425; hind foot 130–160; ear from notch 55–70. Skull: length 118–132, width 64–72. Weight 4–14 (average 6–8) lb.

DISTRIBUTION AND VARIATION The arctic fox is circumpolar in distribution; its main range is restricted to the true tundra. In eastern Canada it is primarily a coastal species occurring around the Hudson and James Bay coasts, along Hudson Strait, and on the Labrador coast. From the east side of James Bay eastward, the name *Alopex lagopus ungava* has been applied. Specimens from this area are said to have slight cranial differences and to be larger than those in the remainder of Canada (*A. l. innuitus*). However, a thorough study may prove them all to be one widespread race. While the main southern limit of range of the arctic fox coincides with the tree line, many animals occasionally wander far south for hundreds of miles (see map 56). It has been suggested that these immigrations occur in years of scarce food supply (normally suggesting a low population of lemming). In Ontario, specimens have been secured from as far south as Ritchie Township, Cochrane District, and Township 10B, Sudbury District, and in Quebec as far south as Lake St John. They have also appeared on Anticosti Island and Cape Breton Island where they were probably transported on ice flows moving south through the Strait of Belle Isle. The arctic fox appears sporadically, yet fairly frequently, on Newfoundland where specimens have been taken as far south as St Shotts on the Avalon Peninsula.

HABITAT The home of the arctic fox is the barren-land tundra, although the coastal regions, including pack-ice, form the habitat of a high percentage of the population.

HABITS The arctic fox may be active at any hour and normally displays little fear of man, often approaching humans quite closely and barking at them much like a small domestic dog. More than one den is used, and each den may have several

Fig. 120 – ARCTIC FOX – *Alopex lagopus*

entrances. Food is varied and includes rodents, stranded marine life, birds and eggs, berries, and scavenged remains of larger mammals, particularly the kills of polar bears. Unlike most foxes, the arctic fox tends to store excess food, and a typical fox den may have a litter of uneaten carcasses of birds, mice, or other food scattered around the entrance.

Breeding starts at about ten months; the mating season begins in February. After fifty to fifty-seven days (usually from April to June) a litter of up to fourteen (an average five or six) pups is born. The young weigh around two ounces at birth and have a thick dark-brown coat. Both parents care for the young, which venture forth from the den at about one month. A life-span of fourteen years has been recorded for captive animals.

REMARKS The arctic fox has long been an important item in the economy of Eskimos and northern Indians. Fluctuations in fox populations and in the prices paid for raw furs have seriously affected the economy of these northern natives.

Ranch raising of the arctic fox, particularly in the blue colour-phase, began about 1865 on the islands along the coast of Alaska, and it soon spread to various points in eastern Canada, although it never became as valuable as the production of the various colour-phases of the red fox. However, the fall in the price of long-haired furs forced most ranches out of business. The last reports of sales in eastern Canada were in 1950–1 when 451 pelts were marketed from Ontario ranches at an average value of $7.80 per pelt. In that same year the total Canadian ranch-raised production was 1,488 pelts.

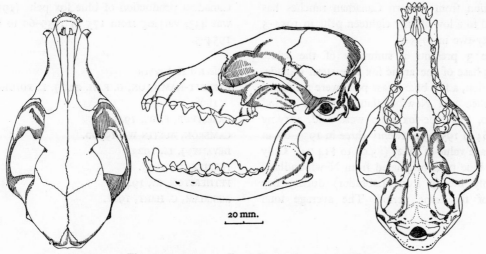

20 mm.

Fig. 121 – SKULL OF *Alopex lagopus* (ROM 20694 ♀)

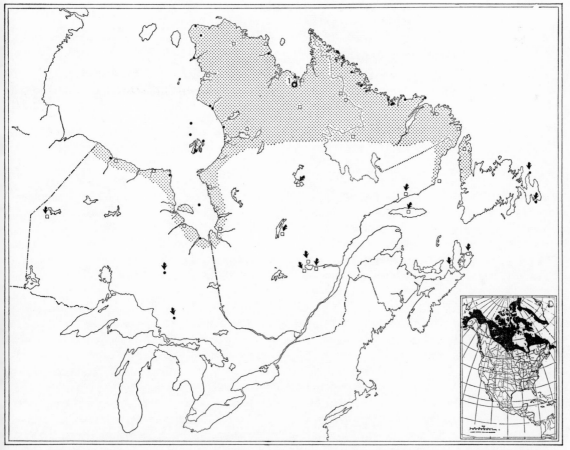

Map 56 – DISTRIBUTION OF THE ARCTIC FOX – *Alopex lagopus* – AND (1) TYPE LOCALITY OF *A. l. ungava* (Merriam)

Production from western Canadian ranches has declined to a low of only eighteen pelts in 1954-5 and forty-two in 1955-6.

Table 3 presents a summary of the white colour-phase of the arctic fox in eastern Canada. In addition, a few blue-phase pelts were produced in Quebec and Newfoundland. In the period 1950-60, 817 blue-fox pelts were sold, varying from 264 in 1954-5 to twenty-three in 1959-60, at an average value of $8.27 ($3.00 to $14.00). Only twenty blue pelts originated from Newfoundland (probably mostly from Labrador) during five years of the same period. The average total

Canadian production of blue fox pelts (1950-60) was 433, varying from 175 in 1959-60 to 870 in 1954-5.

Selected References

BARRETT-HAMILTON, G. E. H. and J. L. BONHOTE, 1898.

BRAESTRUP, F. W., 1941.

CAMERON, AUSTIN W., 1950b.

DEVANY, J. L., 1923.

FAESTER, K., 1945.

FETHERSTON, K., 1947.

MERRIAM, C. HART, 1902.

Table 3

Production of Arctic Fox Pelts (White Colour-Phase) in Eastern Canada, 1950-60

	ALL CANADA	EASTERN CANADA	ONTARIO	QUEBEC	NEW BRUNSWICK	NOVA SCOTIA	PRINCE EDWARD I.	NEW-FOUNDLAND
TOTAL PELTS 1950-60	398,035	63,124	2,312	59,066	—	*18	*2	***1,726
Average Annual Production	39,804	6,312	231	5,907		6		191
Minimum Annual Production	14,457 (1959-60)	2,139 (1957-8)	54 (1955-6)	1,848 (1957-8)		3 (1954-5)		19 (1958-60)
Maximum Annual Production	81,783 (1954-5)	20,213 (1954-5)	635 (1954-5)	19,201 (1954-5)		8 (1958-9)		589 (1950-1)
TOTAL VALUE 1950-60	$5,065,937	$1,036,415	$32,560	$989,029		$385	$29	$14,334
Average Annual Value	$506,594	$103,642	$3,256	$98,903		$128		$1,592
Minimum Annual Value	$353,366 (1959-60)	$29,577 (1957-8)	$243 (1955-6)	$25,872 (1957-8)		$45 (1954-5)		$28 (1959-60)
Maximum Annual Value	$931,607 (1954-5)	$338,337 (1954-5)	$8,509 (1954-5)	$326,417 (1954-5)		$200 (1958-9)		$5,890 (1950-1)
Average Value per Pelt	$12.72	$16.42	$14.10	$16.74		$21.40	$14.50	$8.30
Minimum Average Value per Pelt	$8.16 (1951-2)	$13.18 (1951-2)	$4.50 (1955-6)	$14.00 (1951-4 & 1957-8)		$15.00 (1954-5)		$1.47 (1959-60)
Maximum Average Value per Pelt	$24.44 (1959-60)	$22.82 (1959-60)	$20.00 (1959-60)	$23.00 (1959-60)		$25.00 (1958-9)		$10.00 (1950-1)

* Three years only.　　** One year only, 1952-3.　　*** Nine years only, 1951-60.

Genus **VULPES** Bowdich

Foxes – *Renards*

Dental Formula $\quad$ I $\frac{3-3}{3-3}$ $\quad$ C $\frac{1-1}{1-1}$ $\quad$ P $\frac{4-4}{4-4}$ $\quad$ M $\frac{2-2}{2-2}$ = 42

Vulpes vulpes (Linnaeus) – Red Fox, Coloured Fox – *Renard roux*

In spite of its name, the red fox comes in three basic colours, with the red phase being the most common. The cross fox—a name derived from a fairly distinct cross on the back along the shoulders —is primarily brownish rather than red. The silver and black foxes represent the third and rarest colour-phase. Other minor colour-phases occur occasionally. The bastard samson, which is without the normal long guard-hairs and has only short underfur, is basically a dark sooty-grey colour; its usually matted fur in life gives it a very scruffy appearance.

In all colour-phases of the red fox, the feet and legs and the outside of the ear-tips are black, while the tip of the tail and a varying amount of the underparts are white. In the red colour-phase the shade of red varies considerably from a light yellowish red to a deep auburn red. The cross fox varies both in colour and in the amount of grizzling created by an admixture of black and/or white; the general tone may be described as reddish to reddish brown and it averages darker than the red phase. The basic colour of the silver fox is black with white tips on the guard hairs. The black fox is similar but is without the white 'frosting'. The ratio of the various colour-phases varies geographically, with the rate of occurrence of the silver and cross phases increasing toward the north or northwest where the ratio approaches about one per cent silver, nineteen per cent cross, and eighty per cent red. In the southern part of the range the red predominates at about ninety-nine per cent.

There are eight mammae.

The skull of the red fox is characterized by being relatively larger than the arctic fox *Alopex* and by its longer, narrower rostrum and its less closely spaced teeth, particularly in the lower jaws. The shape of the lower margin of the mandible and the absence of the separated temporal ridges distinguish the red from the gray fox, *Urocyon*.

SIZE Total length 945–1,170 mm.; tail 330–450; hind foot 155–185; ear from notch 75–95. Skull: length 120–160, width 69–85. Weight 6–16 lb.

DISTRIBUTION AND VARIATION The red fox occurs throughout eastern Canada from the agricultural areas of the south to the barren arctic tundras of the north. Representatives of the smallest race, *Vulpes vulpes fulva*, range from the United States into southern Ontario where they intergrade with the larger *V. v. rubricosa* which occurs eastward to the Maritime Provinces, including Newfoundland, and north to Hudson Strait. From the northwest a second larger race, *V. v. abietorum*, ranges into northern Ontario east to near the Quebec border where it merges with *V. v. rubricosa*. In general the Great Lakes have acted as a broad division point about which four geographic races have together: *V. v. regalis* to the southwest, *V. v. abietorum* to the northwest, *V. v. rubricosa* to the northeast, and *V. v. fulva* to the southeast.

HABITAT The red fox is quite adaptable to a wide range of habitats and thrives in close proximity to human habitation. A source of available food and a bit of cover or seclusion for dens seem to fulfil its basic requirements, although it appears to prefer sparsely settled areas broken up by forests or woodlots.

HABITS The red fox is perhaps the most frequently

Fig. 122 – RED FOX – *Vulpes vulpes*

encountered wild canine in eastern Canada. It often ventures forth during the day, and occasionally a whole family may be seen sunning themselves near the entrance to an undisturbed den which may be an enlarged woodchuck hole or one dug by the animals themselves.

Breeding starts in January or February, and after about fifty-two or fifty-three days the young are born, each averaging about four ounces. The litter may be from one to ten but usually averages four or five. The kits resemble domestic pups; their white tail-tips distinguish them from coyotes and wolves. The eyes are closed for eight to ten days. The male or 'dog' hunts for and feeds the female or vixen while she remains in the den with the kits. The young venture out of the den at about one month and are weaned at about two months. Adult size is reached at about six months and breeding starts at about one year. The family unit is maintained until fall, at which time the young start out on their own; they begin a family the following year.

A wide variety of foods is eaten, with mice and rabbits ranking high on the menu. Insects, birds, frogs, snakes, carrion, and vegetation matter are also eaten. The coloured fox can be quite vocal, and is capable of making a variety of howling, barking, yapping, and whining noises not unlike those of a small dog.

REMARKS The red fox's occasional visits to poultry pens have given it a notorious reputation that is further enhanced by its slyness and cunning in eluding the chase—characteristics that have been memorably celebrated by Aesop.

Ranch raising of foxes had its beginning with silver-fox mutations on Prince Edward Island in 1887, and it soon became a thriving industry across Canada and in much of the United States. As fashions in fur changed and prices fell, most

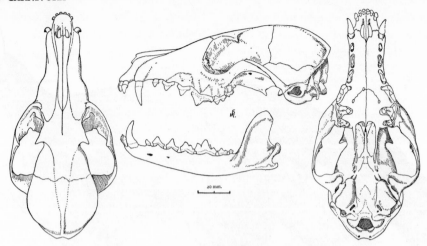

Fig. 123 – SKULL OF *Vulpes vulpes* (ROM 20329)

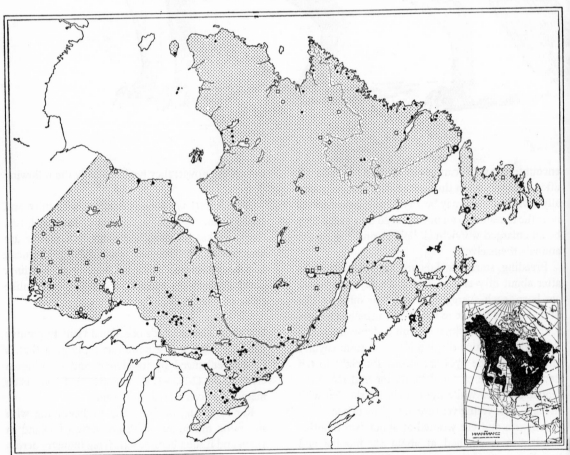

Map 57 – DISTRIBUTION OF THE RED FOX – *Vulpes vulpes* – AND TYPE LOCALITIES OF (1) *V. rubricosa bangsi* Merriam
(= *V. v. rubricosa*); (2) *V. deletrix* Bangs (= *V. v. rubricosa*); (3) *V. v. rubricosa* Bangs

ranchers were forced to discontinue fox ranching. In 1950–1 the ranch production of coloured foxes had dropped to 50,753 for all Canada and 39,464 for eastern Canada with respective values of about $671,000 and $515,000. There was a steady annual decline to 1959–60 when only 1,183 pelts were produced in all Canada (1,057 from eastern Canada) with a value of $14,700 ($14,300 for eastern Canada). Ranch-raised fox pelts averaged from $1.00 to $22.00 apiece during the 1950–60 period.

A summary of wild-caught coloured-fox production is presented in Table 4. The reduction in trapping pressure brought about by declining prices has recently allowed a fairly strong buildup in wild-fox populations in eastern Canada.

Fox hunting, particularly with horse and hound, is limited in eastern Canada. Here the primary sport is in the chase, with comparatively little reduction in the fox population.

Selected References

BANGS, OUTRAM, 1897b, 1898a.

BUTLER, LEONARD, 1951.

CHURCHER, CHARLES S., 1959, 1960.

CROSS, E. C., 1940.

DODDS, D. G., 1955.

HAMILTON, W. J., JR., 1935a.

MERRIAM, C. HART, 1900.

MURIE, ADOLPH, 1936.

SCOTT, THOMAS G., 1947, 1955a, 1955b.

SCOTT, THOMAS G. and WILLARD D. KLIMSTRA, 1955.

SEAGEARS, C. B., 1944.

Table 4

Production of Wild Red, Cross, and Silver Fox Pelts in Eastern Canada, 1950–60

	ALL CANADA	EASTERN CANADA	ONTARIO	QUEBEC	NEW BRUNSWICK	NOVA SCOTIA	PRINCE EDWARD I.	NEW-FOUNDLAND
TOTAL PELTS 1950–60	213,567	153,852	79,600	52,109	*3,698	10,025	2,562	**5,858
Average Annual Production	21,357	15,385	7,960	5,211	411	1,003	256	651
Cross Fox Pelts	10%	4.5%	4%	5.6%	—	2.5%	11%	20.5%
Silver Fox Pelts	2%	1.5%	0.7%	0.7%	—	8.5%	4.5%	9.5%
Minimum Annual Production	8,317 (1956–7)	6,906 (1956–7)	2,886 (1958–9)	2,705 (1956–7)	144 (1954–5)	322 (1956–7)	27 (1957–8)	245 (1956–7)
Maximum Annual Production	42,647 (1950–1)	32,760 (1951–2)	16,258 (1955–6)	10,854 (1950–1)	746 (1950–1)	2,011 (1950–1)	770 (1950–1)	1,025 (1951–2)
TOTAL VALUE 1950–60	$321,859	$185,108	$77,489	$76,220	$2,490	$17,132	$3,491	$9,574
Average Annual Value	$32,186	$18,511	$7,749	$7,622	$276	$1,713	$349	$1,064
Cross Fox Pelts	18%	10.2%	9.4%	10.7%	—	2.9%	21.4%	21%
Silver Fox Pelts	9%	7.2%	5.8%	6.6%	—	16.5%	13.6%	14.5%
Minimum Annual Value	$7,381 (1956–7)	$5,124 (1956–7)	$1,923 (1956–7)	$2,255 (1955–6)	$58 (1954–5)	$230 (1956–7)	$21 (1957–8)	$245 (1956–7)
Maximum Annual Value	$90,175 (1950–1)	$49,697 (1950–1)	$17,879 (1950–1)	$25,600 (1950–1)	$560 (1950–1)	$5,358 (1959–60)	$1,558 (1950–1)	$2,254 (1951–2)
Average Value per pelt								
Red Fox Pelts	$0.95	$0.82	$0.68	$0.93	$0.67	$1.00	$0.85	$1.31
Cross Fox Pelts	$1.95	$1.76	$1.55	$2.00	No cross or silver fox	$1.47	$1.79	$1.63
Silver Fox Pelts	$5.25	$4.61	$5.35	$9.44		$3.67	$4.14	$2.43

* Nine years only, 1950–5 and 1957–60. ** Nine years only, 1957–60.

* Nine years only, 1951–60.

Fig. 124 – GRAY FOX – *Urocyon cinereoargenteus*

Genus **UROCYON** Baird

Gray Foxes – *Renards gris*

Dental Formula   I $\frac{3-3}{3-3}$ C $\frac{1-1}{1-1}$ P $\frac{4-4}{4-4}$ M $\frac{2-2}{3-3}$ = 42

Urocyon cinereoargenteus Schreber – Gray Fox – *Renard gris*

The gray fox is similar in general size to the red fox, although the legs are slightly longer, the body is more slender, and the ears are relatively shorter. A strip of black extends down the middle of the back and along the top of the long bushy tail and terminates in the black tail tip. White bands and black tips on the guard hairs give the remainder of the upper parts a grey appearance. The sides of the neck, the back of the ears, and the legs and feet are yellowish buff. The belly and throat are whitish and the sides of the nose have a brownish patch. There are eight mammae: two pectoral,

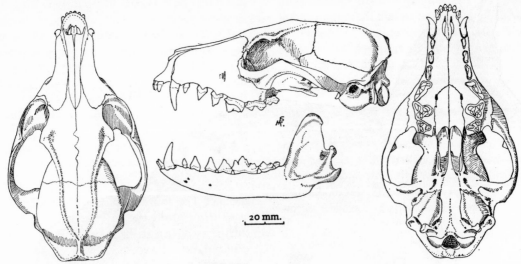

Fig. 125 – SKULL OF *Urocyon cinereoargenteus* (ROM 22493 ♂)

two abdominal, and four inguinal. The skull is characterized by distinct parietal ridges that are widely spaced instead of forming a single sagittal crest, and by an angular emargination in the lower rear section of the mandibles.

SIZE Total length 800–1,125 mm.; tail 275–425; hind foot 110–150; ear from notch 60–85. Skull: length 110–135, width 65–74. Weight 6–18 lb.

DISTRIBUTION AND VARIATION Although primarily a more southern species, the gray fox was apparently present in southern Ontario in pre-Columbian times, for remains have been collected from early Indian middens. It seems to have disappeared completely from this area for almost 300 years and returned to Canada between 1930 and 1940. At present three populations are apparently extending their ranges into eastern

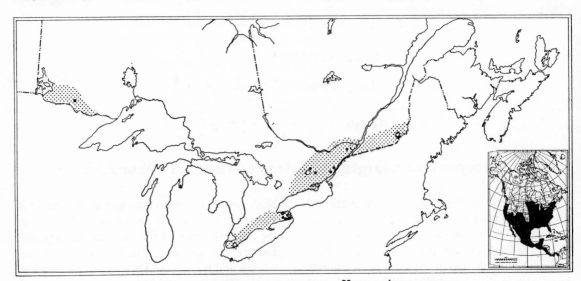

Map 58 – DISTRIBUTION OF THE GRAY FOX – *Urocyon cinereoargenteus*

Canada: *U. c. borealis* into southern Quebec south of the St Lawrence and around the eastern end of Lake Ontario into the province of Ontario; *U. c. ocythous* in the Rainy River region west of Lake Superior; and the third population, probably *U. c. cinereoargenteus*, around each end of Lake Erie.

HABITAT Compared with the red fox, the gray prefers more wooded and less open country. Rocky-river gorges and large woodlots provide suitable habitats, particularly when they are associated with lakes or streams. Hollow logs or trees and rocky cliffs are the preferred den sites, although the gray fox may occasionally use a ground burrow like the red fox.

HABITS The gray fox is unique among the canids in its tree-climbing ability; hence in some areas it is called a 'tree' or 'tree-climbing' fox. When pursued it readily climbs into a tree-top to avoid detection. Although primarily a nocturnal species, the gray fox is frequently active during the daylight hours.

Mating usually takes place about February to March, and one to seven (an average of four) young are born about two months later. The gestation period is thought to be as long as sixty-three days, which is about ten days longer than that of the red fox, although other reports indicate

that it may be as brief as fifty-one days. The pups, weighing about four ounces at birth, are blackish and have their eyes closed for the first eight or nine days. Both parents care for the young, which are weaned at about eight to ten weeks. The males are thought to leave the family circle first, and by fall the family units are broken up entirely.

In food habits the gray fox tends to be similar to, but perhaps more omnivorous than, the red fox.

Less vocal than the red, the gray fox tends to have a lower-pitched call of less intensity.

REMARKS The former occurrence of the gray fox in eastern Canada and its disappearance and re-entry presents one of the more interesting shifts in mammal distribution. Its numbers are so small at present that it is difficult to assess its recent population trends.

Selected References
BANGS, OUTRAM, 1899a.
DOWNING, S. C., 1946.
MERRIAM, C. HART, 1903.
PETERSON, RANDOLPH L., 1957.
PETERSON, R. L., R. O. STANDFIELD, E. H. MCEWEN
    and A. C. BROOKS, 1953.
RICHARDS, STEPHEN H. and RUTH L. HINE, 1953.
SEAGEARS, CLAYTON B., 1944.

Family **URSIDAE**

Bears – *Ours*

Bears are characterized by their large size; their plantigrade feet (i.e. the entire palms or soles are in contact with the ground); five toes on each foot; a short tail; front premolars that are reduced to simple peg-like structures, with usually some missing in most adult specimens; and by molars that are low and flattened to form a crushing dentition not unlike that of man. The molar teeth are progressively larger from front to back.

While only the polar bear, *Thalarctos maritimus*, and the black bear, *Ursus americanus*, are known to occur in eastern Canada today, there have been persistent rumours and reports that an eastern form of grizzly bear, *Ursus horribilis* (or *U. arctos* according to some authors), once lived in the Ungava region of Quebec and persisted until about 1900. Unfortunately the evidence is conflicting. Reports of light-coloured bears in northern Quebec agree in description with the coloration of a grizzly bear, yet there is a strong possibility that the animals described were merely a brown colour-phase of the black bear. Until recently no identified specimen of even a part of a skin or a skeleton of a grizzly bear had been reported from eastern Canada. A western form of grizzly bear is known to have ranged as far east as western Minnesota and western Manitoba up until about 1800.

In November 1964 a remarkably well-preserved grizzly bear skull was recovered from a gravel pit near Orillia, Ont., a site that appears to have been an off-shore island near the western shore of late glacial Lake Algonquin. A carbon-14 collagen test was performed on a portion of a long bone collected in association with the skull which indicated that the animal died some $11,700 \pm 250$ years ago. This skull specimen is in the collections of the Royal Ontario Museum where further studies are being carried out in an effort to establish its relationships with modern grizzly bears on the one hand and with earlier fossil forms on the other.

Although the grizzly bear *Ursus arctos* is still not known to have occurred with certainty in eastern Canada within historic time, this record of a late glacial occurrence calls for a renewed search for evidence to establish when the grizzly disappeared and whether or not there was any connection between it and a possible modern occurrence in the Ungava region of Quebec and perhaps elsewhere.

The bears of the genus *Ursus* are divided into two subgenera. In subgenus *Euarctos*, the black bears, the front claws are approximately the same length as the hind claws; the first lower molar has a broad, open, cuspless valley medially between the metaconid and entoconid; P_4 lacks a medial accessory cusp or a median antero-posterior sulcus on the posterior part; and M^2 is broadest at a point approximately half-way between the anterior and posterior margins. In subgenus *Ursus*, the grizzly and big brown bears, the front claws are much longer than the hind claws; M_1 has one or more cusplets medially in the valley between the metaconid and entoconid; P_4 has median accessory cusps and a median anteroposterior sulcus on the posterior part; and M^2 is broadest at the anterior end.

KEY TO THE EASTERN-CANADIAN GENERA OF *Ursidae*

1 Entire pelage white; combined length of M^1 and M^2 less than the palatal width; dorsal contour of skull (viewed from the side) relatively flat. THALARCTOS p. 222

1′ Pelage not white (usually black in subgenus *Euarctos*); combined length of M^1 and M^2 more than palatal width; dorsal contour of skull strongly arched (in subgenus *Euarctos*). URSUS p. 219

Fig. 126 – BLACK BEAR – *Ursus americanus*

Genus **URSUS** Linnaeus

Subgenus **EUARCTOS** Gray

Black Bears – *Ours noir*

Dental Formula   I $\frac{3-3}{3-3}$ C $\frac{1-1}{1-1}$ P $\frac{4-4}{4-4}$ M $\frac{2-2}{3-3}$ = 42

Ursus americanus Pallas – Black Bear – *Ours noir*

Most bears in eastern Canada have the typical black coat, a brown snout, and occasionally a white patch on the chest. Bears may be encountered that are brownish or some other colour, but no established mutations are found in eastern Canada such as those exhibited by the so-called 'cinnamon', 'blue or glacier', and 'Kermode' bears of western North America. There are three pairs of mammae: one inguinal and two pairs forward in the pectoral region.

The skull is readily distinguished from that of most other carnivores by its large size, its large canines, and by its broad, flattened, crushing molars. The skull of the black bear differs from that of the polar bear in the dorsal contour: it is strongly arched, while the polar bear's skull tends to have an elongate, more flattened contour when viewed from the side.

SIZE Total length 1,375–1,780 mm. (50–71 in.);

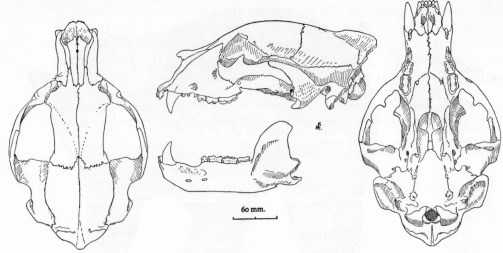

60 mm.

Fig. 127 – SKULL OF *Ursus americanus* (ROM 18896 ♂)

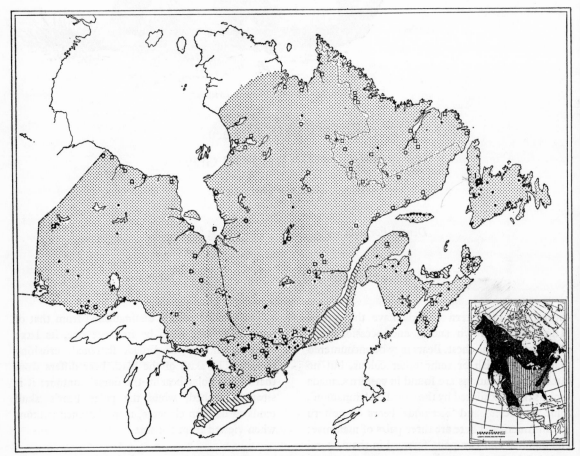

Map 59 – DISTRIBUTION OF THE BLACK BEAR – *Ursus americanus* – AND (1) TYPE LOCALITY OF *U. a. hamiltoni* Cameron

tail 95–125 (3–5 in.); hind foot 200–280 (8–10 in.); ear from notch 125–150 (5–6 in.). Skull: length 250–335, width 150–225. Weight 200–600 (average 300) lb., with females averaging about ten per cent smaller than males.

DISTRIBUTION AND VARIATION The black bear ranges over almost all of eastern Canada except the treeless tundra. However, it has been virtually extirpated from densely settled and agricultural areas.

The entire mainland population is regarded as a single geographic race, *Ursus americanus americanus*. The population occurring on Newfoundland has recently been described as a distinct race, *U. a. hamiltoni*, differing primarily from *U. a. americanus* in having a more highly arched dorsal contour of the skull and a relatively shorter rostrum.

HABITAT Substantial wooded areas.

HABITS The black bear is perhaps more omnivorous than any other native mammal with the possible exception of man. Its diet includes carrion of all types and levels of decay; berries and other fruit; grass and other vegetation such as buds and leaves; fish; small mammals, including farm livestock; and birds, frogs, and insects and their larvae. It is frequently accused of preying on big-game species, including both deer and moose. Undoubtedly some black bears become 'killers' of big game, particularly deer fawns and moose calves, but much of the so-called evidence of their taste for big game is based on 'signs' resulting from their having eaten such species as carrion.

Breeding is thought to begin when the females are three years old; mating takes place in June or July. Apparently there is a delayed implantation, as the fertilized ova show very little development until about December. The young are usually born in late January or February after an estimated 200–225 days' gestation.

At birth the young measure about six to eight inches and weigh only about seven to twelve ounces. Bears have the smallest young in relation to the weight of the mother of any placental mammal and is exceeded in this only by the marsupials.

The mother is usually denned up for an extended sleep during the birth of the young. The newborn have a thin coat of black hair and their eyes are closed. Twins occur most frequently, although one cub or triplets are fairly common (quadruplets are relatively rare). The eyes are opened at about twenty-five to forty days. The young leave the den with the mother in late March or April, at which time they weigh about five or six pounds and are about two months old. They begin feeding on various foods but continue to nurse for several weeks. At one year of age a weight of about sixty (forty to seventy-five) pounds is attained; at two years, 110 (90 to 150); at three years, 160 (125–200); at four years, 200 (175–250); at five years, 250 (225–300) pounds. The full adult dentition is not aquired until the end of the second year. Young cubs are agile climbers and scurry up trees at the approach of danger. As they reach adult size they seldom, if ever, climb. Full maximum size is not attained until about six years of age. Females are thought to breed only every other year. The normal life-span is estimated at ten to fifteen years, with captive animals living as long as twenty-four years.

With the approach of winter, the black bear takes on a thick layer of fat, and when the weather becomes cold it dens up for a deep sleep that differs from true hibernation in that the body temperature remains at a high level. Respiration drops to four or five times per minute but the animal remains conscious and is easily aroused if disturbed. The den site varies from quite sheltered crevices under stumps, logs or rocks to fairly exposed sites where only a bit of brush may be pulled over the sleeping animal. During this prolonged period of inactivity the bear loses little weight; it is only after it awakens and starts searching for the normally scant supply of food available in early spring that there is a marked loss of weight.

Black bears tend to be solitary and remain in a fairly well-defined territory that is thought to be marked with 'bear-claw trees', showing the claw marks made by bears standing upright on their hind feet; these trees are frequently seen in bear country. Black bears are often 'baited' by the use of decayed animal flesh, and they are a common sight at night around garbage dumps left within their range.

REMARKS In the early days of settlement in eastern Canada the skins of black bears were used as rugs and blankets, the meat for food, and the fat or grease for a variety of things, including food, fuel, and medical and even cosmetic purposes. More recently black bears have been reduced to objects of sport hunting; only occasionally are their skins used for rugs or their meat for food. In agricultural areas the black bear's depredations have been serious in isolated cases and owners of cottages have suffered some damage when they have left food behind during absences.

A more thorough study is required of the black bear's food habits to settle the controversy surrounding its effect on the big-game population.

Undoubtedly the black bear has been responsible for more injuries and deaths to humans than any other predator in North America, although most people show less fear of it than of the timber wolf. Perhaps this lack of instinctive fear, coupled with the totally unpredictable behaviour of bears, has contributed to a high percentage of needless human casualties.

Selected References

ALLEN, J. A., 1910.
ANDERSON, R. M., 1945a.
CAMERON, AUSTIN W., 1956.
MATSON, J. R., 1946, 1954.
TENER, J. S., 1955.
WHITLOCK, S. C., 1950.
WRIGHT, WILLIAM H., 1910.

Genus **THALARCTOS** Gray

Polar Bears – *Ours polaires*

Dental Formula $I \frac{3-3}{3-3}$ $C \frac{1-1}{1-1}$ $P \frac{4-4}{4-4}$ $M \frac{2-2}{3-3} = 42$

Thalarctos maritimus (Phipps) – Polar Bear – *Ours polaire*

This large white or yellowish-white bear, with its comparatively long neck and smallish head, is so distinctive that it requires little description. Extra-large males rival the weights of the world's largest carnivores, with a reported 1,600-pound maximum. The skull is more elongated and flattened in dorsal contour than that of the black bear, and the combined lengths of the first and second upper molar teeth is less than the width of the palate.

SIZE Total length 1,500–2,500 mm. (60–100 in.); tail 75–125 (3–5 in.); hind foot 250–400 (10–16 in.); ear from notch 100–150 (4–5 in.). Skull: length 300–460, width 185–265. Weight: males 600–1,600 (av. 800–900) lb., females 500–1,000 (av. 600–700).

DISTRIBUTION AND VARIATION As it is primarily a marine mammal, the polar bear normally does not range far inland and is frequently encountered far

Fig. 128 – POLAR BEAR – *Thalarctos maritimus*

out at sea. It is circumpolar in distribution and is found along all the northern coastal areas south to southern Labrador; there are sporadic occurrences on Newfoundland and on the north shore of the Gulf of St Lawrence. Polar bears occasionally wander far inland and have been taken in such places as Lake St John, Que., approximately 100 miles up the Saguenay River from the Gulf of St Lawrence. Sightings have also been made several miles south of Moosenee, Ont. Most authors have traditionally regarded all Alaskan and Canadian polar bears as belonging to the race *Thalarctos maritimus maritimus*, originally described from Spitzbergen. Two additional forms have been proposed: *T. labradorensis*, described from Okak, Labrador, and *T. m. ungavensis* from near Killinek, Ungava Bay, Que. In all probability these forms do not differ sufficiently to warrant recognition as valid races.

HABITAT Arctic coastlines and pack-ice.

HABITS Like the black bear, the polar bear has an extremely variable diet, although its choice is more limited. The bulk of its food comes from the sea, with seals ranking highest in the diet; wolves, stranded whales, any other available carrion, fish, birds and their eggs, marine invertebrates, and grass and other vegetation constitute the bulk of the rest of its diet. In order to obtain a sustaining supply of food, the polar bear is a ceaseless wanderer, moving about constantly in search of unwary prey or any tid-bit to satisfy the pangs of hunger. Its sense of smell and sight are exceptionally well developed. Though it was known to stalk and kill humans during the winter, prior to the introduction of firearms, more recently its actions have been shown to be highly unpredictable, with most animals exhibiting a healthy fear of humans.

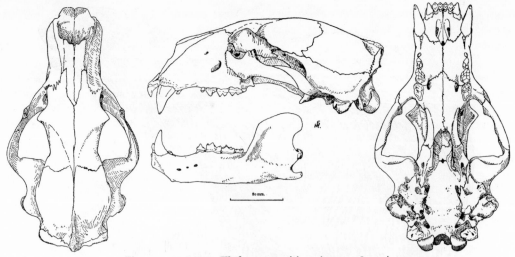

Fig. 129 – SKULL OF *Thalarctos maritimus* (ROM 33.8.23.9)

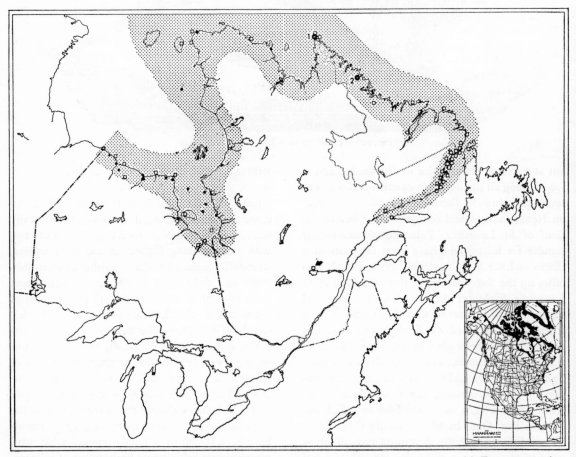

Map 60 – DISTRIBUTION OF THE POLAR BEAR – *Thalarctos maritimus* – AND TYPE LOCALITIES OF (1) *T. m. ungavensis* (Knottnerus-Meyer) [= *T. m. maritimus*]; (2) *T. labradorensis* (Knottnerus-Meyer) [= *T. m. maritimus*]

However, some polar bears, particularly older ones that may have become less facile in hunting seals, are potential 'killers'.

Breeding is thought to start at three or four years of age. Mating takes place in early spring, frequently out on ice floes. Females usually mate every other year. In November or December the pregnant females move inshore where they excavate a den in packed snow. Falling snow covers all but a small air hole and the expectant mother settles down for a long winter's sleep. After a gestation of about eight months, which probably involves some delayed implantation, two small cubs—weighing about two pounds or less and only ten inches long—are born in the ice-bound capsule den. This event takes place during the coldest and darkest part of the winter between December and March. Snuggling close to the mother for warmth and sustenance, the cubs soon become balls of fur and open their eyes at about six weeks. As the daylight returns to the north, the mother and her young become restless and break out of the den and begin their endless search for food along the broken ice or at seal blow-holes.

For such a large animal, the polar bear is extremely agile, and is capable of speeds of up to twenty-five miles per hour. It is a very strong swimmer and is frequently encountered in the open water far from land or ice. It is able to navigate on ice too thin to support a man by spreading its feet widely to distribute its weight more evenly or even by lying flat on the ice and dragging itself along. It occasionally stays on an ice-pack and drifts hundreds of miles away from the place of boarding.

Polar bears have been known to live for thirty-three years—perhaps almost twice the normal life-span in the Arctic. Considering that they are specially adapted for an Arctic environment, it is interesting that polar bears adjust so well to life in zoos.

REMARKS Polar-bear skins became such a popular trophy that conservation measures had to be taken to restrict uncontrolled killing, especially by white hunters. The flesh is quite palatable when it is properly prepared, although the liver has long been known to be unfit for human consumption—it has such a high concentration of vitamin A that it can cause serious illness. Several early explorers have survived a meal of polar-bear liver, but most have suffered from violent headaches, diarrhoea, peeling of the skin, and other ailments.

Though polar bears have become quite common in zoological gardens, they have been studied but little in the wild. Much of our knowledge of them dates from the nineteenth century. A thorough modern study is badly needed.

Selected References

DOUTT, J. K., 1940.
JACKSON, C. F., 1939c.
KNOTTNERUS-MEYER, THEODOR, 1908.
LEWIS, HARRISON and J. K. DOUTT, 1942.
SETON, ERNEST THOMPSON, 1926.

Family **PROCYONIDAE**

Raccoons – *Ratons*

This family is represented in eastern Canada by a single species, the raccoon, a name that derives from the Indian *aroughcun*. The dentition is generalized for an omnivorous diet. It lacks the specialized carnassials as in the *Canidae* but instead has low-crowned molars with rounded cusps (only two lower molars are present). The feet each have five toes and are plantigrade, but they are adapted for semi-arboreal activities.

Genus **PROCYON** Storr

Raccoons – *Ratons*

Dental Formula $I \frac{3-3}{3-3}$ $C \frac{1-1}{1-1}$ $P \frac{4-4}{4-4}$ $M \frac{2-2}{2-2} = 40$

Procyon lotor (Linnaeus) – Raccoon – *Raton laveur*

Its black mask and ringed tail make the raccoon easily identifiable. The fur is long and typically grizzled grey. However, there is a considerable variation in colour from almost black through various shades of brown. There are six mammae. The skull, in general size and shape, closely resembles that of a large mustelid, but it differs in having two upper molars instead of one. The low-crowned cheek teeth with rounded cusps that interlock when they occlude are unique among Canadian carnivores.

SIZE Total length 655–960 mm.; tail 200–275; hind foot 100–125; ear from notch 48–58. Skull: length 110–128, width 69–82. Weight 12–30 lb. Weights of up to 50 and 60 lb. have been reported in the United States.

DISTRIBUTION AND VARIATION Being primarily a southern species, the raccoon reaches its regular northern limit in central Ontario, southern Quebec, and the more southern portions of the Maritime Provinces. The nominate race, *Procyon lotor lotor*, occurs east of Lake Superior, while *P. l. hirtus*, a larger, darker form with a longer pelage that is usually suffused with ochraceous buff, is found west of Lake Superior. A series of recent records well north of the regular range suggests that there has been a general northward movement in the last few years, although a specimen was taken on the upper parts of the Winisk and Attawapiskat Rivers as early as 1904. The raccoon has been reported to be absent from Prince Edward Island, Cape Breton, and Newfoundland. About 1912, raccoons were released on Prince Edward Island and by 1953 a bounty was paid to reduce the population. Fur-return reports indicate that 701 pelts were marketed from Prince Edward Island in the period 1950–9, although in 1955, 1,655 animals were offered for bounty and even more were offered in 1956. While the evidence is not well documented, the raccoon seems to have followed a pattern of occurrence, disappearance, and reappearance in parts of eastern Canada, particu-

Fig. 130 – RACCOON – *Procyon lotor*

larly in the northern parts of Ontario and Quebec as well as in the Maritime Provinces, especially Nova Scotia.

HABITAT The raccoon is usually found in hard-wood areas that provide den sites, normally not far from lakes or streams.

HABITS Breeding is thought to start at about one year and takes place during winter (late January to early March). After a gestation period of sixty-three to sixty-five days, a litter is born of from two to seven (usually four) young, weighing some two or three ounces each. The den is usually in a hollow tree, although fallen logs, excavations under stumps and trees, rock crevices, and other sites are used. At birth the young have dark skin covered with yellowish-grey fur. The face mask is evident at ten days, the ringed tail at about nine-teen days, and at approximately this time the eyes

open (at eighteen to twenty-three days). Solid food is taken at about forty days (weight, $1\frac{1}{2}$ pounds), and the young raccoons begin to wander from the den at about fifty days (weight, two pounds), but they do not travel extensively until they are about ten weeks old. The family group breaks up in the fall and then the young become independent. Captive animals have lived fourteen years, although the average life-span in the wild is probably about half that age.

Primarily nocturnal, the raccoon usually hunts for its food along streams or shore lines, although it frequently ventures inland, especially to nearby cornfields where the corn is in the milk or roasting stage. (Its forays for corn-on-the-cob vex farmers and gardeners operating within the territory of this 'masked bandit'.) The remainder of the diet is highly variable and includes fruit, nuts, insects, cray fish, clams, frogs, birds' eggs, and any small mammal or bird the raccoon happens to catch.

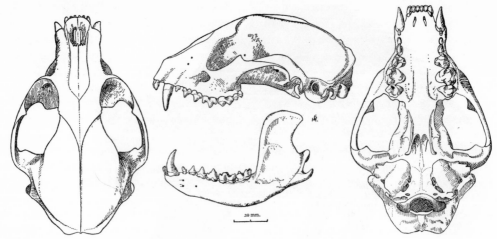

Fig. 131 – SKULL OF *Procyon lotor* (ROM 25570 ♂)

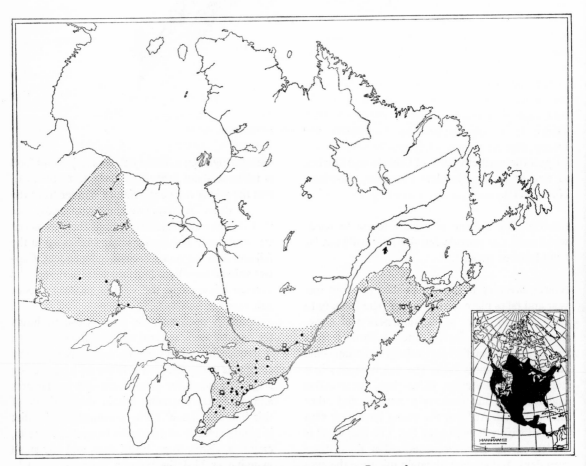

Map 61 – DISTRIBUTION OF THE RACCOON – *Procyon lotor*

Traditionally the raccoon is supposed to wash its food before eating (the species name, *lotor*, comes from the Latin *lutoris*, a washer). However, in practice it fails to live up to such high standards of sanitation. It usually searches for food by feeling under water or beneath debris with its forepaws; much of its food is first picked up with its forepaws and then transferred to its mouth.

Although it is a strong swimmer, the raccoon rarely swims for any distance. It is an agile climber. It has developed a high degree of manual dexterity and a keen sense of touch that allows it to use its forepaws in a manner approaching that of the primates. It has a habit of examining a strange object by picking it up and manipulating it with the forepaws as if to identify it by the sense of touch.

The raccoon makes a variety of vocal sounds, including a high shrill almost like a whistle, a bark, a growl, a snarl, a whine, and several guttural sounds.

Although it is active in all months of the year, the raccoon does not venture forth in extremely cold weather. Instead it becomes torpid and may remain in a state approaching hibernation for several days at a time. Occasionally several raccoons den up together.

REMARKS Raccoons make interesting pets when they are young, but as they mature they almost invariably become rather destructive and unmanageable. In the wild the raccoon adapts well to close association with man and frequently makes nightly forays to the garbage cans of residents in the heart of a metropolitan area.

While raccoon flesh is edible, it must be carefully prepared to be truly palatable. Most of the fat must be removed, as well as the glands under the legs and along the spine to remove a strong, objectionable flavour. The meat should then be parboiled before final cooking.

Raccoon trapping is carried out in all provinces of eastern Canada except Newfoundland. Most of Canada's pelts come from the east, although the total production is not great and the value is not large (see Table 5).

Selected References

CAMERON, AUSTIN W., 1959.

COLE, L. W., 1912.

GILES, LEROY W., 1940.

GOLDMAN, EDWARD A., 1950.

HAMILTON, WILLIAM J., JR., 1936a.

RAND, A. L., 1943.

SANDERSON, GLEN C., 1950, 1951a, 1951b, 1961.

STAINS, HOWARD J., 1956.

STUEWER, FREDERICK W., 1942, 1943a, 1943b.

WHITNEY, LEON F. and ACIL B. UNDERWOOD, 1952.

Table 5

Production of Raccoon Pelts in Eastern Canada, 1950–60

	ALL CANADA	EASTERN CANADA	ONTARIO	QUEBEC	NEW BRUNSWICK	NOVA SCOTIA	PRINCE EDWARD I.	NEW-FOUNDLAND
TOTAL PELTS 1950–60	296,232	292,875	243,411	24,726	7,100	16,937	*701	—
Average Annual Production	29,623	29,288	24,341	2,473	710	1,694	78	
Minimum Annual Production	14,081 (1958–9)	13,820 (1958–9)	10,450 (1958–9)	1,603 (1958–9)	359 (1950–1)	1,247 (1958–9)	4 (1958–9)	
Maximum Annual Production	36,899 (1953–4)	36,817 (1953–4)	31,346 (1955–6)	3,370 (1953–4)	1,046 (1951–2)	2,194 (1950–1)	129 (1952–3 & 1955–6)	
TOTAL VALUE 1950–60	$557,419	$548,757	$434,368	$61,130	$9,026	$43,203	$1,030	
Average Annual Value	$55,742	$51,615	$40,177	$6,113	$903	$4,320	$114	
Minimum Annual Value	$26,698 (1958–9)	$23,774 (1958–9)	$14,108 (1958–9)	$4,008 (1958–9)	$359 (1950–1)	$2,082 (1952–3)	$4 (1958–9)	
Maximum Annual Value	$81,698 (1955–6)	$81,326 (1955–6)	$68,961 (1955–6)	$10,110 (1953–4)	$1,569 (1951–2)	$6,387 (1951–2)	$259 (1950–1)	
Average Value per Pelt	$1.88	$1.87	$1.78	$2.47	$1.27	$2.55	$1.47	
Minimum Average Value per Pelt	$1.39 (1957–8)	$1.39 (1957–8)	$1.30 (1957–8)	$2.00 (1958–9)	$0.75 (1956–8)	$1.00 (1952–3)	$0.84 (1957–8)	
Maximum Average Value per Pelt	$2.49 (1950–1)	$2.51 (1950–1)	$2.55 (1950–1)	$3.00 (1953–5)	$2.50 (1958–9)	$3.50 (1954–5 & 1958–9)	$2.27 (1950–1)	

* Nine years only, 1950–9.

Family MUSTELIDAE

The family *Mustelidae*—commonly referred to as musk carriers or as weasel-like mammals—demonstrates adaptive variation in a rather striking manner. The members of this family vary in size from the least weasel (the smallest carnivore in the world) up to the wolverine; the sea otter, *Enhydra*, in the North Pacific; and the giant otter, *Pteronura*, of South America. The body is usually elongate; the legs are relatively short; and there are five well-developed toes on each foot. The carnassial teeth are well developed and the molar teeth are reduced to one on each side above and two on each side below. The transverse diameter of the single upper molars behind the carnassial is usually as great or greater than the longitudinal diameter. The skull and the auditory bullae are flattened or elongated. Six genera and ten species (plus one now extinct) are native to eastern Canada, including five species of *Mustela* (including the extinct sea mink) and two of *Martes*. The domesticated ferret, *Mustela putorius*, has been imported from Europe for hunting, although its use is now illegal in most areas.

This family contains examples of marked differences in size between sexes.

KEY TO THE EASTERN-CANADIAN GENERA OF *Mustelidae*

1 Premolars four above and four below.

  2 Weight more than 15 lb.; tail relatively short (less than 25 per cent of total length); a pair of light-coloured stripes extending from the upper shoulder region along the sides and joining across the rump; skull 130 mm. or more in length and more than 85 mm. wide.   GULO p. 260

  2' Weight less than 15 lb.; tail relatively long (more than 25 per cent of total length); no stripes present; skull 130 mm. or less in length and less than 85 mm. wide.   MARTES p. 252

1' Premolars fewer than four above and four below.

  3 Premolars four above and three below; total length 900 mm. or more; legs relatively short; tail long and thickest at base and tapering to a point; fur short and dense; colour uniformly dark brown; body modified for aquatic existence; feet with webbed toes.   LUTRA p. 271

  3' Premolars three above and three below; total length less than 900 mm.: 4

    4 Weight 14 lb. or more; tail relatively short; body heavy, wide, and flattened; front claws greatly enlarged for digging; colour yellowish grey with median white stripe extending from the nose over the shoulder; skull more than 100 mm. long and 60 mm. wide.   TAXIDEA p. 263

    4' Weight 14 lb. or less; front claws not greatly elongated for digging; colour not yellowish grey; skull less than 100 mm. long and 60 mm. wide: 5

      5 Weight more than 4 lb.; colour black with a pair of white stripes extending along the back to the tail; skull relatively deep with a pronounced hump at the sinous or frontal region; relatively long and heavy upper molars (approaching a square).   MEPHITIS p. 267

      5' Weight less than 4 lb.; colour brown or white or brown above and whitish below; body elongate, cylindrical, and almost the same diameter as the head; skull relatively shallow with a relatively flat dorsal contour; upper molars relatively narrow and 'dumb-bell'-shaped.   MUSTELA p. 232

Genus **MUSTELA** Linnaeus

Weasels, Ferrets, and Minks – *Belettes, Putois, et Visons*

Dental Formula $\quad$ I $\frac{3-3}{3-3}$ $\quad$ C $\frac{1-1}{1-1}$ $\quad$ P $\frac{3-3}{3-3}$ $\quad$ M $\frac{1-1}{2-2}$ = 34

KEY TO THE EASTERN-CANADIAN SPECIES OF *Mustela*

1 Total length less than 210 mm.; tail less than 40 mm.; skull length less than 33 mm.; mastoid width usually greater than width of brain case; few or no black hairs in tail tip. $\qquad$ MUSTELA RIXOSA p. 241

1′ Total length greater than 210 mm.; tail more than 40 mm.; skull length greater than 33 mm.: 2

2 Skull length less than 55 mm.; skull width less than 30 mm.; tail-tip black; remainder of pelage all white in winter and brown above and white below in summer: 3

3 Tail usually less than 42 per cent of head and body length (usually 30 to 42); insides of hind feet whitish in summer pelage; rostrum (viewed from above and below) relatively short and tapering continuously from the zygoma; postorbital processes blunt and weakly developed, with little postorbital constriction in adults; auditory bullae flattened anteriorly; post-glenoid length usually more than 48 per cent of condylobasal length in males and 50 per cent or more in females. $\qquad$ MUSTELA ERMINEA p. 233

3′ Tail usually more than 42 per cent of head and body length (usually 43 to 55); inside of hind feet brownish in summer pelage; rostrum (viewed from above or below) relatively long with nearly parallel sides; postorbital processes sharp and more strongly developed with more distinct postorbital constriction (in adults); auditory bullae more bulbous anteriorly; post-glenoid length 48 per cent or less of condylobasal length in males and less than 50 per cent in females. $\qquad$ MUSTELA FRENATA p. 239

2′ Skull length more than 55 mm.; skull width more than 30 mm.; pelage not white in winter: 4*

4 Pelage uniformly dark brown; skull relatively long with long brain case and auditory bullae relatively flat and appressed on outer margins. $\qquad$ MUSTELA VISON p. 245

4′ Pelage variable—frequently pale yellowish brown or whitish with dark about the eyes, feet, and tail tip, and with darker-tipped hairs interspersed on other parts of the body; ears fringed with white; skull relatively short and broad with short brain case and well-rounded auditory bullae (domestic introductions only). $\qquad$ MUSTELA PUTORIUS p. 251

*See also *Mustela macrodon*, the extinct sea mink, p. 250.

Mustela erminea Linnaeus – Ermine – *Hermine*

The status of this species, which provides the ermine of royal robes, suffers somewhat when it is referred to as the 'common' or short-tailed weasel of eastern Canada. This little bundle of curiosity and fury has a long slender body, a long neck, and a relatively small head. The legs are relatively short and the tail varies from one-quarter to one-third of the total length and has a black tip. In summer the colour is uniformly dark brown above and along the outsides of the legs. The underparts are white, pale yellowish white, or sometimes straw-coloured to quite yellowish. This whitish (or yellowish) colour extends down the inside of the hind legs and feet. In winter the pelage becomes all white (sometimes stained with yellowish) except for the black tail-tip.

The skull is relatively flattened and is long and narrow. When the sex is known, the weasel skull can usually be identified by size alone; however, there is a small degree of overlap in size between *Mustela erminea* and *M. frenata*. The male of *M. frminea* is about the same size as the female of *M. reenata*, the long-tailed weasel. *M. erminea* adults are always larger than *M. rixosa* adults. The skull of the ermine can usually be distinguished from that of *M. frenata* by the shape of the short rostrum which tapers continuously from the zygomatic processes, by relatively blunt rather than sharp-pointed postorbital processes, and by the shape of the auditory bullae which are usually more flattened anteriorly. The post-glenoid length in *M. erminea* males is usually more than forty-eight per cent of the condylobasal length and fifty per cent or more in females. An additional useful characteristic is the length from the infraorbital foramen to the posterior edge of the anterior insertion of the zygoma compared with the distance from the glenoid fossa to the anterior extension of the auditory bullae. The former represents an average of about fifty per cent in *M. erminea* (males 39 to 66; females 33 to 52), whereas in *M. frenata* the proportion is about seventy-five per cent (males 71 to 116; females 66 to 79).

SIZE Total length: males 270–323 mm.; females 220–262; tail: males 70–100, females 45–75; hind foot: males 33–47, females 25–35; ear from notch 14–22. Skull length: males 38–47, females 34–38; skull width: males 19–24, females 16.5–19.0. Weight: males 80–182 gr., females 45–75.

DISTRIBUTION AND VARIATION The ermine occupies the whole of eastern Canada. Anticosti Island is perhaps the largest discrete land area for which no records of occurrence have been found. The southernmost area, from about the level of Lake Nipigon, Ont., to Lake St John, Que., and southward, is populated by *M. e. cicognanii*, while the remainder of eastern Canada is occupied by the *M. e. richardsonii* which is larger and also differs in that the least width of colour of the underparts averages about two-fifths of the greatest width of colour of the upper parts instead of less than one-third as in *M. e. cicognanii*. West of Lake Superior in the Fort Frances–Lake-of-the-Woods area, *M. e. bangsi* is thought to enter Ontario from Minnesota or Manitoba. Similar to *M. e. cicognanii* in the colour-pattern ratio, *M. e. bangsi* has a relatively large hind foot and a slightly larger skull.

HABITAT Woodlands constitute the primary home of the ermine, although it is able to subsist in a wide variety of situations that provide food and cover.

HABITS It is thought that male ermine start to breed at about one year, while some females breed during their first summer. Mating takes place in the early summer, usually in July or August. However, there is a delayed implantation, and most of the embryonic and foetal development takes place in the last month of an approximately eight- or nine-month gestation period. Four to seven constitute the average litter size, but as many as thirteen have been recorded. The tiny young (weight about two grams each) are born in the spring and are almost naked except for a mane

Fig. 132 – ERMINE – *Mustela erminea*
Top – Female in summer pelage; *Bottom* – Male in winter pelage

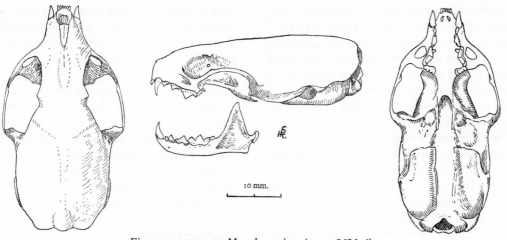

Fig. 133 – SKULL OF *Mustela erminea* (ROM 18686 ♂)

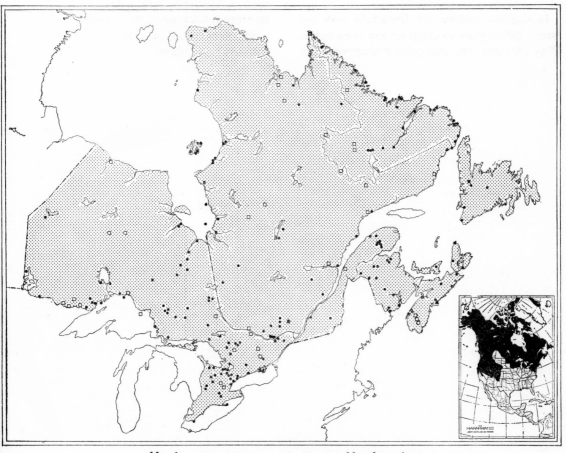

Map 62 – DISTRIBUTION OF THE ERMINE – *Mustela erminea*

of fine white hair on the neck and a few hairs along the back. Within two weeks the brown-and-white colour pattern is apparent. At about one month the eyes are opened and a week or so later the young are weaned. By this time the young males are as large or larger than the mother.

The young are quite playful and vocalize with squeals, squeaks, and purrs. The adults hiss and bark or scream and chatter.

Ermine are persistent hunters and appear fearless and bloodthirsty, especially after a kill. Mice constitute the bulk of the diet, although rabbits, birds, amphibians, and invertebrates are also eaten. Occasional raids on chicken pens have earned for ermine a notorious reputation. Although primarily terrestrial, they climb reasonably well, but they usually avoid heights of more than ten or fifteen feet.

Ermine are curious and frequently peer out from a hiding-place to check on any disturbance. They are quite agile and quickly disappear from sight when they are near cover. They bound along with a curious 'serpentine' gait when travelling out in the open. While primarily nocturnal, they are frequently active during the day.

REMARKS Eastern Canada accounts for less than a quarter of the total Canadian production of ermine pelts (see Table 6). The annual catch of ermine is reasonably stable compared with that of most fur-bearers, although there has been a wide fluctuation in prices. The ermine plays only a minor role in the fur trade in spite of its association with luxury and royalty.

Selected References
ALDOUS, SHALER E. and J. MANWEILER, 1942.
ANDERSON, R. M., 1946.
HALL, E. RAYMOND, 1945, 1951a.
HAMILTON, WILLIAM J., JR., 1933b.
RUST, CHARLES CHAPIN, 1962.
WRIGHT, P. L., 1942a.

Table 6

Production of Ermine Pelts in Eastern Canada, 1950-60

	ALL CANADA	EASTERN CANADA	ONTARIO	QUEBEC	NEW BRUNSWICK	NOVA SCOTIA	PRINCE EDWARD I.	NEW-FOUNDLAND
TOTAL PELTS 1950-60	3,378,143	769,751	319,262	344,154	37,714	40,637	*520	**27,464
Average Annual Production	337,814	76,975	31,926	34,415	3,771	4,064	74	3,051
Minimum Annual Production	255,139 (1958-9)	49,384 (1958-9)	19,997 (1958-9)	22,433 (1955-6)	2,065 (1958-9)	1,302 (1958-9)	15 (1955-6)	1,362 (1955-6)
Maximum Annual Production	536,344 (1952-3)	106,084 (1950-1)	49,180 (1950-1)	47,973 (1950-1)	6,382 (1955-6)	7,023 (1951-2)	162 (1950-1)	6,380 (1951-2)
TOTAL VALUE 1950-60	$4,524,415	$758,861	$308,391	$346,838	$27,817	$50,145	$425	$19,245
Average Annual Value	$452,441	$75,886	$30,839	$34,684	$2,782	$5,015	$60	$2,138
Minimum Annual Value	$246,982 (1958-9)	$28,071 (1958-9)	$11,198 (1958-9)	$14,314 (1958-9)	$826 (1958-9)	$651 (1958-9)	$8 (1955-6)	$681 (1955-6)
Maximum Annual Value	$805,770 (1950-1)	$189,277 (1950-1)	$86,557 (1950-1)	$83,428 (1950-1)	$4,786 (1955-6)	$16,266 (1950-1)	$128 (1950-1)	$6,699 (1951-2)
Average Value per Pelt	$1.34	$0.98	$0.96	$1.00	$0.73	$1.23	$0.82	$0.70
Minimum Average Value per Pelt	$0.95 (1953-4)	$0.56 (1958-9)	$0.56 (1957-9)	$0.60 (1957-60)	$0.35 (1959-60)	$0.50 (1958-9)	$0.43 (1955-6)	$0.50 (1955-60)
Maximum Average Value per Pelt	$2.14 (1950-1)	$1.79 (1950-1)	$1.76 (1950-1)	$1.75 (1950-1)	$1.35 (1950-1)	$2.35 (1950-1)	$1.44 (1950-1)	$1.05 (1951-2)

* Seven years only, 1950-6 and 1957-8.   ** Nine years only, 1951-60.

Fig. 134 – LONG-TAILED WEASEL – *Mustela frenata*

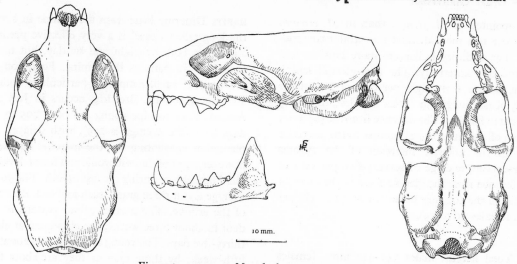

Fig. 135 – SKULL OF *Mustela frenata* (ROM 17225 ♂)

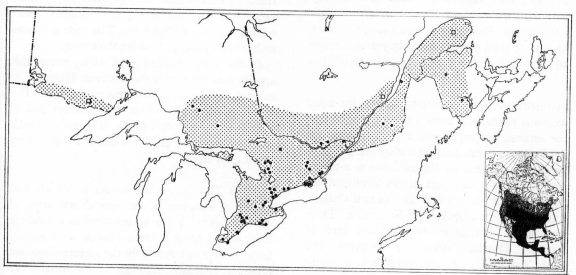

Map 63 – DISTRIBUTION OF THE LONG-TAILED WEASEL – *Mustela frenata*

Mustela frenata Lichtenstein – Long-tailed Weasel – *Belette à longue queue*

Larger than the ermine, the long-tailed weasel is nearer the size of the gray squirrel. Also, the tail is relatively longer than the tail of the ermine, usually averaging more than forty-two per cent of the length of the head and body and more than a third of the total length. In general this weasel superficially resembles the ermine in coloration. However, in summer pelage the white usually does not continue onto the foot or toes. There are eight mammae, four inguinal and four abdominal.

The skull is usually larger than that of *Mustela erminea* of the same sex, although there is a small degree of overlap in size. The skull of *M. frenata* is more angular, and the sides of the rostrum are more parallel when viewed from above. The post-orbital processes are better developed and more sharp-pointed in *M. frenata* than in *M. erminea* and there is a more distinct postorbital constriction. The auditory bullae are more bulbous and are rounded anteriorly. The post-glenoid length of the skull is forty-eight per cent or less of the condylobasal length in males and less than fifty per cent in females. The distance from the posterior margin of the infraorbital process to the posterior edge of the anterior insertion of the zygoma represents an average of seventy-five per cent of the distance from the glenoid fossa to the anterior portion of the auditory bullae (males 71 to 116 per cent, females 66 to 79).

SIZE Total length: males 345–442 mm., females 280–340; tail: males 106–160, females 80–123; hind foot: males 36–51, females 29–40; ear from notch 15–23. Skull length: males 44–51, females 37.5–43.5; skull width: males 23.5–28.2, females 19–23. Weight: males 100–267 gr., females 85–130.

DISTRIBUTION AND VARIATION The long-tailed weasel is primarily a more southern species than the ermine, ranging north from northern and northwestern South America through almost all of central America and the United States to southern Canada. In the east part of the continent the northern limit extends only into central Ontario, southern Quebec, and New Brunswick. There seem to be no valid records west and north of Sudbury District (Metagama, Chapleau, and Pader Township), Ont. *Mustela frenata noveboracensis* is the race found throughout most of eastern Canada, although the easternmost specimens from Quebec and New Brunswick may represent *M. f. occisor* described from Maine, which supposedly averages larger in size and which has a relatively longer tail and a relatively wider skull than *M. f. noveboracensis*.

HABITAT Like the ermine, the long-tailed weasel occupies forests, open country, and a wide variety of other situations; it seldom lives very far from water, however.

HABITS Differing little from the ermine in habits, the long-tailed weasel is a very effective predator and hunts both by night and by day, but not as commonly in pairs as the ermine. Food consists primarily of small mammals, particularly rodents and young rabbits. Breeding occurs in July and August. Four to nine young are born 205 to 337 days later (the average is 279), with delayed implantation accounting for the extreme variation; however, most of the embryonic and foetal development takes place during the last month. The young average about three grams each and lack the mane of the ermine. The normal colour pattern is evident in about three weeks; the eyes open at about thirty-five days. The young are weaned in about the fifth week; by three months they are about two-thirds of their mature size. Females may become sexually mature during the first summer, males when they are a full year old. The male is known to hunt and bring in food for the young.

In the more southern parts of its range, this species does not turn white in winter. However, in eastern Canada it almost invariably does. The moult usually starts about mid-October and is completed by mid-November. The spring moult usually starts early in March and is completed by about early April.

REMARKS The long-tailed weasel is an efficient hunter of rodents. In the agricultural areas of eastern Canada it can be regarded as a valuable asset except when it creates havoc in a poultry flock. It does not appear in the eastern-Canadian fur-trade statistics, although a few weasels are undoubtedly included as ermine.

Selected References
ANDERSON, R. M., 1945b.
BROWN, N. R., 1948.
HALL, E. R., 1951a.
HAMILTON, W. J., JR., 1933b.
PEARCE, JOHN, 1937.
POLDERBOER, EMMET B., LEE W. KUHN, and GEORGE O. HENDRICKSON, 1941.
WRIGHT, PHILIP L., 1942a, 1942b, 1947, 1948a, 1948b, 1950.

Plate I – SOME EASTERN-CANADIAN BATS

1 HOARY BAT – *Lasiurus cinereus*

2 SILVER-HAIRED BAT – *Lasionycteris noctivagans*

3 LITTLE BROWN BAT – *Myotis lucifugus*

4 BIG BROWN BAT – *Eptesicus fuscus*

5 RED BAT – *Lasiurus borealis*

6 EASTERN PIPISTRELLE – *Pipistrellus subflavus*

Plate II – SOME EASTERN-CANADIAN *Sciuridae*

1 EASTERN CHIPMUNK – *Tamias striatus*

2 RED SQUIRREL – *Tamiasciurus hudsonicus*: Winter

3 WESTERN CHIPMUNK – *Eutamias minimus*

4 RED SQUIRREL: Summer

5 FRANKLIN GROUND SQUIRREL – *Citellus franklinii*

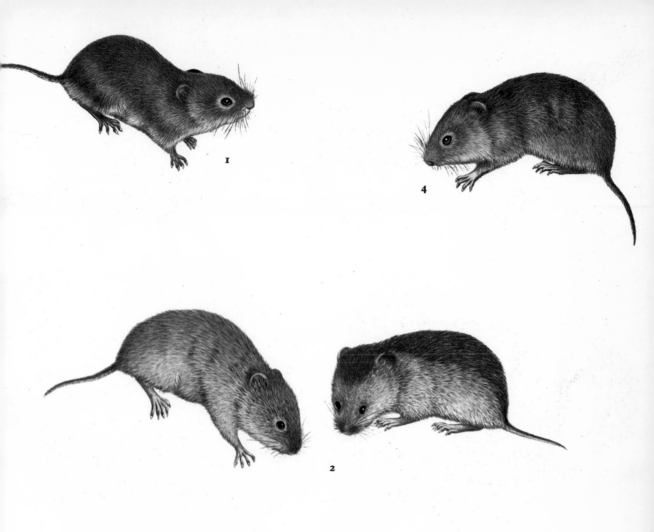

K. S. Pashny

Plate III – SOME EASTERN-CANADIAN MICROTINE RODENTS

1 MEADOW VOLE – *Microtus pennsylvanicus*

2 RED-BACKED MOUSE – *Clethrionomys gapperi* (two colour phases)

3 EASTERN PHENACOMYS – *Phenacomys ungava*

4 ROCK VOLE – *Microtus chrotorrhinus*

5 NORTHERN LEMMING MOUSE – *Synaptomys borealis*

Plate IV – EASTERN-CANADIAN FOXES

I ARCTIC FOX – *Alopex lagopus*
a *Blue colour phase: Winter*
b *White colour phase: Winter*
c *Blue colour phase: Summer*
d *White colour phase: Summer*

2 GRAY FOX – *Urocyon cinereoargenteus*
3 RED FOX – *Vulpes vulpes*
a *Silver colour phase*
b *Cross colour phase*
c *Red colour phase*

Plate v – SOME EASTERN-CANADIAN *Mustelidae*

I ERMINE – *Mustela erminea*
a *Male in winter*
b *Female in summer*

2 MARTEN – *Martes americana*
a *Normal colour phase*
b *Orange colour phase*
3 MINK – *Mustela vison*
4 FISHER – *Martes pennanti*

Plate VI – CANADA LYNX AND BOBCAT

BOBCAT – *Lynx rufus*

CANADA LYNX – *Lynx canadensis*

Plate VII – MOOSE – *Alces alces*

Plate VIII – CARIBOU – Rangifer tarandus

Fig. 136 – LEAST WEASEL – *Mustela rixosa*

Mustela rixosa (Bangs) – Least Weasel – *Petite belette*

The least weasel is the smallest carnivore in the world. It is also the rarest mammal in eastern Canada next to the wolverine, although it is more common to the west and even to the south. This rarity may be more apparent then real since least weasels may be taken by ermine trappers who discard them as worthless 'younguns' (immature) and caught specimens may not be properly identified in the fur trade. In addition to its small size, a short tail without a well-defined black tip quickly identifies this species. A least weasel pelt (even with the tail-tip missing) can be identified under ultra-violet light since its fur will fluoresce to produce a vivid lavender colour (the fur of other weasels, *M. erminea* and *M. frenata*, will remain a dull brown colour).

The summer pelage is a fairly dark brown above

M.E.C.—18

and whitish below. A few scattered black hairs may be present in the tip of the tail. In winter the least weasel is usually entirely white except for a few black hairs in the tail-tip of some animals. The winter pelage is usually acquired about mid-November, although some individuals may not have it until January or February; the summer pelage is acquired about March or April. There are only six mammae, two abdominal and four inguinal.

The skull is smaller than that of the other weasels and is more smoothly rounded in adults. The mastoid width is equal or greater than the greatest width of the brain case, whereas young specimens of similar size in other species have a relatively narrower mastoid width.

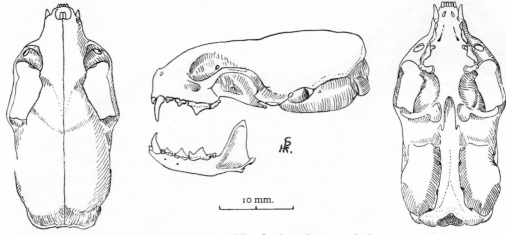

Fig. 137 – SKULL OF *Mustela rixosa* (ROM 17198 ♂)

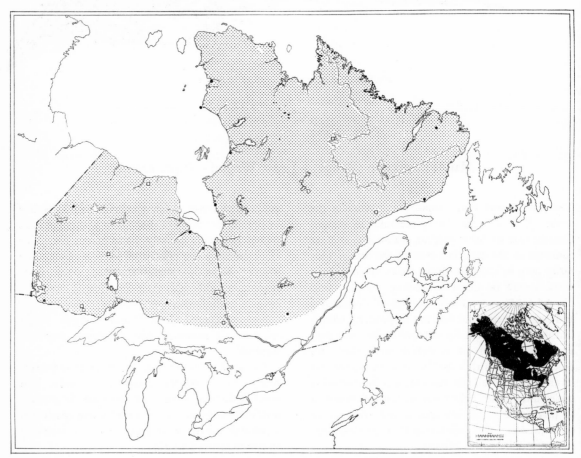

Map 64 – DISTRIBUTION OF THE LEAST WEASEL – *Mustela rixosa*

SIZE Total length: males 189–206 mm., females 172–188; tail: males 30–38, females 23–33; hind foot: males 21–23, females 19–21; ear from notch 10–15. Skull length: males 31.5–32.8, females 30.2–30.5; skull width: males 15.8–17.5, females 14.7–15.9. Weight: males 40–50 gr., females 38–49.

DISTRIBUTION AND VARIATION Records of the least weasel *Mustela rixosa rixosa* are restricted to the area north of the St Lawrence River, with the southernmost records being in Ste Véronique, Labelle Co., Que.; Heaslips, Timiskaming District; and Tatnall, near Oba, Algoma District, Ont. This species has apparently spread eastwards both north and south of the Great Lakes but has not closed the gap to the east.

HABITAT The least weasel is so rare in eastern Canada that its preferred habitat cannot be defined accurately for this area. In Wisconsin it is thought to prefer marshes with a water level at or near the surface during most of the year, although it has been found in meadows, grassy fields, and occasionally around buildings, woodpiles, and brush heaps.

HABITS Unlike the young of the ermine and the long-tailed weasel, the young of the least weasel are born almost every month of the year in its range to the south and to the west. The litter size varies from three to six (one to ten have been reported), with an average of five. More precise breeding data are needed. The dens of this weasel's victim mice are commonly appropriated, and the former occupants' fur is used to line it for winter comfort. Studies to date indicate that small mammals, particularly mice, constitute the main diet, with the possibility that small amounts of insects and other animal matter make up the balance. Captive animals eat thirty per cent of their body weight per day.

REMARKS The least weasel is much too rare to be of any economic importance in eastern Canada. Any new information on this species in this area is much needed.

Selected References

BEER, JAMES R., 1950.

HALL, E. R., 1951a.

LATHAM, ROBERT M., 1953.

POLDERBOER, EMMET B., 1942, 1948.

SNYDER, L. L., 1935.

SWANSON, GUSTAV and P. O. FRYKLUND, 1935.

Fig. 138 – MINK – *Mustela vison*

Mustela vison Schreber – Mink – *Vison*

The mink is a large, dark-coloured weasel. Its pelage is deep brown except for a whitish chin spot, an occasional white marking on the chest, and a tail tip that darkens almost to black. Unlike the true weasel the mink does not change colour in winter. The tail is about half as long as the head and body and is more bushy than the weasel's. As in other mustelids, the musk glands produce a characteristic pungent odour. There are six mammae, two abdominal and four inguinal.

The skull is readily distinguished from that of other *Mustela* by the shape of the auditory bullae which are flattened and extend laterally to form a trapezoidal outline. It is larger than that of the weasel and relatively longer and narrower than that of the domesticated ferret, *Mustela putorius*. (See also the sea mink, *M. macrodon*, p. 250.)

SIZE Total length: males 520–620 mm., females 420–520; tail: males 180–210, females 130–180; hind foot: males 56–68, females 54–60; ear from notch 15–25. Skull length: males 58–70, females 58–68; skull width: males 33–43, females 31–42. Weight: males 565–1,250 gr., females 500–950.

DISTRIBUTION AND VARIATION The mink is found throughout all of eastern Canada except the northern section of the Ungava peninsula. It was apparently not native to Newfoundland, although it has become established there as a result of animals' escaping from fur farms on the island that were first established about 1937. Mink were released on Anticosti Island in the Gulf of St Lawrence in 1912, but by 1936 they were thought to be quite rare, if not extinct, and no subsequent records of their presence on Anticosti are available. Three races are recognized: *M. v. vison* occurring throughout most of the eastern area; *M. v. lowii*, described from Mistassini Lake (occurring from the east coast of James Bay north to Labrador) as a smaller form with a smaller skull that has a lower, more flattened, and proportionally narrower brain case; and *M. v. lacustris*, the so-called Keewatin

mink, originally described from the Echimanish River in Manitoba as a larger dark race with a larger skull than that of *M. v. vison*, more angular, widely flaring zygomatic arches, and with large and rather flat auditory bullae. *M. v. lacustris* occurs in the western portion of Ontario roughly west of a line joining the north shore of Lake Superior and the west shore of James Bay. A detailed study of variations within the species is much needed.

HABITAT This is a water-loving species—mink seldom live very far from lakes, streams, marshes, or the seashore. They frequently follow stream valleys right into the heart of metropolitan areas. Den sites are selected in a wide variety of situations, including burrows in stream banks, muskrat or beaver houses, rock crevices, and cavities in stumps, logs, or standing trees.

HABITS Basically a weasel that has become adapted for an aquatic existence, the mink maintains a position intermediate between other members of the genus *Mustela*, which are terrestrial, and the otter (genus *Lutra*) which is more highly specialized for an aquatic existence. It is an excellent swimmer and is capable of seeking its food both by land and by water. Mink can dive to depths of fifteen to eighteen feet and can swim underwater for distances of up to 100 feet. Small aquatic animals such as frogs, fish, cray-fish and other invertebrates, snakes, birds, small mammals up to the size of muskrats, and rabbits make up the chief items of diet.

Although primarily nocturnal, mink can be seen moving about during the day fairly frequently. They sometimes appear quite curious and fearless as they peer out from behind cover at a human intruder, suddenly disappearing but just as suddenly reappearing at another vantage point to watch developments. Their vocalizations include piercing screams, hoarse barks, guttural purrs, and

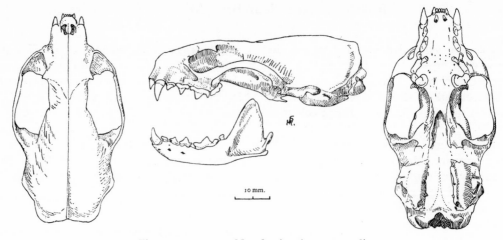

Fig. 139 – SKULL OF *Mustela vison* (ROM 25552 ♀)

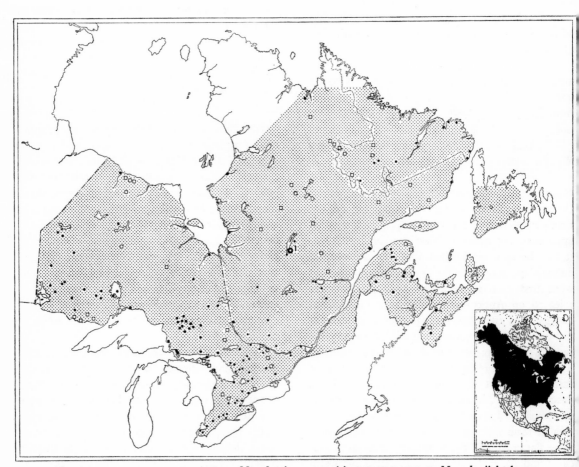

Map 65 – DISTRIBUTION OF THE MINK – *Mustela vison* – AND (1) TYPE LOCALITY OF *M. v. lowii* Anderson

hisses. While not good climbers mink are known to ascend small trees up to a height of at least ten feet. They are rather solitary and are rarely encountered in more than family groups.

Breeding begins at about one year of age, taking place in February or March followed by some thirty-nine to seventy-five days of gestation (the average is fifty-one days). This wide variation results from a delayed implantation of the blastocyst. The actual embryonic attachment is reported to be only thirty to thirty-two days. The litter size averages about four (the range is from three to six), and the young are usually born in April or May. They have a coat of fine hair at birth and their eyes are closed (they open at about twenty-five days). Weaning begins at about five weeks. By eight weeks the young begin to hunt for themselves, though they remain with the mother until autumn. The life-span in the wild is thought to be about eight or nine years, with the average being closer to four or five.

REMARKS The durable pelt of the mink, its glossy softness, and its rich colours make it a fur of distinction. Mink are the most valuable of ranch-raised fur-bearers. Several mutations have been developed, and controlled breeding produces the desirable uniformity in colour and texture. The value of the annual production of ranch-raised mink in Canada in recent years far exceeds that of wild-caught mink (Tables 7 and 8) or of any other fur-bearing species. Ranch production of mink almost doubled during the 1950–60 period to gain an increased percentage of the total fur production in Canada. For all Canada in 1959–60, wild-caught raw furs of all species were valued at approximately $12.4 million (mink, $2.95 million), whereas ranch-raised raw furs were valued at $18.8 million (mink, $18.7 million). Thus ranch production of mink has shown a continued rise and fairly stable prices, whereas wild-caught production has remained fairly constant and has had more widely fluctuating prices.

Occasionally the mink can be a menace to poultry flocks and fish hatcheries, and trappers sometimes accuse it of serious depredations on muskrats.

Selected References

ANDERSON, R. M., 1945b.
BANGS, OUTRAM, 1896e.
ENDERS, ROBERT K., 1952.
ERRINGTON, PAUL L., 1943.
GORHAM, J. R. and H. J. GRIFFITHS, 1952.
HOLLISTER, N., 1913.
MARSHALL, WILLIAM H., 1936.

Table 7

Production of Ranch Mink Pelts in Eastern Canada, 1950–60

	ALL CANADA	EASTERN CANADA	ONTARIO	QUEBEC	NEW BRUNSWICK	NOVA SCOTIA	PRINCE EDWARD I.	NEW-FOUNDLAND
TOTAL PELTS 1950–60	7,837,610	2,916,067	1,942,718	545,549	85,109	207,941	32,060	*101,790
Average Annual Production	783,761	291,607	194,272	54,555	8,511	20,794	3,206	11,310
Minimum Annual Production	574,947 (1950–1)	213,169 (1953–4)	131,192 (1953–4)	49,644 (1950–1)	5,638 (1958–9)	6,505 (1951–2)	1,110 (1950–1)	731 (1951–2)
Maximum Annual Production	1,044,741 (1959–60)	413,602 (1959–60)	284,740 (1959–60)	60,636 (1958–9)	10,867 (1957–8)	32,772 (1959–60)	4,279 (1954–5)	29,764 (1959–60)
TOTAL VALUE 1950–60	$133,327,543	$47,387,998	$32,896,604	$8,466,575	$1,114,063	$2,781,804	$553,407	$1,576,111
Average Annual Value	$13,332,754	$4,738,800	$3,289,604	$846,658	$111,406	$278,180	$55,341	$175,123
Minimum Annual Value	$9,327,522 (1953–4)	$3,311,072 (1951–2)	$1,895,724 (1953–4)	$671,402 (1956–7)	$55,960 (1951–2)	$5,929 (1957–8)	$27,295 (1950–1)	$10,180 (1952–3)
Maximum Annual Value	$18,715,582 (1959–60)	$7,238,949 (1959–60)	$5,115,685 (1959–60)	$1,008,673 (1959–60)	$179,398 (1957–8)	$489,039 (1956–7)	$91,301 (1954–5)	$500,517 (1959–60)
Average Value per Pelt	$17.01	$16.25	$16.93	$15.51	$13.09	$13.37	$17.26	$15.60
Minimum Average Value per Pelt	$15.28 (1956–7)	$12.47 (1956–7)	$12.00 (1956–7)	$13.26 (1952–3)	$10.00 (1951–2)	$12.00 (1955–6)	$14.70 (1958–9)	$10.00 (1952–3)
Maximum Average Value per Pelt	$20.73 (1950–1)	$21.44 (1955–6)	$24.00 (1955–6)	$19.58 (1955–6)	$17.24 (1957–8)	$20.90 (1950–1)	$24.82 (1950–1)	$18.00 (1955–6)

* Nine years only, 1951–60.

Table 8

Production of Wild Mink Pelts in Eastern Canada, 1950–60

	ALL CANADA	EASTERN CANADA	ONTARIO	QUEBEC	NEW BRUNSWICK	NOVA SCOTIA	PRINCE EDWARD I.	NEWFOUNDLAND
TOTAL PELTS 1950–60	1,339,025	601,183	388,900	156,417	18,058	31,167	*648	**7,993
Average Annual Production	133,903	60,118	38,890	15,642	1,606	3,117	72	888
Minimum Annual Production	105,182 (1955–6)	50,012 (1955–6)	32,954 (1955–6)	12,019 (1955–6)	1,011 (1959–60)	1,463 (1959–60)	19 (1959–60)	319 (1954–5)
Maximum Annual Production	173,302 (1957–8)	70,763 (1957–8)	48,205 (1957–8)	20,290 (1950–1)	2,463 (1956–7)	11,510 (1951–2)	129 (1950–1)	1,406 (1951–2)
TOTAL VALUE 1950–60	$26,431,856	$10,342,800	$6,481,136	$2,951,711	$251,507	$519,434	$8,277	$127,735
Average Annual Value	$2,643,186	$1,034,280	$648,114	$295,171	$25,151	$51,943	$919	$14,193
Minimum Annual Value	$1,951,174 (1953–4)	$718,881 (1956–7)	$475,821 (1956–7)	$178,024 (1956–7)	$8,088 (1959–60)	$23,418 (1959–60)	$291 (1958–9)	$12,555 (1953–4)
Maximum Annual Value	$3,964,144 (1950–1)	$1,723,028 (1950–1)	$1,033,575 (1950–1)	$608,700 (1950–1)	$37,349 (1953–4)	$189,915 (1951–2)	$2,483 (1950–1)	$35,150 (1951–2)
Average Value per Pelt	$19.72	$17.21	$16.66	$18.92	$15.62	$16.44	$12.77	$15.98
Minimum Average Value per Pelt	$15.23 (1957–8)	$11.25 (1957–8)	$10.50 (1957–8)	$13.00 (1957–8)	$8.00 (1959–60)	$12.00 (1958–9)	$6.20 (1957–8)	$7.50 (1958–9)
Maximum Average Value per Pelt	$30.41 (1950–1)	$27.97 (1950–1)	$27.45 (1950–1)	$30.00 (1950–1)	$25.00 (1954–5)	$23.50 (1950–1)	$19.25 (1950–1)	$25.00 (1951–2)

* Nine years only, 1950–4 and 1955–60.   ** Nine years only, 1951–60.

Fig. 140 – SKULL OF SEA MINK – *Mustela macrodon* (Type specimen)

Mustela macrodon (Prentiss) – Sea Mink – *Vison de mer*

This very large mink with coarse reddish fur is considered to be extinct. It is reported to have occurred on the southwest coast of Nova Scotia and to have been trapped along the coast of the Bay of Fundy, N.B., in the late nineteenth century. It is thought to have become extinct in Maine between 1860 and 1920; subsequently a mounted specimen was discovered that was reported to have been collected at Campobello Island, N.B., in 1894. Skeletal remains were recovered in 1903 from the shell-heaps at Brooklin, Nancock County, Maine, and described as a distinct species. Other remains have been reported as far south as Middleboro, Massachusetts. *Mustela macrodon* differs from *M.*

vison primarily in its larger size. The premolar-molar toothrow measures over 20 mm. in *M. macrodon* and less in *M. vison*.

It is unfortunate that our knowledge of this species is so sketchy.

Selected References

GOODWIN, G. G., 1935.

LOOMIS, F. B., 1911.

MANVILLE, R. H., 1942.

NORTON, A. H., 1930a.

PRENTISS, D. W., 1903.

SETON, ERNEST THOMPSON, 1921.

WATERS, J. H. and C. E. RAY, 1961.

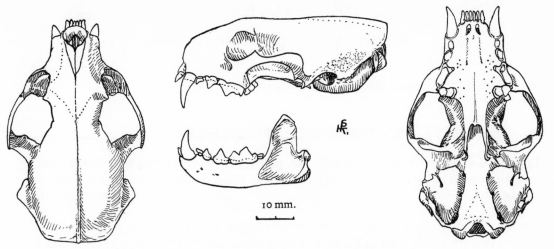

Fig. 141 – SKULL OF DOMESTICATED FERRET *Mustela putorius* (ROM 20334 ♂)

Mustela putorius Linnaeus – Domesticated Ferret – *Putois*

The origin of the domesticated ferret remains uncertain. Linnaeus thought that it came from Africa and gave it the name *Mustela furo*. Later authors considered it a domesticated form of the European polecat and classified it as *Mustela putorius furo*. Certain skull characteristics, such as the shape of the postorbital constriction, suggest that it may be more closely related to the Asian form *M. eversmani* (*M. p. eversmani* of later authors).

The domesticated ferret has been introduced into eastern Canada as an aid in hunting small mammals, particularly cottontail rabbits. Its use has been declared illegal in most areas, although a few specimens have been seen in recent years.

In general the ferret is about the size of a mink but is shorter and more heavily built; its markings are closer to those of a long-tailed weasel. The pelage may be quite variable; it is frequently very pale yellowish brown or whitish with dark about the eyes, feet, and tail-tip. Dark-tipped hairs may be interspersed over the body. The ears are usually fringed with white.

The skull is about the same width as that of a mink but shorter, particularly in the post-glenoid and brain-case lengths. The length of the pre-molar-molar toothrow also averages shorter. Perhaps the most diagnostic character is the shape of the auditory bullae: the ferret has much more inflated and rounded bullae than the mink. The mastoid processes project laterally beyond the brain case to give a distinctive shape to the skull.

Compared with the polecat, the wild form of the ferret in Europe (*M. p. putorius*), the skull of *M. p. furo* can be distinguished by the shape of the post-orbital constriction. In the former this is nearly parallel-sided while in the ferret it has a definite angular constriction.

Selected References

ELLERMAN, J. R. and T. C. S. MORRISON-SCOTT, 1951.

MILLER, GERRIT S., 1912.

Genus **MARTES** Pinel

Martens and Fishers – *Martres et Pékans*

Dental Formula $\quad I\ \frac{3-3}{3-3}\quad C\ \frac{1-1}{1-1}\quad P\ \frac{4-4}{4-4}\quad M\ \frac{1-1}{2-2} = 38$

KEY TO THE EASTERN-CANADIAN SPECIES OF *Martes*

1 Tail more than 275 mm.; skull length more than 90 mm.; length of upper P4 more than 9.5 mm. (measured on the outside) and lower M_1 more than 11 mm.; colour uniform greyish brown to dark brown. MARTES PENNANTI p. 256

1' Tail less than 250 mm.; skull length 90 mm. or less; length of upper P4 less than 9.5 mm. (measured on the outside) and lower M_1 less than 11 mm.; colour variable from a pale yellowish buff, a bright orange, to a rich reddish brown to almost black. The head is usually lighter than the body and a throat or chest patch of buff to orange is usually present. MARTES AMERICANA p. 252

Martes americana (Turton) – Marten – *Martre*

Similar in size to the mink, the marten has longer fur, a bushier tail, and more pronounced ears. The pelage colour varies considerably from a pale yellowish buff to a rich reddish brown to almost black. The head is usually lighter in colour than the rest of the body, and the throat and chest have a light patch that varies from whitish to a pale straw colour to vivid orange. An occasional mutation occurring in Ontario produces animals in which the head is whitish and the rest of the body is bright orange. Abdominal scent glands are present in both sexes (they are larger in the female). The claws are semi-retractable—an aid in tree-climbing. There are six mammae.

The skull of the marten has a more elongate rostrum (it is more dog-like) than that of the mink and can be further distinguished from both the mink and the larger fisher by the shape of the auditory bullae and the last upper molar teeth, and by the fact that there are four instead of three premolars above and below, a characteristic the marten shares with the wolverine, *Gulo*. (*Martes* is readily distinguished from *Gulo* by its smaller, narrower skull.)

SIZE Total length: males 550–675 mm., females 490–602; tail: males 150–220, females 135–200; hind foot: males 80–98, females 70–98; ear from notch 34–48. Skull length: males 80–90, females 69–76; skull width: males 46–53, females 38–46. Weight: males 450–1,500 gr. (1–3 lb.), females 425–950 (1–2 lb.).

DISTRIBUTION AND VARIATION The marten occurs throughout eastern Canada with the exception of the northernmost part of the Ungava peninsula of Quebec and the Cape Henrietta Maria section of Ontario. It has been extirpated from Prince Edward Island and from the southern agricultural areas of Ontario and Quebec. Its current status in New Brunswick and Nova Scotia is uncertain. *Martes americana americana* occurs throughout eastern Canada with the exception of the Labrador coast, where the name *M. a. brumalis* has been applied, and Newfoundland which is occupied by *M. a. atrata*.

HABITAT The boreal coniferous forest.

Fig. 142 – MARTEN – *Martes americana*

HABITS The marten is perhaps best known for its arboreal activities. It is extremely agile in trees where it is able to pursue and catch red squirrels, which form a part of its extremely varied diet. It is also an efficient hunter on the ground where it takes mice, shrews, chipmunks, rabbits, birds and their eggs, amphibians, reptiles, insects, nuts, and fruit. It even enters water to catch crustaceans or fish as food.

A hollow tree is preferred as a den site. The mating season lasts about six weeks during the summer (normally July and August) but the gestation period is prolonged to about nine or ten months as a result of delayed implantation which accounts for over four months. The species is highly polygamous and females are known to mate many times per season in captivity. Only one litter is born per year (March or April) and it consists of from one to six (an average of three or four) young weighing about one ounce each (twenty-five to forty grams) at birth. The eyes of a marten are closed at birth and the body is covered with a fine yellowish hair. In about one week a dark grey cross appears across the shoulders and down the back. This becomes most prominent at about two weeks; at three weeks the greyish tone disappears as the pelage assumes a brownish colour. The young weigh from 175 to 275 grams at about twenty-five days. The eyes have been recorded to open at thirty-nine days, with weaning taking place at about six to seven weeks, by which time the young weigh between 400 and 500 grams. They attain near adult size in about three months when they leave the mother and take up the solitary existence of adults.

Captive animals have lived up to seventeen years with many exceeding ten years. The average life-span in the wild is not known, but it probably does not exceed six to eight years.

REMARKS Marten fur has consistently brought a relatively high price in the past, and this has

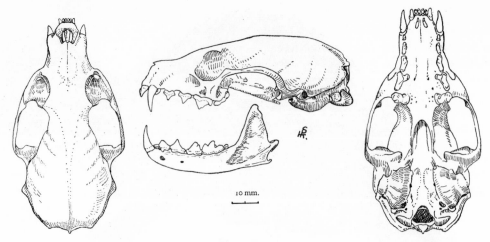

Fig. 143 – SKULL OF *Martes americana* (ROM 25172 ♂)

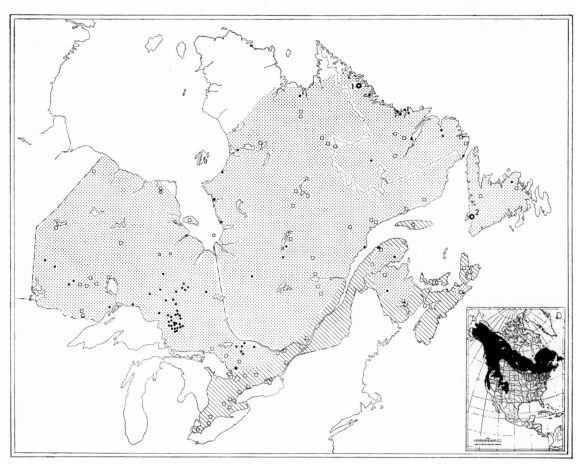

Map 66 – DISTRIBUTION OF THE MARTEN – *Martes americana* – AND TYPE LOCALITIES OF
(1) *M. a. brumalis* (Bangs); (2) *M. a. atrata* (Bangs)

resulted in high trapping pressure on the marten, which has been called the sable of the New World; however, this pressure has declined in recent years, probably owing to a drop in the price of marten pelts (see Table 9). Recent conservation measures, including systems of registered trap lines, have apparently been instrumental in building up marten populations in areas where they had become alarmingly scarce. Marten have become so rare in New Brunswick and Nova Scotia that they are no longer trapped. The apparent success in rebuilding marten populations in Ontario should

be extended to certain areas in the Maritime Provinces.

Selected References

ASHBROOK, FRANK G. and KARL B. HANSON, 1930.
BANGS, OUTRAM, 1897d.
DE VOS, ANTON, 1952.
HAGMEIER, E. M., 1957a, 1958.
MARKLEY, MERLE H. and C. F. BASSETT, 1942.
MARSHALL, W. H., 1951a, 1951b.
RHOADS, SAMUEL N., 1902.
WRIGHT, P. L., 1942a.

Table 9

Production of Marten Pelts in Eastern Canada, 1950–60

	ALL CANADA	EASTERN CANADA	ONTARIO	QUEBEC	NOVA SCOTIA	NEW-FOUNDLAND
TOTAL PELTS 1950–60	170,914	47,589	36,713	10,732	*1	**143
Average Annual Production	17,091	4,759	3,671	1,073		20
Minimum Annual Production	13,381 (1956–7)	1,312 (1950–1)	1,217 (1950–1)	95 (1950–2)		(1955–63)
Maximum Annual Production	29,226 (1959–60)	10,846 (1959–60)	6,644 (1959–60)	4,170 (1959–60)		40 (1953–4)
TOTAL VALUE 1950–60	$1,881,416	$331,154	$250,927	$79,744	$7.00	$1,476
Average Annual Value	$188,142	$33,115	$25,093	$7,975		$211
Minimum Annual Value	$80,968 (1956–7)	$21,330 (1951–2)	$18,779 (1953–4)	$1,520 (1950–1)		$48 (1955–6)
Maximum Annual Value	$536,733 (1950–1)	$58,428 (1959–60)	$35,315 (1954–5)	$27,105 (1959–60)		$478 (1954–5)
Average Value per Pelt	$11.00	$6.95	$6.83	$7.45		$13.00
Minimum Average Value per Pelt	$6.05 (1956–7)	$4.98 (1957–8)	$4.71 (1959–60)	$6.00 (1957–9)		$3.00 (1959–60)
Maximum Average Value per Pelt	$25.52 (1950–1)	$19.74 (1950–1)	$20.00 (1950–1)	$20.00 (1951–2)		$18.33 (1953–4)

* One year only, 1958–9.   ** Seven years only, 1952–6 and 1957–60.

There were no pelts reported for New Brunswick and Prince Edward Island.

Fig. 144 – FISHER – *Martes pennanti*

Martes pennanti (Erxleben) – Fisher – *Pékan*

Larger and darker in colour than the marten, the fisher lacks the marten's characteristic orange throat although a small whitish throat patch is sometimes present. The general body colour varies from pale grey to almost black, with occasionally a reddish-brown tinge. The male pelage is noticeably longer and coarser than the female. There are only four functional mammae. The skull may be distinguished from that of the marten by the size and shape of the auditory bullae. Old males develop particularly high sagittal crests.

SIZE Total length: males 905–1,020 (av. 950) mm., females 790–880 (av. 830); tail: males 330–400 (av. 362), females 300–360 (av. 327); hind foot: males 120–143 (av. 126), females 100–120 (av. 108); ear from notch 40–52. Skull length: males 112–130 (av. 121), females 95–106 (av. 100); skull width: males 62–84 (av. 70), females 52–61 (av. 55). Weight: males 5–13 lb., females 3.0–6.5.

DISTRIBUTION AND VARIATION *Martes pennanti pennanti* is the race occurring in eastern Canada, roughly from a line joining southernmost Labrador to southern James Bay. It has apparently never occurred on Newfoundland. It was introduced to Anticosti Island in the Gulf of St Lawrence and has probably been extirpated from Prince Edward Island. The fisher became extremely rare in New Brunswick but was reintroduced about 1950 in the south-central portion of the province. It was thought to have become extinct in Nova Scotia prior to its reintroduction in the northeast portion of Queen's County, but single specimens were

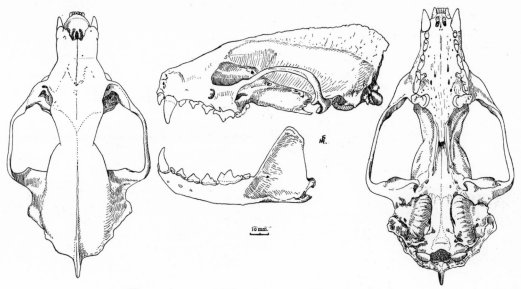

Fig. 145 – SKULL OF *Martes pennanti* (male) (ROM 20158)

Fig. 146 – SKULL OF *Martes pennanti* (female) (ROM 20000)

accidently caught in 1955 and 1958 in nearby areas, suggesting that the species is now re-established there.

HABITAT The fisher seems to prefer heavy mixed forests and rarely ventures far into large open areas.

M.E.C.—19

HABITS The food habits of the fisher are not unlike those of the marten except that larger prey such as porcupine and snowshoe hares are included in the diet, along with the carrion of deer, moose, raccoons, otter, and beaver. In order to satisfy its needs, the fisher travels considerable distances, usually in circuits of up to 100 miles which are

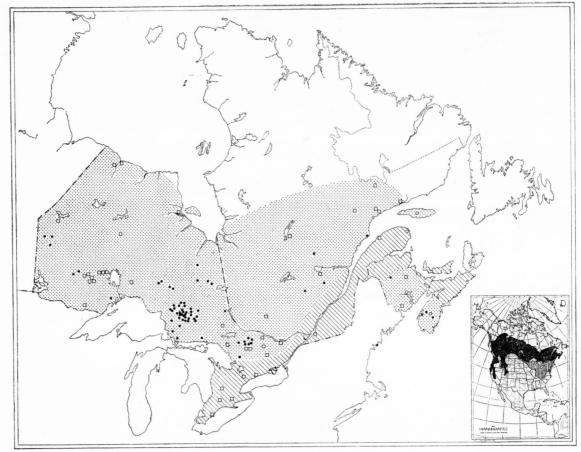

Map 67 – DISTRIBUTION OF THE FISHER – *Martes pennanti*

thought to be completed every three to fifteen days and mostly at night, though some movements occur during the day.

Breeding is thought to begin at one year in females and perhaps at two years in males; it usually takes place around April. The recorded gestation period is about fifteen weeks but, as in marten, there is a delayed implantation of the blastocyst that may account for some nine months. The young, averaging two or three (one to five), are born in the last half of March or April and are not unlike the young of marten (although the eyes open at about seven weeks). They begin to hunt at three months and leave the family circle by late fall.

Polygamous mating takes place some three to eighteen days after the birth of a litter.

The fisher is better as a climber than as a 'fisher-man' and is extremely fast and agile. It is quite solitary and may den up in periods of extreme weather.

REMARKS The prices paid for raw fisher pelts during the period 1950–60 were remarkably stable (Table 10). The solitary fisher rarely becomes abundant in any area. The comparatively high prices paid for female pelts has resulted in more pressure on females than on males. Attempts to rebuild fisher populations in the Maritime

Provinces show some encouraging results, but it is too early to determine their eventual success.

The fur of the fisher is used almost exclusively for making scarves, neck-pieces, or capes; it is rarely made into jackets or used for trimming purposes. For this reason fisher fur is not so well known as the other more common mustelid furs such as ermine, mink, and sable, which are regularly made into coats and jackets.

Selected References

BENSON, D. A., 1959.

DE VOS, ANTON, 1952.

EADIE, R. ROBERT and W. J. HAMILTON, JR , 1958.

ENDERS, R. K. and O. P. PEARSON, 1943.

HAGMEIER, EDWIN M., 1957a.

HAMILTON, W. J., JR. and A. H. COOK, 1955.

RAND, A. L., 1944C.

RHOADS, S. N., 1898.

Table 10

Production of Fisher Pelts in Eastern Canada, 1950–60

	ALL CANADA	EASTERN CANADA	ONTARIO	QUEBEC
TOTAL PELTS 1950–60	55,511	38,719	25,419	13,300
Average Annual Production	5,551	3,872	2,541	1,330
Minimum Annual Production	3,690 (1950–1)	2,211 (1950–1)	798 (1950–1)	1,026 (1951–2)
Maximum Annual Production	6,790 (1954–5)	4,913 (1959–60)	3,281 (1954–5)	1,893 (1959–60)
TOTAL VALUE 1950–60	$1,118,177	$792,243	$494,920	$287,263
Average Annual Value	$111,818	$79,224	$49,492	$28,726
Minimum Annual Value	$84,038 (1958–9)	$62,872 (1950–1)	$27,587 (1950–1)	$22,000 (1952–3)
Maximum Annual Value	$154,485 (1954–5)	$103,944 (1955–6)	$73,062 (1955–6)	$40,977 (1950–1)
Average Value per Pelt	$20.10	$20.48	$19.49	$22.50
Minimum Average Value per Pelt	$17.08 (1957–8)	$17.41 (1958–9)	$15.35 (1953–4)	$19.00 (1959–60)
Maximum Average Value per Pelt	$24.75 (1950–1)	$31.00 (1950–1)	$34.57 (1950–1)	$29.00 (1950–1)

Fig. 147 – WOLVERINE – *Gulo luscus*

Genus **GULO** Pallas

Wolverines – *Carcajous*

Dental Formula I $\frac{3-3}{3-3}$ C $\frac{1-1}{1-1}$ P $\frac{4-4}{4-4}$ M $\frac{1-1}{2-2}$ = 38

Gulo luscus (Linnaeus) – Wolverine – *Carcajou*

Though the largest of the eastern-Canadian mustelids, the wolverine, is rarely encountered in eastern Canada, its reputation as an enemy of trappers is legendary. It is about the size of a medium-large spaniel dog and is superficially bear-like in appearance except for an arched back, a longer bushy tail, and a broad, light-coloured band extending from each shoulder to the rump and onto the tail. The general body colour varies from yellowish brown to nearly black, while the two bands vary from whitish to brown. There is sometimes a light throat patch. There are eight mammae, four abdominal and four inguinal.

The skull is characterized by its massiveness and large size (it is more than 85 mm. wide). The dental formula is the same as that of the marten and fisher.

SIZE Total length 800–1,075 mm. (32–45 in.); tail 170–250 (7–10 in.); hind foot 165–205; ear from notch 45–55. Skull: length 130–175, width 90–107. Weight 18–42 lb.; females average slightly

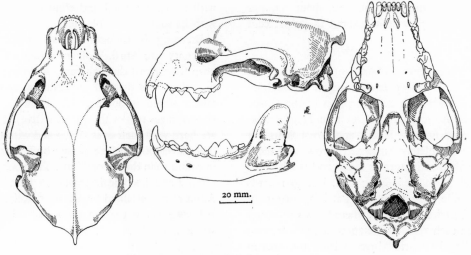

Fig. 148 – SKULL OF *Gulo luscus* (ROM 26432 ♀)

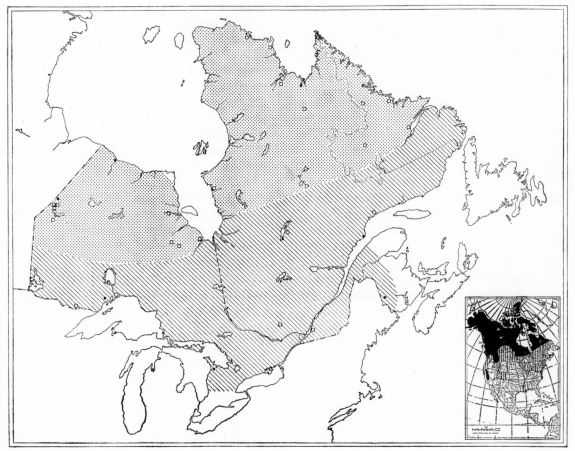

Map 68 – DISTRIBUTION OF THE WOLVERINE – *Gulo luscus*

smaller—their measurements are about ten per cent less and their weight is about thirty per cent less.

DISTRIBUTION AND VARIATION Until the turn of the century, *Gulo luscus luscus* ranged throughout eastern Canada with the exception of the Gaspé Peninsula, Anticosti Island, eastern New Brunswick, Prince Edward Island, and Nova Scotia. It has been completely extirpated throughout more than one half of its former range and has become quite rare in the remaining area. Recent records are available only from the Patricia portion of Kenora District in Ontario, where a few wolverines are taken each year. A fine specimen was secured by the Royal Ontario Museum from this area in 1955. The wolverine's present status in northern Quebec and Labrador is apparently unknown.

HABITAT The habitat requirements are not specialized. The wolverine frequents boreal forests, open areas, and treeless tundra.

HABITS Perhaps the wolverine or *carcajou* has a more prominent place in folklore than any other mustelid, yet there is comparatively little detailed knowledge of it. It is a fairly wide-ranging, solitary animal that is practically omnivorous. Prey as large as deer, caribou, and moose are reported to have been taken under exceptional conditions. However, porcupines and smaller species make up most of its diet. The wolverine feeds on carrion and is perhaps best known for destroying trappers' catches and for breaking into food caches, even in cabins. It is active during all seasons, both by day and by night. It moves with a distinctive lumbering gait with its back arched and climbs reasonably well with its semi-retractable claws.

Breeding is thought to take place between February and April. Wolverine young are usually born from April through June. As in other mustelids, there is a delayed implantation and the gestation period is not precisely known. The litter size averages two or three (one to five). The young are born with their eyes closed and with little hair. The developing pelage is pale buff, much lighter in colour than the fur of adults. The young develop rapidly and become independent by six months. Adult size is attained by one year. Relatively little is known about the life history of this vanishing species.

REMARKS Wolverine fur is especially prized for trimming parkas because it is frost-resistant. As a result, a very small percentage of the wolverine furs taken by trappers reach the commercial market since most of them are used locally. During the ten-year period 1950–60, only seventeen pelts from eastern Canada reached the commercial market. All came from Ontario and were sold for an average of $16.50 each ($8.50 to $18.00). The average number of wolverine pelts marketed from all of Canada each year for the same period was 542 (406 to 780).

Our present knowledge of the wolverine is clouded by much folklore and fantasy. Detailed and accurate information not only about its life history but about its ecology is seriously needed.

Selected References
SETON, E. T., 1926 (vol. 2, pp. 405–449).
WRIGHT, P. L. and R. RAUSCH, 1955.

Fig. 149 – BADGER – *Taxidea taxus*

Genus **TAXIDEA** Waterhouse

Badgers – *Blaireaus*

Dental Formula $I\frac{3-3}{3-3}$ $C\frac{1-1}{1-1}$ $P\frac{3-3}{3-3}$ $M\frac{1-1}{2-2} = 34$

Taxidea taxus (Schreber) – Badger – *Blaireau*

The badger is a robust, flattened, short-legged animal with a yellowish-grey pelage above and a narrow white stripe extending from its nose over its head and shoulders and sometimes down the middle of its back. Its feet are black and there is a black spot on its white cheeks. The underparts and tail are yellowish. The tail and ears are relatively short and the claws on the front feet are exceptionally long. There are eight mammae, four abdominal and four inguinal.

The skull is more triangular in dorsal view (the wide occipital region) and more flattened than that of most mustelids. It is readily distinguished by its size and by its dental formula of thirty-four teeth and the triangular shape of the last upper molar. The auditory bullae are rather large and inflated. The bony palate extends quite far behind the last molar.

SIZE Total length 700–800 mm.; tail 98–158; hind foot 87–150; ear from notch 45–60. Skull: length 109–139, width 64–92. Weight 14–26 lb.

DISTRIBUTION AND VARIATION *Taxidea taxus taxus*

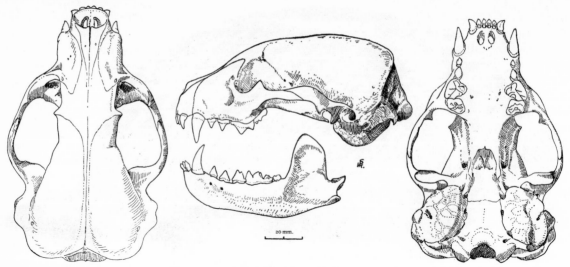

Fig. 150 – SKULL OF *Taxidea taxus* (ROM 33.2.6.1)

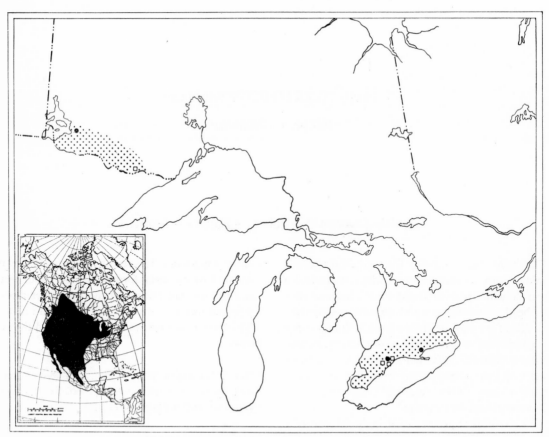

Map 69 – DISTRIBUTION OF THE BADGER – *Taxidea taxus*

occurs in eastern Canada in two areas: the extreme western part of Ontario in the Rainy River region and along the north shore of Lake Erie.

HABITAT Basically an animal of the open grassland prairies, the badger may have invaded Ontario as a result of the clearing of land for agriculture. It is occasionally found in sparse bushland, farmlands, and open woodlots.

HABITS The badger has become highly specialized as a fossorial animal. It constructs long deep burrows for which the long claws of its front feet serve it well. It not only excavates its home but also digs for food, which consists primarily of rodents—particularly ground squirrels—rabbits and insects. North of Lake Erie, where no ground squirrels occur, its main diet is probably made up of woodchucks and cottontail rabbits. Although it is primarily nocturnal, the badger is occasionally active during the day, particularly early in the morning. It seldom remains long in the same den except when it is rearing young, so the most conspicuous sign of its presence is the freshly dug den-opening. It becomes quite fat in the fall and may remain inactive for long periods, especially in extreme weather.

Breeding takes place in the autumn (late August or September), but delayed implantation persists until about February, with development of the unborn young lasting about six to nine weeks. From April to June one to five (usually two or three) young are born covered with fine fur. The eyes are opened at four to six weeks. When the young are about half grown (at approximately eight weeks old) they are weaned, but they continue to remain in the family circle until late summer.

When attacked by dogs or other carnivores, the badger is a formidable foe that is not soon forgotten by its attacker.

REMARKS Badger fur was once in great demand for shaving brushes. Badgers have never been sufficiently abundant in eastern Canada to be of commercial importance.

Selected References

BARTLETT, C. O., 1955.

ERRINGTON, PAUL L., 1937C.

HALL, E. RAYMOND, 1927.

HAMLETT, GEORGE W. D., 1932.

SNEAD, EDWIN and GEORGE O. HENDERSON, 1942.

Fig. 151 – STRIPED SKUNK – *Mephitis mephitis*

Genus **MEPHITIS** Geoffroy-Saint-Hilaire and Cuvier

Striped Skunks – *Mouffettes*

Dental Formula   I $\frac{3-3}{3-3}$ C $\frac{1-1}{1-1}$ P $\frac{3-3}{3-3}$ M $\frac{1-1}{2-2}$ = 34

Mephitis mephitis (Schreber) – Striped Skunk – *Mouffette rayée*

This cat-sized black animal with two white stripes down its back needs little description. There is considerable variation in the extent of the white markings. In some animals the white extends from the head to the end of the tail while in others the white areas are variously reduced to a small white patch on the head. The head is relatively small, sometimes fitting conveniently, if too snugly, into glass jars or opened bean cans. The legs are short, the body is relatively heavy, and the tail is quite long and bushy. There are normally up to fourteen mammae—four pectoral, six abdominal, and four inguinal—though non-functioning mammae sometimes reduce the number to ten.

The skull can be distinguished from that of other mustelids by its relative deepness, and by a squarish upper molar and a swollen sinus area that accounts for a pronounced hump or 'roman nose' in the dorsal contour of the skull. The dental formula is the same as that of *Mustela* and *Taxidea*.

SIZE Total length 540–775 mm.; tail 175–280; hind foot 60–82; ear from notch 25–35. Skull: length 63–84, width 40–55. Weight 3–14 lb.

DISTRIBUTION AND VARIATION The skunk is rather ubiquitous in eastern Canada roughly south of a line joining the southern shore of Hudson Bay and the southern boundary of Labrador. The geographic variation of this species is in need of study. Currently three forms are recognized in the area: *Mephitis mephitis hudsonica* in extreme western Ontario, *M. m. mephitis* in the remainder of Ontario and Quebec north of Georgian Bay to Montreal, and *M. m. nigra* in southern Ontario and south of the St Lawrence River.

HABITAT Skunks seem to prefer semi-open areas of mixed forests and open grassland. However, they have a wide tolerance and seem to turn up almost anywhere, even in the heart of large cities.

HABITS Skunks are truly omnivorous but tend to be more insectivorous than any other of the carnivores of eastern Canada. Small mammals constitute about ten to twenty per cent of their diet. Turtles' and birds' eggs are occasionally eaten; vegetable matter may account for up to another twenty-five or thirty per cent, and insects and other invertebrates make up most of the remainder. Occasionally a skunk enters a poultry pen where it may kill a number of birds. In years of high densities of June beetle larvae a skunk will forage on lawns and golf greens where it may root up and peel back the sod as though it were rolling up a carpet. When the larvae population is less dense, small round holes are dug in the turf as the skunk searches out individual grubs. Closer fraternization with humans often takes place when the mother skunk selects a den site under a porch or under some other part of a house where it can bring forth and rear its young.

Breeding takes place in February or March. A litter of about six (two to ten) is born about early May after a gestation period of sixty-two to sixty-four days. The newborn cubs or kits are born with eyes and ears closed and with very short, fine hair that is quite thin but nevertheless shows the distinctive colour pattern of the adults. The eyes and ears open at about thirty days, by which time the young can operate their musk glands.

While all mustelids have a defence mechanism in the form of well-developed scent glands, the

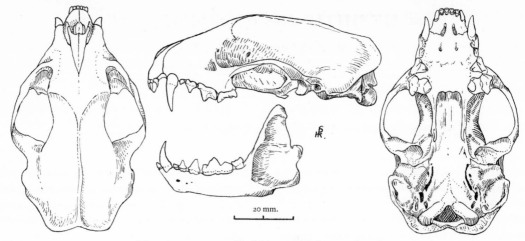

20 mm.

Fig. 152 – SKULL OF *Mephitis mephitis* (ROM 23824 ♂)

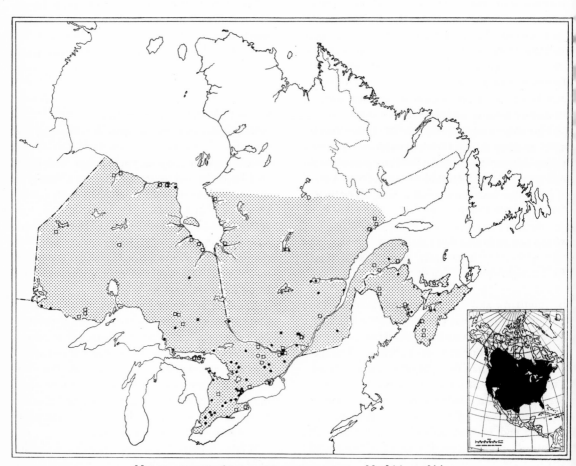

Map 70 – DISTRIBUTION OF THE STRIPED SKUNK – *Mephitis mephitis*

skunk's is almost overdone. Its anal glands are enlarged. There are two, one on each side of the rectum, embedded in a muscle mass. Each gland has a single duct that leads into a nipple-like papilla through which a pungent and malodorous fluid can be ejected ten to fifteen feet or more by the constriction of the muscles surrounding the glands. The use of these glands is a most effective defence action and is respected by any would-be predator that has encountered its effect only once.

In late June or early July the mother and young are sometimes seen scampering about on a lawn. The actions of an inexperienced, overzealous family dog in response to such a development sometimes result in pandemonium and a hasty retreat into the house. The dog's normal reaction of rubbing his fur on the rug to rid the spray of musk from his eyes adds to the consternation of the household. Washing the affected areas (including those of the dog) in tomato juice seems to be an effective remedy. Turpentine has also been reported to be useful.

A family of skunks continues to sally forth in its nightly feeding until late fall when the animals become excessively fat. By late December (sometimes as early as late October) they have selected a deep den in the ground where the whole family and possibly a few neighbours retreat into a state of inactivity for a protracted period, though they may come out briefly at any time during the winter. By late February they begin to reappear and by the end of March full activity is resumed.

Pet skunks are known to live up to ten years. In the wild only large owls appear to be effective predators of the skunk; other carnivores tend to shy away from attacking it. More skunks are killed by automobiles than by anything else outside the wilderness areas.

The skunk has been particularly vulnerable to rabies.

REMARKS Because of their disagreeable odour, relatively few skunks are marketed by most trappers, especially when prices are low as they were during the 1950–60 period (see Table 11) when the annual average was 5,000 pelts sold for only eighty cents each.

The strong odour of the skunk musk results from butylmercaptan, a sulphur-alcohol compound that is highly volatile.

Deodorized skunks make interesting and tractable pets.

Selected References
ALLEN, DURWARD L. and WARREN W. SHAPTON, 1942.
HAMILTON, WILLIAM J., JR., 1936b.
HOWELL, A. H., 1901.
KELKER, GEORGE H., 1937.
LAUN, H. CHARLES, 1962.
SHAW, WILLIAM T., 1928.
STEGEMAN, LEROY C., 1937, 1939.

Table II

Production of Striped Skunk Pelts in Eastern Canada, 1950–60

	ALL CANADA	EASTERN CANADA	ONTARIO	QUEBEC	NEW BRUNSWICK	NOVA SCOTIA	PRINCE EDWARD I.	NEW-FOUNDLAND
TOTAL PELTS 1950-60	67,121	50,373	43,102	6,923	*122	577	**315	—
Average Annual Production	6,712	5,037	4,310	692	20	58	105	
Minimum Annual Production	1,744 (1958-9)	572 (1959-60)	295 (1959-60)	201 (1958-9)	11 (1954-5)	2 (1958-9)	17 (1951-2)	
Maximum Annual Production	16,389 (1950-1)	15,354 (1950-1)	13,435 (1951-2)	1,743 (1950-1)	32 (1952-3)	364 (1957-8)	266 (1953-4)	
TOTAL VALUE 1950-60	$53,739	$40,612	$37,106	$2,941	$27	$380	$158	
Average Annual Value	$5,374	$4,061	$3,710	$294	$4.50	$38	$32	
Minimum Annual Value	$1,422 (1958-9)	$325 (1959-60)	$206 (1959-60)	$60 (1958-9)	$3 (1954-5)	$1 (1955-6 & 1958-9)	$9 (1951-2)	
Maximum Annual Value	$12,872 (1950-1)	$12,022 (1950-1)	$11,009 (1951-2)	$872 (1950-1)	$8 (1953-4)	$182 (1957-8)	$133 (1953-4)	
Average Value per Pelt	$0.80	$0.80	$0.86	$0.42	$0.22	$0.66	$0.50	
Minimum Average Value per Pelt	$0.65 (1951-2)	$0.56 (1959-60)	$0.70 (1959-60)	$0.30 (1957-9)	$0.09 (1952-3)	$0.33 (1955-6)	$0.50 (1950-1)	
Maximum Average Value per Pelt	$1.02 (1952-3)	$1.08 (1952-3)	$1.20 (1952-3)	$0.50 (1950-2 & 1953-6)	$0.27 (1954-5)	$2.00 (1951-2)	$0.53 (1951-2)	

* Six years only, 1950-6.   ** Three years only, 1950-2 and 1953-4.

Fig. 153 – OTTER – *Lutra canadensis*

Genus **LUTRA** Brünnich

Otters – *Loutres de rivière*

Dental Formula $I \frac{3-3}{3-3}$ $C \frac{1-1}{1-1}$ $P \frac{4-4}{3-3}$ $M \frac{1-1}{2-2} = 36$

Lutra canadensis (Schreber) – Otter – *Loutre de rivière*

The otter is more highly adapted for an aquatic existence than any other terrestrial carnivore. It has an efficiently streamlined hydrofoil in its long body, short ears, short legs with fully webbed toes, and long, tapering tail. The fur is short, dense, and dark brown (appearing almost black when wet), with slightly paler tones on the snout and around the mouth. The skull is relatively broad and is flattened dorsally; it has a short, broad rostrum. The dentition is quite heavy and is usually badly worn in older specimens. The dental formula readily identifies the otter.

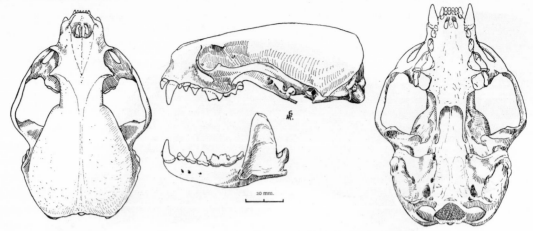

Fig. 154 – SKULL OF *Lutra canadensis* (ROM 25316 ♂)

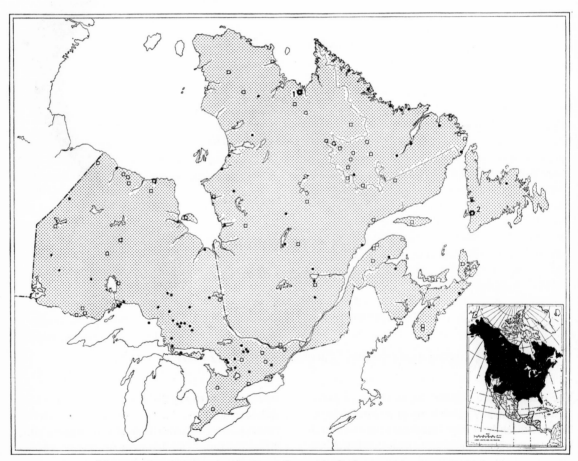

Map 71 – DISTRIBUTION OF THE OTTER – *Lutra canadensis* – AND TYPE LOCALITIES OF
(1) *L. c. chimo* Anderson; (2) *L. c. degener* Bangs

SIZE Total length 900–1,300 mm.; tail 300–500; hind foot 110–140; ear from notch 10–25. Skull: length 95–120, width 60–80. Weight 10–30 lb.

DISTRIBUTION AND VARIATION The otter occupies the whole of eastern Canada more completely than any other carnivore. (A detailed study of the geographic variation of the species is much needed.) It is even able to survive in streams that pass through large cities. Four races are currently recognized: *Lutra canadensis canadensis*, occurring roughly south of James Bay; *L. c. preblei* in the Patricia portion of Kenora District, Ont.; *L. c. chimo* in northern Quebec and Labrador, and *L. c. degener* which is restricted to Newfoundland.

HABITAT Lakes, marshes, streams, and sea shores.

HABITS In keeping with its aquatic habits, the otter feeds on fish, which provide it with much of its food. Amphibians, cray-fish, and other invertebrates; turtles, snakes and other vertebrates such as water fowl; and muskrats and other rodents comprise the balance of the otter's diet. Some vegetation is also eaten in summer. The otter is an extremely graceful and fast swimmer but on land it bounds along, its body undulating. Its short legs sink into deep snow to leave a 'ploughed' furrow trail. For the most part the otter seldom wanders far from water, although it does occasionally take long overland treks, especially during the winter and during the breeding season (which has not been precisely defined).

Breeding age is thought to be reached in about one year. Because of delayed implantation, the gestation period has not been precisely fixed. Ten months to a little over a year have been reported as the elapsed time between breeding and the birth of young, although one captive animal apparently gave birth after a maximum gestation of forty-three days. Births have been reported from January to May, but most young are born in March or April, with an average of two or three (one to six) in the litter. The newborn are about eight inches long and have a black, silky coat. The eyes

are opened at about twenty-five to thirty-eight days, and at about three months the young venture from the den, which may be an abandoned beaver lodge or bank den with an entrance either above or under water. They soon accompany the adults on forays for food, though they always appear to have time for playful antics. An observer canoeing silently down a stream may have the delightful experience of being involved in a game of 'hide-and-go-seek' with otters as a family keeps ahead of the canoe, popping up to look around, giving a snuffle or a snort, and diving out of sight to reappear at some unexpected spot. As otter heads keep appearing and disappearing, it is sometimes difficult to discern how many animals are playing the game. Antics are also performed on otter slides. Otters seem to enjoy the sheer delight of sliding down a deep bank into the water. In winter, sliding becomes a part of their method of travel in the snow.

Adult size is reached at about one year. Captive animals have lived for at least nineteen years and have continued to breed for seventeen years.

REMARKS Otters provide the most durable of furs and are much sought-after by trappers. While never reaching high-population densities, they seem to be able to maintain relatively stable populations from year to year. The average annual production in eastern Canada during the ten-year period 1950–60 averaged 11,156 and varied only from 9,919 to 12,898 otter pelts per year (see Table 12). The prices paid for otter pelts has remained more stable than for most other furs.

Occasionally the otter comes in conflict with fishermen by damaging or stealing fish caught in nets or on lines. The otter is also not very popular around fish hatcheries.

Selected References
ANDERSON, R. M., 1945b.
BANGS, O., 1898a.
HOOPER, EMMET T. and BURTON T. OSTENSON, 1949.
LAGLER, KARL F. and BURTON T. OSTENSON, 1942.
LIERS, EMIL E., 1951, 1953, 1958.
RHOADS, S. N., 1898.

Table 12

Production of Otter Pelts in Eastern Canada, 1950–60

	ALL CANADA	EASTERN CANADA	ONTARIO	QUEBEC	NEW BRUNSWICK	NOVA SCOTIA	PRINCE EDWARD I.	NEW-FOUNDLAND
TOTAL PELTS 1950–60	145,364	111,562	70,992	27,974	1,958	2,425	*1	**8,212
Average Annual Production	14,537	11,156	7,099	2,797	196	243		912
Minimum Annual Production	13,467 (1951–2)	9,919 (1951–2)	6,268 (1951–2)	2,269 (1953–4)	79 (1950–1)	174 (1953–4)		503 (1956–7)
Maximum Annual Production	16,238 (1957–8)	12,898 (1957–8)	8,425 (1957–8)	3,221 (1950–1)	312 (1957–8)	295 (1959–60)		1,505 (1958–9)
TOTAL VALUE 1950–60	$3,546,971	$2,673,214	$1,522,896	$712,964	$54,991	$55,869		$145,517
Average Annual Value	$354,698	$267,321	$152,290	$71,297	$5,499	$5,587	$25.00	$16,168
Minimum Annual Value	$284,096 (1951–2)	$213,515 (1951–2)	$124,733 (1951–2)	$55,062 (1951–2)	$1,920 (1951–2)	$2,764 (1953–4)		$7,545 (1956–7)
Maximum Annual Value	$393,064 (1954–5)	$308,668 (1957–8)	$194,490 (1954–5)	$87,556 (1950–1)	$8,736 (1957–8)	$7,850 (1950–1)		$27,810 (1958–9)
Average Value per Pelt	$24.39	$23.95	$21.45	$25.48	$28.08	$23.03		$17.22
Minimum Average Value per Pelt	$21.10 (1951–2)	$18.23 (1951–2)	$19.90 (1951–2)	$23.00 (1951–2)	$16.00 (1951–2)	$15.89 (1953–4)		$15.00 (1956–7)
Maximum Average Value per Pelt	$27.57 (1950–1)	$27.34 (1950–1)	$27.36 (1950–1)	$30.00 (1955–7)	$35.00 (1955–7)	$31.27 (1950–1)		$30.00 (1958–9)

* One year only, 1950–1. ** Nine years only, 1951–60.

Family **FELIDAE**

Cats – *Chats*

The cat family is characterized by its fully retractable claws. There are five toes in front (the pollex is small and set high above the other toes) and four toes behind. The muzzle is short and broad. The skull is relatively short and broad with a high-arched dorsal contour and large orbital openings. The carnassial teeth are well developed in shortened jaws in which the premolars are reduced to two below and to either two or three above and the molars to only one above and below.

This family is quite conservative in basic morphological variation, differing but little in any species around the world. Eastern-Canadian representatives can be divided into two groups (genera): the long-tailed cats, which include the domestic cat (*Felis catus*) and the cougar (*Felis concolor*), and the short-tailed cats—the Canada lynx (*Lynx canadensis*) and the bobcat (*Lynx rufus*).

KEY TO THE EASTERN-CANADIAN GENERA OF *Felidae*

1 Tail long (more than 25 per cent of head and body); premolars $\frac{2-2}{2-2}$ FELIS p. 275

1' Tail short (less than 25 per cent of head and body); premolars $\frac{3-3}{2-2}$ LYNX p. 280

Genus **FELIS** Linnaeus

Cats – *Chats*

Dental Formula   I $\frac{3-3}{3-3}$ C $\frac{1-1}{1-1}$ P $\frac{3-3}{2-2}$ M $\frac{1-1}{1-1}$ = 30

KEY TO THE EASTERN-CANADIAN SPECIES OF *Felis*

1 Size large, total length over five ft (1.5 m.); skull more than 150 mm. long and 100 mm. wide.

FELIS CONCOLOR p. 276

1' Size small, total length less than three ft (1 m.).; skull less than 110 mm. long and 95 mm. wide.

FELIS CATUS p. 279

Fig. 155 – COUGAR – *Felis concolor*

Felis concolor Linnaeus – Cougar, Mountain Lion, Puma – *Couguar*

The names panther and painter (among others) have also been applied to this species, the largest native cat of Canada. The cougar has the conformation of an oversized domestic cat, but it varies in the colour of its upper parts which range from grizzled grey through dark brown, buff, cinnamon, tawny, and cinnamon rufous. The underparts are dull-whitish overlaid with buff across the abdomen. The backs of the ears are black, though occasional specimens have a greyish patch. The long tail is the same colour as the body except for two or three inches of the tip which is black. There are eight mammae: four pectoral (of which the front two are non-functional), two abdominal, and two inguinal.

The skull is typically cat-like, but it differs from that of other cats in its size and in having three premolars above instead of two as in *Lynx*.

SIZE Total length: males 1,710–2,743 mm., females 1,500–2,332; tail: males 660–900, females 534–815; hind foot: males 240–295, females 220–267; ear from notch 75–100. Skull length: males 172–237, females 158–203; skull width: males 126–165, females 107–141. Weight: males 100–200 lb. females 80–140.

DISTRIBUTION AND VARIATION The last authentic specimens and reliable records indicate that the cougar disappeared from eastern Canada about 100 years ago (*c.* 1860), although in recent years there have been persistent unconfirmed reports of its occurrence, particularly in New Brunswick and occasionally in northern and western Ontario. However, while rather convincing descriptions of cougars and their signs have been provided, no specimen has yet been produced. Originally the

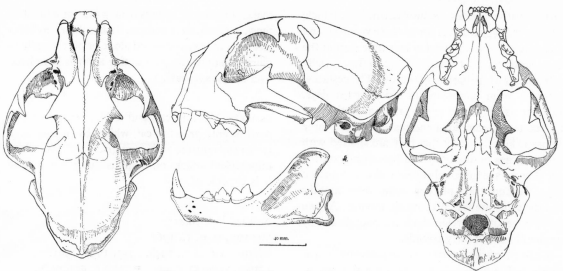

Fig. 156 – SKULL OF *Felis concolor* (ROM 34.5.10.1 ♀)

cougar may have ranged through the southern portion of eastern Canada from about the level of the north shore of Lake Superior to northern New Brunswick. Any specimens west of Lake Superior were thought to have been *Felis concolor schorgeri*, those to the east *F. c. cougar*.

HABITAT   The range of the cougar in North America was once roughly the same as that of the deer (*Odocoileus*). However, it has now been extir-

pated from all but the more remote wilderness areas of the continent—mountainous regions and large swamp areas and extensive rough hilly wood-lands where there is a minimum of interference from man.

HABITS The cougar is active both day and night but is usually more nocturnal and hunts by stalking and leaping rather than by chasing. Deer is its principal food, although domestic animals and

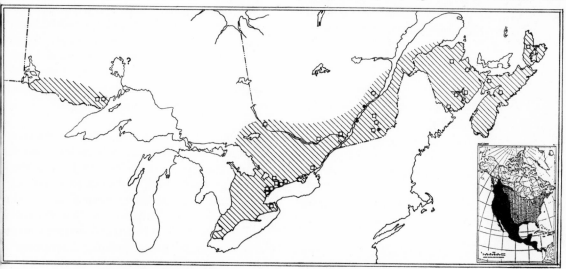

Map 72 – FORMER DISTRIBUTION OF THE COUGAR – *Felis concolor*

smaller native species are also taken. The female starts breeding when it is two or three years old and is apparently able to breed at any time during the year; however, most litters (of one to five, usually averaging two) are born in the spring. The gestation period is from ninety-one to ninety-seven days. The kittens weigh 250 to 500 grams at birth; they are 100 to 150 mm. long and resemble extra-large domestic kittens except that they are spotted with dark blotches on the body and have bands on the tail. The eyes are opened at about nine to fourteen days; weaning takes place at about three months and the spots are lost at about six months. At two months the kittens weigh about ten pounds and by six months about forty pounds.

While primarily a terrestrial species, the cougar climbs well and usually retreats up a tree whenever it is harassed by a dog. It is quite vocal and makes a variety of sounds from a purr or a hiss to a mew, a growl, or a scream. It is solitary in habit and is usually encountered alone or occasionally in pairs or family groups. Captive animals have lived over seventeen years.

REMARKS Much legend and folklore surround this magnificent, graceful cat which by nature is a rather shy creature and is not given to the ferocious unprovoked attacks on humans that many believe it is capable of.

Selected References

JACKSON, H. H. T., 1961.
WRIGHT, BRUCE S., 1948, 1953, 1959, 1961.
YOUNG, STANLEY P. and EDWARD A. GOLDMAN, 1946.

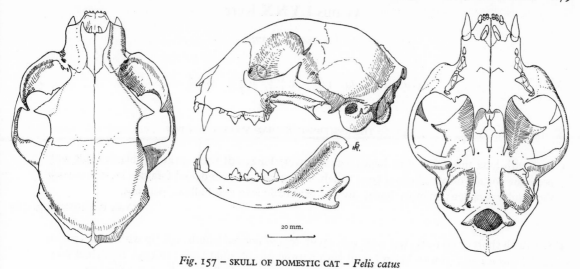

Fig. 157 – SKULL OF DOMESTIC CAT – *Felis catus*

Felis catus Linnaeus – Domestic Cat – *Chat domestique*

As the domestic cat has been associated with man as a pet for over 4,000 years, a great many varieties or breeds have been established. The species is included in this work primarily for osteological purposes. The domestic cat is widely used as a specimen for anatomical study in high schools and universities and it is therefore useful to be able to relate the species to other felids, as well as to other mammals in general. Also, skulls and skeletons of the domestic cat are frequently discovered in the wild under circumstances that make it desirable to distinguish them from those of the native species, and indeed from the skeletal remains of other mammals.

While there are many detailed variations in cranial proportions within the many breeds of cats, on the whole there are remarkably few basic deviations from the average. The skull of the domestic cat is smaller than that of any native cat and rarely exceeds about 100 mm. in length and 75 mm. in width. The basic shape is similar to that of all other species of cats (*Felidae*); it differs from

Lynx not only in being smaller but in having three premolars above and two below instead of two above and below. Occasionally specimens of domestic cats will have the upper front premolar missing on one or both sides, or they will have supernumerary premolars.

Breeding starts at about ten months and may continue up to fourteen years. The peak period of breeding is in February and March, but this may be extended, at intervals of ten days, from December to August. The average gestation period is sixty-two or sixty-three days, varying from fifty-six to sixty-five days. Litters vary from one to eight. The eyes are opened at about ten days. Kittens are usually weaned after four to six weeks. Permanent teeth are acquired at four to seven months. Ages of up to thirty-one years have been reported.

The domestic cat has served as a useful control over rats and mice, but it can be detrimental to desirable native animals such as songbirds and chipmunks.

Genus **LYNX** Kerr

Lynxes – *Lynx*

Dental Formula I $\frac{3-3}{3-3}$ C $\frac{1-1}{1-1}$ P $\frac{2-2}{2-2}$ M $\frac{1-1}{1-1}$ = 28

KEY TO THE EASTERN-CANADIAN SPECIES OF *Lynx*

1 Ears with long tufts; feet very large; legs relatively long; tail with entire tip black; skull with posterior portion of presphenoid bone widely flaring; anterior condyloid foramen located outside the jugular foramen; auditory bullae divided externally into two bulbous portions.

LYNX CANADENSIS p. 280

1′ Ears with short or no tufts; feet relatively small; legs of normal length; tail-tip with black spot on dorsal surface and whitish below; skull with narrow presphenoid bone; anterior condyloid foramen located within the rim of the jugular foramen; auditory bullae not divided externally.

LYNX RUFUS p. 284

Lynx canadensis Kerr – Canada Lynx – *Lynx du Canada*

The Canada lynx is a large, short-tailed cat readily distinguished by its long legs and its large furry feet, by the long tufts on the tip of each ear, and by a completely black-tipped tail. In other features it resembles the bobcat, *Lynx rufus*. The fur is usually buffy grey with indistinct spotting. There are only four mammae, two abdominal and two inguinal.

The skull of the lynx closely resembles that of the bobcat except that it has a much wider presphenoid. The anterior condyloid foramen is distinct and separate from the jugular foramen or foramen lacerum posterius. The auditory bullae have a constriction across them where the inner portion joins the outer section. The skull is smaller than that of the cougar and larger than that of the domestic cat. There are only two premolars above and below.

SIZE Total length: males 790–1,000 (average 876) mm., females 776–870 (av. 838); tail 89–120 (av. 107); hind foot 215–255 (av. 240); ear from notch 70–80 (av. 74). Skull length: males 114–146 (av. 123), females 114–126 (av. 120); skull width: males 80–108 (av. 90), females 83–92 (av. 87). Weight 11–35 (av. 17) lb.

DISTRIBUTION AND VARIATION All of eastern Canada must be included within the range of the Canada lynx. However, it has become quite rare in, if not absent from, most of the agricultural areas of southern Ontario, southern Quebec, southern New Brunswick, and Prince Edward Island. The mainland form is *Lynx canadensis canadensis*, while *L. c. subsolanus* is restricted to Newfoundland.

HABITAT The Canada lynx inhabits wooded and swampy areas where the varying hare is available. The lynx seems to be declining in numbers along the southern portions of its range where the bobcat has recently moved in and is becoming established.

HABITS Although the lynx is an adept climber, most of its hunting is on the ground where the varying hare is its primary food. (The dependence on the varying hare is reflected in population numbers

Fig. 158 – CANADA LYNX – *Lynx canadensis*

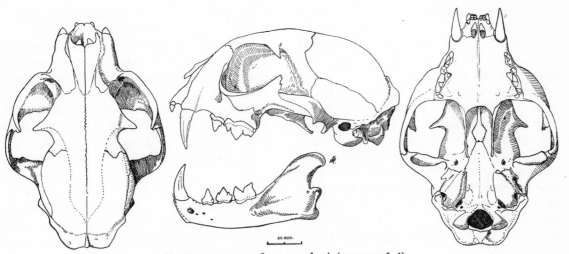

20 MM.

Fig. 159 – SKULL OF *Lynx canadensis* (ROM 20326 ♂)

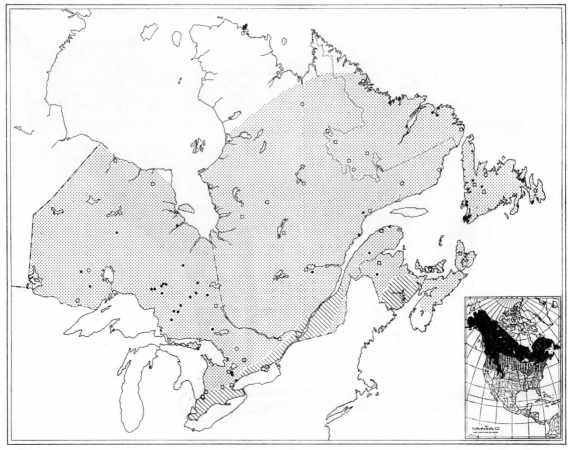

Map 73 – DISTRIBUTION OF THE CANADA LYNX – *Lynx canadensis* – AND (1) TYPE LOCALITY OF *L. c. subsolanus* Bangs

of the lynx which closely follow the cyclic peaks of abundance of the hare, usually lagging about one year behind.) Other small mammals up to the size of a porcupine or fox, ground birds, frogs, and invertebrates are also taken.

Reproduction data are not fully known. Breeding age is thought to be reached at one year; mating takes place from January to March. After about two months, one to four (rarely five) furry kittens are born in a den under a windfall in some natural cavity of the ground. The kittens are much more brownish than the adults and are strongly blotched on the upper parts. The eyes open in about ten days and the young venture forth with the mother at about two months. By fall they leave her to fend for themselves.

The lynx is a shy creature and may become quite submissive when caught in a steel trap.

REMARKS The long, soft, delicately shaded pelt of the lynx is in great demand when long-haired fur is in fashion. There has been an alarming decline in the number of pelts taken in recent years—the number of pelts taken in the years of high production is declining almost steadily. During the period 1950–60, production ranged from about 1,300 to 6,900 pelts, and the average price paid varied from about $3.00 to $16.00 per pelt (see Table 13). The future prospects of this species are not encouraging.

Selected References

BANGS, OUTRAM, 1897a.
CAMERON, AUSTIN W., 1959.
ELSEY, C. A., 1954.
ELTON, CHARLES and MARY NICHOLSON, 1942b.
SETON, ERNEST THOMPSON, 1928.

Table 13

Production of Lynx Pelts in Eastern Canada, 1950–60

	ALL CANADA	EASTERN CANADA	ONTARIO	QUEBEC	NOVA SCOTIA	NEW-FOUNDLAND
TOTAL PELTS 1950–60	138,652	32,315	14,417	13,682	271	*3,945
Average Annual Production	13,865	3,232	1,442	1,368	27	438
Minimum Annual Production	7,324	1,343	215	765	3	272
Maximum Annual Production	40,408	6,928	4,116	2,486	70	648
TOTAL VALUE 1950–60	$1,465,985	$294,466	$136,965	$133,463	$2,208	$23,462
Average Annual Value	$146,599	$29,447	$13,697	$13,34	$221	$2,607
Minimum Annual Value	$38,273	$9,133	$946	$3,673	$18	$1,002
Maximum Annual Value	$704,613	$109,874	$62,152	$47,234	$925	$7,128
Average Value per Pelt	$10.56	$9.11	$9.51	$9.74	$8.18	$5.98
Minimum Average Value per Pelt	$3.62	$3.13	$2.85	$2.50	$3.14	$3.00
Maximum Average Value per Pelt	$17.44	$15.85	$15.10	$19.00	$25.00	$11.00

* Nine years only, 1951–60.

Fig. 160 – BOBCAT – *Lynx rufus*

Lynx rufus (Schreber) – Bobcat – *Lynx roux*

Roughly the same size as the Canada lynx, the bob-cat has relatively shorter legs, smaller feet, shorter ear tufts, and only a black spot on top of the tail instead of a completely black tip. The bobcat is much more variable in colour than the lynx, ranging from light grey to dark reddish brown. The coloration of the upper part varies from a monotone to a quite distinct dark spotting over all. The underparts vary from white to buff, with strong spotting on the belly and inside of the legs. There are four mammae, two abdominal and two inguinal.

The skull, which may average larger than that of the lynx, can be distinguished by the lack of a distinct line of constriction across the auditory bullae, by a narrower presphenoid, and by the anterior condyloid foramen's being confluent with the foramen lacerum posterius.

SIZE Total length: males 853–1,252 (av. 950) mm., females 745–950 (av. 829); tail: 119–190 (av. 145); hind foot: males 170–223 (av. 185), females 155–190 (av. 172); ear from notch 60–75 (av. 66). Skull length: males 126.0–149.5 (av. 135), females 116–138 (av. 123); skull width: males 88–104 (av. 95), females 75–95 (av. 85). Weight: males 12–68 (av. 28) lb., females 10–27 (av. 15).

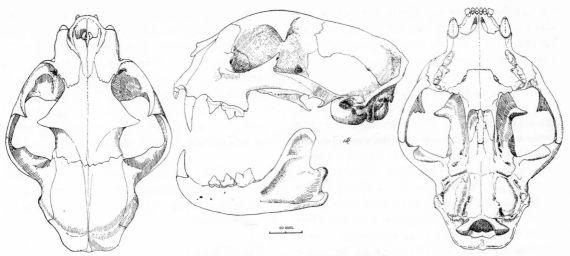

Fig. 161 – SKULL OF *Lynx rufus* (ROM 21418)

DISTRIBUTION AND VARIATION In recent years the bobcat has expanded its range northward in eastern Canada. *Lynx rufus superiorensis* has moved northward in Ontario from the upper peninsula of Michigan via the islands of western Manitoulin and from Minnesota west of Lake Superior; it now completely surrounds Lake Superior. It is a large race. Its skull has a distinctively shaped dorsal contour (an inflated supraorbital region). Compared with the skull of the large eastern race, *L. r.* *gigas*, which occurs from Nova Scotia westward through southern Ontario, the skull of *L. r. superiorensis* has a relatively smaller, thin first upper premolar (P^3) and a relatively wider, shorter palate. *L. r. rufus*, the smaller, more southern race, reaches southwestern New Brunswick and possibly enters Quebec south of the St Lawrence River. It has a relatively wider, shorter skull with an evenly arched dorsal contour and a relatively heavy first upper premolar.

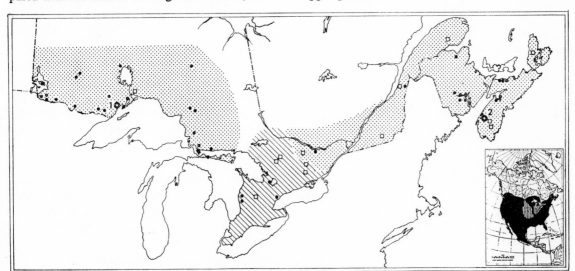

Map 74 – DISTRIBUTION OF THE BOBCAT – *Lynx rufus* – AND TYPE LOCALITIES OF (1) *L. r. superiorensis* Peterson and Downing; (2) *L. r. gigas* Bangs

HABITAT Forested or semi-forested areas that provide suitable den sites. The bobcat thrives much better than the Canada lynx in agricultural and more populated urban areas.

HABITS Like the Canada lynx, the bobcat depends to a large extent on hares and rabbits for food, although a wider variety of animals, including larger prey up to the size of white-tailed deer, is also taken. In agricultural areas the bobcat occasionally preys on chickens, pigs, sheep, and even calves. In general behaviour it is strikingly similar to the domestic cat, even in its vocalization. It is shy and solitary and is seldom observed when free in the wild. Unlike the lynx, which may become submissive when caught in a steel trap, the bobcat almost invariably remains ferocious to the end.

Most breeding is thought to take place about February or March, with one to four (an average of two) kittens being born after a gestation period of about sixty-two days. The newborn weigh about 200 to 800 grams and their eyes remain closed for about the first three to ten days. The fur shows mottling or subdued spotting, and fairly strong facial markings are present. Weaning takes place at about two months. Both parents secure food for the young. By fall, when the young have reached a weight of about ten pounds or more, they are able to fend for themselves.

Captive animals have lived up to twenty-five years. It is probable that wild animals rarely live to be half that age.

REMARKS The fur of the bobcat is not as valuable as the fur of the Canada lynx and comparatively few pelts are marketed annually in eastern Canada (see Table 14).

Selected References

BANGS, OUTRAM, 1897a.
PETERSON, RANDOLPH L. and STUART C. DOWNING, 1952.
POLLACK, E. MICHAEL and WILLIAM G. SHELDON, 1951.
ROLLINS, CLAIR T., 1945.
YOUNG, STANLEY P., 1941a, 1958.

Table 14

Production of Bobcat Pelts in Eastern Canada, 1950–60

	ALL CANADA	EASTERN CANADA	ONTARIO	QUEBEC	NEW BRUNSWICK	NOVA SCOTIA	PRINCE EDWARD I.	NEW-FOUNDLAND
TOTAL PELTS 1950–60	7,243	7,159	—	387	3,633	3,138	*1	—
Average Annual Production	724	716		39	363	314		
Minimum Annual Production	345 (1954–5)	340 (1954–5)		19 (1954–5)	143 (1954–5)	142 (1956–7)		
Maximum Annual Production	1,404 (1955–6)	1,400 (1955–6)		66 (1957–8)	1,145 (1955–6)	384 (1958–9)		
TOTAL VALUE 1950–60	$11,595	$11,250		$523	$4,824	$5,939	$5.00	
Average Annual Value	$1,160	$1,125		$52	$482	$594		
Minimum Annual Value	$360 (1951–2)	$360 (1951–2)		$5 (1954–5)	$98 (1952–3)	$180 (1951–2)		
Maximum Annual Value	$3,820 (1959–60)	$2,881 (1958–9)		$107 (1950–1)	$1,920 (1959–60)	$1,920 (1958–9)		
Average Value per Pelt	$1.60	$1.57		$1.35	$1.32	$1.89		
Minimum Average Value per Pelt	$0.54 (1951–2)	$0.54 (1951–2)		$0.25 (1955–6)	$0.50 (1951–3 & 1957–9)	$1.00 (1952–4)		
Maximum Average Value per Pelt	$3.75 (1958–9)	$3.72 (1958–9)		$2.50 (1959–60)	$4.00 (1959–60)	$5.00 (1958–9)		

* One year only, 1951–2.

Order
Pinnipedia

Marine Carnivores

This group of carnivores is highly adapted for a marine existence. The feet are modified as swimming flippers and the cheek teeth are more simple structures than those of true carnivores. Representatives of two families of this order occur in eastern Canada: *Phocidae*, the hair seals, and *Odobenidae*, the walrus. A third family, *Otariidae*, occurs on the west coast of North America (and elsewhere in the Pacific) and includes eared seals such as the fur seal and the sea-lion. (The California sea-lion is the species commonly used as trained seals.)

KEY TO THE EASTERN-CANADIAN FAMILIES OF *Pinnipedia*

1 Hind limbs capable of rotating forward; upper canines greatly enlarged to form tusks; alisphenoid canals present; all cheek teeth single rooted. ODOBENIDAE, p. 288

1' Hind limbs not capable of rotating forward; upper canines not greatly enlarged; alisphenoid canals absent; posterior cheek teeth double rooted. PHOCIDAE p. 292

Family ODOBENIDAE
Walruses – *Morses*

This family is represented by only one living genus, the walrus. It is best known by its feet, which are modified as flippers, and by the presence of greatly enlarged upper canine teeth. The forelimbs are only free from the elbow. All the teeth are single rooted. The hind feet can be rotated forward as in *Otariidae*, but there is no external ear.

Fig. 162 – WALRUS – *Odobenus rosmarus*

Genus **ODOBENUS** Brisson

Walruses – *Morses*

Dental Formula (functional) $I\frac{1-1}{0-0}$ $C\frac{1-1}{1-1}$ $P\frac{3-3}{3-3}$, $M\frac{0-0}{0-0} = 18$

Odobenus rosmarus (Linnaeus) – Walrus – *Morse*

The large, ponderous size and long tusks of the walrus are well known. The head is relatively short, with a broad squarish muzzle that has coarse, stiff bristles called mystacial vibrissae which measure two to six inches. The hide is quite thick, tough, and wrinkled, with many foldings, and it covers a thick layer of 'blubber' that provides insulation, buoyancy, and a food reserve. Young animals have short greyish-brown hair, but adults are almost hairless. Adult males average about sixteen per cent heavier than females and are more massive, particularly in the neck, chest, and shoulders. The general body colour varies, but usually it is some

shade of grey, brown, or cinnamon and is often suffused with a pink or rose colour. Each flipper has five toes with well-developed nails located well back from the end of the cartilaginous toe-flap. Two pairs of mammary nipples are located within folds of the skin, one pair abdominal and the other inguinal.

The skull is characterized by its large, massive size; by its long canines (which tend to be longer in males—extracted tusks have been reported up to 39.5 in., but they are usually less than 24—and thicker in cross-section); by single peg-like single-rooted cheek teeth; no postorbital process; and by

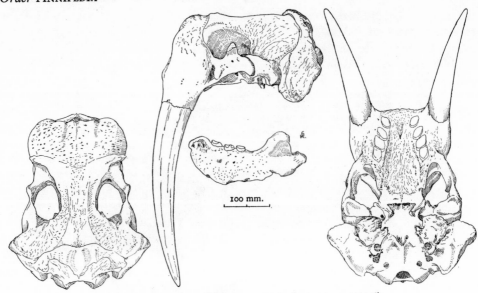

Fig. 163 – SKULL OF *Odobenus rosmarus* (ROM 30.10.4.37 ♂)

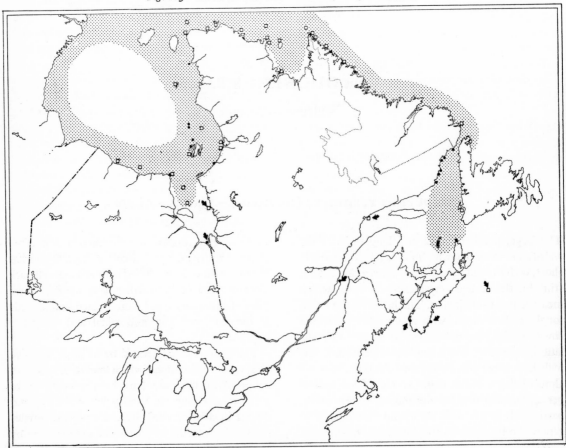

Map 75 – DISTRIBUTION OF THE WALRUS – *Odobenus rosmarus*

the fact that the surface of the mastoid processes is continuous with the auditory bullae. In the milk dentition there are three incisors and a canine both above and below (a total of twenty-eight teeth). Usually only one upper incisor is replaced with a permanent tooth, although occasionally this incisor as well as the lower canine (similar in appearance to other cheek teeth) may not be replaced.

The dentition develops from the deciduous teeth through a so-called successional stage to the final functional set. The deciduous or milk teeth are small, conical in shape, and non-functional. They usually disappear before birth, but are sometimes not shed until soon after. The successional teeth represent the normal permanent dentition of other carnivores, but in the case of the walrus there is a further loss of teeth between birth and middle age by resorption or shedding; the fourth upper premolar develops at the successional stage and may persist to adulthood. The functional dentition is made up of those permanent teeth remaining through the last half of adult life.

The canine tusks have enamel caps or tips for a short time after eruption. Adult tusks consist entirely of dentine or ivory.

SIZE Total length: males 8–13 (av. 9 to 10) ft., females 7–10 (av. 8); tail 2–4 in.; hind foot 18–25 in. Skull length: males 275–400 mm., females 250–375; skull width: males 220–280, females 180–250. Weight: males 1,000–2,500 (av. 1,500) lb., females 1,000–1,800 (av. 1,250).

DISTRIBUTION AND VARIATION The Atlantic walrus, *Odobenus rosmarus rosmarus*, occurs in the North Atlantic and Arctic Oceans. (The Pacific population is regarded as a distinct race, *O. r. divergens.*) In historic times it ranged south along the Labrador coast to the Gulf of St Lawrence where there are records from the Magdalen Islands and from up the St Lawrence River to Rivière Oueille. It also occurred on Sable Island and on the southern coast of Nova Scotia as late as 1937 when a male was said to have been shot near Bear Cove, Meteghham. The walrus still occurs in Hudson Strait and northern Hudson Bay, ranging south to the Belcher Islands, but it has become rare there, although it is still occasionally seen along the Ontario and Quebec shores of Hudson and James Bays north of Agamski Island.

HABITAT Arctic and subarctic waters, especially along shore lines, and in open water around fast and pack ice—wherever the walrus can haul out to sleep or rest and drop quickly back into deep water on the approach of danger. In winter, open water is the primary factor that allows the walrus to subsist in any given area.

HABITS The walrus is primarily an inshore bottom feeder. Bivalve molluscs form the bulk of its diet; sometimes fish and crustaceans are also eaten. Clams are apparently 'shucked' in the mouth, as the shells do not appear in the stomach contents. The large tusks are used in dislodging the clams from the bottom. The walrus is reported to attack seals occasionally (seal-skin has been found in its stomach), but the extent to which seals are taken for food is unknown.

Walrus are reported to be able to dive to a depth of 300 feet (fifty fathoms) and to remain submerged for over ten minutes. A gregarious species, they congregate in close packs, particularly at favourable hauling-out sites or *uglits* on ice or on shore. Their movements are imperfectly known: some groups remain fairly stationary all year while others seem to move considerable distances. There appears to be a general migration pattern in and out of Hudson Bay through Hudson Strait.

The walrus is quite vociferous. Its grunt-like 'oogh' can frequently be heard over considerable distances and often guides hunters in locating feeding or hauled-out herds before they can be sighted.

The gestation period is thought to be ten to eleven months, with no delayed implantation. The females breed no more often than every other year. The single young are born in mid-April to June and continue to nurse for an extended period —up to eighteen to twenty-four months, it is thought. Newborn calves are about four feet long. They lack the characteristic tusks, which erupt at three or four months and are one or two inches long at one year, reaching about three or four inches at two years. Sexual maturity is thought to be reached at about five years in females and six years in males, although most females do not bear young until they are seven years old. The normal life-span is thought to exceed twenty years—it is possibly as long as thirty years.

Although appearing slow and sluggish, the walrus is fairly cautious and has developed a healthy fear of polar bear and man. The only really effective predator other than man is the killer whale.

REMARKS Walrus numbers have been seriously reduced, especially since Eskimo hunters obtained high-powered rifles. Walrus are particularly vulnerable when they have hauled themselves out of the water in large groups; injured animals that are able to reach the water are seldom recovered because they quickly sink. Walrus skins, tusks, and oil have been commercially exploited; the flesh has been eaten by both humans and dogs. Walrus are now used for the most part locally, primarily for dog food (though some fresh meat is eaten by

Eskimos); the tusks are used for carving ivory figurines and tools. It has been estimated that about 1,200 walrus are taken per year in the eastern-Canadian Arctic, of which perhaps less than half come from eastern Canada as it is defined in this work. The average annual increment is estimated to be between twelve and twenty per cent. Strong conservation measures are necessary to prevent further serious decline in walrus numbers.

Selected References
ALLEN, J. A., 1880.
BROOKS, J. W., 1954.
COBB, W. M., 1933.
COLLINS, G., 1940.
DUNBAR, M. J., 1949, 1955a, 1956.
HOWELL, A. BRAZIER, 1930.
LEWIS, HARRISON F. and J. K. DOUTT, 1942.
LOUGHREY, ALAN G., 1959.
MANVILLE, R. H. and P. G. FAVOUR, JR., 1960.
SUTTON, G. M. and W. J. HAMILTON, JR., 1932.
VIBE, CHRISTIAN, 1950.
WRIGHT, BRUCE S., 1951.

Family **PHOCIDAE**

Seals – *Phoques*

All seals in eastern Canada belong to this family— the so-called hair seals. Phocids have no external ears and the rear limbs are permanently directed posteriorly so that they cannot be rotated forward as in *Otariidae* and *Odobenidae*. The fore-flippers are less than one quarter of the length of the body and are flexible and nearly uniform in thickness. The tips of the digits extend only slightly, if at all, beyond the functional claws, which may be quite large. The tympanic bones are large, inflated, and thick-walled. The nasal bones form a wedge

between the frontals. The post-canine teeth usually have three or more distinct cusps. Underfur in the usual sense is never present in the adults, although there may be a sparse substratum of shorter, finer underhairs. The surfaces of all flippers are distinctly haired. Superciliary vibrissae ('whiskers') are well developed. Mammae consist of two or four functional teats.

Seals are rather unique among mammals for the very high butter content of their milk, which in some species exceeds fifty per cent.

KEY TO THE EASTERN-CANADIAN GENERA OF *Phocidae*

1 Single incisor in each lower jaw; premaxillae do not reach nasals; skull wide, almost square in outline, with short rostrum; males with inflatable pouch of skin on top of nose; first and fifth digits on hind feet longer than the middle three. CYSTOPHORA p. 309

1′ Two incisors in each lower jaw; premaxillae in contact with nasals; males without inflatable pouch of skin on top of nose: 2

2 Snout long (distance between the tip of nose and eyes nearly twice the distance between eyes and ear openings); top of skull forms a straight line (viewed laterally). HALICHOERUS p. 305

2′ Snout short (distance between the tip of nose and eyes much less than twice the distance between eyes and ear openings); top of skull forms a convex bent line (viewed laterally): 3

3 First and second digits of front flipper longer than third; jugal bone long and narrow (depth less than half its length); two mammae. PHOCA p. 293

3′ Third digit of front flipper longer than first and second; jugal bone short and deep (depth more than half its length); four mammae. ERIGNATHUS p. 302

Genus **PHOCA** Linnaeus

Hair Seals – *Phoques*

Dental Formula $\text{I} \frac{3-3}{2-2} \quad \text{C} \frac{1-1}{1-1} \quad \text{P} \frac{4-4}{4-4} \quad \text{M} \frac{1-1}{1-1} = 34$

KEY TO THE EASTERN-CANADIAN SPECIES OF *Phoca*

1 Posterior margin of palate broadly U-shaped; bony nasal septum reaching or nearly reaching the posterior margin of the palate; adult males usually have a dark U-shaped band or 'harp' on the back.
(Subgenus *Pagophilus*) PHOCA GROENLANDICA p. 299

1′ Posterior margin of palate V-shaped; bony nasal septum not reaching the posterior margin of the palate: 2

2 Cheek teeth relatively large and set close together; least interorbital width 7 mm. or more; head dog-shaped; pelage usually with dark spots on paler background; hair relatively soft and not consistently directed posteriorly. (Subgenus *Phoca*) PHOCA VITULINA p. 294

2′ Cheek teeth relatively small with spaces between; least interorbital width less than 7 mm.; head round and cat-shaped; pelage usually with rings created by whitish spots with dark centres; hair relatively coarse and stiff and consistently directed posteriorly.
(Subgenus *Pusa*) PHOCA HISPIDA p. 296

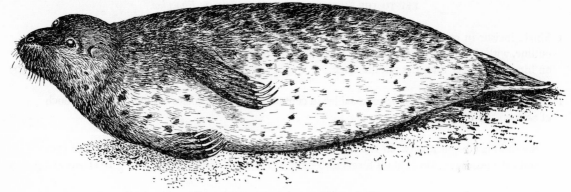

Fig. 164 – HARBOUR SEAL – *Phoca vitulina*

Phoca vitulina Linnaeus – Harbour Seal – *Phoque commun*

A small species with a dog-like face, the harbour seal is usually blotched and/or spotted. The basic colour varies greatly from cream through yellowish grey to dark brown. The darker markings tend to merge along the back. Compared with *Phoca hispida*, the fur is distinctly soft and not consistently directed posteriorly. Experienced observers can distinguish the harbour seal from *P. hispida* by its odour which is neutral compared with the distinctive rank smell of *P. hispida*. The hairs are flattened and arranged in clusters. Oil glands are large and numerous and the dermis is highly vascular.

The posterior margin of the palate is v-shaped; the bony nasal septum does not reach posterior to the margin of the palate; the cheek teeth are relatively large and set close together (they are usually crowded out of line) and the least interorbital width is 7 mm. or more. Compared with the skull of *P. hispida*, the nasals are wider, with sides that are nearly parallel anteriorly instead of flaring.

SIZE Total length 1,350–1,800 mm.; tail 75–105; hind foot 200–300. Skull: length 162–222 (av. 184), width 100–128 (av. 112). Weight: males 130–300 lb., females 100–160.

DISTRIBUTION AND VARIATION The harbour seal is closely associated with land and occurs on both coasts of North America. It ranges further south along coastal waters than the other seals of this family. *P. vitulina concolor* is found along the entire coastline of eastern Canada; it once ranged up the St Lawrence as far west as Lake Ontario, south into Lake Champlain, and northwest up the Ottawa River to the mouth of the Gatineau River where one was killed near Hull in 1865. At the present time it is rarely seen west of Godbout where the St Lawrence River widens into the Gulf. On the east side of Hudson Bay *P. v. mellonae*, a darker race with a slender pointed coronoid process, has become land-locked and remains in Upper and Lower Seal Lakes, Quebec (some 125 miles northeast of Cairn Island, Richmond Gulf, along the coast of Hudson Bay). The harbour seal is represented on the west coast of North America by the race *P. v. richardii*.

The lack of data on recent specific records south of Southampton and Eskimo Point indicates that the harbour seal is now rare in James Bay and western Hudson Bay.

HABITAT As the name implies, the harbour seal is an animal of coastal waters. It commonly enters freshwater streams, especially in the spring (the land-locked *P. v. mellonae* lives permanently in freshwater lakes and streams). This species spends much more time on land than any of the other members of the family.

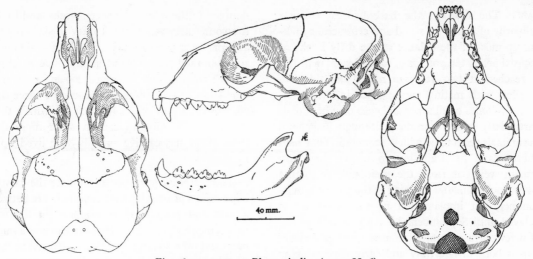

Fig. 165 – SKULL OF *Phoca vitulina* (ROM 18876)

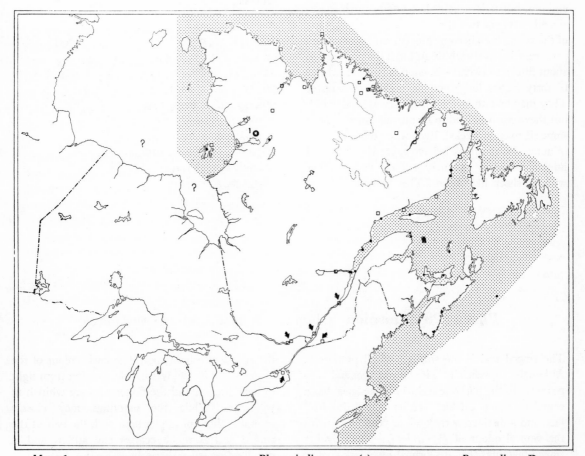

Map 76 – DISTRIBUTION OF THE HARBOUR SEAL – *Phoca vitulina* – AND (1) TYPE LOCALITY OF *P. v. mellonae* Doutt

HABITS The food of the harbour seal consists primarily of fish, with squid and crustaceans making up most of the balance of the daily intake of approximately ten pounds of food. Sexual maturity is reached at two years in males and three in females, with mating taking place in the water. Loose colonies of all sexes and ages may be found, particularly in late summer, although in general the animals seem to be widely scattered. They haul out on land to sleep, but in winter they may remain well out from the mainland. A mating takes place soon after weaning of the young in midsummer, but implantation of the blastocyst is delayed until September. After a gestation period of a few days over nine months, usually a single pup is born in late May and early June. During foetal development fine, silky, white fur covers the embryo, but it is usually lost before birth (occasionally a day or two afterwards). The upper parts of the young soon become greyish while the underparts remain silvery white. At birth the pups weigh about fifteen to twenty-six pounds (they are thirty to forty inches long) and have their eyes open. They may take to water when they are a day old, but they return to land to be nursed (nursing lasts some six to eight weeks). Even when they are a few minutes old, the pups behave aggressively toward human intruders and may call for their mother with a sheep-like bleat. The body weight is doubled in the first six or seven weeks, and by fall the young may weigh about forty to sixty pounds and measure 900 to 1,000 mm. By the following summer they weigh about seventy-five to eighty pounds and measure between 1,000 and 1,200 mm. The teeth of the young appear two or three days after birth; a pup begins to catch fish within three to five weeks. Growth continues for more than three years and captive animals have lived up to nineteen years.

REMARKS Recent attempts to estimate the existing populations of seals indicate that there are between 40,000 and 100,000 *P. v. concolor* (in the total range, of which eastern Canada constitutes a minor part) and only 500 to 1,000 *P. v. mellonae*, the form that is land-locked in the Ungava region of Quebec.

Selected References
ALLEN, J. A., 1880.
ANDERSON, R. M., 1943b.
BARTLETT, ROBERT A., 1927.
DOUTT, J. K., 1942, 1954.
DUNBAR, M. J., 1941, 1949.
FISHER, H. D., 1952, 1954.
MERRIAM, C. HART, 1884.
SCHEFFER, VICTOR B., 1958.
SNYDER, L. L., 1941.
WHEELER, E. P., 1953.

Phoca (Pusa) hispida Schreber – Ringed Seal – *Phoque annelé*

The ringed seal is the smallest of all pinnipeds. Although superficially similar in general appearance to the harbour seal, the ringed seal has a rounder, more cat-like (rather than dog-like) face and a distinctive rank odour (compared with the neutral odour of *P. vitulina*); it usually has ringed markings that are formed by a dark spot in the centre of a light spot. The basic colour of the upper parts is highly variable, ranging from light to dark brown, and the underparts are whitish to yellowish. While the markings may closely resemble those of the harbour seal, the hair of the ringed seal is much coarser and stiffer, and is usually directed posteriorly.

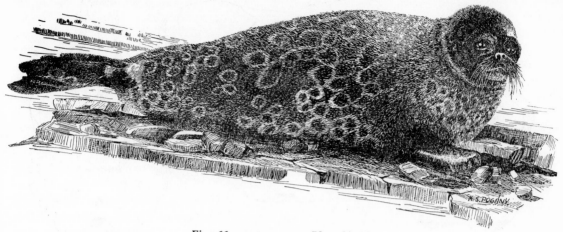

Fig. 166 – RINGED SEAL – *Phoca hispida*

The skull has the same v-shaped posterior margin of the palate as that of *P. vitulina* but it differs in having a narrower least interorbital width (less than 7 mm.) and smaller cheek teeth (not crowded so closely together). The nasals are narrower posteriorly and flare out strongly anteriorly.

SIZE Total length 1,000–1,680 mm.; tail 65–95; hind foot 200–330. Skull: length 155–177 (av. 166), width 90–106 (av. 100). Weight 80–250 lb.

DISTRIBUTION AND VARIATION The ringed seal is closely associated with ice, being circumpolar in distribution, and it is the common seal of the Arctic, but it sometimes ventures south of the Strait of Belle Isle (as far as La Tabitière, Que., and South Brook, Nfld.). One specimen was taken at Manicaugau, near the mouth of the St Lawrence River, in 1888. The ringed seal is common along the Labrador coast, Hudson Strait, Hudson Bay, and James Bay. The entire population is currently regarded as belonging to a single race, *Phoca hispida hispida* (or *Pusa h. hispida* of some authors).

HABITAT Arctic waters and ice floes.

HABITS Unlike the fish-eating harbour seal, the ringed seal feeds on a wide variety of planktonic, nektonic, and benthonic food—primarily crustaceans and other invertebrates, and a limited number of fish, especially the polar cod (*Boreogadus saida*). At least seventy-two species are known to be eaten. Ringed seals feed to a depth of more than twenty fathoms (possibly down to fifty fathoms) and remain submerged for a little over three minutes on the average. They tend to remain in one general area without moving very far. They are known to travel considerable distances over solid ice, however, or even overland, in search of open water. They are usually widely dispersed—they rarely group together in colonies. In winter, particularly in March, they may dig small breathing holes in the ice or larger holes big enough to pass through. They must constantly return to one of these holes, or to natural openings in the ice, after periods of diving or feeding.

Breeding takes place shortly after parturition. The blastocyst is not implanted for a period of three and a half months. About late March or April the female digs a cavity in the snow on landfast ice, or sometimes utilizes natural craters formed by ice push-ups, into which she retreats to bring forth a single white pup (about 25 in. long and weighing about ten pounds). The woolly white coat of the pup lasts about two to four weeks, after which it assumes a greyish colour above and a yellowish-

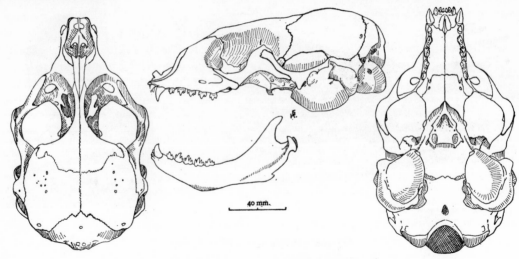

40 mm.

Fig. 167 – SKULL OF *Phoca hispida* (ROM 86.8.24.9)

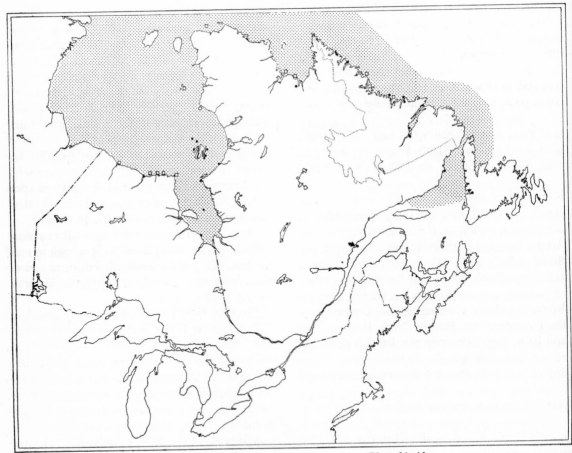

Map 77 – DISTRIBUTION OF THE RINGED SEAL – *Phoca hispida*

grey colour below. These immature seals are then known as 'silver jars'.

In June and early July ringed seals haul out on fast ice and remain there basking in the sun, moulting and fasting. By this time most young are thought to be weaned. Much blubber is lost during this period, but it is soon regained during summer feeding. Full breeding age is not reached until about the seventh year, although some females may ovulate at five or six years. Age can be determined accurately by cross-sectioning the canine tooth which shows an annual deposition that forms rings much like those on a tree trunk. Annuli on the claws also serve to determine the age up to about ten years. Ringed seals are known to live twenty-five years or more under natural conditions—up to forty-three years have been estimated.

REMARKS The economy of coastal Eskimos has been highly dependent on ringed seals, which provide food for both humans and dogs, and foot gear, dog-team harnesses, oil, and other vital needs of the Arctic. The distribution and abundance of the widely dispersed populations are governed by the ice conditions along the coast rather than by food supply.

Selected References
ALLEN, J. A., 1880.
ANDERSON, R. M., 1943b.
DOUTT, J. K., 1942.
DUNBAR, M. J., 1941, 1949.
FISHER, H. D., 1950.
MCLAREN, I. A., 1958a and c.
SCHEFFER, VICTOR B., 1858.
WHEELER, E. P., 1953.

Phoca (Pagophilus) groenlandica Erxleben – Harp or Greenland Seal –
Phoque du Groenland

The name harp seal is derived from the presence of a dark saddle—a harp- or horseshoe-shaped band—on the back of full adults, particularly of males (which also have a black face). The basic colour is light grey. Young adult females may have a less distinct 'harp' and a broken series of blotches instead; their basic colour is dark grey. There is a series of changes in coloration from the 'white-coat' newborn, through 'beaters' which are pale grey with poorly defined spots on the back (after the white coat is shed before the age of one year; 'beaters' are also called 'grey backs', 'grey cubs', or 'rusties'), to 'bedlamers' which become dark grey or tawny with some spotting on the upper sides and back and which have a darker head and flippers, to a sub-adult pelage with blotches instead of a distinct harp, and finally to the full adult pelage. Males are thought to develop the

harp at the end of the fourth year and females at the end of the fifth year. In general shape and size, the harp seal resembles a large harbour seal.

The skull is distinguished from that of other *Phoca* by the broad U-shaped posterior margin of the palate and by the bony nasal septum which almost reaches the posterior margin of the palate.

SIZE Total length 1,460–2,000 (av. 1,600) mm.; tail 95–125; hind foot 250–450. Skull: length 190–228, width 114–124. Weight 100–400 lb.

DISTRIBUTION AND VARIATION *Phoca groenlandica* is primarily an animal of the North Atlantic and the adjoining Arctic Ocean, reaching its normal southern limits in the western Atlantic in the Gulf of St Lawrence, although an occasional harp seal wanders further south. It ranges north to Hudson Strait and northern Hudson Bay but apparently

Fig. 168 – HARP SEAL – *Phoca groenlandica*

rarely moves far south into the Bay proper, although it has been reported as far south as the Belcher Islands.

HABITAT Drifting ice packs out in the deep sea.

HABITS Always on the move, harp seals follow extensive and regular migrations in their constant search for food that combines both fish and planktonic organisms. Capelin are eaten extensively in Newfoundland waters, and herring (*Clupea harengus*) and other fish make up most of the diet in the Gulf of St Lawrence area. Further north, small crustaceans are important items in the diet. During their dives, harp seals can remain submerged for fifteen minutes or more.

By late February to mid-March they reach the Gulf of St Lawrence and Newfoundland area where the 'white-coats' are born on pack-ice after a gestation period of about eleven months. They weigh about twelve pounds at birth. Within two weeks the pups increase their weight by five times, while they remain on the ice (the birth weight is doubled in five days). Seal milk has a high content of fat (forty-two per cent or some twelve times more than a dairy cow's milk) and protein (ten to twelve per cent, some three or four times as much as cow's milk), only about forty-five per cent water (about half the water content of cow's milk), and no milk sugar (there is an average of 4.4 per cent in a dairy cow's milk). The mothers stay on the ice near their pups and establish a small territory

from which they will drive out all intruders. Normally the pups do not enter the water until the white coat is shed. About this time (two to three weeks after birth), the males arrive on the scene and entice the females away from their young to mate.

Mating is apparently completely promiscuous and takes place both on the ice and in the sea. There is no evidence of a harem formation or of any other social organization. Females seem to feed little if at all from the time they haul out to bear young until after mating; during the breeding season males also eat little. Males are thought to become fully mature sexually at eight years, females at between five and eight; females are known to continue to bear young until they are at least sixteen years of age (probably until they are twenty).

Both sexes may live at least twenty-eight years, with some exceeding thirty. Harp seals seldom, if ever, haul out on land outside of the breeding season—they spend their entire time in the water, although they keep fairly close to the coast line. They move northward in the spring (by May or June) to the high Arctic and head back south about December, though some immature seals are thought to remain in the Arctic all year.

REMARKS This species is exploited more than any other by commercial sealers who remove several ship loads (mainly of pups) from the ice-packs

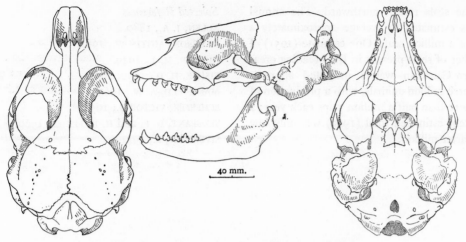

Fig. 169 – SKULL OF *Phoca groenlandica* (ROM 18873)

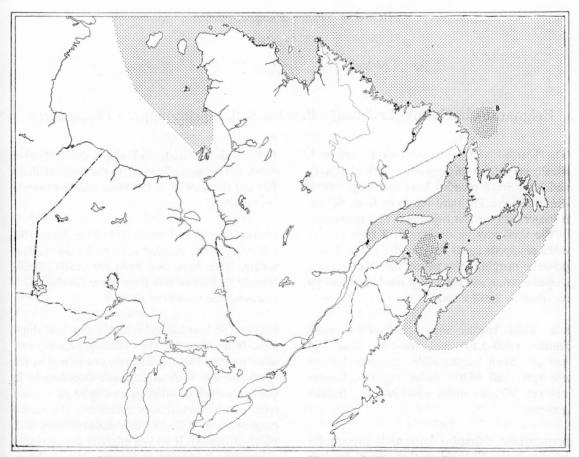

Map 78 – DISTRIBUTION OF THE HARP SEAL – *Phoca groenlandica* (B – *Breeding area*)

before the seals return northward. The annual harvest is estimated to average approximately a quarter of a million seals. One estimate (1951) of the number of seals present in the breeding areas in eastern-Canadian waters indicated approximately three million animals, with a production of a little more than half a million pups each year; a more recent estimated total (1960) was only one and a quarter million.

Selected References

ALLEN, J. A., 1880.
CAMERON, AUSTIN W., 1962.
DUNBAR, M. J., 1949.
FISHER, H. D., 1950, 1955.
MANSFIELD, A. W., 1963.
SCHEFFER, VICTOR B., 1958.
SERGEANT, D. E. and H. D. FISHER, 1960.
SIVERTSEN, E., 1941.

Genus **ERIGNATHUS** Gill

Bearded Seals – *Phoques barbus*

Dental Formula $I \frac{3-3}{2-2}$ $C \frac{1-1}{1-1}$ $P \frac{4-4}{4-4}$ $M \frac{1-1}{1-1} = 34$

Erignathus barbatus (Erxleben) – Bearded Seal, Square-flipper – *Phoque barbu*

The bearded seal is large, variably coloured, usually greyish brown (appearing black when wet), and has a small rounded head and long, coarse, dense vibrissae. The third toe on its front flippers is longer than the first two. It has four mammae.

The skull may be distinguished from that of other pinnipeds by its size, by the widely flaring posterior margin of the palate, the short, wedge-shaped rostrum and short deep jugal bone, and by its relatively small teeth.

SIZE Total length: males 2,100–3,600 mm., females 1,800–2,400; tail 100–150; hind foot 300–400. Skull length: males 225–260, females 200–240; skull width: males 135–140, females 128–137. Weight: males 500–1,000 lb., females 400–700.

DISTRIBUTION *Erignathus barbatus* is circumpolar in distribution, occurring throughout Hudson Bay, Hudson Strait, and along the Labrador coast, and occasionally south to the Strait of Belle Isle and the Gulf of St Lawrence and Newfoundland coasts.

HABITAT Coasts and ice shelves of the Arctic and subarctic, where bearded seals prefer the shallow waters, large bays, and open sea coasts. Occasionally they move into fresh water for short distances up the mouths of rivers.

HABITS The bearded seal is rather slow and sluggish. It feeds on molluscs (clams), prawns, and other bottom-dwelling invertebrates as well as on benthonic fish such as sculpins. Occasionally it takes other fish or other swimming or planktonic species. It is nowhere very numerous and it rarely congregates in colonies but remains solitary and widely dispersed. It seldom migrates any distance.

Breeding is thought to occur in May or June,

Fig. 170 – BEARDED SEAL – *Erignathus barbatus*

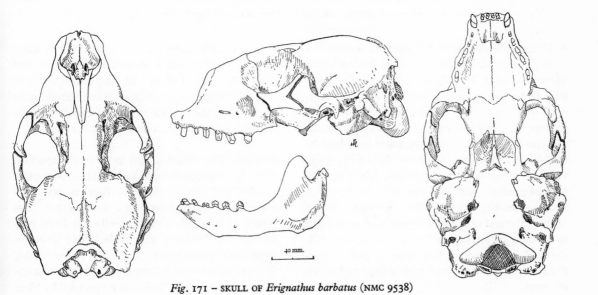

Fig. 171 – SKULL OF *Erignathus barbatus* (NMC 9538)

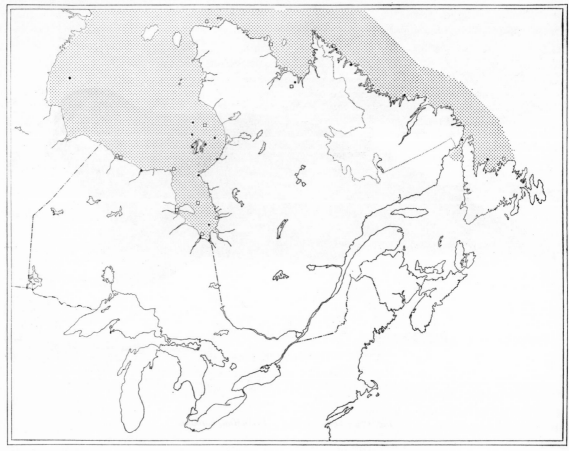

Map 79 – DISTRIBUTION OF THE BEARDED SEAL – *Erignathus barbatus*

and after a gestation period of about eleven months a single long slender pup is born between late March and May. It is about four or five feet long, with large flippers (about one foot long), a well-developed beard, and a long, soft, slightly curly grey or greyish-black coat. In about two weeks this coat is replaced by shorter, more rigid bluish-grey hair. The young apparently do not enter the water until the moult is completed. Adults appear to communicate with the young by means of a shrill, siren-like whistle that becomes deeper towards the end of the call. This sound is thought to be made by forcing air through the water while the head is submerged. It is believed that females reach sexual maturity at six years of age and males at seven.

When undisturbed, the bearded seal is quite curious. Native hunters are said to shout loudly and make other noises when a basking seal is about to make its way into the water. These sounds seem to paralyze the animal with fear and it remains 'frozen' long enough to be approached closely.

REMARKS The bearded seal is a very important species in the economy of the Eskimos, who prize tough hide for boat sails, boat covers, harpoon lines, boot soles, and many other purposes. It is widely eaten (usually not from preference) by Eskimos and their dogs; however, depending apparently on the seal's recent intake, its liver may be toxic because of a hyper-concentration of Vitamin A. This seal is regarded by some as the poorest meat for human consumption of all Arctic species, though the hind flippers are boiled and eaten quite commonly.

Selected References
ALLEN, J. A., 1880.

ANDERSON, R. M., 1934, 1943b.
DEGERBØL, M. and PETER FREUCHEN, 1935.
DUNBAR, M. J., 1941, 1949.
MCLAREN, I. W., 1958b and c.
SCHEFFER, VICTOR B., 1958.
SOPER, J. DEWEY, 1944.

Genus **HALICHOERUS** Nilsson

Gray Seals – *Phoques gris*

$$\text{Dental Formula} \quad \text{I} \frac{3-3}{2-2} \quad \text{C} \frac{1-1}{1-1} \quad \text{P} \frac{4-4}{4-4} \quad \text{M} \frac{1-1}{1-1} = 34$$

Halichoerus grypus (Fabricius) – Gray Seal, Horsehead Seal – *Phoque gris*

A fairly large seal, the gray is perhaps best distinguished by the shape of its 'horse-like' head which has a long snout (the distance between the tip of the nose to the eyes is nearly twice the distance between the eye and the ear opening). In older specimens the nose hangs over slightly. The pelage varies widely in colour: it is usually some shade of grey with indistinct dark mottling on the back and sides; it sometimes appears totally black, especially when wet.

The skull is characterized by its relatively large, massive size and by high-set nasals that form almost a straight line along the dorsal contour. All the cheek teeth except the last two upper and the last lower tooth are single-rooted. Occasionally an extra cheek tooth is present.

SIZE Total length: males 1,600–3,600 mm., females 1,500–2,100; tail 90–125; hind foot 250–375. Skull length: males 260–330, females 208–265; skull width: males 140–200, females 120–140. Weight: males 350–800 lb. females 250–600.

DISTRIBUTION AND VARIATION *Halichoerus grypus* is monotypic and is restricted to the North Atlantic, but it is nowhere abundant on the western side. It is sporadically encountered along the Labrador coast and in Canadian waters is perhaps most common (or best known) in the western half of the Gulf of St Lawrence, particularly around Anticosti Island. It occasionally moves up the St Lawrence River past the Saguenay River; it rarely moves south of Nova Scotia, although specimens have been taken in the Bay of Fundy and a breeding colony is now known to be established south of Cape Cod on Muskeget Island (41° 20′ N, 70° 18′ w) between Nantucket and Martha's Vineyard.

HABITAT The gray seal seems to prefer the turbulent waters off rocks, reefs, cliffs, and exposed shorelines. Its relatively common occurrence in the St Lawrence area might indicate a preference for brackish waters.

HABITS Comparatively little is known of the habits

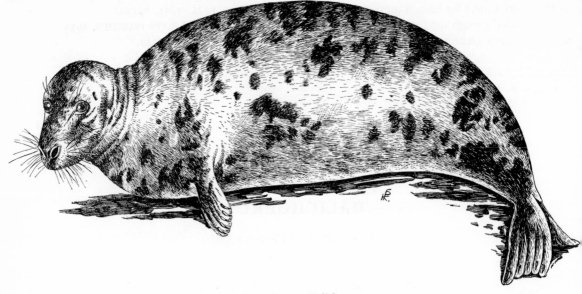

Fig. 172 – GRAY SEAL – *Halichoerus grypus*

of gray seals in eastern Canada. They are apparently quite migratory for they arrive in the western Gulf of St Lawrence about May or June and spend the summer there. In winter they move back northeastward. They tend to localize in colonies where their loud, sustained, distinctive barks can be heard for a considerable distance. Food consists primarily of fish; sculpin and herring are eaten heavily, along with some invertebrate material.

Breeding is thought to occur two or three weeks after the birth of the young. Some authors report pupping in late autumn or early winter, while others indicate that in eastern Canada the pups are born in January or February on a ledge, a sand bar, or on shore ice. However, careful studies in the

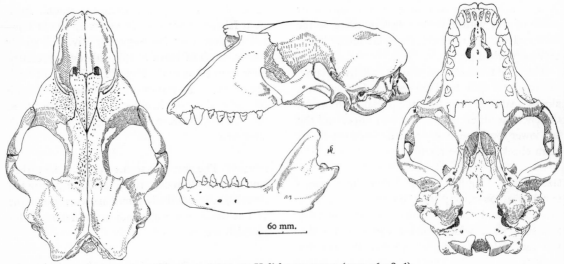

60 mm.

Fig. 173 – SKULL OF *Halichoerus grypus* (NMC 16038 ♂)

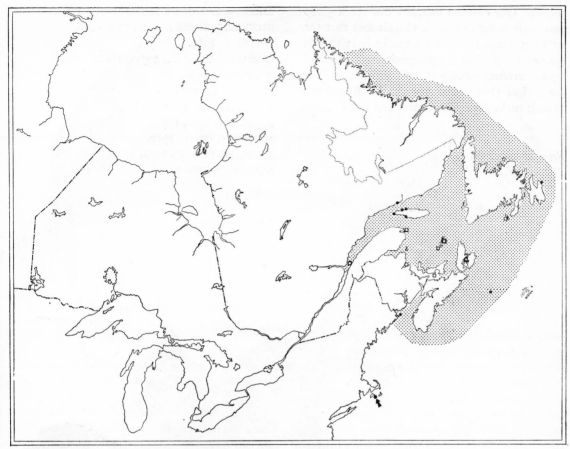

Map 80 – DISTRIBUTION OF THE GRAY SEAL – *Halichoerus grypus*

Outer Hebrides, Scotland, show that the pups there are born on shore in late September and early October (mostly between October 2 and 12) and that mating takes place in the latter part of October, followed by moulting which is completed before the end of November. (There appear to be differences in the breeding cycle in the various geographic localities.) The gestation lasts $11\frac{1}{2}$ months, which includes a delay in the implantation of the blastocyst of about four months. Males are thought to reach full breeding age at six to eight years and females one year earlier.

A young gray seal weighs about thirty-two (twenty to forty-two) pounds at birth (total length: 900 to 1,100 mm.) and has a white coat that lasts during the nursing period of about fourteen to twenty days, after which a blue-grey coat appears. The moult is completed at about thirty days. The milk of the gray seal is thought to be the richest produced by any animal, with up to 52.2 per cent fat, 2.6 per cent lactose, 11.2 per cent protein, and 0.7 per cent ash. During the nursing period the pups gain about 3.3 pounds per day and the mother loses an average of 6.3 pounds per day.

Gray seals tend to be rather slow and deliberate in their movements. They are known to dive to depths exceeding seventy fathoms. Longevity in captivity has exceeded forty years.

REMARKS Not long ago the gray seal was considered extremely rare in eastern Canada, although recent studies have shown the existence of fairly large colonies. One estimate indicates that about 5,000 gray seals occur in eastern Canada and that the total world population of this species is 33,500. In the eastern maritime region, specimens of this seal have been observed with growths of long strands of green algae (*Enteromorpha groenlandica*) attached to their backs during September and October.

Selected References
ALLEN, J. A., 1880

AMOROSO, E. C. and J. H. MATTHEWS, 1951.
BACKHOUSE, K. and H. R. HEWER, 1956.
BAXTER, J., 1963.
CAMERON, AUSTIN W., 1951a, 1962.
DUNCAN, A., 1956.
HEWER, H. R., 1957.
LOCKLEY, R. M., 1945a and b.
MACKENZIE, B. A., 1954.
MATHESON, COLIN, 1950.
MYERS, BETTY JUNE, 1956.
SCHEFFER, VICTOR B., 1958.

Fig. 174 – HOODED SEAL – *Cystophora cristata*

Genus **CYSTOPHORA** Nilsson

Hooded Seals – *Phoques à capuchon*

Dental Formula $I \frac{2-2}{1-1}$ $C \frac{1-1}{1-1}$ $P \frac{4-4}{4-4}$ $M \frac{1-1}{1-1} = 30$

Cystophora cristata (Erxleben) – Hooded Seal, Bladdernose Seal – *Phoque à capuchon*

This is a large seal of variable coloration, usually dark grey or blue-grey with brownish or dark-grey mottling. The male is quite distinctive: it has an inflatable pouch (or hood) on the tip of its snout that gives the species its name. By means of a double-hinged cartilaginous flap in the back of the mouth, a male is able to close the normal passage to the nose and force the exhaled air to the hood or bladder. This bladder is inflated when the male seal is excited or angered and hangs limply over the mouth when deflated. (A fully extended hood will hold the equivalent of about six quarts of water.) Apparently it is self-sealing, as rifle bullets may pass through it without deflating it. The female also has a hood, but it is less well-developed and is not inflatable.

The two outermost digits of the hind feet are longer than the median ones.

The skull, when viewed from above, has an almost square outline behind the noticeably short rostrum. The teeth are relatively heavy; they have swollen roots and are crowded close in the anterior part of the jaws. The upper molar and sometimes the fourth upper premolar are double-rooted. The auditory bullae are greatly expanded.

SIZE Total length: males 1,800–3,300 mm., females 1,500–2,700; tail 100–300; hind foot 250–500. Skull length: males 250–285, females 200–240; skull width: males 210–255, females 160–200. Weight: males 600–900 lb., females 400–800.

DISTRIBUTION *Cystophora cristata* is monotypic and is restricted to the western North Atlantic and Arctic Oceans. It spends the summer in the northern part of its range near Greenland and ranges south in the winter to the level of the Gulf of St Lawrence and Newfoundland, with occasional stragglers going further south. It regularly breeds on the pack-ice off the east coast of Newfoundland, and a few hooded seals whelp on the heavy ice near the Magdalen Islands in the Gulf of St Lawrence. This seal is rarely encountered in Ungava Bay or Hudson Strait, although presumably a rare specimen may wander south into Hudson Bay. It is not common anywhere along the eastern-Canadian coast.

HABITAT The hooded seal is associated with thick sea ice and closely follows the harp seal in its migrations, although it usually stays further out to sea.

HABITS Food is thought to consist mainly of fish, with squid and other invertebrates making up the balance of the hooded seal's diet.

A single pup, which weighs twenty-five to thirty pounds and is three to four feet long, is born on pack-ice about February or early March. Its white coat is usually shed before birth. Both parents guard their pup closely for about two weeks. It may enter the water quite soon after birth, but it apparently returns to the ice to be nursed.

Breeding takes place some three to four weeks after parturition. The rutting season brings on much fighting and loud noise as the males vie for the females. It seems quite probable that there is a delayed implantation of the blastocyst as in other seals. During the pupping and breeding period,

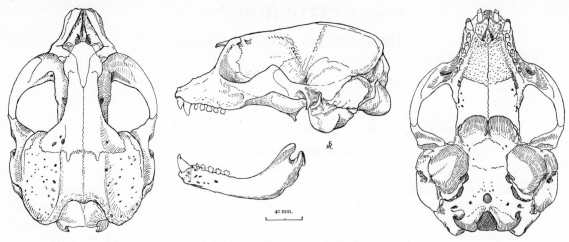

Fig. 175 – SKULL OF *Cystophora cristata* (NMC 17149)

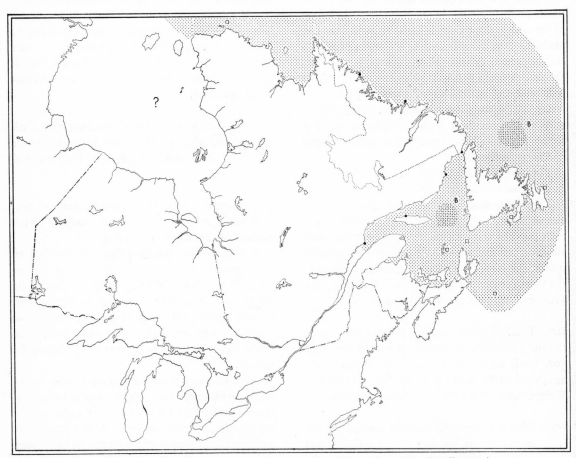

Map 81 – DISTRIBUTION OF THE HOODED SEAL – *Cystophora cristata* (B – *Breeding area*)

while the seals are hauled out on the ice, little or no feeding takes place and family groups remain close-knit. They are quite aggressive when approached by sealers, and the male hisses and snorts as it inflates its hood and stands its ground against any intruder.

REMARKS A number of hooded seals are taken by sealers hunting for harp seals, but pelts of older hooded seals bring a much lower price than those of harp seals and the small number of young do not justify concentrating on them. A total of only twenty pelts was taken in 1957 by local sealers off the Magdalen Islands.

Much remains to be learned about this interesting pelagic seal.

Selected References
ALLEN, J. A., 1880.
BARTLETT, ROBERT A., 1927.
CAMERON, AUSTIN W., 1951a, 1962.
MANSFIELD, A. W., 1963.
OLDS, J. M., 1950.
SCHEFFER, VICTOR B., 1958.

Order
Perissodactyla

This order includes horses, rhinoceroses, and tapirs, and a number of extinct families. *Perisso-dactyla* is distinguished primarily by the feet, especially by the very characteristic astragalus which has a well-grooved trochlea, a short neck, and a flattened, saddle-shaped head, and by the symmetry of the digits—the hind feet always, and the forefeet usually, have the axis of symmetry through the middle or third digit. The number of digits varies from four in the front and three in the back to one on each foot. There is no clavicle or gall-bladder and the stomach is simple.

Family **EQUIDAE**

Horses – *Chevaux*

This family includes many fossil forms and *Equus*, the modern horse, ass, donkey, and zebra. In modern representatives of this family, the feet are reduced to a single digit and bear no trace of other toes. Isolated teeth and skulls and other skeletal material of the horse are frequently presented to museum mammalogists for identification, which suggests that the bone material of this common domestic mammal is unfamiliar and that it should be described here. The palaeontological history of the evolution of the ancestors of the modern horse is perhaps the most classical of its kind and adds further to the desirability of including this living link with the remote past.

Equus caballus is the domesticated horse and *Equus asinus* is the ass or donkey. The offspring of a male ass and a female horse is the mule, which has been widely used as a work animal, for it is superior in some ways to either of the parents—it is docile and withstands hot weather. A cross between a female ass and a male horse produces a hinney, which does not have the useful characteristics of the mule. Both hybrids are usually sterile.

Selected Reference
SIMPSON, GEORGE GAYLORD, 1951.

Genus **EQUUS** Linnaeus

Horses and Asses – *Chevaux et Ânes*

Dental Formula I $\frac{3-3}{3-3}$ C $\frac{1-1}{1-1}$ P $\frac{4-4}{3-3}$ M $\frac{3-3}{3-3}$ = 42

Equus caballus Linnaeus – Domestic Horse – *Cheval domestique*

The domestic horse needs no external description. The skull is characterized by the great elongation of the area in front of the orbits, which are completely surrounded by bone. The mandibles are quite long, with high ascending rami. The incisors are well developed and have broad, flattened biting surfaces; unworn incisors have a cup-like depression. The full set of milk incisors is acquired at six months to one year and persists until the age of two to two and a half years. The first (central) permanent incisors are functional with the second and third milk incisors at $2\frac{1}{2}$ to $3\frac{1}{2}$ years; the first and second permanent incisors are functional with the third milk incisor at $3\frac{1}{2}$ to $4\frac{1}{2}$ years. There is a full set of permanent incisors showing only slightly worn cups at $4\frac{1}{2}$ to 7 years. When the cups are worn away on the first incisor but persist on the second and third, an age of seven to eight years is indicated. When the cups are worn away from the first and second incisors but persist on the third, the age is eight to nine years. When all the incisor cups are worn away and the worn surface on the first incisor is wider (side to side) than it is long (fore to aft), the animal may be considered to be about nine to eighteen years of age. When the worn surface on the first incisor becomes longer than it is wide, the horse is considered to be over eighteen years old. There is some individual variation from

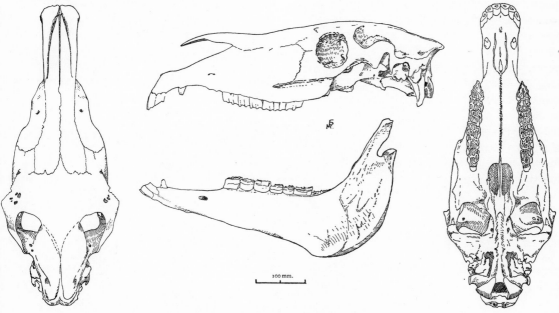

100 mm.

Fig. 176 – SKULL OF DOMESTIC HORSE – *Equus caballus* (ROM 27955)

these averages, but the above criteria for determining age have become established with most judges of horses.

The cheek teeth of horses are quite distinctive, though they are apparently unfamiliar to many casual observers. The central upper premolars and molars are almost square-shaped in cross-section; they are quite long in young animals and become progressively shorter as the crowns are worn away. The lower cheek teeth are much narrower (side to side) than the uppers; they are similar in width (fore to aft) and are about the same length. The enamel patterns are quite distinctive and characteristic.

The gestation period is about eleven to twelve months and averages longer in mares that are carrying a mule rather than a normal horse foal.

Selective breeding has produced many breeds or varieties of horses, ranging from tiny ponies to large draft breeds, including of course the breed that has perhaps become best known today, the racehorse.

Equus asinus Linnaeus – Ass, Donkey, Burro – *Âne*

This species is smaller than the average horse. It has relatively longer ears, a coarse, stiff mane, and a sparsely haired tail. The feet are relatively smaller and the legs are of medium length. Cranially *Equus asinus* differs but little from *E. caballus*. It is much less common than the horse in eastern Canada and is used primarily for producing breeding stock for the production of mules.

Order
Artiodactyla

This order includes the so-called 'cloven-hoofed' or even-toed hoofed animals in which the main axis of the foot lies between the third and fourth digits. The femur lacks a third trochanter. The distal articular surface of the astragalus is divided into two nearly equal facets that rest on the navicular and cuboid bones. The order may be divided into two suborders: *Suiformes*, which includes two living families—*Tayassuidae*, the peccaries, and *Suidae*, the true pigs—and *Ruminantia*, which includes several families of ruminants that possess either horns or antlers such as the *Bovidae*, *Antilocapridae*, and *Cervidae*.

KEY TO THE EASTERN-CANADIAN FAMILIES OF *Artiodactyla*

1 Adults without either horns or antlers; both upper and lower incisors well developed.   SUIDAE p. 315

1′ Adult males normally with either horns or antlers; no upper incisor teeth present; lower canines incisiform: 2

2 Adults of both sexes normally with horns—consisting of a horny sheath covering a bony outgrowth of the frontal bone—which persist throughout the life of the animal; lachrymal bone well developed and in contact with the nasals.   BOVIDAE p. 335

2′ Adult males with antlers consisting of a bony outgrowth of the frontal bone that is covered with skin (velvet) during annual growth but that is rubbed off in the fall, after which the antlers are shed before the following spring; a vacuity in front of the lachrymal bone separates it from the nasal bones.   CERVIDAE p. 317

Suborder
Suiformes

Family **SUIDAE**

Pigs – *Cochons*

This family is represented in eastern Canada only by a domestic mammal, the pig.

Genus **SUS** Linnaeus

Pigs – *Cochons*

Dental Formula $I \frac{3-3}{3-3}$ $C \frac{1-1}{1-1}$ $P \frac{4-4}{4-4}$ $M \frac{3-3}{3-3} = 44$

Sus scrofa Linnaeus – Domestic Pig – *Cochon domestique*

The domestic pig skull is characterized by its triangular outline when it is viewed from the side, by its low-crowned (bunodont) cheek teeth, by its well-developed canines (reaching exceptional lengths in some old males), and by its three well-developed incisors above and below. The original wild boar has quite an elongated rostrum, whereas the domestic varieties of pig tend to have a much shorter and a relatively higher skull, particularly in younger animals.

The average ages at which the permanent teeth erupt in *Sus* are as follows: first incisor, twelve months; second incisor, sixteen to twenty months; third incisor, eight to ten months; canine, nine to ten months; all premolars, twelve to fifteen months; first molar (M = 1), four to six months; second molar (M = 2), eight to twelve months; third molar (M = 3), eighteen to twenty months.

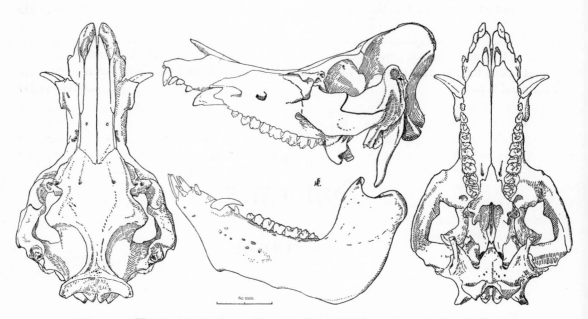

60 mm.

Fig. 177 – SKULL OF DOMESTIC PIG – *Sus scrofa* (ROM 91.11.1.170 ♂)

Suborder
Ruminantia

Family CERVIDAE

Deer – *Cerfs, Chevreuil, Cervidés*

The deer family is characterized by the presence of true antlers (usually in the males only). The antlers proper consist of bony outgrowths from the skull and would be analogous to the horn-core of the bovids and pronghorns except that instead of being persistent they are cast off each year and a new set is grown. Deer antlers are covered with skin during growth, and this skin has fine hair that is usually referred to as the 'velvet'. The velvet, then, is analogous to the horny sheath that covers the bovid horn and to the sheath of the pronghorn (*Antilocapridae*). As soon as the antlers reach full growth the velvet, which is richly supplied with blood vessels, ceases to grow, begins to dry, and is rubbed off as the deer thrashes his antlers against brush or trees. This thrashing activity marks the onset of the rut—the breeding season.

In some bovids—mountain sheep, for example— the age of the animal can be accurately determined by the growth-rings on the horns, but there is no known method by which the age of animals in the deer family can be ascertained from antlers. The size and number of points are subject to a great amount of variation owing basically to heredity and nutrition. Recent studies have shown that body growth takes precedence over antler development in young growing deer, so that larger, better-fed deer grow larger antlers. These studies, based on controlled feeding experiments, also show that animals deficient in calcium and phosphorous produce much smaller antlers than animals fed on balanced rations. Other studies show that there is a pronounced mineral draft (primarily calcium) from the long bones of the legs during the period of antler development. It has been stated that the production of antlers by males each year is just as great a drain on the vitality of the male as the production of young on the female. The size of antlers usually increases each year until the animal reaches the 'prime' of life; it begins to regress as senility approaches, although there may be a tendency for the base of the antlers above the burr (just out from the skull) to continue to increase each year.

Antlers occur only on males in all species except the caribou and reindeer, although occasionally female moose, deer, and wapiti develop them, as a result of some hormone imbalance, perhaps—the phenomenon is poorly understood. (In some cases at least, antler-growing females are hermaphrodites or pseudo-hermaphrodites.) By and large, antlers are a secondary sexual manifestation somewhat comparable to whiskers in man. Although they appear to be formidable weapons of defence or aggression, antlers are rarely used in fighting except when the males fight among themselves during the rutting season. Since the antlers are dropped not long after the rut and are actually a hindrance during the growing period, it is apparent that they are intended primarily for use during the rut. In the final analysis they help to ensure that healthy, vigorous males sire future generations.

KEY TO THE EASTERN-CANADIAN GENERA OF *Cervidae*

1 Vomer high, dividing the posterior nares into two chambers: 2

  2 Skull length less than 350 mm.; antlers (normally on males only) round in cross-section; maxillary canine normally absent; hoofs small.   ODOCOILEUS p. 322

  2' Skull length more than 350 mm.; antlers (present on both sexes) oval to flattened in cross-section; maxillary canine normally present; hoofs large.   RANGIFER p. 330

1' Vomer not dividing the posterior nares into two chambers: 3

  3 Skull length less than 500 mm.; antlers round in cross-section; anterior nasal aperture relatively short; nasals relatively long; premaxillae in contact with nasals; maxillary canine normally present.   CERVUS p. 318

  3' Skull length more than 500 mm.; antlers palmate in adults; anterior nasal aperture quite long; nasals short; premaxillae not in contact with nasals; maxillary canine normally absent.   ALCES p. 326

Genus **CERVUS** Linnaeus

Wapiti – *Cerfs*

Dental Formula   I $\frac{0-0}{3-3}$ C $\frac{1-1}{1-1}$ P $\frac{3-3}{3-3}$ M $\frac{3-3}{3-3}$ = 34

Cervus canadensis Erxleben – Wapiti, American Elk – *Wapiti*

When white men first came to North America they encountered a large, majestic deer, standing about five to five and a half feet at the shoulders, that was a close relative of the stag or red deer of northern Europe and northern Asia. This was the wapiti (an Indian name), also known as the American elk (as opposed to the European elk which is the same species as the Canadian moose).

Male wapiti have large, branching antlers that are more or less round in cross-section. A well-developed mane about the neck and a pale rump-patch help to distinguish the wapiti from other deer. The upper parts of the pelage are greyish brown to dark brown, while the head, mane, and legs are dark brown. The summer pelage is lighter and more tawny. The nose is naked and the lachrymal gland is well developed.

The maxillary canine (the elk tooth of lodge fame) is present in both sexes. The vomer is low posteriorly and does not divide the posterior nares into two chambers. The premaxilla extends up to and makes contact with the nasal bones. As in other cervids, the lachrymal vacuity is widely open and the lachrymal pit is well developed. The antlers of yearling males are normally simple spikes. Those of adults are long and graceful with usually five to seven tines projecting forward from the main beams. The greatest spread of antlers can be as much as sixty inches and the main beam can be over five feet long.

SIZE Total length: males 2,300–2,800 mm., females 2,100–2,400; tail 100–170; hind foot 550–710; ear from notch 130–200. Skull: length

Fig. 178 – WAPITI – *Cervus canadensis*

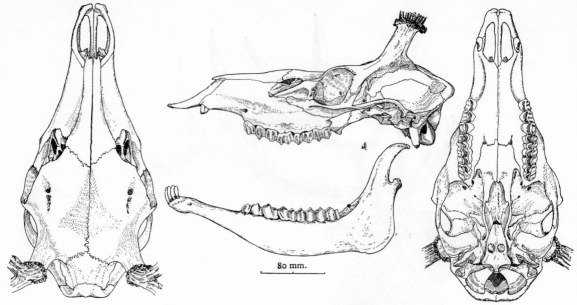

80 mm.

Fig. 179 – SKULL OF *Cervus canadensis* (ROM 18742 ♂)

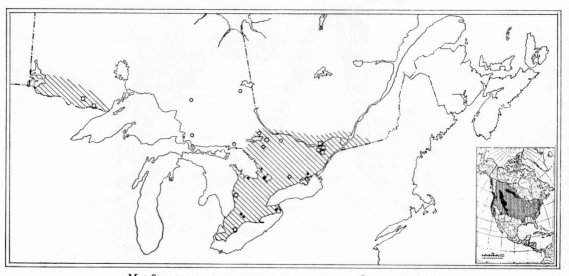

Map 82 – FORMER DISTRIBUTION OF THE WAPITI – *Cervus canadensis*

410–495, width 165–218. Weight: males 500–1,100 (av. 600–700) lb., females 450–650 .

DISTRIBUTION AND VARIATION Originally the wa-piti was widely distributed from southern Ontario and southern Quebec south to Georgia and west to the Pacific coast from southern California to northeastern British Columbia. The eastern form (*Cervus canadensis canadensis*) was slightly smaller, more richly coloured, and it lacked the pale eye-ring of the western races. It occurred in the areas that were first settled and cleared for agriculture. Growing settlement and land-clearing quickly reduced wapiti numbers and by 1850 this animal was completely extinct in Canada; soon the race became totally extinct. All that remains in eastern Canada are the antlers and other bones that are occasionally found in lake bottoms, in excavations, or among the materials collected from Indian midden sites.

Antler fragments from Northern Light Lake and Pickerel Lake in western Ontario seem to be the only available evidence of the original wapiti in Ontario west of Lake Superior. Evidently it was extirpated in western Ontario long before it disap-peared south of the border in Minnesota where a few animals remained until after 1900. A small band was reported to have been observed in the northwest angle of Minnesota as late as 1932. In all probability the wapiti formerly present in northwestern Ontario was the Manitoba wapiti (*C. c. manitobensis*) rather than the eastern race as some have suggested.

C. c. manitobensis or *C. c. nelsoni* have been re-introduced from some of the western game pre-serves into eastern Canada. In 1932 twenty-five were placed in the Pembroke Crown Game Preserve, Ont. The increase of wapiti in this preserve (which was enclosed) was such that in 1935 some animals were transferred from Pem-broke to Algonquin Park and the Bruce Peninsula. In 1933 six carloads were brought from Wain-wright National Park, Alta, and released in the Burwash, Chapleau, and Nipigon-Onaman game preserves in Ontario. The next year distribution was extended to the Goulais River-Ranger Lake

Game Preserve. Introductions were also made at various other points in Ontario, but most have not proved successful. The animals appear to have perished in the Nipigon area.

HABITAT Originally the wapiti had the widest range of any of the native deer of eastern Canada and it lived under widely varying conditions—in the eastern forests, on the western plains, and in the mountains—although it does not appear to have been at home anywhere in dense woods. It seems to have thrived best where natural openings broke up the forests. In view of its wide range and the variety of conditions that apparently suited the wapiti, it is rather surprising that it disappeared so quickly and so completely on the approach of settlement. Furthermore, it thrives better than any other Canadian deer under semi-domesticated conditions in parks.

HABITS The food of the wapiti includes a wide variety of grasses, herbs, shrubs, and trees; the general food habits are much less specialized than those of most other members of the deer family. Peak feeding periods are reached at twilight and dawn, with most activity taking place at night.

The rut extends from early September until after the middle of October and is accompanied by a mating call known as 'bugling' and by brief fights among the adult bulls as they seek to round up and take possession of a harem of cows. The gestation period lasts from 249 to 262 days. A fawn (almost invariably one rather than twins) weighing thirty to forty pounds is born in May or early June and is spotted (as are white-tailed deer at birth). Normally females breed for the first time in the third rutting season after birth. Occasionally males are known to breed one season earlier.

The wapiti has a graceful, pacing-trot gait that reaches forty-five miles per hour. Its gregarious instinct is quite well developed.

REMARKS The introduction of western wapiti to eastern Canada has not proved very successful. Most of the range formerly occupied by the original eastern wapiti is now agricultural. The introductions have been made in areas north of the original range of wapiti where the habitat is not well suited for them. Some of the introduced wapiti were infected with the large liver fluke, *Fascioloides magna*, which presents a serious threat if it is transmitted to white-tailed deer and moose. In Ontario this threat was recognized and legislation was introduced to allow the wapiti to be hunted during the regular hunting season, and steps were taken to eliminate the wapiti from Crown game preserves. The prospects for re-es-

tablishing wapiti as a common game species are not particularly bright or encouraging. However, in view of the possible adverse effect on existing native deer, its establishment is not desirable.

Selected References

CAHN, A. R., 1937.

JOHNSON, DONALD E., 1951.

MURIE, OLAUS J., 1951.

PETERSON, R. L., 1956b, 1957.

QUIMBY, DON C. and DONALD E. JOHNSON, 1951.

QUIMBY, DON C. and J. E. GAAB, 1957.

Genus ODOCOILEUS Rafinesque

Deer – *Cerfs*

Dental Formula $I \frac{0-0}{3-3}$ $C \frac{0-0}{1-1}$ $P \frac{3-3}{3-3}$ $M \frac{3-3}{3-3} = 32$

Odocoileus virginianus (Zimmermann) – White-tailed Deer –
Cerf de Virginie

The white-tailed deer is so well known that little description is needed. Adult males have antlers whose main beams bend forward; unbranched spikes (points or tines) project upwards from them. Yearlings may have only a single spike or tine on one or both sides. The summer pelage is bright reddish, giving way to a greyish winter coat. The underside of the tail is white and is strikingly exposed when an alerted deer bounds away into the bush.

The neck of the buck becomes quite enlarged during the rutting season. The height at the shoulder is between about 31 to 45 inches in bucks and 27 to 33 inches in does.

There are three types of scent glands in both sexes: one between the toes of each foot (interdigital), one on the outside of the shank (metatarsal), and one on the inner surface of the heel or hock joint (tarsal). The latter contains smooth

muscle bundles (*erector pili*) that erect the enlarged hairs covering the gland. This hair erection is thought to serve in a specialized manner for visual communication. The other glands are believed to act as scent depositors; the metatarsal gland comes into use when the animal is lying down, the interdigital gland when it is on the move.

The world-record head of a white-tailed deer, as judged by the Boone and Crockett Club in 1952, came from New Brunswick. The lengths of the main antler beams were $31\frac{3}{4}$ and $31\frac{1}{4}$ inches; the greatest inside spread of the beams was $19\frac{1}{2}$ inches; and the antlers had six and eight points to make a total of fourteen.

In addition to the characteristic antlers of the male, the skull of the white-tailed deer has a high vomer dividing the posterior nares into two chambers, a relatively narrow or pointed rostrum, and usually no upper canine tooth.

Fig. 180 – WHITE-TAILED DEER – *Odocoileus virginianus*

SIZE Total length: males 1,800–2,150 mm. (71–85 in.), females 1,600–2,000 (63–79 in.); tail 200–360 (8–14 in.); hind foot 480–540 (14–21 in.); ear from notch 140–230 (5½–9 in.). Skull length: males 290–350, females 250–290; skull width: males 120–145, females 102–120. Weight: males 100–475 (av. 200–300) lb., females 75–250 (av. 125–180).

DISTRIBUTION AND VARIATION The white-tail is a New World species and occurs throughout most of North America south of a line from Anticosti Island in the Gulf of St Lawrence to James Bay and westward; it extends through Central America to South America. *Odocoileus virginianus borealis* occupies all of the eastern-Canadian portion of the range, with the possible exception of the extreme limits of Ontario (near Kenora and Rainy River) where *O. v. dacotensis*, which is a larger and usually a paler-coloured race with heavier cheek teeth, may range in from the west.

In the last century and a half the range of the

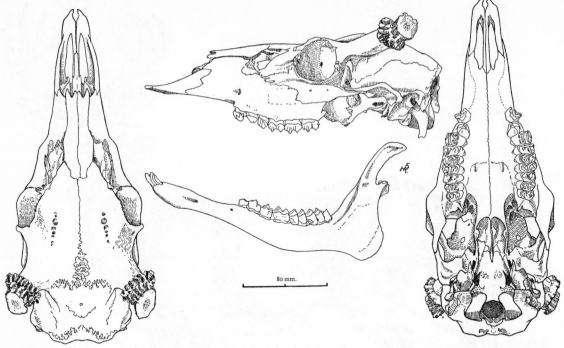

80 mm.

Fig. 181 – SKULL OF *Odocoileus virginianus* (ROM 20963 ♂)

white-tail has been extending northward all across eastern Canada.

HABITAT Areas of second growth in the intermediate stages of forest succession provide the optimum habitat for the white-tailed deer. Logging, burning, settlement, and partial clearing of land have often helped to improve habitat conditions so that quite high concentrations of deer occur in fairly thickly settled country.

HABITS The white-tailed deer is primarily a browser among trees, shrubs, and various species of non-woody plants. In winter and early spring woody plants provide a more limited diet. At this time cedar swamps are a favourite haunt where several deer may congregate in a so-called 'yard'. Extremely alert and agile, the white-tail must be cautious to escape its primary predator, the timber wolf. The normal running speed is about thirty miles per hour, with a reported maximum speed

of fifty. The white-tail is an excellent jumper, capable of clearing heights of seven or eight feet with ease.

Each spring the newly formed antlers of the bucks grow quite rapidly under the velvet and reach full size by fall. They are rubbed free of the velvet just prior to the rut.

Breeding or rutting takes place in the fall, starting in late October, and the peak is reached during the last half of November, with occasional late breeding about one month later. The gestation period lasts about 196 days. One or two fawns, weighing about four to ten pounds, are usually born in May or June. (Twins are quite common—the rate of their occurrence is correlated with food supply; triplets occur rather rarely.) The spotted young are commonly left in hiding for the first month of their lives. The spots disappear at about three and a half months, when the winter coat begins to grow (about September). The young are weaned at about three to four months.

Breeding may take place in does during the

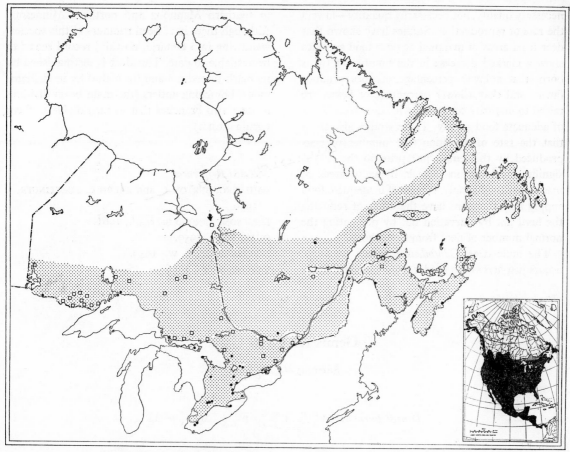

Map 83 – DISTRIBUTION OF THE WHITE-TAILED DEER – *Odocoileus virginianus*

first year (at about seven months), but most does begin to breed in their second year.

The life-span of white-tailed deer in the wild seldom exceeds ten years, although captive animals have lived up to twenty years.

REMARKS In spite of heavy hunting pressure, the white-tailed deer has been able to maintain its numbers and in many cases actually increase to the point of exceeding the optimum carrying capacity of its habitat. It is eastern Canada's most important big-game species and many thousands are taken each year.

The timber wolf is commonly accused of seriously decimating white-tailed deer populations. However, in most cases of declining populations

the major factors usually turn out to be the deterioration of the habitat and its available food, coupled with severe weather and icing conditions, particularly in late winter when the food supply is at its lowest point. Diseases and parasites may also contribute to lack of survival during this critical period.

Mortality from the above factors may be quite violent and clearly evident. On the other hand, and perhaps more important in the long run, we find that food supply has a more subtle and less obvious method of reducing the herds. Deer populations can be reduced to a low level without a single shot being fired, without a single animal being killed by predators or a single animal dying from any other cause. For a deficient diet—one lacking the necessary quality, not necessarily quantity—lowers the rate of reproduction. Studies have shown that deer from areas of marginal or poor food supplies show a marked decrease in the number of twins born, that a lower percentage of does produce fawns, and that a lower percentage of fawns are raised to maturity compared with deer from areas of adequate food supply. These studies also show that the rate of ovulation (the number of eggs produced by the female just prior to the rut) is significantly lower in animals living in areas of inadequate food supply. A state of inadequate food supply may therefore have the effect of reducing the herd not by starvation but by preventing the normal number of deer from being born.

The mule deer, *Odocoileus hemionus hemionus*, occurs just across the border from eastern Canada in southern Manitoba and northern Minnesota. Although there have been rumours of this species' wandering into Ontario, no valid record seems to be available to date. This deer is distinguished by its black-tipped tail and (in males) by its dichotomous, branching antlers (the main beam dividing to form two branches that in turn divide to form terminal tines).

Selected References

DAHLBERG, BURTON L. and RALPH C. GUETTINGER, 1956.
ERICKSON, ARNOLD B., *et al.*, 1961.
QUAY, W. B., 1959.
SEVERINGHAUS, C. W., 1949.
TAYLOR, W. P., 1956.

Genus **ALCES** Gray

Moose – *Orignals*

Dental Formula $\quad$ I $\frac{0-0}{3-3}$ $\quad$ C $\frac{0-0}{1-1}$ $\quad$ P $\frac{3-3}{3-3}$ $\quad$ M $\frac{3-3}{3-3}$ = 32

Alces alces (Linnaeus) – Moose – *Orignal*

The moose is the world's largest living deer. Not only is its size impressive, but its whole form is so unlike that of any other deer that it is as though the moose belonged to some past geological age rather than to our own. It stands some five and a half to six and a half feet at the shoulders.

The moose is characterized by its long face with overhanging muzzle, its heavy front quarters, short neck, and long ears, by a distinctive dewlap or 'bell' under its throat, disproportionately long legs with lighter coloration on the lower parts, and a very short tail. The males have the added distinction of possessing large, palmate antlers. In spring the new coat is short, sleek, and dark brown to almost black; by fall it becomes longer and lighter in colour—usually brownish—and by late spring it may appear quite greyish.

The skull is characterized by a greatly elongated premaxillary region (rostrum), with large nasal apertures and short nasals, by a vomer that is low posteriorly and does not divide the posterior nares into two chambers, and by the absence of upper canine teeth.

SIZE Total length: males 2,440–2,900 mm. (95–115 in.), females 2,000–2,600 (80–100 in.); tail 75–150 (3–6 in.); hind foot 725–830 (29–33 in.); ear from notch 250–275. Skull: length 540–660, width 210–240. Weight: males 725–1,400 lb., females 500–900.

Fig. 182 – MOOSE – *Alces alces*

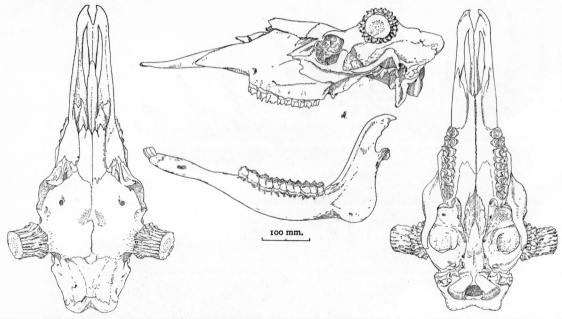

Fig. 183 – SKULL OF *Alces alces* (ROM 18516 ♂)

DISTRIBUTION AND VARIATION The moose is circumpolar in distribution and ranges across the boreal forest of eastern Canada north to a line from Anticosti Island to central James Bay and along the main tree-line limit in Ontario. It is absent from Ontario south of the Precambrian Shield and has been extirpated from the more densely settled areas of southern Quebec, especially south of the St Lawrence. There is some doubt that it ever occurred on Prince Edward Island in recent times. It has been introduced to Newfoundland (in 1878 and 1904) and Anticosti Island in the Gulf of St Lawrence. Only a few moose still persist on Anticosti Island, but the Newfoundland introductions have now populated most of that island. In 1953 twelve moose from Newfoundland were introduced to southeastern Labrador near the St Lewis River. Reports in 1962 indicate that these animals had reproduced and that the herd had increased. *A. a. americana* occurs east of Lake Superior and *A. a. andersoni* to the west.

There has been an extension of range northward since white men first came to eastern Canada.

HABITAT The boreal forest, especially in areas of second growth, or intermediate stages of forest succession interspersed with lakes and streams.

HABITS In addition to a basic diet of broad-leafed trees and shrubs, moose seek out aquatic vegetation during the summer months. They are most easily observed during this period as they make daily trips to a good feeding area in lakes or streams. In early spring they sometimes become completely submerged as they dive for tender aquatic plants growing up from the bottom. In winter, balsam fir becomes an important staple in the diet. Bark is also peeled from certain species of trees as an additional source of food, particularly in late winter, or in early spring as the sap begins to rise.

The moose is a solitary animal, living alone much of the time; it is seldom found in more than family groups. However, during the summer several moose may be observed in one good aquatic feeding area; in this event, though, each animal moves about independently and after feeding returns to its solitary existence. In winter a particularly favourable feeding area may bring several animals together

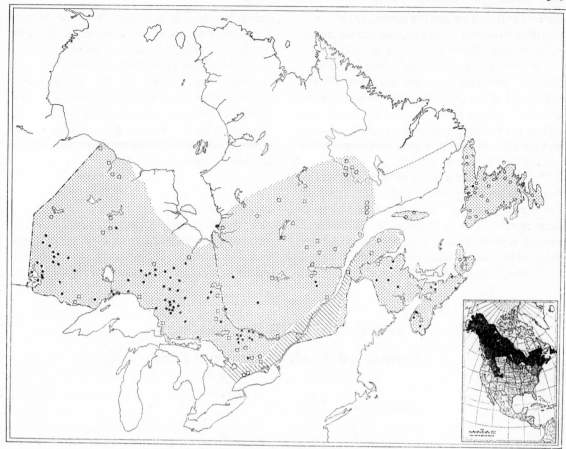

Map 84 – DISTRIBUTION OF THE MOOSE – *Alces alces*

into a 'yard'. In eastern Canada the snow seldom becomes deep enough to prevent the moose from moving on its independent way should it so desire.

The breeding or rutting season starts after the middle of September and may continue until late October. The gestation period lasts about 240 to 246 days. A calf weighing twenty-five to thirty-five pounds is born in late May or early June. It is reddish brown with a paler head, unspotted, and has a dark eye-ring and a dark muzzle. It grows at a remarkable rate and may reach a weight of 400 to 600 pounds in twelve months. Twins occur on the average in about ten to twenty-five per cent of the births of full adult cows, occasionally more often in some populations. They occur less frequently in the first breeding of young cows.

Breeding may start at sixteen months in females, but probably many females and most males do not breed until they are over two years old.

Antlers are shed during the winter; the larger sets are shed first and young animals shed last. New antlers start to grow in early spring and develop extremely rapidly, reaching full size by late August.

The moose is an excellent swimmer and spends more time in the water, perhaps, than any other deer. Its long legs serve it well in wading and running—it can attain running speeds of thirty to thirty-five miles an hour (its normal gait is about twenty to twenty-five miles an hour).

REMARKS Recent trends indicate that the moose is

thriving well in many parts of eastern Canada, and that there have been marked population increases in many regions. There has been a general spread into the fringe areas of its range where moose were formerly quite rare or largely unknown. On the other hand, where the white-tailed deer is more or less dominant—in Nova Scotia, New Brunswick, and in the southern part of its range in Quebec and Ontario—the moose have failed to reach the level of their former abundance.

Data from eastern Canada indicate that a relatively high percentage of cow moose fail to produce calves each year (over fifty per cent according to some reports). This of course limits the potential rate of reproduction. The moose is a solitary mammal and needs a relatively large area to sustain it. As moose are so thinly distributed during the breeding season, it is difficult for a bull to mate with more than one or two cows, especially when it is faced with belligerent competition from other males during the short period when the cows are receptive. This, coupled with the possible breeding limitations brought about by inadequate food supply (as discussed for white-tailed deer), results in a relatively low rate of reproduction—an increase of only some fifteen to twenty per cent in the adult population each year.

Selected References

EDWARDS, R. Y. and R. W. RITCEY, 1958.
PETERSON, RANDOLPH L., 1950, 1952, 1953a, 1955.
PIMLOTT, DOUGLAS H., 1959, 1961.
PIMLOTT, D. H. and W. J. CARBERRY, 1958.

Genus **RANGIFER** Hamilton-Smith

Caribou and Reindeer – *Caribou et Renne*

$$\textit{Dental Formula} \quad \text{I} \frac{0-0}{3-3} \quad \text{C} \frac{1-1}{1-1} \quad \text{P} \frac{3-3}{3-3} \quad \text{M} \frac{3-3}{3-3} = 34$$

Rangifer tarandus (Linnaeus) – Caribou – *Caribou*

The caribou is a unique member of the deer family in that both males and females have antlers, although the female antlers are much smaller in size. Several types of caribou occur in the arctic and subarctic of both North America and Eurasia, including reindeer which have been domesticated in several areas. The best-known caribou of North America are the western barren-ground caribou that have been the basic commodity in the economy of the mainland Eskimos for centuries. Perhaps the least known are the woodland caribou that inhabit the boreal forests from Newfoundland to the Mackenzie Delta. The woodland caribou average larger than the barren-ground (the shoulder height of males is 1,081 to 1,400 mm., averaging 1,290 mm. or about 50 inches) and their antlers are usually heavier, more flattened in cross-section, and more compact (they usually lack the long, graceful upsweep characteristic of the barren-ground caribou). The ears of all caribou are short, broad, and well furred. The squarish nose or muzzle is covered with short whitish hair and there is a whitish eye-ring. The long ventral mane, the small rump patch, the underside of the tail, the inside of the ears, the hair around the feet, and an area on the flanks are also whitish. The rest of the body colour is brownish to greyish. The winter pelage consists of long, brittle guard-hairs and dense, fine, curly underfur. In summer the pelage is much shorter and softer and becomes ideal for Eskimo parkas.

The hoofs are relatively large and crescentic and

Fig. 184 – WOODLAND CARIBOU – *Rangifer tarandus caribou*

in the barren-ground caribou are as wide as (or wider than) they are long (the hoofs of males average 86 × 86 mm. wide, of females 80 × 84 mm.) while in the woodland form the male hoofs are 100 to 135 mm. long (av. 113.5) and 75 to 118 mm. wide (av. 98) and the female hoofs are 75 to 105 mm. long (av. 100) and 75 to 95 mm. wide (av. 83.6). With the toes spread, the track is wider than it is long. In summer the edges of the hoofs are worn flat and the soft pad of each hoof rests on the ground. In winter the foot-pads shrink and become horny, while the edges of the hoofs grow quite long and the hair between the toes lengthens to form tufts that cover the pads. Thus the caribou

walks on the thin crescentic horny rim of its hoofs in winter and has its inner foot-pads protected by hair.

The posterior nares of the skull are divided by the vomer. Small upper canines are usually present but they do not pierce the gum. The incisors are small and graduated in size (the largest are in the centre). The last lower molar has a weak posterior third lobe. The nasal bones are relatively long and flare widely posteriorly to form a rough T-shape. The rostrum is much broader than that of *Odocoileus*.

SIZE *Rangifer tarandus caribou*. Total length:

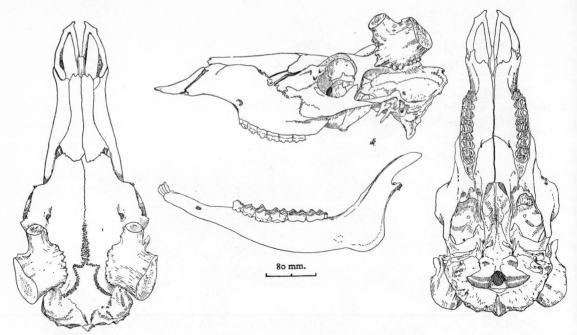

Fig. 185 – SKULL OF Rangifer tarandus caribou (ROM 19880 ♂)

males 1,840–2,472 (average 2,175) mm., females 1,730–2,045 (av. 1,870); tail 125–225; hind foot 500–600; ear from notch 110–150. Skull length: males 342–427 (av. 374.3), females 306–368 (av. 333.4); skull width: males 157–198 (av. 175.5), females 140–174 (av. 159.3). Weight: males 350–550 (av. 395) lb., females 200–350 (av. 290).

Rangifer tarandus groenlandicus. Total length: males 1,600–2,096 (av. 1,800 mm.), females 1,370–1,860 (av. 1,660); tail 110–200; hind foot 432–570; ear from notch 100–140. Skull length: males 296–372 (av. 334), females 273–326 (av. 297); skull width: males 157–198 (av. 175.5), females 140–174 (av. 159.3). Weight: males 175–340 (av. 242) lb., females 135–210 (av. 180).

DISTRIBUTION AND VARIATION Based on skeletal findings and early reports, it appears that the range of caribou in North America prior to the coming of Europeans included all of eastern Canada except the region south of the French River, Lake Nipissing, and the Mattawa and Ottawa Rivers in Ontario and the southern townships of Quebec west of the Sutton Mountains. At present the caribou is restricted to the regions north of a line joining the north shore of Lake Superior, Lake Abitibi, Lake St John, and the Saguenay River. It has disappeared from the entire area south of the St Lawrence River, except for a small isolated population that is still present in the mountains of the Gaspé Peninsula, Que.

The taxonomy of the genus *Rangifer* has been in a rather confused state. Until recently the woodland-form caribou has been regarded as a distinct species (*R. caribou*) and the New World barren-land form as another full species (*R. arcticus*), while the Old World reindeer was regarded as *R. tarandus*. Additional races, such as *R. caboti* of the Ungava-northern Labrador region, have been treated as full species. But in 1961 Banfield reviewed the entire genus and concluded that all caribou and reindeer are but one species, *R. tarandus*. The caribou occurring regularly in eastern Canada are regarded as a single race, *R. t. caribou*, which in-

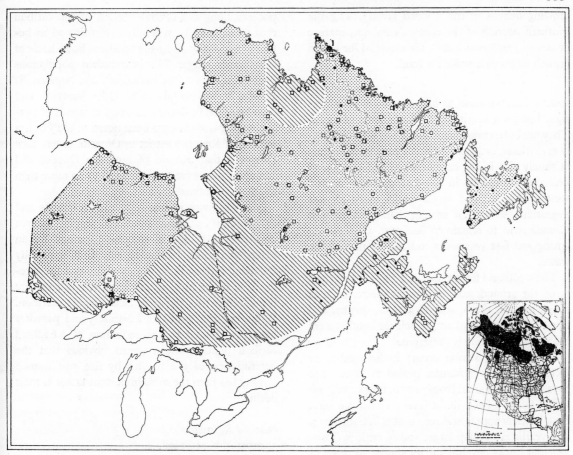

Map 85 – DISTRIBUTION OF THE CARIBOU – *Rangifer tarandus* – AND TYPE LOCALITIES OF (I) *R. arcticus caboti*
G. M. Allen [=*R. t. caribou*]; (2) *R. terraenovae* Bangs [=*R. t. caribou*]

cludes the forms described as *R. caribou sylvestris* (a name that has been applied to the population from northwestern Ontario westward to the Mackenzie Delta); *R. caboti* or *R. arcticus caribou* (representing the northern-Quebec and Labrador populations); and *R. terranovae* (the Newfoundland form).

In this system of classification the barren-land caribou becomes *R. tarandus groenlandicus* (instead of *R. arcticus arcticus*), which is thought to have entered Ontario some time in the last fifty years and to have ranged along the Hudson Bay coast as far east as Cape Henrietta Maria at the junction of Hudson and James Bays. Averaging smaller in

size than the woodland type, the barren-ground caribou has also been characterized by the shape of its antlers, which are more round in cross-section, smaller in beam, and rise higher in a longer, more graceful arch than those of the woodland type. No specific record of this race has been reported from eastern Canada in the past few years.

HABITAT Caribou occupy two basic habitats: the barren ground of the Arctic and the boreal coniferous forest. In both habitats lichens provide the essential elements for caribou—ground-growing fructicose lichens (reindeer moss) in the barren grounds or open areas and various species of tree-growing lichens in the wooded areas. Along the southern portion of the caribou's habitat, mature or climax coniferous forests are essential for lichen growth to provide sufficient food.

HABITS Caribou seem to have relatively poor eyesight but good hearing and a keen sense of smell. They are both curious and shy. They are inherently gregarious, gathering in herds from small bands of family size in the case of woodland caribou to herds of thousands in the barren lands of the western Arctic. The larger herds make regular migrations while the smaller bands of eastern Canada tend to remain in one area. Caribou are strong and fast swimmers and readily take to the water.

The woodland form eats lichen growing on trees or on the ground, and other plant species such as fungi, mosses, herbs, sedges, grasses, shrubs, and trees. Of the woody plants, which are lightly eaten, the mountain maple is preferred.

The breeding season occurs in September or October and the gestation period is about 240 days. The fawns are fulvous brown, unspotted, and weigh ten to fifteen lb. at birth. Twins are rare. Small antlers appear at three months in both sexes, and yearlings develop larger spiked antlers. Two-year-old bucks develop antlers similar to those of mature does. (Occasionally some females do not develop antlers.) Yearling does are thought to be sexually mature but bucks normally do not breed until they are two or three years old. Caribou reach full maturity and size at about four to five years and probably have a potential longevity of about twelve to fifteen years.

REMARKS The recent population trends in caribou are not encouraging across most of their range in North America; eastern Canada supports only a pitifully small number of these majestic mammals.

The woodland-caribou populations of eastern Canada have become reduced to rather isolated pockets along the central portion of the caribou range and have been totally exterminated in between, especially along the southern boundaries of the former range. The best-known populations have been insular (the islands of Lake Nipigon, St Ignace, and Slate Islands in Lake Superior, and Newfoundland). Some encouraging trends of persisting populations have been noted in the Patricia portion of Kenora District in Ontario. It has been estimated that caribou of northern Quebec and Labrador may have been reduced to no more than about 6,000 animals.

Man's activity in removing mature forests and in opening up these areas for second growth destroys the habitat of woodland caribou for an extended period. Lichen regeneration, especially following intense fires, is very slow, and the tree-forms of lichen must await the growth of a mature forest before they can again be available to caribou. While hunting, predation, diseases, and parasites have contributed to the reduction of woodland caribou populations, it seems obvious that the deterioration of the habitat by fire and human activity has been the most important factor in their decline.

Selected References

ANDERSON, R. M., 1938.

BANFIELD, A. W. F., 1949, 1954, 1955, 1960a, 1961a.

BANFIELD, A. W. F. and J. S. TENER, 1958.

BANGS, OUTRAM, 1896b.

CAMERON, AUSTIN W., 1959.

CRINGAN, A. T., 1957.

DE VOS, A. and R. L. PETERSON, 1951.

DUGMORE, A. A. RADCLIFFE, 1913.

EDWARDS, R. Y., J. SOOS and R. W. RITCEY, 1960.

HARPER, FRANCIS, 1955, 1961.

JACOBI, A., 1931.

KELSALL, J. P., 1957.

MANNING, T. H., 1948.

MOISAN, GASTON, 1956–7.

QUAY, W. B., 1955.

Family **BOVIDAE**

Oxen, Bison, Muskoxen, Sheep, Goats, and Antelopes –
Boeufs, Bisons, Ovibos, Moutons, Chèvres, et Antilopes

The family *Bovidae* is a large one and includes oxen or cattle, bison, muskoxen, sheep, goats, and antelopes. It is represented by native species on all major land-masses except South America and Australia. There apparently have never been any native bovids occurring in eastern Canada in the Recent epoch, although the bison is known to have ranged along the border in New York, Pennsylvania, Ohio, Michigan, Minnesota, and Manitoba. The bison has been introduced into eastern Canada on a limited scale; other bovids are domestic species.

Bovids are characterized by the presence of permanent horns, usually in both sexes, that grow from the frontal bones. Under domestication some breeds have been developed that have no horns (polled cattle and sheep). The lachrymal bone is in contact with the nasals. There are no upper canine teeth. The lateral toes are always incomplete and are sometimes absent. There is no gall-bladder.

KEY TO THE EASTERN-CANADIAN GENERA OF *Bovidae*

1 Size large (weight 500 to 2000 lb.): 2

2 Premaxillae not extending to make contact with the nasals; skull broad and massive with heavy and long maxillary toothrow (over 110 mm.); fore-quarters quite heavy with pronounced hump at shoulders. BISON p. 336

2′ Premaxillae extending to and in contact with the nasals; skull relatively narrow and less massive, with lighter and shorter maxillary toothrow (usually less than 110 mm.); fore-quarters not especially heavy and without pronounced hump at shoulders. BOS p. 337

1′ Size medium to small (weight usually less than 300 lb.): 3

3 Deep lachrymal pit in front of orbit; premaxilla not wedged between nasal and maxilla; horns (when present) usually with outwardly directed spiral; feet with glands between the hoofs; pelage dense (wool) with no tendency for elongation on chin, throat, and neck. OVIS p. 338

3′ No lachrymal pit in front of orbit; premaxilla wedged between nasal and maxilla; horns not forming an outward or inward spiral; feet without glands; pelage coarse (usually not woolly), with males developing a beard under chin. CAPRA p. 339

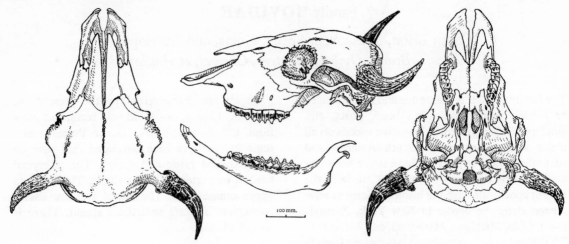

Fig. 186 – SKULL OF BISON – *Bison bison* (ROM 20126 ♂)

Genus **BISON** Hamilton-Smith

Bisons

Dental Formula $\text{I}\frac{0-0}{3-3}$ $\text{C}\frac{0-0}{1-1}$ $\text{P}\frac{3-3}{3-3}$ $\text{M}\frac{3-3}{3-3} = 32$

Bison bison (Linnaeus) – Bison, North American Buffalo – *Bison d'Amérique*

The bison has become a familiar species as an inmate of most zoos. It has been introduced into eastern Canada in large fenced areas such as Burwash, Ont., but it has not become established under wild conditions. The postcranial skeleton is quite similar to that of *Bos*, the domestic cow, and it needs to be compared carefully with *Bos* specimens of similar age in order to distinguish between the two species. The broad massive skull is readily distinguished by the short nasal extension of the premaxilla which does not reach the nasal. The maxillary cheek teeth average larger than those of domestic cattle.

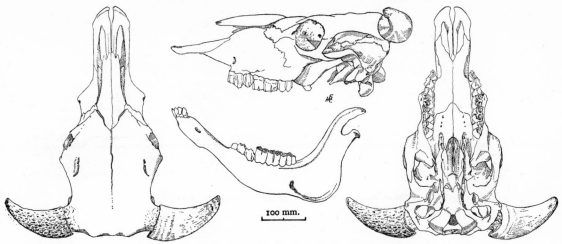

Fig. 187 – SKULL OF DOMESTIC COW – *Bos taurus* (ROM 20181)

Genus **BOS** Linnaeus

Cattle – *Vaches*

Dental Formula $\quad$ I $\frac{0-0}{3-3}$ $\quad$ C $\frac{0-0}{1-1}$ $\quad$ P $\frac{3-3}{3-3}$ $\quad$ M $\frac{3-3}{3-3}$ = 32

Bos taurus Linnaeus – Domestic Cow – *Vache domestique*

A wide variety of breeds of cattle has been de-veloped, largely from ancestral stock descending from *Bos primigenius*, the original wild cattle of Europe, although there probably have been other ancestral forms included in modern breeds, such as the various Asiatic cattle, including *Bos banteng*.

The skull of the domestic cow may be distin-guished from that of the bison, its nearest North American relative, by the position of the posterior part of the premaxilla which is in contact with the nasal bone. Also, the skull of the domestic cow is much narrower than that of the bison, and is much longer than that of other common bovids such as sheep, goats, and muskoxen. The skull of *Bos* as well as of other bovids differs from that of cervids by having the lachrymal bone in contact with the nasals (it is not separated by a prelachrymal vacuity).

The postcranial skeleton is quite similar to that of the bison, but it differs from that of cervids of comparable size (moose and wapiti) in being heavier in general and in having shorter, heavier long bones in the legs.

Compared with native cervids, the eruption of the permanent dentition in *Bos* is extended over a longer period—about four years instead of a year and a half. The first permanent tooth to appear is the first molar (M = 1) at five to six months. Between one and one-and-a-half years the second molar appears (M = 2); between one-and-a-half and two years the first lower incisor (I_1); and between one-and-a-half and two-and-a-half years the middle premolar (P = 3). When the animal is between two and two-and-a-half the second lower incisor (I_2), the front premolar (P = 2), and the last molar (M = 3) move into functional posi-tions. The last premolar (P = 4) appears between two-and-a-half and three years. The third incisor (I_3) erupts at three years and the lower permanent canine (C) finally erupts between three-and-a-half and four years.

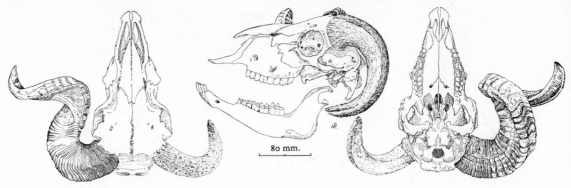

Fig. 188 – SKULL OF DOMESTIC SHEEP – *Ovis aries* (ROM 18438 ♂)

Genus **OVIS** Linnaeus

Sheep – *Moutons*

Dental Formula   I $\frac{0-0}{3-3}$ C $\frac{0-0}{1-1}$ P $\frac{3-3}{3-3}$ M $\frac{3-3}{3-3}$ = 32

Ovis aries Linnaeus – Domestic Sheep – *Mouton domestique*

The domestic sheep skull is readily identified by the presence of a deep lachrymal or pre-orbital pit and by the premaxillae which are not wedged in between the nasals and the maxilla. The infra-orbital foramen is small and has a well-defined rim around it. Many domestic breeds have no horns, but when horns are present they tend to spiral outward, or after a full turn the horn tip may project forward or slightly inward.

Native mountain sheep of western North America are a distinct species, *Ovis canadensis*.

The eruption of the permanent dentition in *Ovis*

starts with the lower first molar (M_1) at about three months and the upper (M^1) at about five months. The second molars appear between nine and twelve months. At twelve to eighteen months the first lower incisor (I_1) appears and the second (I_2) erupts between eighteen and twenty-four months —the same period in which all the premolars and the last molars ($M = 3$) appear. The third lower incisor (I_3) erupts between thirty and thirty-six months, and the lower canine does not appear until the animal is between three-and-a-half and four years old.

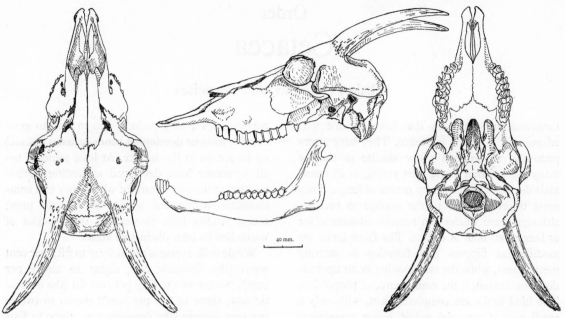

Fig. 189 – SKULL OF DOMESTIC GOAT – *Capra hircus* (ROM 84.6.1.5)

Genus **CAPRA** Linnaeus

Goats – *Chèvres*

Dental Formula I $\frac{0-0}{3-3}$ C $\frac{0-0}{1-1}$ P $\frac{3-3}{3-3}$ M $\frac{3-3}{3-3}$ = 32

Capra hircus Linnaeus – Domestic Goat – *Chèvre domestique*

The skull of the domestic goat can be recognized by the absence of a lachrymal or pre-orbital pit and by the premaxilla which extends back as a wedge between the nasal and the maxilla. The infraorbital foramen is large and does not have a well-defined rim anteriorly. Horns are consistently present and are usually scimitar-like and bent back in a more or less vertical plane, or they may be twisted like a corkscrew and point up or bend backwards over the neck in a single spiral turn with the tips directed inwards and up.

The sequence of eruption of the permanent teeth approximates that of the domestic sheep *Ovis aries*.

Native mountain goats of western North America are not closely related to the domestic goat as they are of a different genus, *Oreamnos americanus*.

Order

Cetacea

Whales, Dolphins, and Porpoises

Cetaceans are mammals that have become well adapted for a marine existence. They have a torpedo-like, streamlined shape similar to that of many fish but they nurse their young, as all mammals do, and breathe air by means of lungs. They must therefore come to the surface to breathe, although some whales can remain submerged for as long as an hour at a time. The front limbs are modified as flippers that function as steering mechanisms, while the tail, moving in an up-and-down oscillation, is the main source of propulsion. The hind limbs are completely lost, with only a small pair of vestigial pelvic bones remaining; these bones are located internally near the genital opening, well down from the backbone. Hair has been completely lost in the adults; although it may be present in the unborn young, it is shed by the time of birth. The body is covered with a thick layer of blubber that serves as insulation against the low marine temperatures. Cetaceans have developed adaptations for maintaining a high body temperature (95°–100° F.) even in frigid arctic waters. The vascular system is adapted for long utilization of oxygen that permits the whale to be submerged for long periods, and to dive to great depths, without developing bends (caisson disease) on its return to the surface. At least some, if not all, cetaceans have developed an auditory echolocation system by means of which they can communicate within the species and locate prey: recent studies have shown that each species of whale has its own distinctive voice.

Whale milk averages about forty to fifty per cent water (the domestic cow, eighty to ninety per cent); twenty-two to fifty per cent fat (the domestic cow, three to five per cent); eleven to twelve per cent protein (the domestic cow, three to four per cent); and lactose (sugar) from a trace to two per cent (the domestic cow, three to five per cent).

The skull is highly modified and is often strikingly asymmetrical.

Whales include the largest living animals either now or in the past, and they greatly exceed the biggest dinosaurs in size. The largest whale is the blue or sulphur-bottom, *Sibbaldus musculus*.

All modern whales are divided into two groups (suborders): *Odontoceti*, the toothed whales, and *Mysticeti*, the baleen or toothless whales.

KEY TO THE EASTERN-CANADIAN SUBORDERS OF *Cetacea*

1 Whales with ordinary teeth (no baleen plates); single narial opening (blowhole). ODONTOCETI p. 341

1' Whales with baleen plates instead of teeth; paired narial openings. MYSTICETI p. 381

Selected References

FRASER, F. C. and P. E. PURVES, 1954.
GRIFFIN, D. R., 1955.
HOWELL, A. BRAZIER, 1930.
KELLOGG, R., 1928, 1938, 1940.
KELLOGG, W. N., R. KOHLER and H. N. MORRIS, 1953.

NORMAN, J. R. and F. C. FRASER, 1937.
SCHEVILL, WILLIAM E., 1961.
SLIJPER, E. J., 1962.
TOMILIN, A. G., 1957.
TRUE, F. W., 1889, 1904.

Suborder
Odontoceti

Toothed Whales – *Denticètes ou Cétodontes*

The number of teeth of living odontocets varies from a single elongate tusk in the male narwhal to as many as 240 in some of the porpoises. The number of teeth present gives a rough correlation with the food habits of the species: large numbers of teeth are associated with the fish-eating species while reduced numbers of larger, firmly anchored, sharp teeth are found in the killer whale, a marine mammal predator; further reductions in number are found in more specialized feeders. All toothed whales have a single nostril opening or 'blowhole'. Of six living families, representatives of five have been found in waters adjoining eastern Canada. All traces of hair, normally characteristic of mammals, are lost in the adults of this group, although hair may be found in some areas at certain stages of the developing embryo.

KEY TO EASTERN-CANADIAN FAMILIES OF *Odontoceti*

1 Snout extending well beyond lower jaws; mandibles with well-developed teeth (18 or more); narial opening (blowhole) located left of median line of skull: 2

  2 Size large (over 25 ft.); head enormous (about one third of total body) with truncate snout; narial opening located at anterior end of snout (the blow pattern is directed forward of vertical); dorsal fin low and thick; skull an elongated triangle (when viewed from above); lower jaws united anteriorly (more than half of the total length) to form a Y-shape.   PHYSETERIDAE p. 351

  2′ Size small (under 15 ft.); head not greatly enlarged; snout not truncate; narial openings located near the middle of the head; dorsal fin well developed; skull a short triangle (approximately as wide as it is long); mandibular symphysis short (lower jaws not forming an elongated Y-shape).   KOGIIDAE p. 354

1′ Snout not extending well beyond lower jaw; narial opening medial: 3

  3 Head blunt without well-developed beak; no dorsal fin; size medium (10 to 18 ft.); all cervical vertebrae are free (they are not fused together); colour usually white, greyish white, blue grey, or mottled.   MONODONTIDAE p. 357

  3′ Head variable (usually beaked or dolphin-shaped); dorsal fin well developed; first two or more vertebrae fused together; colour variable (not all white): 4

    4 Teeth reduced to one pair in lower jaws and none in the upper; throat with two longitudinal grooves forming a V; flukes without median notch; dorsal fin located well behind the centre of the back; lachrymal bone distinct from the jugal; from two to all of the cervical vertebrae fused together.   ZIPHIIDAE p. 342

    4′ Teeth present in both upper and lower jaws; no groove on throat; flukes with median notch; dorsal fin located near the centre of the back; lachrymal bone indistinctly separated from jugal; first two cervical vertebrae fused together   DELPHINIDAE p. 362

Family **ZIPHIIDAE**

Beaked Whales – *Baleines à bec*

These are whales with elongated rostrums and teeth reduced to one or two pairs in the lower jaw; none is functional in the upper. Two longitudinal grooves form a v on the throat. A dorsal fin is located well behind the middle of the body. Most members of this family are rarely encountered anywhere and records in eastern-Canadian waters are restricted to isolated beach strandings.

Only two genera, *Mesoplodon* and *Hyperoodon*, have definitely been recorded—one species of the latter and three of the former. *Ziphius cavirostris* have been recorded from Newport, Rhode Island, and further south, and might occasionally enter eastern-Canadian waters. *Mesoplodon europaeus* has been recorded on the Atlantic coast of the United States.

KEY TO THE EASTERN-CANADIAN GENERA OF *Ziphiidae*

1 Head with large bulbous swelling above beak; mouth short (reaching only about half-way to the level of the eyes); skull with crests formed by elevated maxillary bones on either side of pre-maxillae, anterior to external nares; all cervical vertebrae fused together.　　　　HYPEROODON p. 349

1' Head without large bulbous swelling above the beak; mouth long (almost reaching the level of the eyes); skull without large maxillary crests; only four or less of the cervical vetebrae are fused together.　　　　MESOPLODON p. 342

Genus **MESOPLODON** Gervais

Beaked Whales – *Baleines à bec*

KEY TO THE EASTERN-CANADIAN SPECIES OF *Mesoplodon*

1 Functional teeth in lower jaw situated at the anterior tip of mandible; rostrum without basi-rostral groove.　　　　MESOPLODON MIRUS p. 347

1' Functional teeth in lower jaws situated posterior to the mandibular symphysis; rostrum with basi-rostral groove: 2

2 Mandibular tooth of males small, its height above the alveolus never more than the depth of the mandible at its shallowest point; rostrum vertically thin.　　　　MESOPLODON BIDENS p. 343

2' Mandibular tooth of males large, its height above the alveolus much more than the depth of the mandible at its shallowest point; rostrum extremely dense with deep basi-rostral groove.　　　　MESOPLODON DENSIROSTRIS p. 345

Fig. 190 – SOWERBY BEAKED WHALE – *Mesoplodon bidens*

Mesoplodon bidens (Sowerby) – Sowerby Beaked Whale –
Baleine à bec de Sowerby

This species resembles fairly closely other species of *Mesoplodon* in general body proportions, size, and colour. It is black to slate grey, shading to pale grey below. The Sowerby beaked whale was the first species described and is perhaps the most common of the genus. The generic name *Mesoplodon* indicates that it is 'armed with a tooth in the middle of the jaw'; however, this applies only to *M. bidens* and *M. densirostris*. The tooth in *M. bidens* is much smaller than in *M. densirostris*; it is not elevated and is located about a third of the way back from the tip of the long, fairly slender jaw. The rostrum is vertically thin and the head tends to be more slender and tapering, with a more receding forehead, than that of other species of this genus.

SIZE Total length 13–22 ft; pectoral flipper 13–20 in.; fluke span 35–44 in. Skull: length 24–30 in., length of rostrum 18–20 in.; width 11–13 in. Weight: up to about 1½ tons.

DISTRIBUTION AND VARIATION This is primarily a North Atlantic species with records on both the European and North American sides, including the waters off Newfoundland. Two specimens have been collected from Newfoundland: a male at

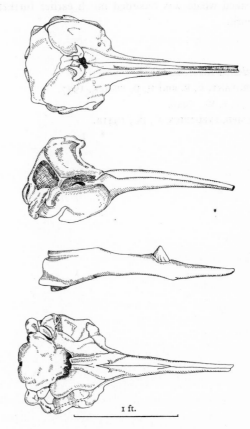

1 ft.

Fig. 191 – SKULL OF *Mesoplodon bidens*

Chapel Arm, Trinity Bay, on August 26, 1952 and a female at Wild Bight, Notre Dame Bay, on September 23, 1953.

HABITS It has been suggested that the summer range of the Sowerby beaked whale is normally in the northern offshore waters, as it is for other species of this genus, but that occasional specimens are attracted to the Newfoundland banks by dense populations of squid, a favourite food.

Breeding is thought to take place in late winter or early spring, with a gestation period of approximately one year. The young are about five to eight feet long at birth and suckle for about one year.

REMARKS The records for 1952 and 1953 referred to above are apparently the first authentic ones for eastern-Canadian waters, although the Sowerby beaked whale was recorded much earlier further south.

Selected References

SERGEANT, D. E. and H. D. FISHER, 1957.
TRUE, F. W., 1910.
ULMER, FREDERICK A., JR., 1941a.

Map 86 – DISTRIBUTION OF THE SOWERBY BEAKED WHALE – *Mesoplodon bidens*

Fig. 192 – BLAINVILLE BEAKED WHALE – *Mesoplodon densirostris*

Mesoplodon densirostris (Blainville) – Blainville Beaked Whale – *Baleine à bec de Blainville*

In general body form and in the shape of the flukes, flippers, and dorsal fin, this species is very similar to True's and to other beaked whales of the genus. It is almost completely black except for light patches on the underside between the flippers and other irregular spots on the belly. It differs most strikingly from other beaked whales in the size and shape of the lower jaw. In fully adult males the entire middle third of the mandible is dominated by a huge tooth (about $6 \times 3\frac{1}{2} \times 1\frac{3}{4}$ inches) that is elevated above the level of the top of the beak. In females the teeth remain small and apparently do not erupt above the gum line. The rostrum (or beak) is characterized by a deep basirostral groove; by a lateral constriction in the basal third of its length; and by the very dense texture of the rostral bones which exceed the denseness of ivory (their specific gravity is 34 per cent greater than that of elephant ivory, making them the densest of any vertebrate structure).

SIZE Total length 13–15 ft; pectoral flipper 18–20 in.; fluke span 38–42 in. Skull: length 22–32 in., length of rostrum 14–20 in.; greatest width 11–14 in. Weight 1,500–1,900 lb.

DISTRIBUTION AND VARIATION Since the original discovery of the Blainville beaked whale in 1817,

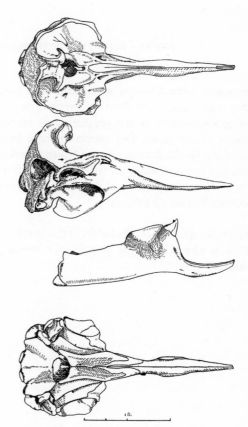

Fig. 193 – SKULL OF *Mesoplodon densirostris*

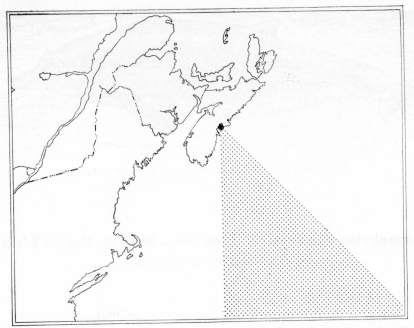

Map 87 – DISTRIBUTION OF THE BLAINVILLE BEAKED WHALE – *Mesoplodon densirostris*

apparently some fourteen specimens have been taken and these have been widespread in the Indian Ocean and in the northern and central Atlantic Ocean. Some four specimens have been recorded from the Atlantic coast of North America, including one well-documented adult male from Peggy's Cove near Halifax, N.S. in 1940 (the ninth specimen known up to 1942).

HABITS Needless to say, the habits of this species—which is almost certainly pelagic—are virtually unknown.

REMARKS It is of interest that this species has not been reported either from the south Atlantic Ocean or the north Pacific Ocean.

Selected References

HARMER, SIDNEY F., 1924.
MOORE, JOSEPH CURTIS, 1958.
RAVEN, H. C., 1942.
TRUE, FREDERICK W., 1910.
ULMER, FREDERICK A., JR., 1941a.

Fig. 194 – TRUE BEAKED WHALE – *Mesoplodon mirus*

Mesoplodon mirus True – True Beaked Whale – *Baleine à bec de True*

The True beaked whale is slate black on the back; the lower side is a yellowish purple flecked with black. The median line of the belly is somewhat darker, with a greyish area in front of the vent. The fins are black. There is a dorsal fin and the fluke is without a median notch. The skull is characterized by the presence of a pair of teeth at the anterior end of the mandible. In males these teeth protrude through the gums but in females they are embedded below the surface of the skin. The mandibular symphysis extends about a quarter or more of the length of the mandible. There is no basirostral groove on the sides of the posterior portion of the rostrum as there is in other locally recorded species of *Mesoplodon*.

SIZE Total length 15–18 ft; pectoral flipper 14–20 in.; fluke span 42–52 in. Skull: length 30–33 in., length of rostrum 15–21 in.; greatest width 12–14 in. Weight 1,800–2,000 lb.

DISTRIBUTION AND VARIATION The extent of distribution of the True beaked whale is unknown. It has been recorded from the western Atlantic from the coast of Florida to Cape Breton Island where a specimen was taken at South Gut, Ste Anne's Bay, N.S., on August 5, 1938. Specimens have also been reported from the coasts of Ireland and the Outer Hebrides.

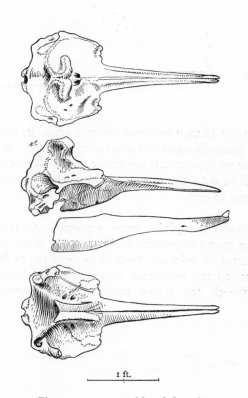

1 ft.

Fig. 195 – SKULL OF *Mesoplodon mirus*

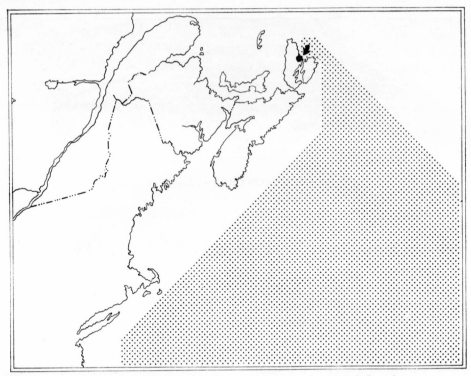

Map 88 – DISTRIBUTION OF THE TRUE BEAKED WHALE – *Mesoplodon mirus*

HABITS Little is known of this rare whale. Its food is primarily squid and other cuttlefish, and some fish are also eaten. It apparently spends most of its life far out to sea and is therefore seldom encountered by man.

REMARKS *Mesoplodon mirus* apparently occupies the temperate western North Atlantic while the related *M. europaeus* tends to be restricted to the tropical and subtropical western North Atlantic, although the known ranges broadly overlap. Specimens of the latter have been taken from New York to Trinidad, with one European record from the English Channel.

Selected References

ALLEN, GLOVER M., 1939a.
HARMER, SIDNEY F., 1924.
MOORE, JOSEPH CURTIS, 1960.
MOORE, JOSEPH CURTIS and F. G. WOOD, JR., 1957.
RAVEN, HENRY C., 1937.
TRUE, FREDERICK W., 1910, 1913.

Fig. 196 – BOTTLENOSE WHALE – *Hyperoodon ampullatus*

Genus **HYPEROODON** Lacépède

Bottlenose Whales – *Baleines à bec communes*

Hyperoodon ampullatus (Forster) – Bottlenose Whale – *Baleine à bec commune*

Adult males have an inflated forehead that rises rather abruptly from a short rostrum or beak; the lower jaw carries a single, rather small tooth or tusk at the front end. The large forehead surrounds two crests of bone, above the rostral portion of the skull, which continue to grow throughout the life of the whale and thus expand this region of the head. In young whales and females the head lacks the abrupt swelling of the forehead and the teeth usually do not protrude through the gums. The v-shaped grooves of the throat, characteristic of members of this family, are fairly prominent. The dorsal fin is situated well behind the middle of the back.

The colour is quite variable and changes with age. Young calves are fairly dark, varying from black to greyish black with a lighter grey tinge.

Yellowish-white or whitish spots appear on their flanks and underparts as they approach maturity. This spotting produces a marbled effect in females that may become a fairly uniform yellowish white or may occasionally produce a white band around the neck.

Old males are distinctive, having an irregular whitish patch on the forehead and a whitish dorsal fin.

A spermaceti reservoir, somewhat similar to that of the sperm whale, is found in the head of this species. The brain of an adult is reported to weigh 6.6 pounds. The intestines measure some 820 per cent of the body length. The bottlenose whale is unique among the *Ziphiidae* in that the teeth have enamel caps.

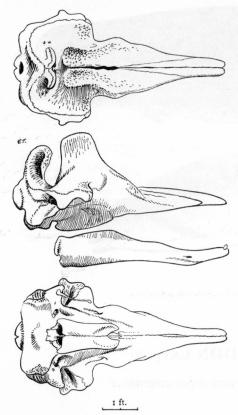

1 ft.

Fig. 197 – SKULL OF *Hyperoodon ampullatus*

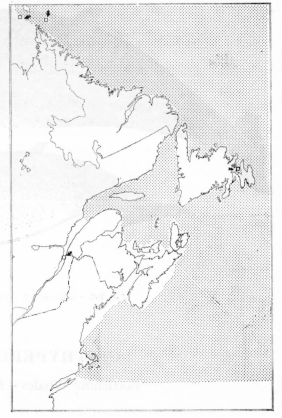

Map 89 – DISTRIBUTION OF THE BOTTLENOSE WHALE – *Hyperoodon ampullatus*

SIZE Total length: males up to 38 ft, females to 24 ft; pectoral flipper 24–36 in.; tail fluke span 52–72 in. Skull: total length 55–75 in., length of rostrum 35–45 in.; greatest width 26–36 in. Weight: about $1\frac{1}{2}$ to $3\frac{1}{2}$ tons; one 36.5 ft specimen weighed 5,000 lb. although a female—21 ft 8 in. in length—is reported to have weighed about 6,000 lb.

DISTRIBUTION AND VARIATION In summer this species occurs in the arctic and subarctic Atlantic and apparently moves south in winter. There are fairly frequent occurrences of young whales in the Labrador-current waters. A 22-foot-long female was taken at Cape Martin in the estuary of the St Lawrence River on September 4, 1940, and a male about the same length was taken at Dildo Arm, Trinity Bay, Nfld, on July 27, 1953. Other sight-

ings have been made in Newfoundland waters. This species apparently has not been reported south of the level of Rhode Island in the west and the northern coast of Europe in the east. The only other species of this genus, *Hyperoodon planifrons*, occurs in the southern hemisphere.

HABITS The bottlenose whale is noted for its sudden and very speedy dives. Apparently it dives to great depths (to at least 250 fathoms) to find squid and cuttlefish, its principal food. The contents of one bottlenose-whale stomach showed a count of 10,000 cuttlefish beaks. In its deep feeding, this whale occasionally takes herring and other fish. It usually remains submerged for only ten to twenty minutes, although harpooned animals have been known to remain submerged for over an hour. One report recorded a submergence of 120 minutes. The 'blow' is low, averaging only about three feet in height.

This species tends to remain in small pods of four to a dozen (less commonly in larger groups), each with a recognized leader according to some reports. The bottlenose whale is also said to remain persistently with a wounded member of its group.

Newborn bottlenose whales are about ten feet in length and are presumed to be born in the spring after a gestation period of about one year.

REMARKS This species was harvested commercially in eastern-Canadian waters on a small scale prior to 1900.

Selected References
BEAUGÉ, CDR., 1942.
GRAY, D., 1882.
LINDSAY, D. M., 1911.
MURRAY, J. and J. HJORT, 1912.
NORMAN, J. R. and F. C. FRASER, 1937.
SERGEANT, D. E. and H. D. FISHER, 1957.
SLIJPER, E. J., 1962.
TRUE, FREDERICK W., 1910.

Family **PHYSETERIDAE**

Sperm Whales – *Cachalots*

A single world-wide species represents this family today, although at least ten genera are known as fossils.

Genus **PHYSETER** Linnaeus

Sperm Whales – *Cachalots*

Physeter catodon Linnaeus – Sperm Whale – *Cachalot macrocéphale*

The sperm whale has been widely hunted since the early days of whaling and has become one of the most colourful and the best-known species. (Moby Dick was an albino sperm whale.) It is the largest of living toothed whales and has perhaps the most distinctive shape of all whales. It has an enormous head ending in a large blunt nose, with a single 'blowhole' located on the left side on the top front end of the head. The long, narrow jaws are Y-shaped, with narrow stem-like front ends armed with eighteen to thirty heavy conical teeth on each side. The teeth lack any enamel. The jaws appear almost ridiculously weak in comparison with the rest of the head, which constitutes about one-third of the total body. There are no functional teeth in the upper jaw, although small vestigial teeth have occasionally been found exposed; they are mostly embedded in the gum and escape notice.

There is a low dorsal fin, and shallow corrugations on the back and flanks. The colour is a rather uniform grey or dark bluish grey.

The enormous head or 'nose' contains a large reservoir of spermaceti, an oily substance that

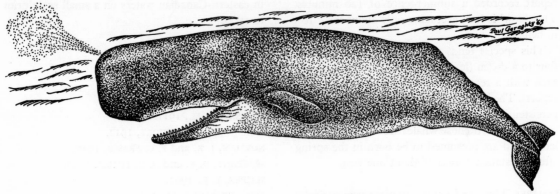

Fig. 198 – SPERM WHALE – *Physeter catodon*

turns white on exposure to air. This has been widely used for making candles (especially the standard candle of physics labs), pharmaceutical preparations, and cosmetics. As much as a ton of spermaceti has been recovered from one whale.

SIZE Total length: males up to 65 ft, females up to 40 ft; pectoral flipper 3.5–6 ft; fluke span 12–15 ft. Skull: length up to about 18 ft, length of rostrum 12–14 ft, greatest width 7–8.5 ft. Weight: up to approximately 60 (av. 33) tons in adult males and 10 to 15 tons in females. One 54-foot male weighed 41.73 metric tons and one 59-foot male weighed 53.36 metric tons.

DISTRIBUTION AND VARIATION The sperm whale is almost world-wide in distribution. Females and young tend to remain in more tropical waters (between about 40 degrees north and south latitudes), while adult older males appear to wander into both polar regions. Occurrences in the North Atlantic are generally between April and September. The sperm whale has been recorded off the coast of both Newfoundland and Nova Scotia, where it is considered quite rare. About March 1964 a young whale, measuring approximately 28 feet in length, was washed ashore near Broad Cove, Lunenberg County, Nova Scotia. A small portion

of the skeleton, including both lower jaws, was later recovered by William Christie of Boreal Biological Laboratories Limited and presented to the Royal Ontario Museum. The sperm whale has also been sighted in the outer Gulf of Maine, but it rarely ventures inshore of the 100-fathom line. It is more common in the eastern North Atlantic, particularly in the Azores region.

HABITS The sperm has been described as the most colourful and pugnacious of all whales. Like most of the toothed whales previously discussed, it feeds principally on squid and octopus, although some fish are occasionally taken. In 1955 a 47-foot sperm whale was taken near the Azore Islands that had swallowed whole a giant squid weighing 405 pounds and measuring 34 feet, 5 inches from the tip of the tail to the tip of the longest tentacle. About a ton of food is required each day.

When diving or 'sounding' the sperm whale lifts its flukes high in the air and heads almost straight down, sometimes to amazing depths—perhaps deeper than any other whale (620 fathoms or 3,720 feet is a depth recorded by one author). Maximum submersion usually lasts up to ninety minutes but averages about thirty minutes. The sperm whale commonly re-surfaces near the point where it sounds. The vapour of the 'blow' extends some

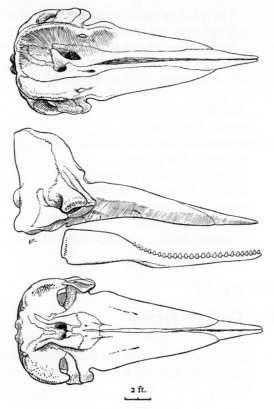

Fig. 199 – SKULL OF *Physeter catodon*

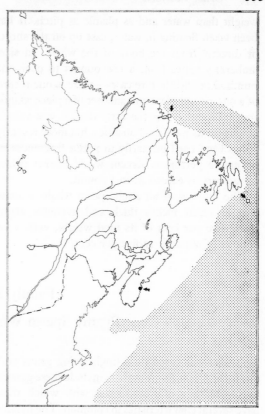

Map 90 – DISTRIBUTION OF THE SPERM WHALE –
Physeter catodon

ten to twenty feet above the surface and is distinctive in that it is ejected obliquely forward instead of straight up as in most whales. The sperm
whale is a relatively fast swimmer, often reaching
a speed of up to ten knots and as high as twenty
knots for short distances.

The newly born young range from 12 to 15 feet
long (the average, 3.92 m.). By six months the calf
may be 18 to 20 feet in length. Nursing continues
for at least thirteen months.

The gestation period is sixteen months. Oestrus
follows some seven months after weaning of the
calves, so that female sperm whales produce offspring (usually one calf) once every three years.
Sexual maturity is thought to be reached at four or
five years.

It was formerly suggested that sperm whales
lived only eight or nine years on the average, but
marked individuals show that males live up to at
least thirty-two years and females to at least twenty-
two years.

REMARKS The intestines of the sperm whale are
extremely long—1,200 feet in a 55-foot whale.

This species is famous for its production of
ambergris, a highly valuable substance that origi-
nates in its intestines, apparently as the result of
some irritation. As the hard, horny beaks of cuttlefish are frequently found embedded in ambergris,
they are thought to be the possible initiators of its
production. Ambergris is a wax-like, greyish, dark
brown or blackish substance that is lighter in

weight than water and as pliable as pitch. It has been taken floating in water, cast up on the shore, or directly from the body of the whale. In size, ambergris varies from a few ounces to over one hundred pounds in rare cases—there is one record of a 975-pound piece and another of a piece weighing 918 pounds. In the early days it was valued chiefly for its medicinal qualities, but more recently it has been used primarily to retain fragrances in expensive perfumes. Recent world-market prices for ambergris exceed $100 a pound.

The blubber of an adult sperm whale is some five to seven inches thick and averages about thirty-two per cent of its total weight, with a fat content of about forty-five per cent.

The eye of one forty-ton sperm whale weighed only 290 grams—a little over half a pound.

In the season 1952–3, 8,317 sperm whales were taken throughout the world (this number is second only to the annual catch of fin whales).

Selected References
CLARKE, ROBERT, 1956.
HEEZEN, B. C., 1957.
MATTHEWS, L. H., 1938a.
NORMAN, J. R. and F. C. FRASER, 1937.
RAVEN, H. C. and W. K. GREGORY, 1933.
SLIJPER, E. J., 1962.
TOMILIN, A. G., 1957.
WORTHINGTON, L. V. and W. E. SCHEVILL, 1957.

Family **KOGIIDAE**

Pygmy Sperm Whales – *Cachalots pygmées*

This family is based on a single living genus and one fossil genus. Some authors include these genera in a subfamily of *Physeteridae* with which they have several characteristics in common. The pygmy sperm whale nevertheless has quite distinct features and can be regarded as representing a separate family.

Genus **KOGIA** Gray

Pygmy Sperm Whales – *Cachalots pygmés*

Kogia breviceps (Blainville) – Pygmy Sperm Whale – *Cachalot pygmée*

This is a small and consequently little-known whale. Like the true sperm whale, the pygmy has a spermaceti organ on the top of the nose, but this reservoir is not nearly so inflated as the true sperm whale's, so that a relatively blunt nose overhanging a small, round, lower jaw distinguishes the pygmy sperm whale from almost all others. Instead of comprising about one-third of the total body length the head is only about a sixth as long as the body. The pygmy sperm whale has a single blowhole, crescentic in shape, located a little to the left of the midline but near the centre of the head instead of at the front end as in the true sperm whale. It also has a well-developed hooked or sickle-shaped dorsal fin near the middle of the body. The body colour is black on the back and greyish on the undersurface. Adults have no trace of hair, but the foetus has four short, tapering bristles in an oblique row in front of the eye.

There are no functional teeth in the upper jaws, but the lower jaws each have nine to sixteen (usually no more than thirteen or fourteen)

Fig. 200 – PYGMY SPERM WHALE –*Kogia breviceps*

slender, conical, and fairly sharp pointed teeth without enamel. Up to four (two on each side) rudimentary teeth have been found embedded in the gum of the upper jaws. All the cervical vertebrae are fused together. The skull has a short triangular rostrum, so that when viewed from above or below it forms almost an equal-sided triangle.

SIZE Total length 9–13 ft; pectoral flipper 13–26 in.; tail fluke span 22–34 in. Skull: total length 13–18 in., length of rostrum 6–9 in., greatest width 11–14 in. Weight 300–1,000 lb.

DISTRIBUTION AND VARIATION Records of this rare little whale have been quite widespread in both the Atlantic and Pacific Oceans. Its only known occurrence in eastern-Canadian waters is based on a well-documented specimen taken at Herring Cove, Halifax Co., N.S., on January 17, 1920, where it was discovered dead beneath the ice. It was a female, eight and a half feet long and weighing approximately 400 pounds.

HABITS Very little is known of the activities of this species. It appears to be quite solitary in its behaviour, as more than a pair or a mother and calf have not been observed. The pygmy sperm whale apparently feeds on squid and cuttle-fish, as its larger relatives do. Other remains found in the stomachs of stranded specimens have been crabs (including shore crabs) and prawns. The

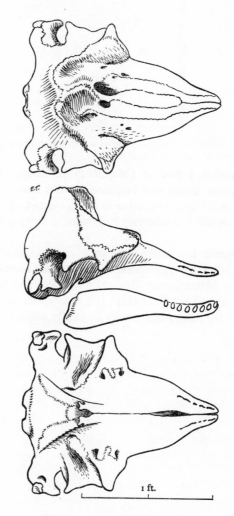

1 ft.

Fig. 201 – SKULL OF *Kogia breviceps*

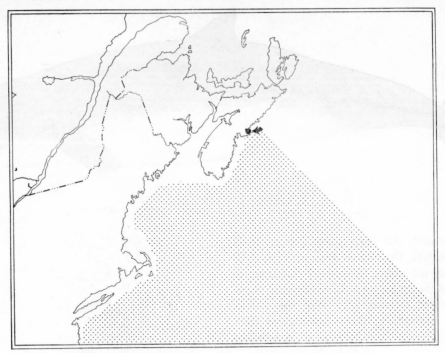

Map 91 – DISTRIBUTION OF THE PYGMY SPERM WHALE –*Kogia breviceps*

gestation period is thought to be about nine months. Births and pregnant females have been recorded from December to April, suggesting that the breeding season may be prolonged or irregular.

REMARKS In addition to the single eastern-Canadian record, the pygmy sperm whale has been recorded from Massachusetts Bay and off the coast of New Jersey and South Carolina. It is so rare everywhere that the main range cannot be clearly defined.

Selected References

ALLEN, GLOVER M., 1941.

ENDERS, R. K., 1942.

GUNTER, GORDON, CARL L. HUBBS and M. ALLAN BEAL, 1955.

HUBBS, CARL L., 1951.

MOORE, JOSEPH CURTIS, 1953.

PIERS, H., 1923.

SLIJPER, E. J., 1962.

ULMER, F. A., JR., 1941b.

Family **MONODONTIDAE**

White Whales and Narwhals – *Bélugas et Narvals*

There are only two living genera in this family (called *Delphinapteridae* by some authors). Both are relatively small (average length 10 to 15 feet) and inhabit arctic waters. They are similar in general body shape and have no dorsal fin. They have a single narial opening and all their cervical vertebrae are free. Apparently no trace of hair has been found either on the embryo or on the adult.

Some authors have regarded these whales as a subfamily of the *Delphinidae*, but they differ in various ways, particularly in the lack of fusion of any of the cervical vertebrae. They differ sufficiently from one another, particularly in their dentition, to be regarded as representing two subfamilies within the family *Monodontidae*: *Delphinapterinae* (white whales) and *Monodontinae* (narwhals).

KEY TO THE EASTERN-CANADIAN GENERA OF *Monodontidae*

1 Teeth present in both upper and lower jaws (a total of at least 32); colour of adults whitish throughout. (*Delphinapterinae*) DELPHINAPTERUS p. 357

1′ Teeth absent in lower jaw and only one or two in the upper (males with one extremely elongate tusk extending forward as a spiralled tusk beyond the end of the nose); females without functional teeth; colour of adults yellowish or greyish, marbled or mottled, with darker shades above and paler below. (*Monodontinae*) MONODON p. 360

Subfamily **DELPHINAPTERINAE**

Genus **DELPHINAPTERUS** Lacépède

White Whales – *Béluga*

Delphinapterus leucas (Pallas) – White Whale, Beluga – *Béluga ou Marsouin blanc*

The name 'beluga' is derived from a Russian word meaning white whale. This species has no dorsal fin. Both upper and lower jaws have eight to ten teeth on each side. Young whales of the St Lawrence area are dark brownish in colour the first year; they turn bluish grey or mottled during the second year, yellowish or greyish white the third year, and become milk white after four years.

In Hudson Bay this whale is slaty blue rather than brownish during the first year.

SIZE Total length 9–18 ft (av. males 12–14, females 10–12); pectoral flipper 14–20 in.; fluke span 30–48 in. Skull: length 20–26 in., length of rostrum 9–12 in., greatest width 10–14 in. Weight 800–4,000 (av. 800–1,500) lb.

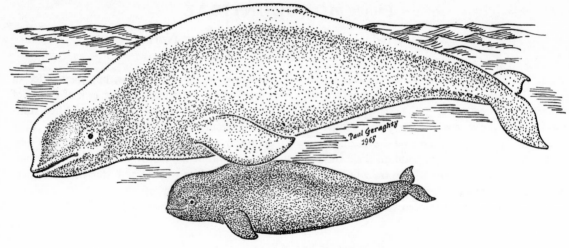

*Fig. 202 – * WHITE WHALE *– Delphinapterus leucas*

DISTRIBUTION AND VARIATION The white whale is typically a northern species and is circumpolar in distribution. It is found in Hudson and James Bays, east through Hudson Strait and Ungava Bay. It is apparently quite rare along the Labrador coast and around Newfoundland. A substantial number of white whales occupy the upper reaches of the Gulf of St Lawrence and the lower part of the river as far as Quebec City. Early records indicate sightings as far upriver as Montreal. In June 1952 an adult female was taken in a fish weir at Maces Bay, N.B., in the Bay of Fundy where additional sightings have since been made. More southerly occurrences have been recorded from Cape Cod, Massachusetts, and Atlantic City, New Jersey.

HABITS The white whale is typically an inshore species, often ascending larger rivers and estuaries during the summer. It is gregarious, usually travelling in pods of three or four to several dozen. The normal swimming speed has been estimated at six knots and the maximum at ten knots. Submergence of up to fifteen minutes between surfacing has been recorded.

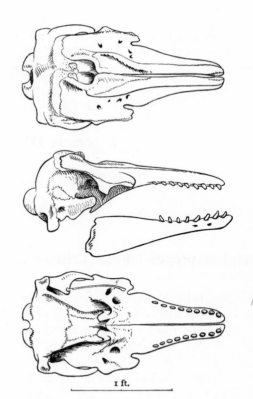

1 ft.

*Fig. 203 – * SKULL OF *Delphinapterus leuças*

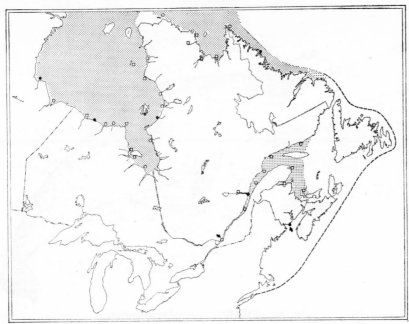

Map 92 – DISTRIBUTION OF THE WHITE WHALE – *Delphinapterus leucas*

Sexual maturity is thought to be reached by the females in their third summer and by males in their fourth. Mating is thought to take place about May. The gestation period is about one year. Normally a single calf, measuring about five feet in length, is born during the summer months. (Twins occur occasionally.) It is nursed about six or eight months before weaning. Females are thought to produce young about every other year.

Food consists of small fish such as capelin, sand lounce, herring, cod, and squid, octopi and other molluscs, crustaceans, polychaete worms (*Nereis*), and other invertebrate species.

Recent studies show that white whales make high-pitched resonant whistles and squeals under water, as well as ticking and clucking sounds. Some of these sounds are bell-like and a few somewhat resemble an echo-sounder. Occasionally the calls include a trilling sound, and for this reason the name 'sea canary' has been applied to the white whale. Some of the calls have been described as sounding like a crowd of children shouting in the distance.

REMARKS The protective blubber of white whales

forms a layer four to eight inches thick which when rendered produces twenty-five to fifty gallons of whale oil; large specimens have produced as much as 150 gallons. The skin has been widely used commercially, particularly as superior quality shoe and boot laces. In the Churchill, Man., area, white whales were processed not only for their oil but for their meat, which was used as food for mink and other fur-bearers. This species is regularly hunted in the St Lawrence River, where hunting methods include shooting, harpooning, netting, and the use of special weirs. The white whale or beluga is an important species in the economy of the Eskimos wherever it occurs in sufficient numbers to be available to them.

Selected References

DOAN, K. H. and C. W. DOUGLASS, 1953.
FISHER, H. D. and D. E. SERGEANT, 1955.
HOWELL, A BRAZIER, 1935.
SCHEVILL, W. E. and BARBARA LAWRENCE, 1949.
SERGEANT, D. E. and H. D. FISHER, 1957.
SLIJPER, E. J., 1962.
TOMILIN, A. G., 1957.
VLADYKOV, VADIM D., 1944, 1946.

Fig. 204 – NARWHAL – *Monodon monoceros*

Subfamily **MONODONTINAE**
Genus **MONODON** Linnaeus
Narwhals – *Narvals*

Monodon monoceros Linnaeus – Narwhal – *Narval*

The fabled unicorn was said to have a long, sharp, twisted horn similar to the tusk of the narwhal, the most bizarre structure to be found among whales. Reaching a length of up to nine feet, the left tusk is spirally grooved sinistrally. The single right tusk is normally undeveloped and does not extend through the bone of the upper jaw. Neither tusk is developed in the female. However, females with tusks and males with a right tusk, or even two tusks, have occasionally been reported. No adaptive function has been definitely established for narwhal tusks. Perhaps they can best be regarded as secondary sexual characters, comparable in function to the antlers of the deer family. Neither sex has any teeth in the lower jaw. All cervical vertebrae remain free (they are not fused together).

Young narwhals differ very little in general size, shape, and body proportions from young white whales. They are usually darker and more solid in colour than the adults. The colour varies considerably from dark mottled, yellowish, or greyish with mottling, to almost pure white. The underparts are lighter than the back and sides. No trace of hair has been found in either the embryo or the adult.

SIZE Total length 10–18 ft (not including tusk); pectoral flipper 13–19 in.; fluke span 30–48 in. Skull: length 20–26 in., length of rostrum 9–13 in., greatest width 13–19 in. Weight 700–3,000 lb.

DISTRIBUTION The narwhal is the most truly Arctic of all whales, rarely venturing very far south. It occurs rarely in Hudson Bay and along the northern Labrador coast. In eastern Canada, only Hudson Strait and Ungava Bay are within the regular range of this species. In 1949 a narwhal was found badly decomposed well up on the beach some ten miles north of Weenisk Post, Ont., on Hudson Bay. It was thought to have been dead for about a year, and from its position on the beach it seemed to have been washed up by either the spring or the fall high tides of 1948. The animal may have been shot, but no Indian at either Weenisk or Fort Severn recalled ever having seen a narwhal. The body may have been carried down from a considerable distance north. A small portion of the tusk was eventually recovered and deposited in the collections of the Royal Ontario Museum.

HABITS Narwhals appear to be always migrating in and out of bays and fiords and up and down coastlines. They tend to stay in groups of from four or five to several dozen. They are thought to produce one offspring (rarely twins) every other year. The gestation period and breeding season are apparently not precisely known, though it has been suggested that breeding extends over a prolonged period. The newborn are four to six feet long and remain close to the mother well into the winter. Foods

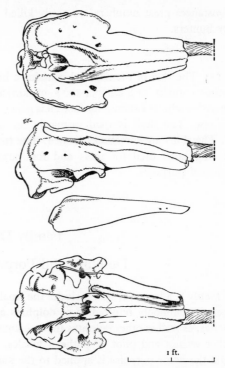

Fig. 205 – SKULL OF *Monodon monoceros*

include fish such as polar cod and Greenland halibut, and northern shrimps, squid, and other invertebrates. Occasionally narwhals become trapped in bays or fiords and are forced to return repeatedly to any openings in the ice to breathe. Under such

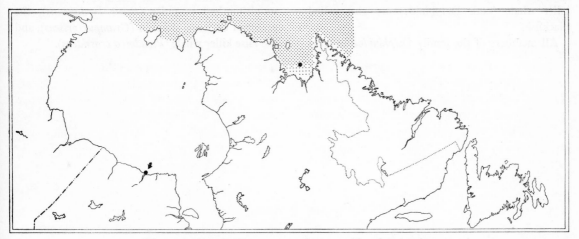

Map 93 – DISTRIBUTION OF THE NARWHAL – *Monodon monoceros*

circumstances great numbers are easily killed by native hunters.

REMARKS The skin of the narwhal contains a high vitamin-C content (31.8 mg. per 100 g. of skin) and is eagerly sought by Eskimos for food; it is generally eaten raw. The flesh is used primarily for dog food. The skins are sometimes tanned. The tusks have long been used for tools and for various ornamental purposes.

The narwhal gained prominence in 1955 when the handle of the mace of the government of the Northwest Territories was made from a narwhal tusk by Eskimos of Cape Dorset.

Selected References

DEGERBØL, MAGNUS and P. FREUCHEN, 1935.
PORSILD, MORTON P., 1922.
SLIJPER, E. J., 1962.
TOMILIN, A. G., 1957.

Family **DELPHINIDAE**

Dolphins and Porpoises – *Dauphins et Marsouins*

This family is a large one and includes the smaller cetaceans, commonly referred to as dolphins and porpoises, as well as other dolphins that are known as killer whales and pilot or pothead whales. In general the name porpoise is applied to the small forms that do not have a well-defined beak, while the name dolphin is applied to the larger forms, many of which have a well-developed beak. Unfortunately there has been wide usage of common names that do not follow this classification and much confusion has arisen. This has been increased by the use of the name dolphin for a fish and by the fact that the pothead or pilot whale and killer whale (both Delphinids) are also called blackfish.

All members of the family *Delphinidae* have at least the first two cervical vertebrae fused together; a single crescentic blowhole situated well back from the tip of the snout; and the bony septum between the nares displaced to the left. The eastern-Canadian species have a dorsal fin and functional teeth in both upper and lower jaws.

The porpoise (*Stenella styx*) has been recorded from Greenland and points south, including Woods Hole, Massachusetts, and Jamaica, but apparently no valid record is yet available from eastern-Canadian waters. Other species that normally occur in the western North Atlantic, south of Canadian waters, include *Stenella frontalis*, the rough-toothed porpoise (*Steno bredanensis*), the grampus or Risso dolphin (*Grampus griseus*), and the false killer whale (*Pseudorca crassidens*).

KEY TO THE EASTERN-CANADIAN GENERA OF *Delphinidae*

1 Head with a distinct beak set off by a deep crease or angle: 2

  2 Beak long (averaging 4 to 6 in.); a distinct black patch usually surrounds the eye; 40 to 50 teeth in each jaw; palate with deep lateral groove on each side; size 5.5 to 8.5 ft.   DELPHINUS p. 364

  2' Beak short (averaging 2 to 3 in.); no distinct black eye patch; normally 20 to 34 teeth in each jaw; palate without deep lateral groove on each side; size 6 to 12 ft: 3

    3 Colour-pattern dark above and light below, without variable colour-patterns on sides; size 8 to 12 ft; skull with 20 to 25 teeth in each jaw, about 10 mm. in diameter; rostrum longer than cranial portion of the skull.   TURSIOPS p. 366

    3' Colour-pattern dark above and light below, with variable colour-patterns on each side; size 6 to 10.5 ft; skull with 22 to 34 teeth in each jaw, about 5 or 6 mm. in diameter; rostrum length approximately the same as that of the cranial portion of the skull.   LAGENORHYNCHUS p. 369

1' Head without a distinct beak set off by a crease or angle: 4

    4 Body length less than 6 ft; teeth spade-shaped, with 22 to 27 in each jaw; dorsal fin low and triangular.   PHOCOENA p. 379

    4' Body length more than 10 ft; teeth conical: 5

      5 Dorsal fin high with straight posterior edge especially in adult males; pectoral flippers broad and rounded; head bluntly rounded; colour strikingly black and white with white spot behind the eye; teeth 25 mm. or more in diameter and number 10 to 14 in each jaw.   ORCINUS p. 373

      5' Dorsal fin low with concave posterior edge; pectoral flippers long, tapering, and sharply pointed; head bulged forward, especially in males; colour almost all black except for chest and a narrow stripe along mid-ventral line; teeth about 12 mm. in diameter and numbering 9 to 12 in each jaw.   GLOBICEPHALA p. 376

Fig. 206 – COMMON DOLPHIN – *Delphinus delphis*

Genus **DELPHINUS** Linnaeus

Common Dolphins – *Dauphins communs*

Delphinus delphis Linnaeus – Common Dolphin – *Dauphin commun*

The common dolphin is relatively rare in eastern-Canadian waters. In more temperate areas it is one of the familiar species encountered by sea travellers as it playfully jumps out of the water ahead of ships, sometimes far out at sea. It has a well-developed beak that is relatively narrow, some five or six inches in length and set off from the forehead by a well-defined deep v-shaped groove or crease. The dorsal fin is fairly well developed, tapering to a sharp tip with a concave posterior margin. The back, flippers, and fluke are usually black or nearly so and the underside is whitish. The sides have bands of grey, yellow, and white. The eye is surrounded by a black patch that usually extends forward in a narrow streak towards the beak. The skull is characterized by the elongate rostrum and by long, narrow, lower jaws, both of which have forty to fifty small teeth on each side.

SIZE Total length 5.5–8.5 ft; pectoral flipper 9–15 in.; fluke span 14–22 in. Skull: length 15–19 in., length of rostrum 8.5–12.5 in., greatest width 6.0–7.5 in. Weight approximately 100–180 lb.

DISTRIBUTION AND VARIATION The common dolphin is widespread in temperate waters. At least two specimens have been taken well off the coast of Nova Scotia where common dolphins are thought to appear in numbers during the late summer and autumn (43° 30′ N., 63° 00′ W. and 44° 00′ N., 61° 00′ W.) Apparently the first record close to shore was of a specimen taken in Dildo Arm, Trinity Bay, Nfld., on July 22, 1957—a 6-foot-3-inch male weighing 175 pounds. It was alone in association with a herd of some 155 pilot whales, *Globicephala melaena*. An earlier report based on a specimen shot in a sheltered tidal passage near the mouth of the Coxipi River, Saguenay County, Que., remains open to question.

The common dolphin is normally a pelagic species that does not move close to shore.

HABITS The leaping antics of common dolphins as they move in close to ships at sea are well known. Common dolphins are thought to be about the fastest swimmers of all whales, since they commonly 'zig-zag' in front of ships travelling close to twelve knots. However, recent studies indicate that a part of this apparent speed may be the result of the dolphins' actually riding on the bow-waves of the ship; they do this by placing their flukes at an angle in the upswelling water. They often leap clear of the water, usually returning with a graceful dive but frequently falling back sideways or with a splashing 'belly flop'. This species does not engage in deep dives and normally remains submerged for only $1\frac{1}{2}$ to 3 minutes before re-surfacing.

The common dolphin is gregarious, travelling in schools of from less than a dozen up to several hundred. Fish of various species, swallowed whole, constitute the major food, although squid are also eaten. The gestation period is thought to be about nine or ten months and a calf—usually only one—is born in late winter or early spring in temperate waters. Mating is thought to follow soon after birth of the young. The normal life-span has been estimated to be about fifteen years.

REMARKS The common dolphin is said to give active aid to sick or wounded comrades or to weak and ailing young by pushing them to the surface and supporting them while swimming. However, specific evidence of this seems to be lacking, at least for the western North Atlantic.

Like other dolphins, this species is capable of making a series of sounds under water.

Selected References

NORMAN, J. R. and F. C. FRASER, 1937.
SERGEANT, DAVID E., 1958.
SERGEANT, DAVID E. and H. D. FISHER, 1957.
SLIJPER, E. J., 1962.
TOMILIN, A. G., 1957.
TRUE, F. W., 1889.

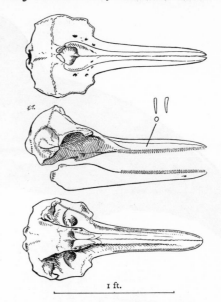

Fig. 207 – SKULL OF *Delphinus delphis*

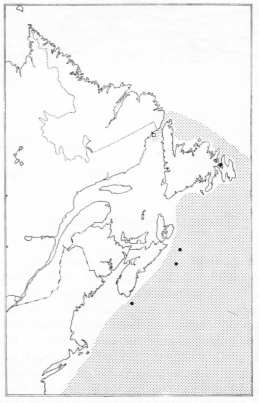

Map 94 – DISTRIBUTION OF THE COMMON DOLPHIN – *Delphinus delphis*

Fig. 208 – BOTTLE-NOSED DOLPHIN – *Tursiops truncatus*

Genus **TURSIOPS** Gervais

Bottle-nosed Dolphins – *Dauphins à gros nez*

Tursiops truncatus (Montagu) – Bottle-nosed Dolphin – *Dauphin à gros nez*

The common name is derived from the shape of the small beak. The bottle-nosed dolphin is even rarer in eastern-Canadian waters than the common dolphin. Only one specimen has been recorded here, although it is the most familiar dolphin along the Atlantic coast of the United States. It is a larger species than the common dolphin and is distinguished by its purplish lead-grey upper parts and whitish underparts and by its short beak which is normally less than three inches long. The teeth are comparatively large (about 10 mm. or $\frac{3}{8}$ in.

wide) and there are twenty to twenty-six in each side of each jaw.

SIZE Total length 8–12 ft; pectoral flipper 12–18 in.; fluke span 20–28 in. Skull: length 15–23 in., length of rostrum 8–12 in., greatest width 7–12 in. Weight 300–400 lb.

DISTRIBUTION AND VARIATION Primarily an animal of the temperate and tropical Atlantic, the bottle-nosed dolphin is common along the coast from

Maine to Mexico. The single Canadian record was a female taken from the Petitcodiac River at Salisbury, N.B., about September 15, 1950.

HABITS Of all cetacea, perhaps the bottle-nosed dolphin is known most intimately. It survives well in large marine aquarium tanks where it becomes quite tame and has been the subject of intensive study.

In captivity it is most active during the day and rests at night. Its playful antics are similar to those of the common dolphin, but it tends to be less pelagic, staying closer inshore. Swimming speeds of up to ten or twelve knots have been measured for some distances, and short spurts of much greater speeds are thought to be possible. It is believed that the bottle-nosed dolphin rarely dives deeper than ten or fifteen fathoms. Submergence rarely exceeds fifteen minutes. In captivity it demonstrates a high order of intelligence and learns to perform many feats. Reports of co-operation in assisting young or injured comrades have been confirmed by studies in captivity.

The gestation period is approximately one year. Usually a single calf is born every other year weighing about twenty-five pounds and measuring 36 to 45 inches. The calf is able to swim fast enough to keep up with the mother almost immediately after birth. The young nurse for short periods quite frequently (about every twenty to thirty minutes at first), and continue to nurse for sixteen to twenty-two months. Solid food is taken in small quantities at about six or seven months and is slowly increased until the calf is weaned.

The food of adults is almost exclusively fish, swallowed whole head first, but invertebrates may be eaten by some. Captive animals can subsist on about eighteen to twenty-five pounds of fish a day. The estimated maximum life-span is thirty years.

Bottle-nosed dolphins commonly travel in large schools, of both sexes and all ages, that are without any apparent leader or other obvious social organization. However, under captive conditions the males apparently establish a strict hierarchical order; the largest is usually dominant.

Recent research has proved that when the

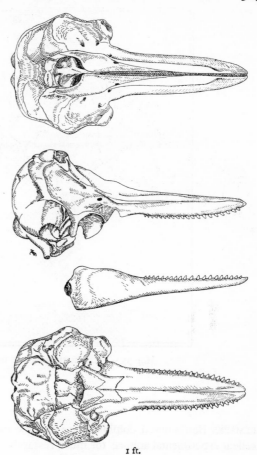

1 ft.

Fig. 209 – SKULL OF *Tursiops truncatus*

bottle-nosed dolphin is under water, it can not only detect a sound for distances of at least eighty feet but it can quickly locate the source of the sound. It has a repertoire of various sounds of its own, including a shrill whistle in the 7,000-to-15,000-cycle-per-second range. Young have been observed to keep in constant contact with their mothers by whistling. Sounds between seven and fifteen kilocycles are emitted with continuously changing pitch, while sounds between twenty and 110 kilocycles consist of very short blasts of variable duration. Thus the bottle-nosed dolphin, and perhaps most cetaceans, are able to locate objects as well as food in the dark by a principle not unlike the echo-location of bats.

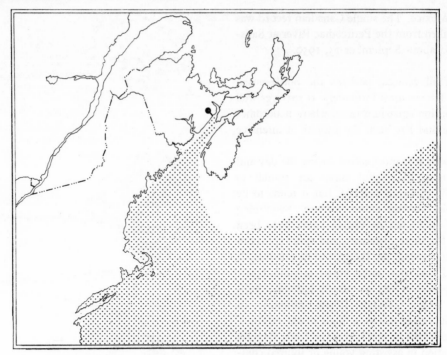

Map 95 – DISTRIBUTION OF THE BOTTLE-NOSED DOLPHIN – *Tursiops truncatus*

REMARKS Bottle-nosed dolphins have become excellent experimental animals for much research on behaviour and on many other aspects of cetology including physiology, echo-location, and general biology. They are star performers in marineland or sea-water aquariums in Florida and California. They breed and produce young in captivity.

Selected References
ALLEN, GLOVER M., 1931.
BROWN, D. H. and K. S. NORRIS, 1956.
ESSAPIAN, FRANK S., 1953, 1955.
KELLOGG, W. N., 1953, 1961.

KELLOGG, W. N., R. KOHLER and H. N. MORRIS, 1953.
LAWRENCE, BARBARA and W. E. SCHEVILL, 1954.
LILLY, JOHN C., 1961.
MCBRIDE, A. F. and H. KRITZLER, 1951.
MOORE, JOSEPH CURTIS, 1953.
NORRIS, K. S., J. H. PRESCOTT, P. V. ASA-DORIAN, and P. PERKINS, 1961.
SCHEVILL, W. E. and BARBARA LAWRENCE, 1953, 1956.
SERGEANT, D. E. and H. D. FISHER, 1957.
SLIJPER, E. J., 1962.
TAVOLGA, MARGARET C. and F. S. ESSAPIAN, 1957.
TRUE, F. W., 1890.

Genus **LAGENORHYNCHUS** Gray

White-sided Dolphins – *Dauphins à côtés blancs*

KEY TO THE EASTERN-CANADIAN SPECIES OF *Lagenorhynchus*

1 Beak white or dark; side colours black, grey, and white; teeth about 6 or 7 mm. in diameter and number 22 to 27 on each side above and below; rostrum not especially narrow or pointed.

LAGENORHYNCHUS ALBIROSTRIS p. 369

1' Beak black; side colours black, grey, yellow, and white; teeth about 5 mm. or less in diameter and number 30 to 34 on each side above and below; rostrum narrow and pointed.

LAGENORHYNCHUS ACUTUS p. 371

Lagenorhynchus albirostris Gray – White-beaked Dolphin – *Dauphin à nez blanc*

Although quite similar in form to the white-sided dolphin (*L. acutus*), the white-beaked dolphin is slightly larger and can be easily distinguished when its beak is white (see below). The lower margin of the flipper is less curved and the dorsal fin is slightly larger and more reclined than in *L. acutus*. There is usually a greyish band along the sides. The flipper, flukes, and dorsal fin are black and the belly is white. The upper and lower lips are usually white (hence the name), but they may be greyish or darkly pigmented. A dark streak usually extends from the corners of the mouth to the flippers. Considerable variations are found in the colour pattern, some of which are apparently correlated with age. Each jaw has twenty-two to twenty-seven pairs of teeth that are about a quarter of an inch in diameter (6 or 7 mm.).

SIZE Total length 8–10.5 ft; pectoral flipper 12–19 in.; fluke span 15–29 in. Skull: total length 16–19 in., length of rostrum 8.0–9.5 in, greatest width 9.0–10.5 in. Weight about 300–600 lb.

DISTRIBUTION AND VARIATION The white-beaked dolphin is primarily an arctic species of the North Atlantic and rarely ventures very far south of the

Gulf of Maine. It appears in small numbers in the spring and fall in Newfoundland waters. On March 20, 1953, seven specimens were driven ashore by advancing sea ice at Seal Cove, Conception Bay, Nfld, and were killed by local residents. Another specimen was harpooned at Port de Grave, Conception Bay, on May 10, 1954. Sight records include Trinity Bay, Newfoundland, and Hamilton Inlet, Labrador. The white-beaked dolphin is more commonly encountered along the northern European coast where very large schools have been reported, particularly off Norway.

HABITS Although the range of this species is similar to that of the white-sided dolphin, the white-beaked dolphin apparently prefers colder waters. The white-sided dolphin, for instance, appears only during the summer in Newfoundland waters, whereas the white-beaked dolphin appears there only in spring and fall. The white-beaked dolphin is apparently much less gregarious on the west side of the Atlantic, since schools observed rarely exceed a dozen; however, this may be an expression of low population density in the area. (The white-sided dolphin usually occurs in schools of forty or fifty or more.) The white-beaked dolphin

Fig. 210 – WHITE-BEAKED DOLPHIN – *Lagenorhynchus albirostris*

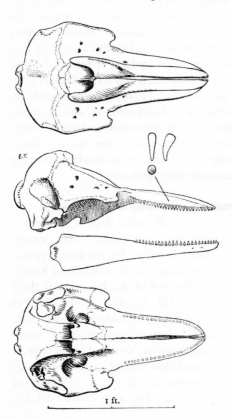

Fig. 211 – SKULL OF *Lagenorhynchus albirostris*

Map 96 – DISTRIBUTION OF THE WHITE-BEAKED
DOLPHIN – *Lagenorhynchus albirostris*

appears to be less active than the white-sided dolphin.

The young, measuring about 4 feet at birth, are born in midsummer. The gestation period is thought to be ten months.

This species is known locally as 'squid hound' and its food is thought to be made up of fish and squid.

REMARKS Much remains to be learned of this in-teresting dolphin. Its voice was recently recorded in the Gulf of Maine.

Selected References

NORMAN, J. R. and F. C. FRASER, 1937.

SCHEVILL, WILLIAM E. and WILLIAM A. WATKINS, 1962.

SERGEANT, D. E. and H. D. FISHER, 1957.

TOMILIN, A. G., 1957.

TRUE, F. W., 1889.

Fig. 212 – WHITE-SIDED DOLPHIN – *Lagenorhynchus acutus*

Lagenorhynchus acutus (Gray) – White-sided Dolphin – *Dauphin à flancs blancs*

The white-sided dolphin has distinctive colour patterns on the sides. A light, almost whitish area extends backward from about the dorsal fin approximately two-thirds of the distance to the flukes. A greyish band usually extends below the full length of the whitish one and forward to the eye. Below this there is a yellowish band just above the white of the belly and lower jaws. A dark stripe extends from the corner of the mouth below the eye to the pectoral flipper. The upper part of the beak and the flipper, back, dorsal fin, and flukes are all black. The short beak (about two inches long) is separated from the head by a deep groove.

The upper and lower jaws each have thirty to

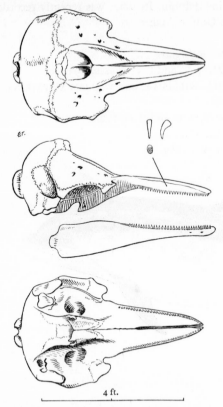

4 ft.

Fig. 213 – SKULL OF *Lagenorhynchus acutus*

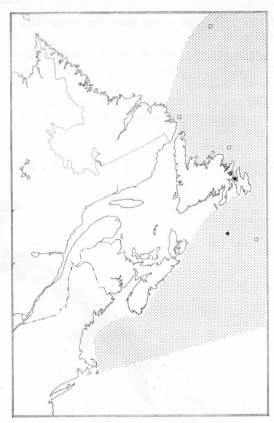

Map 97 – DISTRIBUTION OF THE WHITE-SIDED
DOLPHIN – *Lagenorhynchus acutus*

thirty-four pairs of small pointed teeth (up to about 5 mm. or $\frac{3}{16}$ in. in diameter). Males are only slightly larger than females. The rostrum is narrower and usually more pointed than that of the white-beaked dolphin, and the teeth are smaller and more numerous.

SIZE Total length 6–9.5 ft; pectoral flipper 10–14 in.; fluke span 24–28 in. Skull: length 15–18 in., length of rostrum 7.5–9 in., greatest width 8.5–10 in. Weight about 200–500 lb.

DISTRIBUTION AND VARIATION The white-sided dolphin is restricted to the northern North Atlantic, including the North Sea, although a closely related species, *Lagenorhynchus obliquidens*, occurs in the North Pacific and south as far as Baja California. The white-sided dolphin is fairly common off the east coast of Newfoundland where it occurs in

summer, often associated with pilot whales. This dolphin is occasionally driven inshore and stranded by whalers. Two stranded specimens were taken at Chapel Arm, Trinity Bay, Nfld., on July 30, 1954. The white-sided dolphin has been recorded as far south as Cape Cod, Massachusetts, but it occurs more commonly north of Newfoundland. It has been seen along the coast of southern Labrador (one was sighted twenty miles north of St Lewis Sound on August 21, 1954) and is commonly encountered in the Grand Banks area, often in large schools.

HABITS The white-sided dolphin prefers cold water, although it ranges further south than *L. albirostris*. It is quite gregarious and usually travels in schools of forty or fifty to over a hundred. It is often observed in close association with other whales, particularly pilot whales. Local residents often refer to this species as a 'jumper'. It is apparently much more active than the white-beaked dolphin.

The gestation period is about ten months. The young are usually born in the spring and measure 3 to 4 feet. Food consists primarily of squid and fish, the latter apparently predominating.

REMARKS The white-sided dolphin is reported to be less prone to panic than some gregarious whales when one of its group is injured or killed.

Selected References
JONSGÅRD, A. and O. NORDLI, 1952.
NORMAN, J. R. and F. C. FRASER, 1937.
SERGEANT, D. F. and H. D. FISHER, 1957.
SCHEVILL, WILLIAM E., 1956.
TOMILIN, A. G., 1957.
TRUE, F. W., 1889.

Genus ORCINUS Fitzinger
Killer Whales – *Épaulards*

Orcinus orca (Linnaeus) – Atlantic Killer Whale – *Épaulard*

The killer whale is one of the most feared predators of the sea. The male, up to 31 feet in length, was thought to be almost twice as large as the female, but recent studies indicate that both sexes average about 18 feet. This species is characterized by a striking development of the dorsal fin. Situated about midway along the back, the fin of the male extends upward to a maximum of six feet above the contour of the body and terminates in a sharp point at the apex. Young and females have much shorter dorsal fins, generally ranging up to about 3 feet. There is no beak present on the bluntly rounded head, which is streamlined into the body. The teeth—ten to fourteen in number in each side of each jaw—are somewhat flattened transversely (about 2-to-3 inches long and averaging slightly less than 1×2 inches or 25×50 mm. in diameter) and, as in other delphinids, interlock when the mouth is closed—the prey has little opportunity to free itself from such an efficient grasping mechanism. The pectoral flippers are disproportionately large for the size of this whale and are broadly rounded—they do not taper to a point as in most delphinids. The surface of the tail fluke is likewise expanded to provide the killer with amazing speed and stamina for catching its prey. The colour and markings of this black-and-white whale are quite distinctive. The dorsal fin, back, flukes, and pectoral flippers are black, while a white area extends along the lower jaw to the flippers, along the belly and up the flanks about midway between the dorsal fin and fluke. There is a white patch above the eye.

SIZE Total length: males 18–31 ft, females 10–24 ft; pectoral flippers: males 47–70 in., females 22–59 in.; fluke span: males 76–92 in., females 35–55 in. Skull length: males 34–48 in., females 28–38 in.; length of rostrum: males 20–24 in., females 14–18 in.; greatest width: males 27–32 in., females 15–24

Fig. 214 – ATLANTIC KILLER WHALE – *Orcinus orca*

in. Weight: males 3,000–8,000 lb. (there is a report of one male weighing 8 tons), females 1,600–5,000 lb.

DISTRIBUTION AND VARIATION This genus is cosmopolitan but is more common toward the polar regions. The Atlantic and Pacific forms are considered by some authors to be different species (*Orcinus rectipinna* in the Pacific) while others consider both as belonging to the single species, *O. orca*. Other names that have been applied to this genus include *Grampus* and *Orca*. The killer whale is not common in eastern-Canadian waters. In the ten-year period 1947–56 some dozen and a half reports of occurrences have been recorded, including three or four killers taken by whalers from the Trinity Bay area of the east coast of Newfoundland. One specimen was stranded near Economy, Minas Basin, N.S., in 1950 and another

near Chapel Arm, southern Trinity Bay, Nfld, in 1955. On April 27, 1957, a herd of between nineteen and twenty-five was stranded at New Melbourne, Trinity Bay, Nfld, apparently as a result of being forced ashore by drifting ice. Sight records include the Labrador coast, the Strait of Belle Isle, and the St Lawrence estuary. There has apparently been no record of killer whales from Hudson Bay. It is thought that there is a general northward movement in the spring, with killers passing the east coast of Newfoundland in June, and the Strait of Belle Isle in June and July, as they proceed north along the Labrador coast to the true Arctic where they are more common. A return migration occurs with the onset of autumn.

HABITS The killer whale truly lives up to its name. Killers travel in groups of from two or three up to forty or fifty, usually maintaining a tight formation.

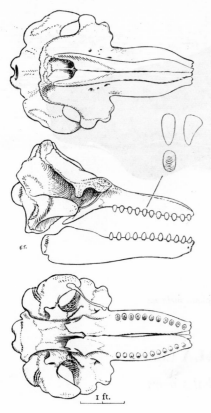

Fig. 215 – SKULL OF *Orcinus orca*

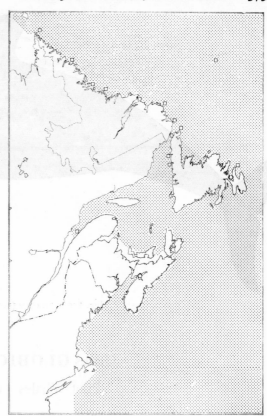

Map 98 – DISTRIBUTION OF THE ATLANTIC
KILLER WHALE – *Orcinus orca*

They hunt in packs in much the same manner as wolves, often attacking large whales many times their own size. Other prey include seals, walrus, porpoises, and other dolphins. Smaller prey are sometimes swallowed whole, while larger whales are torn bit by bit until they are literally ripped to pieces or until all appetites are satisfied. Killers are reported to swim up under ice floes and bump them with their bodies in order to dislodge seals or other prey that have taken refuge there. They are also reported to attack carcasses of whales captured by whalers and occasionally to make off with an entire specimen.

The gestation period is thought to be between twelve and sixteen months. The young measure about 7 to 9 feet long at birth. Nursing is thought to continue for about a year. Breeding may take place soon after parturition. The maximum life span has been estimated to be about twenty years.

REMARKS Various reports have shown that the killer whale has an amazing stomach capacity. Remains of up to thirteen porpoises and fourteen seals have been recorded in one specimen. The intestines of the killer measure about 8.2 times its total length.

Selected References

DEARDEN, J. C., 1958.

ELLERMAN, J. R. and T. C. S. MORRISON-SCOTT, 1951.

ESCHRICHT, D. F., 1866.

KELLOGG, R., 1940.

NORMAN, J. R. and F. C. FRASER, 1937.

SERGEANT, D. E. and H. D. FISHER, 1957.

SLIJPER, E. J., 1962.

TOMILIN, A. G., 1957.

Fig. 216 – PILOT WHALE – *Globicephala melaena*

Genus **GLOBICEPHALA** Lesson

Pilot Whales – *Globicéphales noirs*

Globicephala melaena (Traill) – Pilot Whale, Blackfish, Pothead Whale – *Globicéphale noir*

The generic name *Globicephala* and the common name 'pothead' both stem from the peculiar shape of the head of this whale. The forehead is greatly swollen, resembling a large globular projection above the upper jaw. Except for a light greyish patch under the throat region that narrows and extends backward as a stripe along the belly to the vent, and sometimes a darker greyish saddle behind the dorsal fin, the coloration of this species is all blackish (slate grey when wet and dark chocolate when dry)—thus the name 'blackfish'. The dorsal fin is rather low and has a long base, a bluntly rounded tip, and a deep concavity in the rear margin. The pectoral flipper is relatively long, slender and pointed. The skull is broad and short, with nine to eleven (sometimes twelve) teeth in each

side of the upper and lower jaws measuring almost half an inch (12 mm.) in diameter. The teeth are restricted to the front portions of the jaws. In older animals as few as six teeth are to be found.

SIZE Total length: males 15–21 ft, females 12–17 ft; pectoral flipper 26–48 in.; fluke span 42–58 in. Skull: length 24–28 in., length of rostrum 12–17 in., greatest width 16–20 in. Weight approximately 1–3 tons.

DISTRIBUTION AND VARIATION Although the genus is widespread in both the Atlantic and Pacific, this species is restricted in the Atlantic to the northern portion, ranging from the northern Scottish Islands to the Faeroe Islands and Iceland. On the

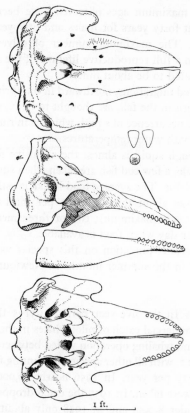

Fig. 217 – SKULL OF *Globicephala melaena*

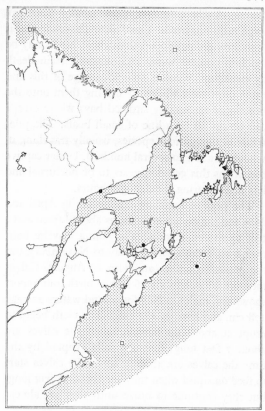

Map 99 – DISTRIBUTION OF THE PILOT WHALE –
Globicephala melaena

western side it ranges from southern Greenland south to about northern New Jersey. The pilot is the most common whale of the east coast of Newfoundland during the summer months, entering the bays about mid-May and leaving about October. (A commercial whaling operation has been carried on there since 1947.) This species is uncommon in the closer inshore waters of the continental coast. However, a herd was stranded at St Mary Bay near Digby, N.S., on August 2, 1949, and a single specimen was stranded near Yarmouth, N.S., in August 1954. Pilot whales have been sighted off the southernmost coast of Nova Scotia as well as in the Gulf of St Lawrence. In 1930 there was an unusually large number stranded on both the north and south coasts of Prince Edward Island, including about 200 at Percival and Enore Rivers and about fifty near Borden. About two dozen were observed and a few were shot at

Summerside, P.E.I. Pilot whales occasionally enter the estuary of the St Lawrence River. A herd of twenty-one was stranded at Trois Pistoles on August 31, 1930. Other records for the same year include Boischatel, Île d'Orléans, and Ste Anne de la Pocatière. In 1934 twenty-three pilot whales were stranded at Métis, eight near Tartague (Tartigou) and Rivière Blanche, and forty at Boule Rock. In 1936 pilot whales were again reported in the St Lawrence River area. Records also include the coast of Labrador north to Ungava Bay. The overall distribution pattern for this species varies from year to year and from season to season. It is thought that its occurrence is largely governed by the distribution of squid, *Illex illecebrosus*, which forms almost the whole diet of the pilot whale.

HABITS The name pilot whale is thought to be derived from the habit these whales have of following closely a lead or pilot whale—usually a large male—in herds. This follow-the-leader habit is so strongly developed that whole herds may be led into shallow water and almost certain death by stranding. Whalers take advantage of this and catch most pilot whales by driving them onto the beaches of favourably situated bays where escape can be cut off by a line of small boats. The pilot whale is a gregarious species, usually travelling in schools of a few to several hundred. Under captive conditions this genus appears to be nocturnal and less active during the daylight hours.

The peak of breeding takes place in April and May and the gestation period is about fifteen and a half to sixteen months. The young may be born over a six-month period (May to November), but the greatest number are born in August. Calves measure between 5 and 6 feet at birth (one report shows that males in Newfoundland waters average 178 cm. and females 174 cm.). The teeth begin to erupt at about six months when the calves are about 7 feet long; they are fully erupted by the time the calves are about 9 feet. The calves start to feed on squid when they are about 7½ feet long, but they continue to nurse until they are almost two years old.

The female begins to breed at about six years (four-and-a-half to eight), by which time it averages about 12 feet in length. The male does not become fully mature sexually until it is about twelve years and measures about 16 feet. At this age the male continues to grow while the female has normally reached its maximum size.

The reproductive cycle is some forty months long, with twenty-one to twenty-two months of lactation. It has been calculated that about ten to thirteen per cent of the mature reproducing females produce calves each year. The mortality rate is apparently much greater for males than for females. In Newfoundland waters the sex ratio of the adults was recently found to be about three females for every male.

On the basis of recently developed techniques of determining age by sectioning the teeth and counting the number of annual growth-layers of dentine,

normal maximum ages observed have been estimated at forty years for males and fifty years for females. The maximum number of calves produced in a full reproductive lifetime of the female is estimated to be about nine.

Marked migrations, northward in the spring and southward in the fall, are thought to be correlated with the occurrence of squid, which is in turn correlated with water temperatures.

Although squid is almost the exclusive food of this whale, a few cod fish are taken when squid are not available. The average food intake is estimated to average about thirty pounds per meal (up to sixty pounds maximum); two or three meals are eaten per day when food is available.

No serious predation on this species was discovered in the summer months in Newfoundland waters.

REMARKS In the five-year period 1951–5 the annual commercial catch of pilot whales in the Newfoundland whaling operation varied between 2,298 and 6,412, with all other species accounting for less than sixty per year. In 1956 nearly 10,000 pilot whales were taken. In 1957 the catch dropped to a little under 8,000, and in 1958 only about 1,000 were captured. Approximately 2,000 were taken in 1959 and 1960; however, in 1961 the take was 6,262.

The average adult pilot whale produces about forty gallons of blubber oil and about two gallons of head oil. The flesh has recently been processed as fox or mink food for fur farms.

Selected References
BROWN, S. G., 1961.
HARRISON, R. J., 1949.
KRITZLER, H., 1952.
MATHEWSON, S. J., 1935.
NEEDLER, A. W. H., 1931.
SERGEANT, D. E., 1962.
SERGEANT, D. E. and H. D. FISHER, 1957.
STARRETT, A. and P. STARRETT, 1955.

Fig. 218 – HARBOUR PORPOISE – *Phocoena phocoena*

Genus **PHOCOENA** G. Cuvier

Common Porpoises – *Marsouins communs*

Phocoena phocoena (Linnaeus) – Harbour Porpoise, Common Porpoise – *Marsouin commun*

The harbour porpoise is quickly identified by its small size, a beakless rounded head, and a triangular dorsal fin. It is the only true porpoise in eastern-Canadian waters. It is stoutly built; its greatest diameter is reached about midway between the flipper and the dorsal fin, which is situated just behind the middle of the body. The flippers are quite oval in outline and are relatively small in proportion to the body. The rostrum, back, flukes, and flippers are black and the throat and belly are white. The skull is unique among the cetaceans of eastern Canada in having twenty-two to twenty-seven pairs of spade-shaped teeth in each jaw.

SIZE Total length 3–6 ft; pectoral flipper 7.5–10.5 in., fluke span, 14–16 in. Skull: length 9.5–12.5 in., length of rostrum 4.0–5.5 in.; greatest width 5.5–7.0 in. Weight 100–150 lb.

DISTRIBUTION AND VARIATION The harbour porpoise is restricted to the North Atlantic from about the level of Iceland and Davis Strait south to the New Jersey coast in the west and to the Strait of Gibraltar in the east. During the summer months it is a fairly common species along the coast of the Maritime Provinces from the west side of the Bay of Fundy to Newfoundland. It is less well known in the Gulf of St Lawrence and along the Labrador coast.

HABITS This species is appropriately named harbour porpoise because it is shore-loving and frequently enters well into harbours and stream estuaries: it is rarely encountered very far out at sea. Fish—such as herring, hake, and pollack—constitute the principal diet, although squid and other invertebrates are also eaten. A single calf,

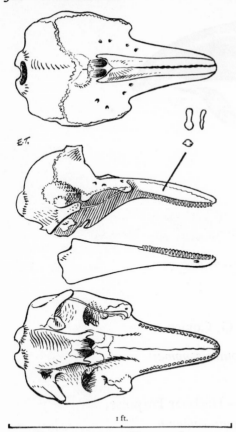

Fig. 219 – SKULL OF *Phocoena phocoena*

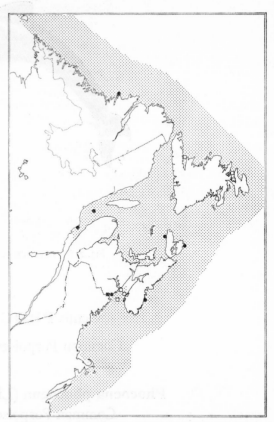

Map 100 – DISTRIBUTION OF THE HARBOUR PORPOISE – *Phocoena phocoena*

measuring some 30 to 34 inches at birth, is born after a gestation period of about ten or eleven months, usually in June or later. The mother suckles the young by swimming slowly partly on one side to allow the calf to breathe while nursing. The young are thought to continue to nurse for about eight months.

Harbour porpoises usually travel in schools and swim just below the surface, emerging about four times a minute to breathe. When the air is expelled from the lungs a low puffing or hissing sound is made. This characteristic sound has given rise to the local name of 'puffing pig'. The harbour porpoise arrives at the coast of eastern Canada suddenly in the spring and disappears before winter; its winter range is still largely unknown.

REMARKS Porpoises were hunted by the Micmac Indians in the Bay of Fundy prior to the turn of the century. The oil was rendered and sold to early settlers and the flesh was eaten.

Selected References

ANDERSON, RUDOLPH M., 1947.

KELLOGG, R., 1940.

LEIGHTON, A. H., 1937.

MØHL-HANSEN, U., 1954.

SERGEANT, D. E. and H. D. FISHER, 1957.

SLIJPER, E. J., 1962.

TOMILIN, A. G., 1957.

Suborder
Mysticeti

Whalebone Whales – *Cétacés à baleine*

In this group no functional teeth are present in either jaw. Ordinary teeth are present during foetal development but disappear before birth and a series of plates of whalebone (called baleen) develop in the roof of the mouth. These plates are of a horny substance about 6 to 12 mm. ($\frac{1}{4}$ to $\frac{1}{2}$ inches) thick, rather hard yet flexible, and have a glossy finish. The shorter plates are roughly triangular in outline and grow out of the palate at right angles to the long axis of the body. The outer edge of the plates is smooth while the inner edge is frayed into brushlike strands. There are 200 to 400 plates, with about 6 millimeters ($\frac{1}{4}$ of an inch) between, in each side of the mouth. They make an effective sieve through which these whales are able to strain out the small organisms they require as food. In the Suborder *Mysticeti* the nasal openings or blow-holes are paired, not single as in the *Odontoceti*. Unlike the toothed whales (Suborder *Odontoceti*), which have no trace of hair in the adults, the whalebone whales characteristically retain a few hairs in the head region that apparently function much like the vibrissae or bristles of other mammals. The local representatives of this Suborder are divided into two distinct families, *Balaenopteridae* and *Balaenidae*. A third family, *Eschrichtiidae*, includes only the grey whale of the Pacific.

Most of the representatives of *Mysticeti* are truly the giants among whales.

KEY TO THE EASTERN-CANADIAN FAMILIES OF *Mysticeti*

1 Dorsal fin present; external grooves present on throat; upper border of lower lip not strongly arched; whalebone short; skull with straight or slightly arched rostrum; lower jaws with well-developed coronoid process. BALAENOPTERIDAE p. 382

1' Dorsal fin absent; no external grooves present on throat; upper border of lower lip strongly arched; whalebone long and narrow; skull with strongly arched rostrum; lower jaws without well-developed coronoid process. BALAENIDAE p. 397

Family **BALAENOPTERIDAE**

Fin-backed Whales – *Rorquals*

The members of this family are commonly called fin whales or rorquals. They are characterized by the presence of a dorsal fin (thus the name); a series of parallel grooves running longitudinally on the undersurface of the throat and chest region; relatively short and stiff whalebone plates with thick bristles measuring from 0.2 to 1.0 mm. in diameter; a relatively flattened and shortened head; long tapered pectoral flippers; and unfused neck vertebrae. They feed on relatively large crustaceans and fish. Three genera and five species have been recorded from waters adjacent to eastern Canada. One genus, the humpback whale (*Megaptera*), is sometimes treated as distinct (subfamily *Megapterinae*) from other finbacks which are thus included in the subfamily *Balaenopterinae*. Another genus (*Sibbaldus*), the blue whale, is considered by some authors to be the same as *Balaenoptera*; this arrangement would reduce the family to two living genera.

KEY TO THE EASTERN-CANADIAN GENERA OF *Balaenopteridae*

1 Pectoral flippers extremely long (about one third of total body length) and scalloped; body relatively short and stout; knobby protuberances present on head and lower jaws; flukes strongly serrate; width between throat grooves 5 to 8 in.; skull with relatively deep and broad rostrum with sides tapering gradually from the middle to a sharp point in front.   MEGAPTERA p. 394

1′ Pectoral flippers relatively short (less than 20 per cent of body length) and not scalloped; body relatively long and tapering; knobby protuberances absent from head and lower jaws; flukes not serrate; width between throat grooves 2 to 3 in.; skull not as described above: 2

  2 Body coloration usually without white on the undersurface; throat grooves extending back to the level of the navel; rostrum parallel-sided posteriorly and curved inward at tip (viewed from above); total length 70–110 ft; skull length 16–21 ft.   SIBBALDUS p. 391

  2′ Body coloration with white on lower jaws or mid-ventral area; throat grooves may not extend as far back as the navel; rostrum triangular with straight sides, tapering to a sharp point (viewed from above); total length up to 82 ft; skull length up to 17 ft.   BALAENOPTERA p. 383

Genus **BALAENOPTERA** Lacépède

Finback Whales – *Rorquals*

KEY TO THE EASTERN-CANADIAN SPECIES OF *Balaenoptera*

1 Whalebone plates (baleen) yellowish white or slate coloured or both: 2

  2 Size less than 35 ft in total length; baleen all white or yellowish with longest plates about 12 in. long or less; pectoral flippers with a white patch or band in the middle of the dark top-side and white below; skull less than 7 ft (2.3 metres) long.   BALAENOPTERA ACUTOROSTRATA p. 388

  2′ Size 65 ft or more in total length; baleen yellow and slate coloured except in front right side of jaw where it is white with longest plates less than 36 in.; pectoral flippers dark above and white below; skull 12–17 ft long.   BALAENOPTERA PHYSALUS p. 383

1′ Whalebone plates black: 3

  3 Size 40 to 60 ft; baleen fringes fine, soft, and white; white area on throat; throat grooves extend only a short distance behind flippers; skull length 9–14 ft.   BALAENOPTERA BOREALIS p. 386

  3′ Size 70 to 110 ft; baleen fringes coarse and black; usually no white coloration on throat; throat grooves extend well back of flippers to the level of the navel; skull length 16–21 ft.
    (*Balaenoptera musculus*). See SIBBALDUS MUSCULUS p. 391

Balaenoptera physalus (Linnaeus) – Common Finback or Fin Whale –
Rorqual commun

This long, streamlined whale is second only to the blue whale in length and weight. Its second position in weight is approached only by the sperm whale and the bowhead. When viewed from above, the head is quite wedge-shaped (the sides of the head of the blue whale are nearly parallel). The back is distinctly ridged towards the tail, and the dorsal fin is quite high and has a concave posterior border. The colour pattern is unique among mammals in that it is strikingly asymmetrical in the head region. The general body colouring varies from light grey to dull greyish brown above and pure white below, including the undersurfaces of the flippers and flukes. In the head region the right lower jaw is white, the left pigmented. This asymmetry extends into the mouth where the left side of the tongue and the front section of the right series of whalebone plates are white with the opposite parts pigmented. The baleen plates number about 430 on each side, the longest of which are 20 to 36 inches; the frayed inner surfaces of both the pigmented (greyish) and white blades are yellowish white. Two series of short, greyish bristles are present on each side of the upper jaw. The skull is characterized by its large size and by a rostrum that has a flat dorsal contour and a wedge or triangular shape with straight sides (viewed from above).

SIZE Total length 60–82 (av. 68–72) ft; pectoral flipper 6.5–9.5 ft; fluke span 12–16 ft. Skull: length 12–17 ft, length of rostrum 8.5–10.5 ft,

Fig. 220 – COMMON FINBACK WHALE – *Balaenoptera physalus*

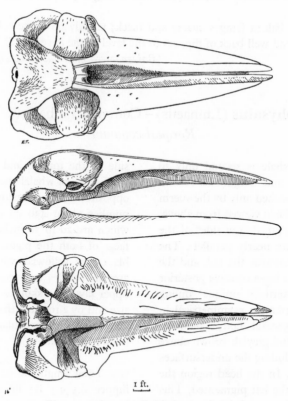

Fig. 221 – SKULL OF *Balaenoptera physalus*

greatest width 5.5–7.5 ft. Weight 40–70 (av. 58) tons. One 74-ft female from the Pacific weighed 69.54 metric tons.

DISTRIBUTION AND VARIATION The common fin-back occurs the world over in all oceans. On the west side of the Atlantic it is uncommon north of Davis Strait. It has been recorded from the Bay of Fundy, the Gulf of St Lawrence, and even up the St Lawrence River as far as Montreal where one was located in 1901; about 1870 a specimen is reported to have been killed on the shores of the Island of Orleans. However, it occurs more commonly off the shores of Newfoundland and Labrador. It moves into Canadian waters in summer and returns southward in winter.

HABITS The common finback whale is the most gregarious in its habits of all the larger whales, with small groups being the rule. Upwards of 300 in a school have been recorded, and some reports are as high as 1,000. Pods of ten or fifteen seem to be the usual number.

This streamlined whale is one of the faster whales. It has been reported to cruise at speeds of up to twenty-six knots, although its average speed is about ten to twelve knots. At an average speed the flukes beat up and down about once or twice a second. The 'blow' is strong, reaching thirteen to twenty feet in height as it rises vertically—first in a narrow column, then expanding into an elongated ellipse. When swimming slowly the finback usually surfaces almost horizontally; the blowhole comes up first and is followed by a section of the back and finally the dorsal fin. When it swims at a fast speed it surfaces at an angle and the snout breaks water first; the body is arched to display a great deal of the back and tail region, and the animal then dives at an angle without showing the flukes. The finback is said to swim sometimes on its side when feeding, presumably because it can roll more easily than it can turn.

The types of food eaten by the finback vary more than with most whalebone whales: crustaceans, squid, and small fish are the basic diet in various proportions.

M.E.C.—27

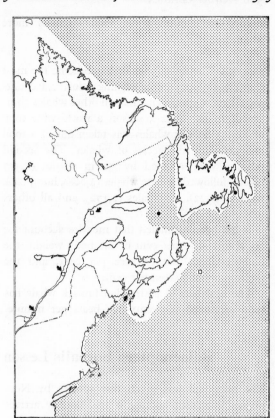

Map 101 – DISTRIBUTION OF THE COMMON FINBACK WHALE – *Balaenoptera physalus*

Single calves (occasionally twins) are born after a gestation period of about 360 days and measure about 20 to 22 feet in length and weigh up to about 4,000 pounds. The young nurse for only about five to seven months, by which time they are 35 to 40 feet long. By the second or third year, when sexual activity may begin, they measure about 64 to 66 feet. They are not fully mature sexually until they are six to eight years of age. Full size and the 'prime' of life is thought to be reached at ten to fifteen years.

Reproduction has been reported to continue until about thirty years of age, with females producing a calf in alternate years. Recent research on aging based on the lamination of the whale's wax ear-plug indicates that some finback whales live at least forty-three years. Further studies are needed to confirm these vital statistics more accurately.

REMARKS The finback whale has become the most important species for the whaling industry, accounting for more specimens than all other whales combined. In the 1952–3 season a world-wide total of 25,553 finback whales was taken out of a total of 43,669 for all species of whales. The second position was occupied by sperm whales (8,317 taken), followed by blue whales (4,208), humpback whales (3,322), sei whales (2,172), and all others (97).

It has been estimated that muscles account for about forty-five per cent of the body weight, the blubber about twenty-three per cent, and the skeleton about sixteen per cent.

The heartbeat of a stranded finback whale has been measured at twenty-five beats per minute. The normal rate has been estimated at about eight times per minute.

The brain may weigh up to 18.3 pounds. The length of the intestines is about four times the total length of the whale. The average blubber thickness is about three inches. The testes may weigh up to sixty pounds and the non-gravid ovaries about twenty-two pounds.

Selected References

ALLEN, GLOVER M., 1916.
DIONNE, C. E., 1902.
GUNTHER, E. R., 1949.
LAWS, R. M., 1959.
NORMAN, J. R. and F. C. FRASER, 1937.
SLIJPER, E. J., 1962.
TOMILIN, A. G., 1957.
TRUE, F. W., 1904.

Balaenoptera borealis Lesson – Sei or Pollack Whale – *Rorqual sei*

The name sei was given this species by Norwegian fishermen because it traditionally arrives along their coast with the sei fish, or pollack as it is known in the western Atlantic. The throat grooves of the sei whale are characteristically short, reaching only a small distance beyond the flippers. The number of grooves is quite variable, ranging from thirty-two to sixty. The baleen or whalebone measures up to 29 inches in length and is quite diagnostic in this species: the main blades (averaging about 330 on each side) are usually black and occasional ones are partly white, while the frayed inner edges are white and extremely fine and silky, almost resembling sheep's wool. A few hairs occur on the upper and lower jaws and on the rostrum. The body is thickest just behind the insertion of the pectoral flippers. As in most finback whales, the tail is laterally compressed; two thin ridges, one above and one below, join the flukes rather abruptly. The body colour is usually bluish black or greyish. There is a whitish area stretching back from the chin, narrowing between the flippers and then widening out again. When viewed from the side, the skull is slightly more arched than that of other species of this genus.

SIZE Total length 40–60 ft; pectoral flipper 3.5–5 ft; fluke span 8–13 ft. Skull: length 9–14 ft, length of rostrum 6–9 ft, greatest width 4.5–6.5 ft. Weight approximately 10–48 (av. 13) tons. One 43-ft female weighed 15.43 metric tons.

DISTRIBUTION AND VARIATION The sei whale is truly cosmopolitan, ranging almost from pole to pole, although it tends to occur more commonly in warmer waters and makes only brief visits to the polar regions in midsummer. In the western North Atlantic it is known off Iceland and the Labrador and Newfoundland coasts but is nowhere common in eastern-Canadian waters now. In the early days of whaling, specimens were taken by whalers off Newfoundland. The first specimen to be recorded there was taken in 1902; a second was taken in 1903, 39 were taken in 1904, and two each in 1905, 1906, 1909, and 1912.

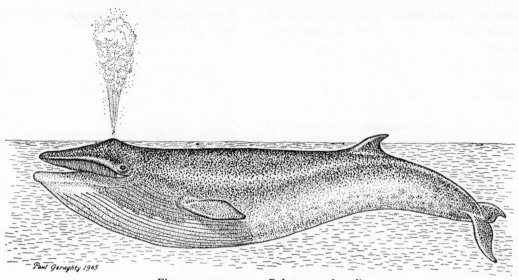

Fig. 222 – SEI WHALE – *Balaenoptera borealis*

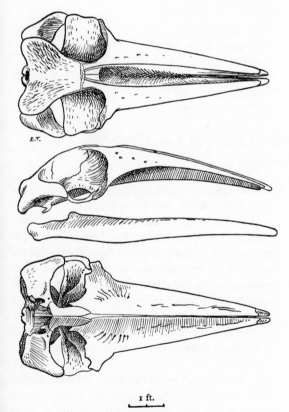

1 ft.

Fig. 223 – SKULL OF *Balaenoptera borealis*

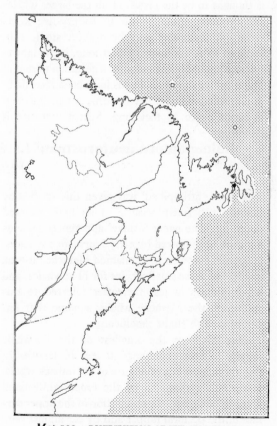

Map 102 – DISTRIBUTION OF THE SEI WHALE –
Balaenoptera borealis

HABITS Primarily a pelagic species, the sei whale tends to migrate into polar regions in midsummer but avoids the extreme cold by arriving late and leaving early. It appears to remain fairly solitary as it is rarely encountered in large pods. Food consists primarily of small crustaceans that are strained out by the fine fibrous baleen fringes. The stomach of one 40-foot sei whale contained 450 pounds of recently caught krill.

The sei whale usually surfaces obliquely, exposing first the beak, the top of the head, and finally the 'blow' which is smaller and not as high (usually 6 to 8 feet) as that of the common fin whale (13 to 20 feet). When it submerges it does not arch its body or expose its flukes but rather remains rigid and exposes little of its body on the surface. It rarely jumps above the water but it is an extremely fast swimmer for short distances—it is thought to be the fastest of all the larger whales and reaches speeds of up to twenty-five knots (which it maintains only briefly). A single calf, some 12 to 18 (average 15) feet long, is thought to be born about November after a gestation period of about twelve months. (Twins have been recorded.) It is weaned at about five months, at which time it is about 25 to 28 feet long. Sexual maturity is reached at about eighteen months, when the animimal is 44 to 48 feet long.

REMARKS Sei whales accounted for 2,172 of the total of 43,669 whales reported to have been taken by whalers around the world in the 1952–3 season. This was the least number of commercially caught whales identified. In measurements for whaling purposes, six sei whales equal one *blue-whale unit*.

The muscles account for about fifty-four per cent of the total body weight (the highest among the larger finback whales), the skeleton thirteen per cent, and the blubber only twenty per cent (the lowest average among commercially caught whales). The testes weigh about fifteen pounds.

Selected References
ALLEN, GLOVER M., 1916.
ANDREWS, R. C. 1916.
LAWS, R. M., 1959.
MATTHEWS, L. H., 1938b.
NORMAN, J. R. and F. C. FRASER, 1937.
SLIJPER, E. J., 1962.
TOMILIN, A. G., 1957.
TRUE, F. W., 1904.

Balaenoptera acutorostrata Lacépède – Little Piked or Minke Whale – *Petit rorqual*

The name 'little piked' was given this species by Scottish fishermen because of its high, pointed dorsal fin. The name 'Minke' apparently arose as a nickname bestowed by early Norwegian whalers. It appears that a crewman named Meincke mistook a school of these small whales for blue whales, and his shipmates in jest thereafter referred to this species as the Meincke whale, a name that has persisted with slight modification.

This whale is the smallest of the fin-whale family, seldom exceeding 30 feet in length. In general shape it is a miniature of the finback whale. It is easily recognized by the broad white band that extends across the midsection of the upper surface of the pectoral flipper and by the almost pure white or yellowish-white whalebone plates that seldom reach one foot in length (usually no more than eight inches) and number about 300 (287 to 320) on each side of the mouth. The head, lower jaws, and back are bluish grey, brownish grey, or greyish black, grading into a light colour on the sides. With the exception of four or five outer throat grooves, the entire throat, belly, and undersurface of the flukes are white. The throat grooves vary in number from fifty to seventy.

The skull is readily distinguished by its small size which seldom exceeds six feet in length.

SIZE Total length 15–33 (av. 25) ft; pectoral flipper 20–48 in.; fluke span 50–96 in. Skull: length 52–78 in., length of rostrum 30–48 in., greatest width 26–47 in. Weight approximately 1–3 tons.

Fig. 224 – LITTLE PIKED WHALE – *Balaenoptera acutorostrata*

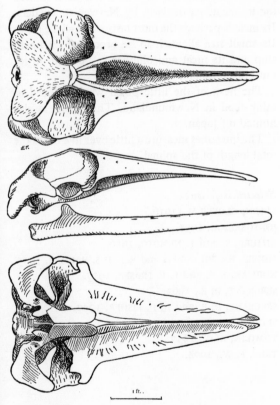

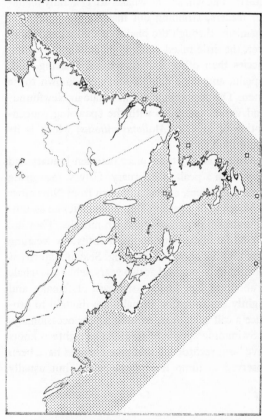

Fig. 225 – SKULL OF *Balaenoptera acutorostrata*

Map 103 – DISTRIBUTION OF THE LITTLE PIKED
WHALE – *Balaenoptera acutorostrata*

DISTRIBUTION AND VARIATION   The little piked whale ranges throughout the major oceans of the world. It tends to be an inshore species, preferring the colder waters north of the warm Gulf Stream current. It penetrates further into polar regions than other finback whales and has been observed peering up from cracks in the ice. In eastern-Canadian waters it has been reported from near Sugluk in the southwestern part of Hudson Strait and from Ungava Bay. It is fairly common along the Labrador and Newfoundland coasts and occasionally enters the Gulf of St Lawrence and the Bay of Fundy. It has been recorded from the coasts of New York, New Jersey, and Florida (including the Gulf of Mexico side). Since 1947 a small number have been taken each year by Newfoundland whalers (240 between 1947 and 1955; a high of fifty-five in 1951, a low of three in 1950).

HABITS   The whalebone whales are generally plankton feeders, straining out many small species of organisms through the blades of the baleen. However, the little piked whale is more of a fish-eating species than other finback whales. Herring, cod, capelin, and even dogfish shark are known to be eaten. The appearance of this whale in Newfoundland waters coincides with the spawning concentration of capelin (*Mallotus villosus*) which is its major food there.

Mating usually takes place between January and May, with a peak in February. Calves, measuring some 7 to 9 feet, are usually born from November to March with a peak in December, after an assumed gestation period of about ten months. They are nursed for about four or five months; by weaning time they are about 16 feet long. Sexual maturity is thought to be reached at two years, when the whale is about 24 feet long in the case of females and slightly less in males. Females are thought to produce a calf each year, missing a year occasionally.

Swimming speeds of fourteen to eighteen knots have been recorded. Little piked whales have been observed to jump free of the water, but usually half their body remains submerged during most jumps. Their manner of normal surfacing is not unlike that of the other finback whales, but the blow is much smaller, usually no more than three feet—about the same height as the blow of the white whale. A captive specimen was observed in a tank in Japan for a month, during which time it apparently did not sleep but merely increased its respiration and its activities from nightfall until about midnight and reduced its respiration and became quieter thereafter.

The little piked whale usually travels in small pods of less than 100 (usually no more than ten or twenty).

The normal maximum life span is estimated to be about thirty years.

REMARKS   Because of its small size, the little piked whale has not been subjected to heavy whaling pressure, although since 1940 it has been hunted for its meat, particularly by Norwegian whalers. Its meat is perhaps the most tasty of all whale meat. Its small size allows it to be processed on board ship and its meat and blubber to be held on ice until taken ashore.

The flesh of the little piked whale is used as mink food in Newfoundland. This whale is also hunted off Japan.

The intestines measure a little over five times the total length of the animal.

Selected References

ALLEN, GLOVER M., 1916.

JONSGÅRD, A., 1951.

KIMURA, S. and T. NEMOTO, 1956.

MOORE, JOSEPH CURTIS and RALPH S. PALMER, 1955.

NORMAN, J. R. and F. C. FRASER, 1937.

SERGEANT, D. E., 1963.

SERGEANT, D. E. and H. D. FISHER, 1957.

SLIJPER, E. J., 1962.

TOMILIN, A. G., 1957.

TRUE, F. W., 1904.

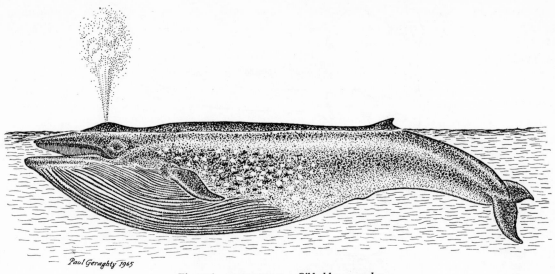

Fig. 226 – BLUE WHALE – *Sibbaldus musculus*

Genus **SIBBALDUS** Gray

Blue Whales – *Baleines bleues*

Sibbaldus musculus (Linnaeus) – Blue Whale, Sulphur-Bottom Whale – *Baleine bleue*

The largest animal that ever lived, either past or present, is the undisputed record of the blue whale. It has the same basic shape as the preceding finback whales; indeed, it is regarded as the same genus (*Balaenoptera musculus*) by some authors. It is generally dark slate blue over the entire body, with the exception of the tip and undersurface of the flippers which may be partially white. There is considerable variation in the shades of blue and in the amount of mottling on the upper surface of the body. The undersurface may have a film of diatoms that give a yellowish colour to the entire undersurface—thus the name 'sulphur bottom'. Sulphur-bottom specimens occur primarily in the Antarctic where these diatoms are prevalent.

The dorsal fin is located well back on the body and is quite small and low. The throat grooves extend back to the level of the navel—much further than in other finback whales. The pectoral fins are long and tapering and have a convex posterior border. The head is less than a quarter of the body length and is not arched or narrowed anteriorly. There are twenty to forty hairs around the upper jaw, as in other finback whales. The sides of the rostrum are nearly parallel almost to the tip. The baleen, including the coarse frayed ends, is jet black, averaging about 370 (250 to 400) plates per side and 23 to 39 inches in length.

SIZE Total length 70–100 (av. 85) ft.; pectoral flipper 7–12 ft; fluke span 16–24 ft. Skull: length, 16–21 ft, length of rostrum 11–15 ft, greatest width 8–11 ft. Weight 70–140 tons (av. 106 tons). One specimen caught on January 27, 1948 by a Japanese whaler measured 90 ft and weighed 2,684 cwt. or 136.4 metric tons.

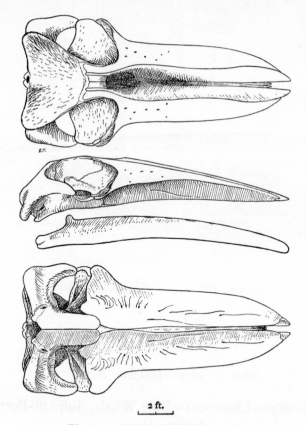

2 ft.

Fig. 227 – SKULL OF *Sibbaldus musculus*

DISTRIBUTION AND VARIATION   The blue whale occurs in the major oceans of the world. The greatest concentrations are toward the higher latitudes of both hemispheres, but there are rather regular migrations to warmer regions during breeding seasons. Concentrations sufficient for commercial whaling have persisted longer in the Antarctic regions. In the early days of whaling the blue whale was relatively common off the Newfoundland coast; several were taken as late as 1900–5. It has been recorded in the Gulf of St Lawrence as far west as Seven Islands. Southerly records in the western North Atlantic include a 60-foot juvenile specimen stranded at Ocean City, New Jersey, and a 98-foot specimen in the Panama Canal (Atlantic end).

HABITS   The blue whale rarely congregates in schools and is usually found singly or in pairs. It cruises at a speed of twelve to fourteen knots, but is capable of speeds of up to eighteen to twenty knots for short distances. It has been observed to jump almost free of the water, although it commonly surfaces in much the same way as the fin whale. The blow averages about twenty feet in height and is pear-shaped, getting longer at the top. Food consists almost entirely of krill (small shrimp-like crustaceans)—the stomach of one Antarctic specimen contained nearly a ton of krill.

Mating usually takes place during the summer months, and a calf (usually one but occasionally two) is born about one year later (gestation ten to eleven months). At birth the calf is about 25 feet long and weighs about two to four tons. It is weaned after about five to seven months, at which time it is about 50 feet long. The female becomes sexually mature at about four and a half years, when it is approximately 70–75 feet long; it is thought to produce calves only every two or three years. At ten to fifteen years the blue whale is fully grown and may live to an age of twenty to thirty years (or perhaps much longer).

REMARKS Because of its enormous size, the blue whale is the species most sought after by commercial whalers. It has been used as the standard of international whaling agreements, with one *blue whale unit* equalling two fin whales, 2.5 humpbacks, or six sei whales. The world catch of blue whales, in the 1952–3 season, totalled 4,208—just under ten per cent of all whales taken. There has been a decrease from seventy-five per cent in 1930 to twenty-five per cent in 1950 to only about six per cent more recently.

In spite of its great length, the blue whale has only sixty-three vertebrae compared with the harbour porpoise which has sixty-six, the common dolphin which has seventy-five, and the white-sided dolphin which has ninety-three (the maximum for living cetacea).

Muscles account for an average of forty per cent of the total weight, the skeleton seventeen per cent, and the blubber—which averages about six inches thick—makes up about twenty-seven per cent. There is no gall bladder; the liver may weigh up to a ton and provides 1,000 to 9,000 (average 4,000) International Units of vitamin A.

The brain of a 100-ton specimen weighs about 15¼ pounds and the tongue roughly four tons. The testes measure about 2½ feet long and weigh up to 100 pounds. The ovaries of one 83-foot pregnant specimen weighed sixty-five pounds. The non-gravid ovaries are about 12 inches long and weigh

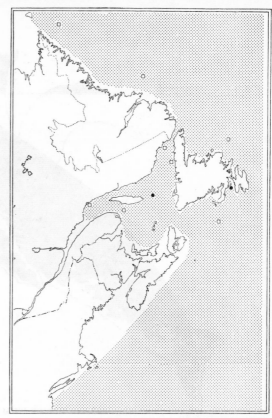

Map 104 – DISTRIBUTION OF THE BLUE WHALE –
Sibbaldus musculus

about twenty pounds. The surface area of an average blue whale is about 223 square yards (an elephant measures about 42 square yards).

Selected References

ALLEN, GLOVER M., 1916.

HARMER, SIDNEY F., 1923.

KELLOGG, R., 1940.

LAWS, R. M., 1959.

NORMAN, J. R. and F. C. FRASER, 1937.

SLIJPER, E. J., 1962.

TOMILIN, A. G., 1957.

TRUE, F. W., 1904.

Fig. 228 – HUMPBACK WHALE – *Megaptera novaeangliae*

Genus **MEGAPTERA** Gray

Humpbacked Whales – *Mégaptères*

Megaptera novaeangliae (Borowski) – Humpback Whale –
Baleine à bosse, Mégaptère

The humpback whale—also called *Megaptera nodosa* by some authors—is readily distinguished by its relatively short, stout body; its extremely long, scalloped pectoral flippers; knobby protuberances on the head and lower jaws; and by broad serrated flukes and broad pleats on the throat, measuring from 5 to 8 inches and numbering only fourteen to twenty. The back is black while the undersurface usually has varying amounts of whitish. The flippers are commonly white but may be blackish above. The baleen is brownish, grey-black or black, and is rarely longer than 24 inches (though it is sometimes as long as 30); it has about 300–400 blades on each side. The skull is relatively wide, with a broad rostrum that tapers gradually from the middle to a fairly sharp anterior point (the sides of the rostrum are not parallel as in *Sibbaldus* or straight as in *Balaenoptera*).

SIZE Total length 35–60 ft; pectoral flipper 11–17 ft; fluke span 15–21 ft. Skull: length 6.5–14.0 ft,

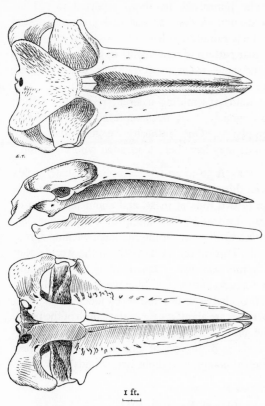

Fig. 229 – SKULL OF *Megaptera novaeangliae*

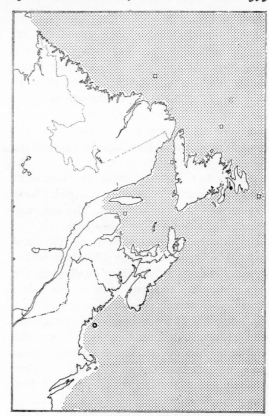

Map 105 – DISTRIBUTION OF THE HUMPBACK WHALE – *Megaptera novaeangliae*

length of rostrum 4–9 ft, greatest width 4.0–8.2 ft. Weight 25 to 45 tons.

DISTRIBUTION AND VARIATION The humpback whale is generally distributed in all oceans of the world but makes rather regular migrations to the polar regions in spring and returns to warmer latitudes in the winter. It tends to be a more shore-loving species than other large finback whales. In the early days of whaling the humpback was quite commonly taken off the Newfoundland and Labrador coasts. It is now fairly rare in eastern-Canadian waters.

HABITS Like the finback whale, the humpback feeds heavily on krill (small crustaceans), but it also consumes a large quantity of small fish, par-

ticularly capelin, herring, mackerel and whiting, as well as squid. One North Atlantic specimen had six cormorants in its stomach and a seventh in its throat.

The mating of humpback whales takes place about April (January to May) in the northern hemisphere. At this time they indulge vigorously in amorous antics; they 'caress' or flail each other with their powerful long flippers and rub each other with the knobby protuberances on the head, lower jaws, and flippers. The gestation period is thought to be slightly less than a year (ten months in the North Atlantic). The young are born from November to March, measuring some 9 to 17 feet long and weighing 2,500 to 4,000 pounds. Twins are produced occasionally. When it nurses the mother rolls over on its side in a rather relaxed-appearing position, thus exposing the teats which are held between the jaws of the calf. Weaning takes place after five to ten months (five in the North Atlantic, ten in the southern hemisphere), at which time the calf may be about 15 to 30 feet long. Estimates of the age at which sexual maturity is reached vary from two to five years, with the shorter period applying in the North Atlantic population where the length of the males is estimated to be about 22 feet and the females 24 feet. Mature females are thought to produce young about every other year, giving birth twice in three years at the most. The estimated maximum life-span is about thirty years.

The humpback is apparently more active and playful at the surface than any other large whale. Its antics consist of 'lob-tailing'—rolling on the surface, slapping the water with its flukes and flippers and frequently swimming on its back for a while, exposing its white belly—and 'breaching', when it jumps straight up, completely clear of the water, to fall back on its side with a terrific splash. The humpback has been seen to turn complete somersaults both above and under the water. It is a surprisingly slow swimmer, with an average speed of only three or five knots; however, it can make short bursts of up to nine or ten knots. Prior to diving, the body may be exposed in an arch above the water, and as it dives, the flukes may be exposed almost vertically—especially prior to deep dives. The depths to which a humpback can dive are not precisely known, but evidence suggests that it descends to at least sixty fathoms, perhaps much deeper. When it surfaces, the blow averages about six feet in height.

The humpback has been reported to aid injured comrades and in one case assistance lasted for forty minutes. It has been observed to follow a regular pattern of movements in which it appeared in the same area at about the same time on successive days.

Sounds resembling a siren, rising and falling continuously, have been reported from a pod of humpbacks. One authority suggests that these sounds may have been associated with courtship.

REMARKS A 30-to-40-foot humpback usually yields about thirty to fifty barrels of oil (about eight tons), one to two tons of meat, and about half a ton of meal. Two and a half humpbacks equal one *blue whale unit* in terms of international whaling agreements. During the 1952–3 season the world catch of humpbacks was 3,322, ranking fourth behind the finback, sperm, and blue whales. The blubber averages between five and seven inches thick. The intestines are about 5.5 times the length of the body. The brain averages about eleven (up to fifteen) pounds and an eye of one forty-ton specimen weighed 980 grams (about two pounds).

Selected References

ALLEN, GLOVER M., 1916, 1942.
CHITTLEBOROUGH, R. G., 1954, 1958.
MATTHEWS, L. H., 1937.
NORMAN, J. R. and F. C. FRASER, 1937.
SCHEVILL, WILLIAM E. and RICHARD H. BACKUS, 1960.
SLIJPER, E. J., 1962.
TOMILIN, A. G., 1957.
TRUE, F. W., 1904.
WILLIAMSON, GORDON R., 1961.

Family **BALAENIDAE**

Right Whales and Bowhead Whales – *Baleines noires et Baleines boréales*

The common name of members of this family was first applied in the early days of whaling when these whales were the most sought-after of all species because they floated when killed and provided easy access to much oil and whalebone—they were the 'right' whales to be pursued. They are readily distinguished from the other whalebone whales (family *Balaenopteridae*) by the following characteristics: the absence of a dorsal fin; the absence of grooving or furrowing under the throat; very long, narrow, flexible whalebone plates equipped with fine, hair-like bristles from 0.1 to 0.2 mm. in diameter; well-developed lower lips, which project upward on either side in a great arch; strongly arched upper jaws; pectoral fins that are relatively short, broad, and rounded; and the fusion into a single unit of all seven cervical vertebrae. The lower jaws lack the well-developed coronoid processes that are present in the *Balaenopteridae*. Members of the *Balaenidae* family feed on very small organisms. They are slow swimmers, rarely exceeding five knots, usually averaging about two. (This slow speed was another important factor in making them the 'right' whales to pursue in the primitive boats used by early whalers.) There are only three living genera, two of which occur in the North Atlantic while the third, a small and little-known genus (*Caperea*) that seldom exceeds 20 feet in length, is found in the southern hemisphere.

KEY TO THE EASTERN-CANADIAN GENERA OF *Balaenidae*

1 Head length more than thirty per cent of total body length; throat and chin yellowish white; no 'bonnet' on upper jaw; nasal bones long and narrow; dorsal contour of entire skull a strong and evenly symmetrical arch; posterior portion not excessively short and wide; longest baleen up to 10 or 15 feet.   BALAENA p. 400

1' Head length less than thirty per cent of total body length; throat and chin black; a 'bonnet' present on the upper jaw; nasal bones short and broad; dorsal contour of skull less strongly arched and the curvature interrupted by a bulge at the nasal and cranial region; posterior portion of skull excessively short and wide, giving the skull an over all T-shape (when viewed from above); longest baleen up to 7 or 8 feet.   EUBALAENA p. 398

Fig. 230 – NORTH ATLANTIC RIGHT WHALE – *Eubalaena glacialis*

Genus **EUBALAENA** Gray

Right Whales – *Baleines noires*

Eubalaena glacialis (Borowski) – North Atlantic Right Whale, Biscayan Right Whale – *Baleine noire*

This species is thought by some authors to belong to the same genus (i.e. *Balaena glacialis*) as the bowhead. However, while it is obviously closely related to the bowhead (*Balaena mysticetus*), it differs in having a relatively smaller head (it is about twenty-five instead of thirty-three per cent of the total length). The head is less arched and passes more evenly into the contour of the body. The baleen is black with brownish fringes and is much shorter than that of the bowhead (usually less than 7 or 8 feet). It consists of about 230 to 250 blades on each side. *Eubalaena* also lacks the white chin. The body is quite commonly all black or it may have white patches that are distributed irregularly on the undersurface of the body. A unique 'bonnet' is developed on the front portion of the upper jaw, which consists of a horny excrescence about 11 inches long and 8 inches wide. This bonnet is characteristically infested with parasitic worms and crustaceans, including barnacles and whale lice. Light-coloured horny bumps are found on the lower lips and on the upper jaw behind the bonnet. Hairs or bristles occur on both the upper and lower jaws—up to 100 to 150 on each.

Compared with the skull of *Balaena*, the rostrum

of *Eubalaena* is less arched and the dorsal contour is interrupted by a bulge at the nasal and cranial region and has distinctly shorter and wider nasal bones. The posterior portion is excessively short and wide, giving the skull an over all T-shape when viewed from above.

SIZE Total length 40–60 ft; pectoral flipper 5.5–8 ft; fluke span 12–21 ft. Skull: length 9–14 ft, length of rostrum 7.5–11.5 ft, greatest width 7–10 ft. Weight approximately 35–60 tons.

DISTRIBUTION AND VARIATION As its English name indicates, *E. glacialis* is confined to the North Atlantic. *E. australis* occurs in the southern hemisphere and *E. sieboldii* in the North Pacific. All three are closely related forms which some authors consider are merely geographic races of *E. glacialis*.

The species formerly ranged from Greenland to as far south as the Florida coast in winter, although is soon disappeared in this latitude with early whaling and became too scarce for successful operation throughout the west Atlantic before 1800. It began to reappear about 1850 and was again soon decimated. It was hunted in the Gulf of St Lawrence and off the coast of Newfoundland and Labrador. It is now quite rare and is protected by an international agreement prohibiting its capture. This species was recently observed off the New England coast; it is likely that at least a few right whales still enter eastern-Canadian waters.

HABITS Right whales are specially adapted for feeding on plankton or on small forms of life. They are fond of floating on the surface and are given to playful antics, sometimes jumping almost clear of

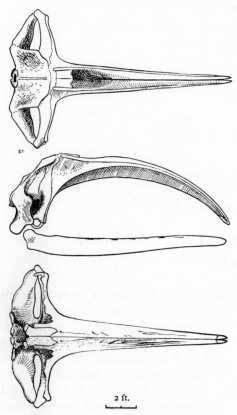

2 ft.

Fig. 231 – SKULL OF *Eubalaena glacialis*

Map 106 – DISTRIBUTION OF THE RIGHT WHALE – *Eubalaena glacialis*

the water. The blow or 'spout' of the North Atlantic right whale is double or v-shaped—two diverging cones extending upwards to about 10-to-15 feet. When surfacing, this whale normally exposes much of its back and the top of its head; the flukes are briefly raised above the surface of the water prior to a deep dive. It is said to blow usually five or six times and then dive deeply for ten to twenty minutes. In the early days, when it was abundant, the North Atlantic right whale schooled in large numbers. Today it is a rare sight to find more than two or three in a pod.

Comparatively little is known of the life history of this species. The gestation period is thought to be about ten months, with mating taking place early in the year (February to March). The new-born young measure approximately 10 to 15 (one specimen was 20) feet long and are thought to nurse for about a full year. Early reports indicate that the mother will refuse to abandon an injured or dying calf. The maximum life-span is estimated to be about forty years.

The vocal sounds of this rare species were recently recorded for the first time.

REMARKS The North Atlantic right whale was one of the first whales to be exploited on a commercial scale, perhaps as early as the year 890 or before. The Basques, living along the coast of the Bay of Biscay, began to hunt this species around the eleventh century. Meat, oil, and baleen or whale-bone were all in great demand and the industry expanded far afield as the species became over-exploited. In 1578 thirty Basque whaling ships are known to have lain at anchor in Newfoundland waters. Oil production apparently varied from 30 to 130 barrels per whale, depending upon size, and the baleen weighed from 500 to 1,500 pounds. Since the recent reappearance of the North Atlantic right whale off New England—the first evidence of this species in northeastern waters—we are encouraged to hope that it will become sufficiently common to allow further study that will fill in many of the serious gaps in our knowledge of this most interesting whale.

Selected References

ALLEN, GLOVER M., 1916, 1942.

ALLEN, J. A., 1908.

KELLOGG, R., 1940.

NORMAN, J. R. and F. C. FRASER, 1937.

SCHEVILL, WILLIAM E. and WILLIAM A. WATKINS, 1962.

SLIJPER, E. J., 1962.

TOMILIN, A. G., 1957.

Genus **BALAENA** Linnaeus

Bowhead Whales – *Baleines boréales*

Balaena mysticetus Linnaeus – Bowhead Whale, Greenland Right Whale – *Baleine boréale*

The bowhead, once the most common whale of the Arctic, is now quite rare. For about 100 years following 1719 there was a thriving industry in Davis Strait that virtually exterminated this species there; whaling activities in the remainder of the North Atlantic near Greenland, Iceland, Spitzbergen, and Jan Meyen had the same effect. It is now regarded as one of the rarest of the large whales anywhere in the world.

The bowhead is characterized by an enormous head that comprises about a third of the total length of the body and is strongly arched, as the name suggests. The head has an elevated protuberance in the region of the blowholes and is narrowed along the rostrum which fits between the huge lower lip. The sides of the lower lip arch upward from 5 or 6 feet on each side of extremely long black baleen plates with brownish frayed fibres.

Fig. 232 – BOWHEAD WHALE – *Balaena mysticetus*

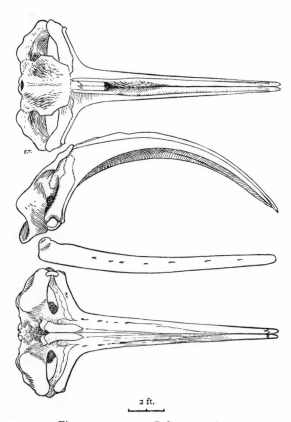

2 ft.

Fig. 233 – SKULL OF *Balaena mysticetus*

There are some 300 plates that extend down some 10 to 12 feet (maximum 14.5) in the middle of each side and become progressively shorter toward the front and back. Each blade is some 10 to 12 inches wide at the gum. The bowhead might also be called 'the hairy one' for it has about 250 bristles on its chin and on the tip of its upper jaw.

The body is thickest just behind the fins and tapers as a cone to a relatively small tail in front of quite large flukes. The flippers are quite large, and they are broadly rounded rather than long and tapered as in the finback whales. The bowhead has no dorsal fin and no throat grooves, unlike the finback group. The colour varies considerably, but basically the entire body is black or blackish except for a whitish 'chin' and perhaps some white on the belly.

SIZE Total length 40–65 ft; pectoral flipper 6–9 ft; fluke span 14–28 ft. Skull: length 11–21 ft, length of rostrum 8.5–15 ft, greatest width, 5.5–10.0 ft. Weight approximately 40–75 tons.

DISTRIBUTION AND VARIATION The bowhead is an arctic species that does not migrate into the temperate regions. During the early days of whaling it moved as far south as the Gulf of St Lawrence, and Basque whalers were thought to have taken it on the south coast of Newfoundland. In 1949 a part of a skull of a bowhead was excavated at Ste Anne des Monts, Gaspé County, Que., thus confirming a former occurrence in the Gulf of St Lawrence. This is the only species of whalebone whale to enter or remain in Hudson Bay. A small number entered the north part of the Bay

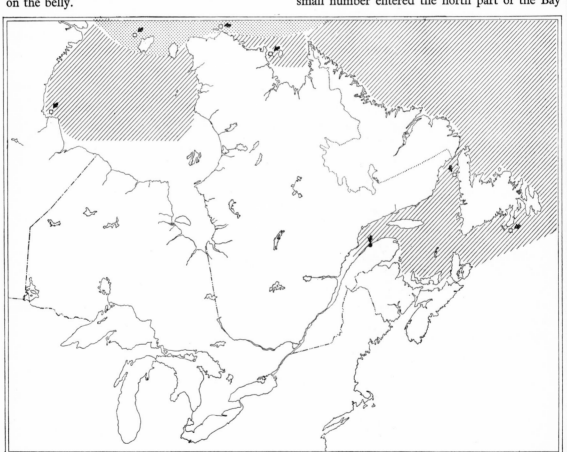

Map 107 – DISTRIBUTION OF THE BOWHEAD WHALE – *Balaena mysticetus*

near Southampton Island at least until around 1930, and earlier they moved as far south as Churchill; many were thought to remain in Hudson Bay all year round. A small number still persist in the North Pacific near Alaska and are thought to be increasing since they have been protected by an International Treaty of 1937. The past distribution of bowheads corresponded with the movements of the edge of the arctic pack-ice—the whales migrated north along the edge of the ice in spring and retreated southward with the advent of winter.

HABITS The bowhead is a solitary species, usually staying alone or in family groups. Small shrimp-like crustaceans form the great bulk of the diet. The young, measuring some 10 to 18 feet long, are thought to be born in February or March after a gestation period of from nine to ten months. The calves apparently continue to nurse for about a full year. The bowhead is relatively timid—less active and slower than most large whales (usually cruising at about three or four knots). This, coupled with its tendency to float when killed, contributed greatly to its early decimation. Normal submergence lasts up to twenty or thirty minutes, with a maximum of about sixty minutes. The surfacing is accompanied by a double-coned blow reaching some 10 or 15 feet in height. After a prolonged dive, the bowhead usually remains on the surface six or seven minutes before diving again. The flukes are exposed prior to deep dives and are said to shake in the air sometimes before they disappear under water. The bowhead often remains floating at the surface for prolonged periods and is reported to be a sound sleeper. It is thought to be especially vulnerable to infestation by external parasites—particularly whale lice, a crustacean (*Cyamus*

species); hundreds of thousands have been encountered on a single whale. Like other whales, the bowhead may have an accumulation of barnacles.

There are reports of the bowhead's coming to the aid of an injured comrade. It is known to live at least forty years and perhaps longer.

REMARKS During the seventeenth and eighteenth centuries the bowhead was the most valuable of all the whales that were hunted at that time.

The blubber is quite thick on this species, with reports of thicknesses of 15 to 28 inches (up to forty-five per cent of the total weight, the maximum for all whales). The oil yield is reported to be upwards of twenty-five tons or over 5,000 gallons. The baleen from a single whale may weigh up to a ton or more. A number of skulls of this species—monuments to wholesale slaughter—were observed by the author in 1956 along the coast of Melville Peninsula on the Fox Basin side.

The present status of the bowhead remains obscure. There is little positive evidence that it is not still a vanishing species.

Selected References

ALLEN, GLOVER M., 1942.

ANDERSON, R. M., 1937, 1947.

CAMERON, AUSTIN W., 1951b.

DEGERBØL, MAGNUS and PETER FREUCHEN, 1935.

KELLOGG, R., 1940.

NORMAN, J. R. and F. C. FRASER, 1937.

PAYNE, F. F., 1887.

PREBLE, EDWARD A., 1902.

SLIJPER, E. J., 1962.

SUTTON, GEORGE M. and WILLIAM J. HAMILTON, JR., 1932.

TOMILIN, A. G., 1957.

Glossary

Containing terms that are most frequently encountered in mammalian literature and that may not be familiar to the new student of mammalogy. Names and terms associated with the skull or skeleton as outlined in *Figs.* 1, 2, and 3 under 'The Mammalian Skeleton' are not included here but can be readily located by referring to the Index.

ABDOMINAL POUCH   A fur-lined pouch on the belly of female marsupials; the marsupium. It contains mammae and is used for carrying young.

AESTIVATION   Inactivity during the summer. Compare HIBERNATION.

ALVEOLUS   A small cavity or pit; commonly the socket for a tooth.

ANGLE OF MANDIBLE   Posterior, lower part of lower jaw; also called angular process.

ANTERIOR   Before, or towards the front; opposite to posterior.

ANTLER   Bony growth of the head of members of the family Cervidae; it is covered during growth with skin called velvet and is shed annually. Compare HORN.

ANTORBITAL PROCESS OR PROJECTION   Forward expanded arm of the supraorbital process of the frontal bone in rabbits.

ARBOREAL   Inhabiting or frequenting trees.

ASTRAGALUS   The ankle bone; a bone of the foot that articulates with the tibia and fibula above and with the calcaneum below.

BACULUM   Os penis, or bone in the penis, found in many Carnivora, Chiroptera, Pinnipedia, and some Rodentia.

BASAL LENGTH   Distance on the skull from the anterior-most inferior border of the foramen magnum to a line connecting the anterior-most parts of the premaxilla.

BASILAR LENGTH   Distance on the skull from the anterior-most inferior border of the foramen magnum to a line connecting the posterior-most margins of the alveoli of the first upper incisor.

BLASTOCYST   A body that develops from a cleavage of the fertilized ovum or egg.

BRACHYDONT   Of teeth: having short crowns and well-developed roots; opposite of hypsodont.

BROWSE   Leaves and twigs; to feed on same. Compare GRAZE.

BUCCAL   Of or pertaining to the cheeks or the cavity of the mouth; oral; when applied to teeth, opposite of lingual (synonymous with labial).

BUNODONT   Of teeth: having tubercles on the crowns; opposite to lophodont.

CAECUM (also CECUM)   A blind pouch; the dilated intestinal pouch into which the ileum, the colon, and (when present) the appendix vermiformis open.

CALCAR   Cartilaginous structure attached to the inside of the foot of some bats; it supports the interfemoral membrane.

CARNASSIAL   Flesh-eating; shearing teeth of carnivores consisting of the upper fourth premolar and the lower first molar in all living forms.

CARNIVOROUS   Feeding on flesh; preying on animals; opposed to herbivorous.

CAUDAL   Of or pertaining to the tail.

CEMENT   Of a tooth: a bone-like substance or tissue that forms a layer investing the root and neck of a tooth and sometimes parts of the crown; cementum.

CERVICAL   Of or pertaining to the neck.

CHEEK TEETH   All teeth behind the canines; premolars and molars.

CINGULUM   A band or girdle forming a ridge on the base of a tooth below the crown.

CLAW   A pointed horny structure, commonly curved, at the end of a toe. Compare NAIL, HOOF.

CLINE   A continuous gradient in which a taxonomic character changes gradually in one direction from one value to another without perceptible breaks, gaps, or steps; a type of geographic variation.

CONCH   The entire external ear; also called pinna.

CONDYLE   An articular prominence on a bone.

CONDYLOBASAL LENGTH   The least distance on the skull from a line connecting the posterior-most projections of the exoccipital condyles to a line connecting the anterior-most projections of the premaxillary bones.

CRANIUM   The skull; or (more restricted) the part of the skull that encloses the brain; the brain case.

CREPUSCULAR   Of, pertaining to, or like twilight; active in the twilight periods.

CROWN   Of a tooth: the part above the gum; also the top of a tooth.

CUSP   Of a tooth: a point (sometimes blunt or rounded) on the crown.

DECIDUOUS TEETH   Teeth that are shed; milk teeth.

DELAYED IMPLANTATION   Postponed embedding of the blastocyst in the uterine epithelium for several days or longer.

DENTAL FORMULA   A brief method of expressing the number and kinds of teeth in the form of fractions representing the teeth on each side above and below. For example, the full dentition of placental mammals is:

$$I \frac{3-3}{3-3} \quad C \frac{1-1}{1-1} \quad P \frac{4-4}{4-4} \quad M \frac{3-3}{3-3} = 44$$

DENTINE   A calcareous material like bone, but harder and denser, that composes the principal mass of a tooth; ivory.

DENTITION   The number, kind, and arrangement of teeth; the teeth of an animal considered collectively.

DIASTEMA   A vacant space; a gap between teeth in a jaw.

DIURNAL   Active by day; opposed to nocturnal.

DORMANCY   A period of inactivity usually lasting some weeks or longer.

DORSAL   Pertaining to the back or its parts; opposed to ventral.

ECHO-LOCATION   Detection or location by means of echoes from sounds transmitted by a mammal.

ENAMEL   The intensely hard calcareous substance that forms a thin layer capping or partly covering the teeth of most mammals; the hardest substance of the animal body.

ENAMEL LOOPS   Loops formed by enamel ridges bordered by dentine on the grinding surface of the tooth.

ENDEMIC   Confined and indigenous to a certain region.

EPIPHYSIS   A piece of bone separated from a long bone in early life by cartilage, but later becoming part of the larger bone.

ESTIVATION   See AESTIVATION.

FAECES   Intestinal excrement; droppings.

FENESTRA   A small opening in a bone, especially one that does not transmit a nerve or a blood vessel.

FORAMEN   An opening, perforation, or orifice; particularly an opening in a bone that transmits a nerve or blood vessel or both.

FOREARM   The long wing-bone in bats between the elbow and the wrist.

FOSSA   A pit, cavity, or depression.

FOSSORIAL   Fitted for digging; applied to animals that live underground.

GENITALIA   The external sexual organs.

GESTATION   Development, or period in the womb, between conception and birth.

GRAZE   To feed on grass or herbs.

GUARD HAIRS   The long, stiff hairs that grow up through the shorter underfur of a mammal's pelage.

HERBIVOROUS   Feeding on plants, especially grass and weeds.

HETERODONT   Having a dentition in which the teeth are differentiated as incisors, canines, premolars, and molars.

HIBERNATION   Inactivity during winter period. More restricted: this inactivity accompanied by a drop in body temperature and a reduction of the rate of heart beat and of respiration. Compare AESTIVATION.

HOLOTYPE   See TYPE SPECIMEN.

HOME RANGE   The area normally used by an animal for its activities.

HOOF   The horny covering that protects the ends of the digit and supports the weight of the animal. Compare CLAW and NAIL.

HORN   The horny sheath covering an outgrowth of bone from the skull, circular or oval in cross-section and pointed at the extremity (it is not shed). The true horn is found only in bovids, although the term horn is commonly associated with other families (e.g. pronghorns, rhinoceri).

HYOID   Designating or pertaining to a bone or several connected bones situated at the base of the tongue and developed from the second and third visceral arches.

HYPSODONT   Having teeth with high crowns and short roots, as in the molars of the horse; opposite to brachydont.

IMPLANTATION   The attachment of the blastocyst to the lining of the uterus; the penetration of the blastocyst through the epithelium of the uterus and its embedding in the endometrium (the lining of the uterus); the early stage of pregnancy.

INCISIFORM TEETH   Teeth which, though shaped like incisor teeth, are not necessarily incisors; as in the lower canine teeth in the families Cervidae and Bovidae.

INFRAORBITAL CANAL OR FORAMEN   A canal or opening through the zygomatic plate of the maxillary bone from the orbit to the side of the rostrum, transmitting nerves, blood vessels, and in some cases muscles.

INGUINAL   In or pertaining to the region of the groin.

INNOMINATE BONE   The hip bone; a bone consisting of the ilium, the ischium, and the os pubis.

INSECTIVOROUS   Feeding on insects.

INTERDIGITATION   Interlocking, like the fingers of clasped hands; in mammal distribution an intertwining of two races or species, each of which is usually restricted to a specific habitat that penetrates in finger-like projections into the range of the other.

INTERFEMORAL MEMBRANE   The membrane in bats that extends from one leg to the other and usually encloses a part or all of the tail; the uroptagium.

INTERGRADATION   A gradual merging through a series of intermediate forms or populations; a blending of a taxonomic characteristic as the result of the interbreeding of two or more geographic races in a zone where the different populations come together.

INTERORBITAL CONSTRICTION   The least distance across the top of the skull between the orbits or eye sockets.

KEEL   The free flap of skin in bats attached along the calcar beyond the interfemoral membrane; also the ventral expansion of the sternum in bats.

LABIAL   Of or pertaining to the lips; when applied to teeth, the opposite of lingual (synonymous with buccal).

LACHRYMAL (also LACRIMAL)   Pertaining to tears; associated with the eyes (e.g. lachrymal gland, ~ bone).

LOPHODONT   Having molar teeth with transverse ridges on the grinding surface, as in most ungulates and many rodents; opposed to bunodont.

MARSUPIUM   See ABDOMINAL POUCH.

MASTOID BREADTH   Greatest distance across the mastoid bones perpendicular to the long axis of the skull.

MEATUS   A natural passage or canal, or the opening of such a passage (e.g. the external auditory opening in the skull).

METATARSAL GLAND   A gland on the inside of the hind leg between the foot and the hock.

MID-DORSAL   Of or pertaining to something along the top of the back.

MOLARIFORM   Of or pertaining to teeth, the form of which is like that of the molar; premolars and molars when similar in shape.

MONOTREMES   Egg-laying mammals of the Order Monotremata.

MUTATION   A genetic change in the characters of an offspring from those of its parents resulting in a mutant or 'sport'.

NAIL   The horny plate on the upper surface of the ends of the fingers and toes, as in man and other species; differs from claw and hoof only in shape and form.

NAPE   The back of the neck.

NARES   Nostrils, or nasal openings. *Anterior or external nares:* the openings into the nasal cavity at the anterior end of the skull. *Posterior or internal nares:* the openings connecting the nasal cavity with the pharynx.

NASAL   Of or pertaining to the nose; nasal bones.

NOCTURNAL   Active by night; opposed to diurnal. Compare CREPUSCULAR.

OCCIPUT   The back part of the head or skull; the posterior aspect of the four occipital bones in the skull that surround the foramen magnum.

OCCLUSAL   Of or pertaining to the grinding or biting surface of a tooth.

OESTRUS (also ESTRUS)   The period of sexual receptivity in females; the stage in the reproductive cycle during which the uterus is prepared for implantation of the ovum.

OMNIVOROUS   Feeding on both animal and plant material.

ORBIT   The eye socket of the skull.

OVIPAROUS   Egg laying; hatched from an externally laid egg. Compare VIVIPAROUS.

OVUM   Egg.

PALATAL LENGTH   The distance on the skull from the anterior-most point on the posterior border of the palate (palatine bones) to a line connecting the anterior-most parts of the premaxillary bones.

PALATE   Of the skull: the bony roof of the mouth comprised of the two palatine bones, the two maxillary bones, and the premaxillary bones.

PALATILAR LENGTH   The distance on the skull from the anterior-most point on the posterior border of the palate (palatine bones) to a line connecting the posterior-most margins of the alveoli of the first upper incisors.

PARIETAL RIDGES   Temporal ridges—a pair of bony ridges rising just back of each orbit and passing back over the brain case to converge posteriorly; present in only certain species.

PECTORAL   Of, pertaining to, situated in, or occurring in or on the chest.

PELAGE   The covering or coat of a mammal; hair, wool, or fur.

PELAGIC   Of or related to the open sea; living in the open sea distant from land.

PENICILLATE   Ending in a tuft of fine hair (e.g. the end of the tail).

PHALANGEAL   Pertaining to *phalanges* (sing., *phalanx*)—bones of the fingers and toes.

PINNA   The external ear; conch.

PLACENTA   The round flat organ within the uterus that establishes communication between the mother and the embryo by means of the umbilical cord.

PLANTAR   Of or pertaining to the sole of the foot.

PLANTIGRADE   Walking on the sole with the heel touching the ground.

POLLEX   The first digit of the forelimb; the thumb,

POLYGAMOUS   Having more than one mate.

POSTERIOR   At or toward the hind end of the body; opposite to anterior.

PREDATOR   A species that kills and feeds on another.

PROGNATHOUS   With jaws projecting beyond the upper part of the face.

QUILL   A pointed, stiff, specialized hair, as in the porcupine.

RE-ENTRANT ANGLE   An infold of the enamel layer on the side, front, or back of a cheek tooth.

RETRACTABLE   Capable of being drawn back or in, as in the claws of a cat.

ROSTRUM   The anteriorly projecting part of a mammalian skull in front of the orbits; snout.

SECONDARY SEXUAL VARIATION   A difference, apart from the primary sexual organs, distinguishing individuals of one sex from the other.

SECTORIAL   Cutting; opposing teeth modified for cutting in a scissor-like fashion.

SINUS   A cavity in the substance of a bone of the skull that communicates with the nasal cavity and contains air.

SUTURE   The line of union in an immovable articulation, as in the bones of the skull.

TACTILE   Of or relating to the sense of touch (e.g. tactile organ).

TEMPORAL RIDGES   See PARIETAL RIDGES.

TENTACLES   Elongate, finger-like projections; usually fleshy in mammals.

TERRESTRIAL   Inhabiting the land rather than the air, trees, or water.

THORACIC   Of or pertaining to the region surrounded by the ribs.

TAIGA   The northernmost boreal or coniferous forest extending below the arctic tundra; an interspersion of treed and treeless areas.

TOPOTYPE   A specimen, in addition to the holotype of a species, taken from the type locality.

TOTAL LENGTH   The distance in mammals from the tip of the nose to the end of the fleshy part of the tail when the animal is laid out straight in its normal position (not stretched).

TRAGUS   Outgrowth in front of the external opening of the ear; the prominent, leaf-like projection in the ear of many bats.

TROCHLEA   The surface of the astragalus bone that articulates with the tibia and fibula bones; a pulley-shaped part or structure.

TRUNCATE   With a square or even end; blunt as if cut off.

TUBERCLES   Nodules or small prominences; the small fleshy pads on the soles of some species; protrusions on the crown of a tooth.

TYPE LOCALITY   The place where the type specimen (holotype) was collected.

TYPE SPECIMEN   The original specimen on which the scientific name and accompanying diagnosis of a species or subspecies are based. Holotype.

UNGULATE   Mammal with hoofs as opposed to claws or nails.

UROGENITAL SYSTEM   The combined structures of the excretory and reproductive systems.

UROPTAGIUM   See INTERFEMORAL MEMBRANE.

VENTRAL   Designating, pertaining to, or situated on the lower side; the belly side; opposed to dorsal.

VIBRISSA   Stiff tactile hairs on the wrists or face; the 'feelers' or 'cat whiskers'.

VIVIPAROUS   Born alive; as opposed to oviparous (externally hatched from an egg) or oviviparous (hatched from an egg retained within the body cavity).

WIDTH OF SKULL   The greatest width, usually across the zygomatic arches; zygomatic breadth.

ZYGOMATIC PLATE   The flattened expanded part of the maxillary in front of the orbit from which the anterior part of the zygomatic arch arises.

Bibliography

A List of the Publications and Serials abbreviated in this Bibliography will be found on page 446.

ALDOUS, C. M.
1936. Food habits of *Lepus americanus phaeonotus*. *Jour. Mamm.*, vol. 17, no. 2, pp. 175–6.
1937. Notes on the life history of the snowshoe hare. *Jour. Mamm.*, vol. 18, no. 1, pp. 46–57.

ALDOUS, SHALER E.
1941. Food habits of chipmunks. *Jour. Mamm.*, vol. 22, no. 1, pp. 18–24.

ALDOUS, SHALER E., and J. MANWEILER
1942. The winter food habits of the short-tailed weasel in northern Minnesota. *Jour. Mamm.*, vol. 23, no. 3, pp. 250–5.

ALLEN, DURWARD L.
1944. Michigan fox squirrel management. *Mich. Dept. Conserv., Game Div. Pub.*, no. 100, 404 pp.

ALLEN, DURWARD L., and WARREN W. SHAPTON
1942. An ecological study of winter dens, with special reference to the eastern skunk. *Ecology*, vol. 23, no. 1, pp. 59–68.

ALLEN, ELSA G.
1938. The habits and life history of the eastern chipmunk, *Tamias striatus lysteri*. *N.Y. State Mus. Bull.*, no. 314, 122 pp.

ALLEN, GLOVER M.
1906. Sowerby's whale on the American coast. *Am. Nat.*, vol. 40, no. 473, pp. 357–67.
1915. The water shrew of Nova Scotia. *Proc. Biol. Soc. Washington*, vol. 28, pp. 15–18.
1916. The whalebone whales of New England. *Memoirs Boston Soc. Nat. Hist.*, vol. 8, no. 2, pp. 107–322.
1919. The American collared lemmings (*Dicrostonyx*). *Bull. Mus. Comp. Zool.*, vol. 62, no. 13, pp. 509–40.
1920. Hoy's shrew in Labrador. *Jour. Mamm.*, vol. 1, no. 3, p. 139.
1930. The walrus in New England. *Jour. Mamm.*, vol. 11, no. 2, pp. 139–45.
1931. Ocean dolphins. *Bull. Boston Soc. Nat. Hist.*, vol. 61, pp. 3–7.
1933. Geographic variation in the big brown bat (*Eptesicus fuscus*). *Can. Field-Nat.*, vol. 47, no. 2, pp. 31–2.
1939a. True's beaked whale in Nova Scotia. *Jour. Mamm.*, vol. 20, no. 2, pp. 259–60.
1939b. *Bats.* Harvard Univ. Press, Cambridge, Mass., 368 pp.
1941. Pygmy sperm whale in the Atlantic. Papers on Mammalogy. *Field Mus. Nat. Hist., Zool. Ser.*, vol. 27, pub. 511, pp. 17–36.
1942. Extinct and vanishing mammals of the western hemisphere with the marine species of all the oceans. *Am. Comm. for International Wildlife Protection, Spec. Pub.*, no. 11, 620 pp.

ALLEN, GLOVER M., and THOMAS BARBOUR
1937. The Newfoundland wolf. *Jour. Mamm.*, vol. 18, no. 2, pp. 229–34.

ALLEN, H.
1893. A monograph of the bats of North America. *U.S. Natl. Mus. Bull.*, no. 43, 198 pp.

ALLEN, J. A.

1880. History of North American pinnipeds, a monograph of the walruses, sea-lions, sea-bears and seals of North America. *U.S. Geol. and Geogr. Surv. of the Terr., Misc. Pub.*, no. 12, 785 pp.

1894a. Notes on mammals from New Brunswick, with description of a new species of *Evotomys. Bull. Am. Mus. Nat. Hist.*, vol. 6, pp. 99–106.

1894b. Remarks on a second collection of mammals from New Brunswick, and on the rediscovery of the genus *Neotoma* in New York State. *Bull. Am. Mus. Nat. Hist.*, vol. 6, pp. 359–64.

1896. Description of new North American mammals. *Bull. Am. Mus. Nat. Hist.*, vol. 8, pp. 223–34.

1898. Revision of the chickarees, or North American red squirrels (subgenus *Tamiasciurus*). *Bull. Am. Mus. Nat. Hist.*, vol. 10, pp. 249–98.

1901. A preliminary study of the North American opossums of the genus *Didelphis. Bull. Am. Mus. Nat. Hist.*, vol. 14, pp. 149–88.

1908. The North Atlantic right whale and its near allies. *Bull. Am. Mus. Nat. Hist.*, vol. 24, pp. 277–329.

1910. The black bear of Labrador. *Bull. Am. Mus. Nat. Hist.*, vol. 28, pp. 1–6.

ALLIN, A. E.

1940. The vertebrate fauna of Darlington Township, Durham County, Ontario. *Trans. Roy. Can. Inst.*, vol. 23, pt. 1, no. 49, pp. 83–118.

1942. Bats hibernating in the District of Thunder Bay, Ontario. *Can. Field-Nat.*, vol. 56, no. 6, pp. 90–1.

1943. Some additions to the vertebrate fauna of Darlington Township, Durham County, Ontario. *Can. Field-Nat.*, vol. 56, nos. 8–9, p. 140.

1950. European hare introduced into the District of Thunder Bay, Ontario, *Can. Field-Nat.*, vol. 64, no. 3, pp. 122–4.

AMOROSO, E. C., and J. H. MATTHEWS

1951. The growth of the grey seal (*Halichoerus grypus*) from birth to weaning. *Jour. Anat.*, vol. 85, pp. 426–8.

ANDERSON, R. M.

1934. Mammals of the eastern Arctic and Hudson Bay. *Canada's Eastern Arctic*. Dept. Int., Ottawa, pp. 67–137.

1937. Mammals and birds of the western Arctic district, Northwest Territories, Canada. *Canada's Western Northland*. Land, Parks and Forests Branch, Ottawa, pp. 97–122.

1938. The present status and distribution of the big game mammals of Canada. *Trans. Third N. Am. Wildlife Conf.*, pp. 390–406.

1939. Mammals of the Province of Quebec. *Ann. Report Provancher Soc. of Nat. Hist. 1938*, pp. 50–114.

1940. Mammifères de la Province de Québec. *Ann. Report Provancher Soc. of Nat. Hist. 1939*, pp. 37–111.

1941. Two species of bats added to the list of Quebec mammals. *Ann. Report Provancher Soc. of Nat. Hist. 1940*, pp. 23–30 (English), 31–7 (French).

1942a. Six additions to the list of Quebec mammals with descriptions of four new forms. *Ann. Report Provancher Soc. of Nat. Hist. 1941*, pp. 31–43 (English), 45–57 (French).

1942b. Canadian voles of the genus *Phenacomys* with description of two new Canadian subspecies. *Can. Field-Nat.*, vol. 56, no. 4, pp. 56–61.

1943a. Summary of the large wolves of Canada, with description of three new Arctic races. *Jour. Mamm.*, vol. 24, no. 3, pp. 386–93.

1943b. Two new seals from Arctic Canada with key to the Canadian forms of hair seals (Family *Phocidae*). *Ann. Report Provancher Soc. of Nat. Hist. 1942*, pp. 23–34 (English), 35–47 (French).

1943c. Nine additions to the list of Quebec mammals with descriptions of six new forms. *Ann. Report Provancher Soc. of Nat. Hist. 1942*, pp. 49–62 (English), 63–77 (French).

1945a. Summary of Canadian black bears with description of two new northwestern species. *Ann. Report Provancher Soc. of Nat. Hist. 1944*, pp. 17–33 (English), 34–52 (French).

1945b. Three mammals of the weasel family (*Mustelidae*) added to the Quebec list with descriptions of two new forms. *Ann. Report Provancher Soc. of Nat. Hist. 1944*, pp. 56–61 (English), 62–8 (French).

1946. Richardson's ermine added to the list of Quebec mammals, with a survey of the weasels found in the Province. *Ann. Report Provancher Soc. of Nat. Hist. 1945*, pp. 19–26.

1947. Catalogue of Canadian Recent mammals. *Natl. Mus. Can., Bull.*, no. 102, *Biol. Ser.*, no. 31, 238 pp.

1948. A survey of Canadian mammals of the north. *Ann. Report, Prov. Quebec Assoc. Protection Fish and Game*, pp. 9–17.

ANDERSON, R. M., and A. L. RAND

1943a. A new lemming mouse (*Synaptomys*) from Manitoba with notes on some other forms. *Can. Field-Nat.*, vol. 57, no. 6, pp. 101–3.

1943b. Variation in the porcupine (genus *Erethizon*) in Canada. *Can. Jour. Res.*, vol. 21, pp. 292–309.

1944. Notes on chipmunks of the genus *Eutamias* in Canada. *Can. Field-Nat.*, vol. 57, nos. 7 and 8, pp. 133–5.

1945. The varying lemming (genus *Dicrostonyx*) in Canada. *Jour. Mamm.*, vol. 26, no. 3, pp. 301–6.

ANDERSON, SYDNEY

1962. A new northern record of *Synaptomys borealis* in Ungava. *Jour. Mamm.*, vol. 43, no. 3, pp. 421–2.

ANDREWS, R. C.

1916. The sei whale. Monographs of the Pacific Cetacea. *Mem. Am. Mus. Nat. Hist., New Ser.*, vol. 1, pt. 6, pp. 291–388.

ANONYMOUS

1915. The Canadian fisheries museum. *Ottawa Nat.*, vol. 29, no. 8, pp. 99–100.

1953. Expedition to Ungava, summer 1953. *Arctic*, vol. 6, no. 4, pp. 277–8.

ANTHONY, H. E., and G. G. GOODWIN

1924. A new species of shrew from the Gaspé Peninsula. *Am. Mus. Novitates*, no. 109, pp. 1–2.

ARLTON, A. V.

1936. An ecological study of the mole. *Jour. Mamm.*, vol. 17, no. 4, pp. 349–71.

ASH, C. E.

1952. The body weights of whales. *Norsk Hvalf.*, vol. 41, p. 364.

ASHBROOK, FRANK G.

1948. Nutrias grow in United States. *Jour. Wildlife Mgt.*, vol. 12, no. 1, pp. 87–95.

ASHBROOK, FRANK G., and KARL B. HANSON

1930. The normal breeding season and gestation period of martens. *U.S. Dept. Agr., Circ.*, no. 107, pp. 1–6.

ATWOOD, EARL L.

1950. Life history studies of nutria, or coypu, in coastal Louisiana. *Jour. Wildlife Mgt.*, vol. 14, no. 3, pp. 249–65.

BACKHOUSE, K., and H. R. HEWER

1956. Delayed implantation in the grey seal, *Halichoerus grypus* (Fab.). *Nature*, vol. 178, p. 550.

BAILEY, VERNON

1893. The prairie ground squirrels or spermophiles of the Mississippi Valley. *U.S. Dept. Agr., Bull. Div. Ornith. and Mamm.*, no. 4, 69 pp.

1897. Revision of the American voles of the genus *Evotomys*. *Proc. Biol. Soc. Washington*, vol. 11, pp. 113–38.

1898. Descriptions of eleven new species and subspecies of voles. *Proc. Biol. Soc. Washington,* vol. 12, pp. 85–90.

1900. Revision of the American voles of the genus *Microtus. N. Am. Fauna,* no. 17, 88 pp.

1913. Two new subspecies of North American beavers. *Proc. Biol. Soc. Washington,* vol. 26, pp. 191–3.

1927a. Beaver habits and experiments in beaver culture. *U.S. Dept. Agr. Tech. Bull.,* no. 21, 40 pp.

1927b. How beavers build their houses. *Ann. Report Smithsonian Inst. for 1926,* pub. 2895, pp. 357–60.

BAILEY, VERNON, and J. KENNETH DOUTT
1942. Two new beavers from Labrador and New Brunswick. *Jour. Mamm.,* vol. 23, no. 1, pp. 86–8.

BAILLIE, JAMES L.
1955. The golden eagle nesting in the Gaspé Peninsula, Quebec. *Can. Field-Nat.,* vol. 69, no. 1, pp. 13–14.

BAIN, FRANCIS
1890. *The natural history of Prince Edward Island.* G. Herbert Haszard, Publisher, Charlottetown, 123 pp.

BANFIELD, A. W. F.
1948. Longevity of the big brown bat. *Jour. Mamm.,* vol. 29, no. 4, p. 418.

1949. The present status of North American caribou. *Trans. 14th N. Am. Wildlife Conf.,* pp. 477–91.

1954. Preliminary investigation of the barren-ground caribou. *Wildlife Mgt. Bull.,* ser. 1, no. 10A, pp. 1–79, 10B, pp. 1–112.

1955. A provisional life table for the barren-ground caribou. *Can. Jour. Zool.,* vol. 33, no. 3, pp. 143–7.

1956. Records of two microtine rodents from the Quebec tundra. *Can. Field-Nat.,* vol. 70, no. 2, p. 99.

1960a. The use of caribou antler pedicels for age determination. *Jour. Wildlife Mgt.,* vol. 24, no. 1, pp. 99–102.

1960b. Some noteworthy accessions to the National Museum mammal collection. *Natl. Mus. Can., Nat. Hist. Papers,* no. 6, pp. 1–2.

1961a. A revision of the reindeer and caribou, genus *Rangifer. Natl. Mus. Can., Bull.,* no. 177, *Biol. Ser.,* no. 66, 137 pp.

1961b. A red bat on Southampton Island, Northwest Territories. *Can. Field-Nat.,* vol. 75, no. 4, p. 264.

BANFIELD, A. W. F., and J. S. TENER
1958. A preliminary study of the Ungava caribou. *Jour. Mamm.,* vol. 39, no. 4, pp. 560–73.

BANGS, OUTRAM
1894a. Description of a new field mouse (*Arvicola terraenovae* sp. nov.) from Codroy, Newfoundland. *Proc. Biol. Soc. Washington,* vol. 9, pp. 129–32.

1894b. Description of a new muskrat from Codroy, Newfoundland. *Proc. Biol. Soc. Washington,* vol. 9, pp. 133–8.

1896a. Preliminary description of a new vole from Labrador. *Am. Nat.,* vol. 30, pp. 1051–2.

1896b. Preliminary description of the Newfoundland caribou. Privately printed, Boston, Nov. 11, 1896, at 5 o'clock p.m.

1896c. On a small collection of mammals from Lake Edward, Quebec. *Proc. Biol. Soc. Washington,* vol. 10, pp. 45–52.

1896d. A revision of the squirrels of eastern North America. *Proc. Biol. Soc. Washington,* vol. 10, pp. 145–67.

1896e. Notes on the synonymy of the North American mink with description of a new subspecies. *Proc. Boston Soc. Nat. Hist.,* vol. 27, pp. 1–6.

1897a. Notes on the lynxes of eastern North America, with descriptions of two new species. *Proc. Biol. Soc. Washington,* vol. 11, pp. 47–51.

1897b. Description of a new red fox from Nova Scotia. *Proc. Biol. Soc. Washington*, vol. 11, pp. 53-5.

1897c. On a small collection of mammals from Hamilton Inlet, Labrador. *Proc. Biol. Soc. Washington*, vol. 11, pp. 235-40.

1897d. Preliminary description of the Newfoundland marten. *Am. Nat.*, vol. 31, pp. 161-2.

1898a. Descriptions of the Newfoundland otter and red fox. *Proc. Biol. Soc. Washington*, vol. 12, pp. 35-8.

1898b. A list of the mammals of Labrador. *Am. Nat.*, vol. 32, no. 379, pp. 489-507.

1898c. The eastern races of the American varying hare, with description of a new subspecies from Nova Scotia. *Proc. Biol. Soc. Washington*, vol. 12, pp. 77-82.

1898d. A new rock vole from Labrador. *Proc. Biol. Soc. Washington*, vol. 12, pp. 187-8.

1899a. A new gray fox from the upper Mississippi Valley. *Proc. New England Zool. Club*, vol. 1, pp. 43-4.

1899b. Notes on some mammals from Black Bay, Labrador. *Proc. New England Zool. Club*, vol. 1, pp. 9-18.

1900. Three new rodents from southern Labrador. *Proc. New England Zool. Club*, vol. 2, pp. 35-41.

1910. List of the mammals of Labrador in *Labrador, the country and the people*, by Wilfred T. Grenfell and others. Macmillan Co., New York, app. 4, pp. 458-68.

1913. The land mammals of Newfoundland. *Bull. Mus. Comp. Zool.*, vol. 54, no. 18, pp. 509-16.

BANKS, J. W.
1911. Mammals of Rockwood Park, New Brunswick (abstract-list). *Bull. Nat. Hist. Soc. New Brunswick*, vol. 6, pt. 3, pp. 346-8.

BARRETT-HAMILTON, G. E. H., and J. L. BONHOTE
1899. Ontario subspecies of the arctic fox (*Canis lagopus*). *Ann. Nat. Hist.*, 7th ser., vol. 1, no. 4, pp. 287-9.

BARTLETT, C. O.
1955. Badgers in Kent and Elgin Counties, Ontario. *Can. Field-Nat.*, vol. 69, no. 1, pp. 12-13.

BARTLETT, ROBERT A.
1927. Newfoundland seals. *Jour. Mamm.*, vol. 8, no. 3, pp. 207-12.

BATCHELDER, CHARLES F.
1930. The voice of the porcupine. *Jour. Mamm.*, vol. 11, no. 2, pp. 237-9.

1948. Notes on the Canada porcupine. *Jour. Mamm.*, vol. 29, no. 3, pp. 260-8.

BATEMAN, ROBERT
1953. Observations on the natural history of the Leaf-Bay—Fort Chimo Region, Ungava, Quebec. *Intermediate Nat.*, no. 8, pp. 1-7.

BAXTER, J.
1963. The horseheads of Nantucket. *Massachusetts Audubon*, vol. 47, No. 4, pp. 169-71.

BEAUGÉ, cdr.
1942. Sur l'apparition et l'échouage d'un *Hyperoodon rostratus* à Sainte Anne de la Pocatière. *Ann. Report Provancher Soc. of Nat. Hist. 1941*, pp. 23-30.

BEER, JAMES R.
1950. The least weasel in Wisconsin. *Jour. Mamm.*, vol. 31, no. 2, pp. 146-9.

1954. A record of the hoary bat from a cave. *Jour. Mamm.*, vol. 35, no. 1, p. 116.

1956. A record of a silver-haired bat in a cave. *Jour. Mamm.*, vol. 37, no. 2, p. 282.

BELL, J. M.
1905. Iron ranges of Michipicoten West, Game and Fish. *14th Rept. Ont. Bureau Mines*, vol. 14, pt. 1, p. 297.

BELL, ROBERT
1885. Mammals of the vicinity of Hudson's Bay and Labrador. *Geol. and Nat. Hist. Surv. of Can.*, *New Ser.*, vol. 1, Dawson Bros., Montreal, app. 2, pp. 48D-53D.

BENDELL, JAMES F.

1959. Food as a control of a population of white-footed mice, *Peromyscus leucopus noveboracensis* (Fischer). *Can. Jour. Zool.*, vol. 37, pp. 173–209.

1961. Some factors affecting the habitat selection of the white-footed mouse. *Can. Field-Nat.*, vol. 75, no. 4, pp. 244–5.

BENEDICT, FRANCIS G., and ROBERT C. LEE

1938. Hibernation and marmot physiology. *Carnegie Inst. of Washington Pub.*, no. 497, 239 pp.

BENSON, D. A.

1957. Abnormal dentition in white-tailed deer. *Jour. Mamm.*, vol. 38, no. 1, p. 140.

1959. The fisher in Nova Scotia. *Jour. Mamm.*, vol. 40, no. 3, p. 451.

BENTON, ALLEN H.

1955. Observations on the life history of the northern pine mouse. *Jour. Mamm.*, vol. 36, no. 1, pp. 52–62.

BIRD, RALPH D.

1955. Melanism in the varying hare, *Lepus americanus* Erxleben. *Can. Field-Nat.*, vol. 69, no. 1, p. 11.

BISHOP, SHERMAN C.

1947. Curious behaviour of a hoary bat. *Jour. Mamm.*, vol. 28, no. 3, pp. 293–4.

BLAIR, W. FRANK

1941. Some data on the home ranges and general life history of the short-tailed shrew, red-backed mouse, and woodland jumping mouse in northern Michigan. *Am. Midl. Nat.*, vol. 25, no. 3, pp. 681–5.

1942. Size of home range and notes on the life history of the woodland deer-mouse and eastern chipmunk in northern Michigan. *Jour. Mamm.*, vol. 23, no. 1, pp. 27–36.

BLEAKNEY, J. SHERMAN

1965. First specimens of eastern pipistrelle from Nova Scotia. *Jour. Mamm.*, vol. 46, no. 3, pp. 528–9.

BLOSSOM, PHILLIP M.

1932. A pair of long-tailed shrews (*Sorex cinereus cinereus*) in captivity. *Jour. Mamm.*, vol. 13, no. 2, pp. 136–43.

BRAESTRUP, F. W.

1941. A study of the arctic fox in Greenland. *Meddelelser om Grønland*, vol. 131, no. 4, 101 pp.

BROOKS, ALLAN

1905. The mammalia of northern Wellington. *Ont. Nat. Sci. Bull.*, no. 1, pp. 25–6.

BROOKS, J. W.

1954. A contribution to the life history and ecology of the Pacific walrus. *Alaska Coop. Wildlife Res. Unit, Spec. Rept.*, no. 1, 103 pp.

BROWN, D. H., and K. S. NORRIS

1956. Observations of captive and wild cetaceans. *Jour. Mamm.*, vol. 37, no. 3, pp. 311–26.

BROWN, LOUIS G., and LEE E. YEAGER

1945. Fox squirrels and gray squirrels in Illinois. *Bull. Ill. Nat. Hist. Survey*, vol. 23, no. 5, pp. 449–536.

BROWN, N. R.

1948. First New Brunswick specimen of the northeastern long-tailed ermine, *Mustela frenata occisor* (Bangs). *Can. Field-Nat.*, vol. 62, no. 1, pp. 43–4.

1953. An addition to the list of the mammals of Nova Scotia, the eastern red bat. *Can. Field-Nat.*, vol. 67, no. 3, p. 139.

BROWN, N. R., and R. G. LANNING

1955. The mammals of Renfrew County, Ontario. *Can. Field-Nat.*, vol. 68, no. 4, pp. 171–80.

BROWN, S. G.

1961. Observations of pilot whales (*Globicephala*) in the North Atlantic Ocean. *Norsk Hvalf.*, no. 6, pp. 225–54.

BURT, WILLIAM HENRY

1938. A new water shrew (*Sorex palustris*) from Labrador. *Occas. Papers Mus. Zool., Univ. Mich.*, no. 383, pp. 1–2.

1946. *The mammals of Michigan.* Univ. Mich. Press, Ann Arbor, 288 pp.

1947. *Mammals of the Great Lakes region.* Univ. Mich. Press, Ann Arbor, 246 pp.

1958. Some distribution records of mammals from Hudson Bay. *Jour. Mamm.*, vol. 39, no. 2, p. 291.

BUTLER, LEONARD

1951. Population cycles and colour-phase genetics of the coloured fox in Quebec. *Can. Jour. Zool.*, vol. 29, no. 1, pp. 24–41.

CABOT, WILLIAM BROOKS

1920. *Labrador.* Small, Maynard & Co., Boston, 354 pp.

CAHALANE, VICTOR H.

1947. *Mammals of North America.* Macmillan Co., New York, 682 pp.

CAHN, ALVIN R.

1930. Auditory ossicles of living and giant beavers. *Jour. Mamm.*, vol. 11, no. 3, pp. 292–9.

1937. The mammals of the Quetico Provincial Park of Ontario. *Jour. Mamm.*, vol. 18, no. 1, pp. 19–30.

CAMERON, AUSTIN W.

1949. Report on biological investigations of game and fur-bearing animals in Nova Scotia, 1948. *Ann. Report, Nova Scotia Dept. Lands and Forests*, pp. 123–47.

1950a. A new chipmunk (Tamias) from Ontario and Quebec. *Jour. Mamm.*, vol. 31, no. 3, pp. 347–8.

1950b. Arctic fox on Cape Breton Island. *Can. Field-Nat.*, vol. 64, no. 4, p. 154.

1951a. The mammals of southeastern Quebec. *Ann. Report Provancher Soc. of Nat. Hist. 1950–1951*, pp. 20–86.

1951b. Greenland right whale recorded in Gaspé County, Quebec. *Ann. Report Natl. Mus. Can., 1949–50, Bull.*, no. 123, pp. 116–19.

1952. Notes on a small collection of mammals from Prince Edward Island. *Ann. Report Natl. Mus. Can., 1950–51, Bull.*, no. 126, pp. 185–7.

1953. The mammals of the Trois Pistoles area and the Gaspé Peninsula. *Ann. Report Natl. Mus. Can., 1951–52, Bull.*, no. 128, pp. 168–88.

1956. A new black bear from Newfoundland. *Jour. Mamm.*, vol. 37, no. 4, pp. 538–40.

1958a. New mammal records for Prince Edward Island. *Jour. Mamm.*, vol. 39, no. 2, pp. 291–2.

1958b. A record of *Sorex arcticus* for New Brunswick. *Jour. Mamm.*, vol. 39, no. 2, p. 292.

1958c. *Canadian mammals.* Natl. Mus. Can., Dept. Northern Affairs and Natl. Res., Ottawa, 80 pp.

1959. Mammals of the Islands in the Gulf of St Lawrence. *Natl. Mus. Can., Bull.*, no. 154, *Biol. Ser.*, no. 53, 165 pp.

1962. Mammalian zoogeography of the Magdalen Islands archipelago, Quebec. *Jour. Mamm.*, vol. 43, no. 4, pp. 505–14.

CAMERON, AUSTIN W., and WILLIAM A. MORRIS

1951. The mammals of the Lake Mistassini and Lake Albanel regions, Quebec. *Bull. Natl. Mus. Can.*, no. 123, pp. 120–30.

CAMERON, AUSTIN W., and PHILLIP A. ORKIN

1950. Mammals of the Lake St. John region. *Ann. Report Natl. Mus. Can., 1948–1949, Bull.*, no. 118, pp. 95–108 .

CARTWRIGHT, GEORGE

1792. *A journal of transactions and events, during a residence of sixteen years on the coast of Labrador* . . . Newark [England], vol. 1, pp. 1–287; vol. 2, pp. 1–505; vol. 3, pp. 1–248.

CHAMBERLAIN, M.
1884. List of the mammals of New Brunswick. *Bull. Nat. Hist. Soc. New Brunswick*, no. 3, art. 4, pp. 37–41.

CHITTLEBOROUGH, R. G.
1954. Studies on the ovaries of the humpback whale, *Megaptera nodosa* (Bonnaterre), on the western Australian coast. *Aust. Jour. Marine and Freshwater Res.*, vol. 5, no. 1, pp. 35–63.
1958. The breeding cycle of the female humpback whale, *Megaptera nodosa* (Bonnaterre). *Aust. Jour. Marine and Freshwater Res.*, vol. 9, no. 1, pp. 1–18.

CHITTY, DENNIS, and CHARLES ELTON
1937. Canadian arctic wild life enquiry, 1935–6. *Jour. Animal Ecol.*, vol. 6, no. 2, pp. 368–85.

CHRISTIAN, JOHN J.
1951. The mammals of the Mazinaw Lake region of Ontario; their reproduction and population dynamics. *Annals Carnegie Mus.*, vol. 31, art. 18, pp. 339–86.

CHURCHER, CHARLES S.
1959. The specific status of the New World red fox. *Jour. Mamm.*, vol. 40, no. 4, pp. 513–20.
1960. Cranial variation in the North American red fox. *Jour. Mamm.*, vol. 41, no. 3, pp. 349–60.

CLARKE, C. H. D.
1938. A study of the mammal population of the vicinity of Pancake Bay, Algoma District, Ontario. *Natl. Mus. Can., Bull.*, no. 88, *Biol. Ser.*, no. 23, pp. 141–52.
1944. Gleanings from the natural history of Huron County, Ontario. *Can. Field-Nat.*, vol. 58, no. 3, pp. 82–4.

CLARKE, ROBERT
1956. A giant squid swallowed by a sperm whale. *Proc. Zool. Soc. London*, vol. 126, pt. 4, p. 645.

CLOWES, A. J.
1929. A note on the composition of whale milk. *Discovery Repts.*, vol. 1, pp. 472–5.

COBB, W. M.
1933. The dentition of the walrus, *Odobenus obesus*. *Proc. Zool. Soc. London*, pt. 3, pp. 645–68.

COGNAC, MARCEL
1963. Winter hunter's wily prey. *Telegram Weekend Mag.*, vol. 13, no. 11, pp. 24–6.

COLE, L. W.
1912. Observations on the senses and instincts of the raccoon. *Jour. Animal Behavior*, vol. 2, no. 5, pp. 299–309.

COLEMAN, A. P.
1899. Copper regions of the upper lakes. *8th Rept. Ont. Bureau Mines*, vol. 8, pt. 2, pp. 121–74.

COLLINS, G.
1940. Habits of the Pacific walrus (*Odobenus divergens*). *Jour. Mamm.*, vol. 21, no. 2, pp. 138–44.

COMEAU, NAPOLEON A.
1909. Life and sport on the north shore of the lower St Lawrence and Gulf. Quebec Telegraph Printing Co., 2nd ed., 440 pp.

COMEAU, NOEL M.
1940 Notes preliminaires sur la presence du *Canis tundrarum ungavensis*, n. ssp. dans la province de Québec. *Annales Assoc. Canadienne-Francaise Avancement Sciences*, vol. 6, pp. 121–2.

CONIBEAR, FRANK, and J. L. BLUNDELL
1949. *The wise one.* Wm. Sloane Associates, New York, 265 pp.

COPELAND, M., and M. L. CHURCH
1906. Notes on the mammals of Grand Manan, N.B., with a description of a new subspecies of white-footed mouse. *Proc. Biol. Soc. Washington*, vol. 19, pp. 121–6.

COURTNEY, T. J.
1947. Baby beavers. *Jour. Mamm.*, vol. 28, no. 3, pp. 228–30.

COVENTRY, A. F.
1931. Amphibia, reptilia, and mammalia of the Temagami District, Ontario. *Can. Field-Nat.*, vol. 45, no. 5, pp. 109–13.
1932. Notes on the Mearns flying squirrel. *Can. Field-Nat.*, vol. 46, no. 4, pp. 75–8.
1937. Notes on the breeding of some *Cricetidae* in Ontario. *Jour. Mamm.*, vol. 18, no. 4, pp. 489–96.

COWAN, IAN MCTAGGART
1936. Nesting habits of the flying squirrel, *Glaucomys sabrinus*. *Jour. Mamm.*, vol. 17, no. 1, pp. 58–60.

CRIDDLE, STUART
1943. The little northern chipmunk in southern Manitoba. *Can. Field-Nat.*, vol. 57, nos. 4–5, pp. 81–6.

CRINGAN, A. T.
1957. History, food habits and range requirements of the woodland caribou of continental North America. *Trans. 22nd N. Am. Wildlife Conf.*, pp. 485–501.

CROSS, E. C.
1937a. Wolf! Wolf! *Rod and Gun in Can.*, vol. 38, no. 8, pp. 18–19; 32–3.
1937b. The white-tailed deer of Ontario. *Rod and Gun in Can.*, vol. 38, no. 9, pp. 14–15; 32.
1938. *Synaptomys borealis* from Godbout, Quebec. *Jour. Mamm.*, vol. 19, no. 3, p. 378.
1940. Periodic fluctuations in numbers of the red fox in Ontario. *Jour. Mamm.*, vol. 21, no. 3, pp. 294–306.
1941. Colour-phases of the red fox (*Vulpes fulva*) in Ontario. *Jour. Mamm.*, vol. 22, no. 1, pp. 25–39.

CROSS, E. C., and J. R. DYMOND
1929. The mammals of Ontario. *Handbook, Royal Ontario Mus. Zool.*, no. 1, Univ. Toronto Press, Toronto, 52 pp.

CURTIS, JAMES D., and EDWARD L. KOZICKY
1944. Observations on the eastern porcupine. *Jour. Mamm.*, vol. 25, no. 2, pp. 137–46.

DAHLBERG, BURTON L., and RALPH C. GUETTINGER
1956. The white-tailed deer in Wisconsin. *Wis. Cons. Dept., Tech. Wildlife Bull.*, no. 14, 282 pp.

DALKE, PAUL D.
1942. The cottontail rabbits in Connecticut. *Conn. State Geol. and Nat. Hist. Surv. Bull.*, no. 65, 97 pp.

DALKE, PAUL D., and PALMER R. SIME
1941. Food habits of the eastern and New England cottontails. *Jour. Wildlife Mgt.*, vol. 5, no. 2, pp. 216–28.

DAVIS, DAVID E.
1936. Status of *Microtus enixus* and *Microtus terraenovae*. *Jour. Mamm.*, vol. 17, no. 3, pp. 290–1.

DAVIS, ELI
1931. Some notes on mammals, birds and ferns of Kazabazua District, Quebec. *Can. Field-Nat.*, vol. 45, no. 8, pp. 193–4.

DAVIS, WAYNE H.
1959. Disproportionate sex ratios in hibernating bats. *Jour. Mamm.*, vol. 40, no. 1, pp. 16–19.

DAVIS, WAYNE H., and WILLIAM Z. LIDICKER
1956. Winter range of the red bat, *Lasiurus borealis*. *Jour. Mamm.* vol. 37, no. 2, pp. 280–1.

DAWSON, G. M.
1896. Summary report on operations of the geological survey for the year 1895. *Geol. Surv. Dept., Ottawa*, vol. 8, pp. 1A–154A.
1901. Summary report of the Geological Survey Dept. for the year 1900. *Geol. Surv. of Can., Ann. Report*, vol. 13, pp. 109A–160A.

DEARDEN, J. C.
1958. A stranding of killer whales in Newfoundland. *Can. Field-Nat.*, vol. 72, no. 4, pp. 166–7.

DEGERBØL, MAGNUS, and PETER FREUCHEN

1935. Mammals. Parts 1 and 2. *Rept. Fifth Thule Exped. 1921–24.* Gyldendalske Borhandel, Nordisk Forlag. Copenhagen, vol. 2, nos. 4–5, 278 pp.

DEGERBØL, MAGNUS, and U. MØHL-HANSEN

1943. Remarks on the breeding conditions and moulting of the collared lemming (*Dicrostonyx*). *Meddelelser om Grønland*, vol. 131, no. 11, 40 pp.

DEVANY, J. L.

1923. Arctic fox shot in Cape Breton. *Can. Field-Nat.*, vol. 37, no. 6, p. 118.

DE VOS, A.

1949. Timber wolves (*Canis lupus lycaon*) killed by cars on Ontario highways. *Jour. Mamm.*, vol. 30, no. 2, p. 197.

1951. Peak populations of *Peromyscus maniculatus gracilis* in northern Ontario. *Jour. Mamm.*, vol. 32, no. 4, p. 462.

1952. The ecology and management of fisher and marten in Ontario. *Ont. Dept. Lands and Forests, Tech. Bull.*, 90 pp.

1962. Changes in the distribution of the snowshoe hare in southern Ontario. *Can. Field-Nat.*, vol. 76, no. 4, pp. 183–9.

DE VOS, A., and A. E. ALLIN

1949. Some notes on moose parasites. *Jour. Mamm.*, vol. 30, no. 4, pp. 430–1.

DE VOS, A., and R. L. PETERSON

1951. A review of the status of the woodland caribou (*Rangifer caribou*) in Ontario. *Jour. Mamm.*, vol. 32, no. 3, pp. 329–37.

DICE, LEE R.

1932a. The songs of mice. *Jour. Mamm.*, vol. 13, no. 3, pp. 187–96.

1932b. Variation in a geographic race of the deer mouse, *Peromyscus maniculatus bairdii*. *Occas. Papers Mus. Zool., Univ. Mich.*, no. 239, 26 pp.

1933. Longevity in *Peromyscus maniculatus gracilis*. *Jour. Mamm.*, vol. 14, no. 2, pp. 147–8.

1936. Age variation in *Peromyscus maniculatus gracilis*. *Jour. Mamm.*, vol. 17, no. 1, pp. 55–7.

1937a. Additional data on variation in the prairie deer-mouse, *Peromyscus maniculatus bairdii*. *Occas. Papers Mus. Zool., Univ. Mich.*, no. 351, 9 pp.

1937b. Variation in the wood-mouse, *Peromyscus leucopus noveboracensis*, in the northeastern United States. *Occas. Papers Mus. Zool., Univ. Mich.*, no. 352, 32 pp.

DICE, L. R., and R. M. BRADLEY

1942. Growth in the deer-mouse, *Peromyscus maniculatus*. *Jour. Mamm.*, vol. 23, no. 4, pp. 416–27.

DIONNE, C. E.

1902. *Les mammifères de la Province de Québec.* Dussault and Proulx, Quebec, 285 pp.

DOAN, K. H., and C. W. DOUGLASS

1953. Beluga of the Churchill region of Hudson Bay. *Bull. Fish. Res. Bd. Can.*, no. 98, pp. 1–27.

DODDS, D. G.

1955. Food habits of the Newfoundland red fox. *Jour. Mamm.*, vol. 36, no. 2, p. 291.

1958. Observations of pre-rutting behaviour in Newfoundland moose. *Jour. Mamm.*, vol. 39, no. 3, pp. 412–16.

1962. Late breeding in Newfoundland snowshoe hare. *Can. Field-Nat.*, vol. 76, no. 1, pp. 60–1.

DONALDSON, HENRY H.

1924. The rat: data and reference tables. *Mem. of the Wistar Inst. Anat. and Biol.*, 2nd Ed., no. 6, 469 pp.

DOUTT, J. KENNETH

1939. The expedition to Hudson Bay. *Carnegie Mag.*, vol. 12, no. 8, pp. 227–36.

1940. Polar bears in the Gulf of St Lawrence. *Jour. Mamm.*, vol. 21, no. 1, pp. 90–2.

1942. A review of the genus *Phoca. Annals Carnegie Mus.*, vol. 29, art. 4, pp. 61–125.

1954. Observations on mammals along the east coast of Hudson Bay and the interior of Ungava. *Annals Carnegie Mus.*, vol. 33, art. 14, pp. 235–49.

DOWNING, S. C.
1938. Second Ontario record for the pipistrelle. *Jour. Mamm.*, vol. 19, no. 1, p. 103.
1940. First Ontario record of the subgenus *Mictomys*. *Can. Field-Nat.*, vol. 54, no. 7, pp. 109–10.
1946. The history of the gray fox in Ontario. *Can. Field-Nat.*, vol. 60, no. 2, pp. 45–6.

DOWNING, S. C., and D. H. BALDWIN
1961. Sharp-shinned hawk preys on red bat. *Jour. Mamm.*, vol. 42, no. 4, p. 540.

DUGMORE, A. A. RADCLYFFE
1913. *The romance of the Newfoundland caribou.* J. B. Lippincott Co., Philadelphia, 191 pp.
1914. *The romance of the beaver.* Heinemann, London, 225 pp.

DUNBAR, M. J.
1941. On the food of seals in the Canadian eastern arctic. *Can. Jour. Res.*, vol. 19, pp. 150–5.
1949. The Pinnipedia of the arctic and subarctic. *Bull. Fish. Res. Bd. Can.*, no. 85, 22 pp.
1952. The Ungava Bay problem. *Arctic*, vol. 5, no. 1, pp. 4–16.
1955a. The status of the Atlantic walrus, *Odobenus rosmarus* (L), in Canada. *Arctic*, vol. 8, no. 1, pp. 11–14.
1955b. The present status of climatic change in the Atlantic sector of northern seas, with special reference to Canadian eastern arctic waters. *Trans. Roy. Soc. Can.*, vol. 49, ser. 3, pp. 1–7.
1956. The status of the Atlantic walrus, *Odobenus rosmarus* (L), in Canada. *Proc. and Pap. 5th Tech. Meet.*, Internatl. Union for the Prot. of Nat., Brussels, pp. 59–61.

DUNCAN, A.
1956. Notes on the food and parasites of the grey seal, *Halichoerus grypus* (Fabricius), from the Isle of Man. *Proc. Zool. Soc. London*, vol. 126, pp. 635–44.

DYMOND, J. R.
1928. The mammals of the Lake Nipigon region. *Trans. Roy. Can. Inst.*, vol. 16, pt. 2, pp. 239–50, (*Contrib. Roy. Ont. Mus. Zool.*, no. 1).
1936. Life history notes and growth studies on the little brown bat, *Myotis lucifugus lucifugus. Can. Field-Nat.*, vol. 50, no. 7, pp. 114–16.

EADIE, W. R.
1947. The accessory reproductive glands of *Parascalops* with notes on homologies. *Anat. Rec.*, vol. 97, pp. 239–52.

EADIE, W. ROBERT, and W. J. HAMILTON, JR.
1958. Reproduction in the fisher in New York. *New York Fish and Game Jour.*, vol. 5, no. 1, pp. 77–83.

EDWARDS, R. L.
1963. Observations on the small mammals of the southeastern shore of Hudson Bay. *Can. Field-Nat.*, vol. 77, no. 1, pp. 1–12.

EDWARDS, R. Y., and R. W. RITCEY
1958. Reproduction in a moose population. *Jour. Wildlife Mgt.*, vol. 22, no. 3, pp. 261–8.

EDWARDS, R. Y., J. SOOS, and R. W. RITCEY
1960. Quantitative observations on epidendric lichens used as food of caribou. *Ecology*, vol. 41, no. 3, pp. 425–30.

EIDMANN, HERMAN
1935. Zur Kenntnis der Säugetierfauna von Südlabrador, 2. Beitrag zur Kenntnis der Fauna von Südlabrador. *Zeitschrift für Säugetierkunde*, vol. 10, no. 3, pp. 39–61.

EKLUND, CARL R.

1957. Bird and mammal notes from the interior Ungava Peninsula. *Can. Field-Nat.*, vol. 70, no. 2, pp. 69–76.

ELLERMAN, J. R., and T. C. S. MORRISON-SCOTT

1951. *Checklist of palaearctic and Indian mammals, 1758 to 1946.* Brit. Mus. (Nat. Hist.), 810 pp.

ELLIOT, D. G.

1901. List of mammals obtained by Thaddeus Surber . . . in the provinces of New Brunswick and Quebec, Canada. *Field Columb. Mus. Pub.*, no. 54, pp. 15–29.

ELSEY, C. A.

1954. A case of cannibalism in Canada lynx (*Lynx canadensis*). *Jour. Mamm.*, vol. 35, no. 1, p. 129.

ELTON, C. S.

1942. *Voles, mice and lemmings.* Oxford Univ. Press, 496 pp.

1954. Further evidence about the barren-ground grizzly bear in northeast Labrador and Quebec. *Jour. Mamm.*, vol. 35, no. 3, pp. 345–57.

ELTON, C., and M. NICHOLSON

1942a. Fluctuations in numbers of muskrat in Canada. *Jour. Animal Ecol.*, vol. 11, no. 1, pp. 96–126.

1942b. The ten-year cycle in numbers of the lynx in Canada. *Jour. Animal Ecol.*, vol. 11, no. 2, pp. 215–44.

ENDERS, R. K.

1942. Notes on a stranded pygmy sperm whale (*Kogia breviceps*). *Notulae Naturae*, no. 111, 6 pp.

1952. Reproduction in the mink (*Mustela vison*). *Proc. Am. Philos. Soc.*, vol. 96, no. 6, pp. 691–755.

ENDERS, R. K., and O. P. PEARSON

1943. The blastocyst of the fisher. *Anat. Rec.* vol. 85, no. 3, pp. 285–7.

ERICKSON, ARNOLD B., *et al.*

1961. The white-tailed deer of Minnesota. *Minn. Dept. Cons., Tech. Bull.*, no. 5, 64 pp.

ERRINGTON, PAUL L.

1937a. Habitat requirements of stream-dwelling muskrats. *Trans. Second N. Am. Wildlife Conf.*, pp. 411–16.

1937b. Drownings as a cause of mortality in muskrats. *Jour. Mamm.*, vol. 18, no. 4, pp. 497–500.

1937c. Summer food habits of the badger in northwestern Iowa. *Jour. Mamm.*, vol. 18, no. 2, pp. 213–16.

1940. Natural restocking of muskrat vacant habitats. *Jour. Wildlife Mgt.*, vol. 4, no. 2, pp. 173–85.

1941. Versatility in feeding and population maintenance of the muskrat. *Jour. Wildlife Mgt.*, vol. 5, no. 1, pp. 68–89.

1943. An analysis of mink predation upon muskrats in north-central United States. *Iowa Exp. Sta. Res. Bull.*, no. 320, pp. 799–924.

1948. Environmental control for increasing muskrat production. *Trans. 13th N. Am. Wildlife Conf.*, pp. 596–607.

1951. Concerning fluctuations in populations of the prolific and widely distributed muskrat. *Am. Nat.*, vol. 85, no. 824, pp. 273–92.

ESCHRICHT, D. F.

1866. On the species of the genus *Orca* inhabiting the northern seas. *Recent memoirs on the Cetacea* by Eschricht *et al.*, London, Ray Soc. Inst., pub. 40, pp. 151–88.

ESSAPIAN, FRANK S.

1953. The birth and growth of a porpoise. *Nat. Hist.*, vol. 57, no. 9, pp. 392–9.

1955. Speed-induced skin folds in the bottle-nosed porpoise, *Tursiops truncatus*. *Breviora*, Mus. Comp. Zool., no. 43, 104 pp.

EVANS, FRANCIS C.

1949. A population study of house mice (*Mus musculus*) following a period of local abundance. *Jour. Mamm.*, vol. 30, no. 4, pp. 351–63.

EWER, D. A.

1945. Acoustic control in the flight of bats. *Nature*, vol. 156, p. 692.

FAESTER, K.

1945. Effect of the climatic amelioration of the past decade on the autumn change of coat of the arctic fox in Greenland. *Meddelelser om Grønland*, vol. 142, no. 2, 18 pp.

FAY, FRANCIS H., and EDWIN H. CHANDLER

1955. The geographical and ecological distribution of cottontail rabbits in Massachusetts. *Jour. Mamm.*, vol. 36, no. 3, pp. 415–24.

FETHERSTON, K.

1947. Geographic variation in the incidence of occurrence of the blue phase of the arctic fox in Canada. *Can. Field-Nat.*, vol. 61, no. 1, pp. 15–18.

FISHER, H. D.

1950. Seals of the Canadian east coast. *Fish. Res. Bd. Can., Gen. Ser.*, Atlantic Biol. station, no. 18, 4 pp.

1952. The status of the harbour seal in British Columbia, with particular reference to the Skeena River. *Bull. Fish. Res. Bd. Can.*, no. 83, 58 pp.

1954. Delayed implantation in the harbour seal, *Phoca vitulina* L. *Nature*, vol. 173, pp. 879–80.

1955. Utilization of Atlantic harp seal populations. *Trans. 20th N. Am. Wildlife Conf.*, pp. 507–18.

FISHER, H. D., and D. E. SERGEANT

1955. A record of the white whale in the Bay of Fundy. *Can. Field-Nat.*, vol. 68, no. 3, pp. 138–9.

FOSTER, J. BRISTOL

1961. Life history of the phenacomys vole. *Jour. Mamm.*, vol. 42, no. 2, pp. 181–98.

FOSTER, J. BRISTOL., and R. L. PETERSON

1961. Age variation in *Phenacomys*. *Jour. Mamm.*, vol. 42, no. 1, pp. 44–53.

FOWLE, C. DAVID., and R. Y. EDWARDS

1954. The utility of break-back traps in population studies of small mammals. *Jour. Wildlife Mgt.*, vol. 18, no. 4, pp. 503–8.

1955. An unusual abundance of short-tailed shrews, *Blarina brevicauda*. *Jour. Mamm.*, vol. 36, no. 1, pp. 36–41.

FRASER, F. C., and P. E. PURVES

1954. Hearing in cetaceans. *Bull. Brit. Mus. (Nat. Hist.)*, vol. 2, no. 5, pp. 103–14.

GABBUTT, PETER D.

1961. The distribution of some small mammals and their associated fleas from central Labrador. *Ecology*, vol. 42, no. 3, pp. 518–25.

GALAMBOS, R., and D. R. GRIFFIN

1940. The supersonic cries of bats. *Anat. Rec.*, vol. 78, p. 95.

1942. Obstacle avoidance by flying bats; the cries of bats. *Jour. Exp. Zool.*, vol. 89, pp. 475–90.

GIANINI, CHARLES A.

1923. Caribou and fox. *Jour. Mamm.*, vol. 4, no. 4, pp. 253–4.

GILES, LEROY W.

1940. Food habits of the raccoon in eastern Iowa. *Jour. Wildlife Mgt.*, vol. 4, no. 4, pp. 375–82.

GILLETT, J. M.

1955. A plant collection from the Mealy Mountains, Labrador, Canada. *Can. Field-Nat.*, vol. 68, no. 3, pp. 118–22.

GILPIN, J. BERNARD

1870. On the mammalia of Nova Scotia. *Trans. N.S. Inst. Nat. Sci.*, vol. 2, no. 4, pp. 58–69.

GOLDMAN, EDWARD A.

1937. The wolves of North America. *Jour. Mamm.*, vol. 18, no. 1, pp. 37–45.

1950. Raccoons of North and Middle America. *N. Am. Fauna*, no. 60, 153 pp.

GOODWIN, G. G.

1924. Mammals of the Gaspé Peninsula, Quebec. *Jour. Mamm.*, vol. 5, no. 4, pp. 246–57.

1929. Mammals of the Cascapedia Valley, Quebec. *Jour. Mamm.*, vol. 10, no. 3, pp. 239–46.

1935. The mammals of Connecticut. *Conn. State Geol. and Nat. Hist. Surv. Bull.*, no. 53, 221 pp.

GORHAM, J. R., and H. J. GRIFFITHS

1952. Diseases and parasites of minks. *U.S. Dept. Agr., Farmers' Bull.*, no. 2050, 41 pp.

GORHAM, STANLEY W., and DAVID H. JOHNSTON

1962. Notes on New Brunswick bats. *Can. Field-Nat.*, vol. 76, no. 4, p. 228.

GOTTSCHANG, J. L.

1956. Juvenile molt in *Peromyscus leucopus noveboracensis*. *Jour. Mamm.*, vol. 37, no. 4, pp. 516–20.

GOULD, E.

1955. The feeding efficiency of insectivorous bats. *Jour. Mamm.*, vol. 36, no. 3, pp. 399–407.

1959. Further studies on the feeding efficiency of bats. *Jour. Mamm.*, vol. 40, no. 1, pp. 149–50.

GOULD, V. E.

1936. Nova Scotia mammal notes. *Can. Field-Nat.*, vol. 50, no. 6, pp. 103–4.

GRANGE, WALLACE B.

1932a. Observations on the snowshoe hare, *Lepus americanus phaeonotus* Allen. *Jour. Mamm.*, vol. 13, no. 1, pp. 1–19.

1932b. The pelage and colour changes of the snowshoe hare, *Lepus americanus phaeonotus* Allen. *Jour. Mamm.*, vol. 13, no. 2, pp 99–116.

GRAY, D.

1882. Notes on the characters and habits of the bottlenose whale (*Hyperoodon rostratus*). *Proc. Zool. Soc. London*, pt. 4, pp. 726–31.

GREEN, MORRIS M.

1928. Some unusually large specimens of North American voles. *Jour. Mamm.*, vol. 9, no. 3, p. 255.

1930. Notes on some small Canadian rodents. *Can. Field-Nat.*, vol. 44, no. 3, p. 69.

GREENE, EUNICE C.

1935. Anatomy of the rat. *Trans. Am. Philos. Soc.*, vol. 28, new series, 370 pp.

GRENFELL, WILFRED T.

1922. *Labrador. The country and the people.* Macmillan, New York, 529 pp.

GRIFFIN, D. R.

1940. Notes on the life histories of New England cave bats. *Jour. Mamm.*, vol. 21, no. 2, pp. 181–7.

1946a. Supersonic cries of bats. *Nature*, vol. 158, pp. 46–8.

1946b. The mechanism by which bats produce supersonic sounds. *Anat. Rec.*, vol. 96, p. 519.

1950. Measurements of the ultrasonic cries of bats. *Jour. Acoust. Soc. Am.*, vol. 22, no. 2, pp. 247–55.

1951. Audible and ultrasonic sounds of bats. *Experientia*, vol. 7, no. 12, pp. 448–53.

1952. Mechanisms in the bat larynx for production of ultrasonic sounds. *Federation Proc.*, vol. 11, p. 59.

1953. Bat sounds under natural conditions, with evidence for the echolocation of insect prey. *Jour. Exp. Zool.*, vol. 123, no. 3, pp. 435–66.

1955. Hearing and acoustic orientation in marine animals. *Deep-sea Res.*, Suppl. to vol. 3, pp. 406–17.

1958. *Listening in the dark.* Yale Univ. Press, New Haven, 413 pp.

GRIFFIN, D. R., and R. GALAMBOS
  1940. Obstacle avoidance by flying bats. *Anat. Rec.*, vol. 78, p. 95.
  1941. The sensory basis of obstacle avoidance by flying bats. *Jour. Exp. Zool.*, vol. 86, no. 3, pp. 481–506.

GRIFFIN, D. R., and A. D. GRINNELL
  1956. The sensitivity of echolocation in bats. *Anat. Rec.*, vol. 125, p. 634.
  1958. Ability of bats to discriminate echoes from louder noise. *Science*, vol. 128, no. 3316, pp. 145–7.

GRIFFIN, D. R., and A. NOVICK
  1955. Acoustic orientation of neotropical bats. *Jour. Exp. Zool.*, vol. 130, no. 2, pp. 251–300.

GRIFFIN, D. R., F. A. WEBSTER, and C. R. MICHAEL
  1960. The echolocation of flying insects by bats. *Animal Behaviour*, vol. 8, nos. 3–4, pp. 141–54.

GRINNELL, A. D., and D. R. GRIFFIN
  1958. Sensitivity of echolocation in bats. *Biol. Bull.*, vol. 114, no. 1, pp. 10–22.

GRIZZELL, ROY A., JR.
  1955. A study of the southern woodchuck, *Marmota monax monax*. *Am. Midl. Nat.*, vol. 53, no. 2, pp. 257–93.

GRÜNEBERG, HANS
  1943. *The genetics of the mouse*. Univ. Press, Cambridge, England, 412 pp.

GUNTER, GORDON, CARL L. HUBBS, and M. ALLAN BEAL
  1955. Records of *Kogia breviceps* from Texas, with remarks on movements and distribution. *Jour. Mamm.*, vol. 36, no. 2, pp. 263–70.

GUNTHER, E. R.
  1949. The habits of fin whales. *Discovery Repts.*, vol. 25, pp. 113–42.

HAGMEIER, EDWIN M.
  1957a. Distribution of marten and fisher in North America. *Can. Field-Nat.*, vol. 70, no. 4, pp. 149–68.
  1957b. A red bat from New Brunswick. *Can. Field-Nat.*, vol. 71, no. 1, p. 35.
  1958. Inapplicability of the subspecies concept to North American marten. *Syst. Zool.*, vol. 7, no. 1, pp. 1–7.

HALKETT, A.
  1905. A naturalist in the frozen north. *Ottawa Nat.*, vol. 19, no. 4, pp. 81–6.

HALL, A.
  1861–2. On the mammals and birds of the district of Montreal. Parts 1–6. *Can. Naturalist and Geologist*, vol. 6, art. 22; vol. 7, arts. 4, 17, 30, 33, and 39.

HALL, E. RAYMOND
  1927. The muscular anatomy of the American badger. *Univ. Calif. Pub. Zool.*, vol. 30, no. 8, pp. 205–19.
  1945. A revised classification of the American ermines with description of a new subspecies from the western Great Lakes region. *Jour. Mamm.*, vol. 26, no. 2, pp. 175–82.
  1951a. American weasels. *Univ. Kans., Pub. Mus. Nat. Hist.*, vol. 4, 466 pp.
  1951b. Synopsis of North American *Lagomorpha*. *Univ. Kans., Pub. Mus. Nat. Hist.*, vol. 5, no. 10, pp. 119–202.

HALL, E. RAYMOND, and E. LENDELL COCKRUM
  1952. Comments on the taxonomy and geographic distribution of North American Microtines. *Univ. Kans., Pub. Mus. Nat. Hist.*, vol. 5, no. 23, pp. 293–312.
  1953. A synopsis of the North American Microtine rodents. *Univ. Kans., Pub. Mus. Nat. Hist.*, vol. 5, no. 27, pp. 273–498.

HALL, E. RAYMOND., and KEITH R. KELSON
  1959. *The mammals of North America*. Ronald Press Co., New York, vol. 1, pp. 1–546; vol. 2, pp. 547–1083.

HALL, JOHN S., ROGER J. CLOUTIER, and DONALD R. GRIFFIN

1957. Longevity records and notes on toothwear of bats. *Jour. Mamm.*, vol. 38, no. 3, pp. 407–9.

HALL, J. S., and W. H. DAVIS

1958. A record of homing in the big brown bat. *Jour. Mamm.*, vol. 39, no. 2, p. 292.

HAMILTON, WILLIAM J., JR.

1929. Breeding habits of the short-tailed shrew, *Blarina brevicauda. Jour. Mamm.*, vol. 10, no. 2, pp. 125–34.

1930. The food of the *Soricidae. Jour. Mamm.*, vol. 11, no. 1, pp. 26–9.

1931a. Habits of the short-tailed shrew, *Blarina brevicauda* (Say). *Ohio Jour. Sci.*, vol. 31, no. 2, pp. 97–106.

1931b. Habits of the star-nosed mole, *Condylura cristata. Jour. Mamm.*, vol. 12, no. 4, pp. 345–55.

1933a. The insect food of the big brown bat. *Jour. Mamm.*, vol. 14, no. 2, pp. 155–6.

1933b. The weasels of New York: their natural history and economic status. *Am. Midl. Nat.*, vol. 14, no. 4, pp. 289–344.

1934. The life history of the rufescent woodchuck, *Marmota monax rufescens* Howell. *Annals Carnegie Mus.*, no. 23, pp. 85–178.

1935a. Notes on food of red foxes in New York and New England. *Jour. Mamm.*, vol. 16, no. 1, pp. 16–21.

1935b. Habits of jumping mice. *Am. Midl. Nat.*, vol. 16, no. 2, pp. 187–200.

1936a. The food and breeding habits of the raccoon. *Ohio Jour. Sci.*, vol. 36, no. 3, pp. 131–40.

1936b. Seasonal food of skunks in New York. *Jour. Mamm.*, vol. 17, no. 3, pp. 240–6.

1937a. Activity and home range of the field mouse, *Microtus pennsylvanicus pennsylvanicus* (Ord). *Ecology*, vol. 18, no. 2, pp. 255–63.

1937b. Growth and life span of the field mouse. *Am. Nat.*, vol. 71, no. 5, pp. 500–7.

1937c. The biology of microtine cycles. *Jour. Agr. Res.*, vol. 54, no. 10, pp. 779–90.

1938. Life history notes on the northern pine mouse. *Jour. Mamm.*, vol. 19, no. 2, pp. 163–70.

1939a. *American mammals: their lives, habits and economic relations.* McGraw-Hill Book Co., New York, 434 pp.

1939b. Observations on the life history of the red squirrel in New York. *Am. Midl. Nat.*, vol. 22, no. 3, pp. 732–45.

1940a. The summer food of minks and raccoons on the Montezuma Marsh, New York. *Jour. Wildlife Mgt.*, vol. 4, no. 1, pp. 80–4.

1940b. Breeding habits of the cottontail rabbit in New York State. *Jour. Mamm.*, vol. 21, no. 1, pp. 8–11.

1940c. The molt of *Blarina brevicauda. Jour. Mamm.*, vol. 21, no. 4, pp. 457–8.

1940d. The biology of the smoky shrew (*Sorex fumeus fumeus* Miller). *Zoologica*, vol. 25, no. 4, pp. 473–92.

1941. The food of small forest mammals in eastern United States. *Jour. Mamm.*, vol. 22, no. 3, pp. 250–63.

1943. *The mammals of eastern United States. An account of Recent land mammals occurring east of the Mississippi.* Comstock Publishing Co., Ithaca, N.Y., 432 pp.

1944. The biology of the little short-tailed shrew, *Cryptotis parva. Jour. Mamm.*, vol. 25, no. 1, pp. 1–7.

1958. Life history and economic relations of the opossum (*Didelphis marsupialis virginiana*) in New York State. *Mem. Cornell Univ. Agr. Exp. Sta.*, no. 354, 48 pp.

HAMILTON, WILLIAM J., JR., and ARTHUR H. COOK

1955. The biology and management of the fisher in New York. *New York Fish and Game Jour.*, vol. 2, no. 1, pp. 13–35.

HAMILTON, WILLIAM J., JR., and W. J. HAMILTON III.

1955. The food of some small mammals from the Gaspé Peninsula, P.Q. *Can. FieldNat.*, vol. 68, no. 3, pp. 108–9.

HAMILTON, WILLIAM J., JR., and RUSSELL P.
HUNTER
1939. Fall and winter food habits of Vermont bobcats. *Jour. Wildlife Mgt.*, vol. 3, no. 2, pp. 99–103.

HAMLETT, GEORGE W. D.
1932. Observations on the embryology of the badger. *Anat. Rec.*, vol. 53, no. 3, pp. 283–303.
1938. The reproductive cycle of the coyote. *U.S. Dept. Agr. Tech. Bull.*, no. 616, 12 pp.

HANSEN, R. M.
1957. Remarks on the bifid claws of the varying lemming. *Jour. Mamm.* vol. 38, no. 1, pp. 127–8.

HANTZSCH, BERNARD
1931. Contributions to the knowledge of extreme northeastern Labrador. *Can. Field-Nat.*, vol. 45, no. 4, pp. 85–90; vol. 45, no. 6, pp. 143–6; vol. 46, no. 1, pp. 7–12; vol. 46, no. 2, pp. 34–6; vol. 46, no. 7, pp. 153–62.

HARDY, C.
1870. On the beaver in Nova Scotia. *Proc. N.S. Inst. Nat. Sci.*, vol. 2, pt. 1, pp. 17–25.

HARMER, SIDNEY F.
1923. Cervical vertebrae of a gigantic blue whale from the Panama. *Proc. Zool. Soc. London, Part 4*, pp. 1085–9.
1924. On *Mesoplodon* and other beaked whales. *Proc. Zool. Soc. London*, pp. 541–87.
1928. The history of whaling. *Proc. Linnean Soc. London, Session 140, 1927–28*, pp. 51–95.

HARPER, FRANCIS
1930. Notes on certain forms of the house mouse (*Mus musculus*) particularly those of eastern North America. *Jour. Mamm.*, vol. 11, no. 1, pp. 49–52.

1955. The barren ground caribou of Keewatin. *Univ. Kans. Mus. Nat. Hist., Misc. Pub.*, no. 6, 163 pp.
1961. Land and fresh-water mammals of the Ungava Peninsula. *Univ. Kans. Mus. Nat. Hist., Misc. Pub.*, no. 27, 178 pp.

HARRISON, R. J.
1949. Observations on the female reproductive organs of the pilot whale *Globicephala melaena* Traill. *Jour. Anat.*, vol. 83, no. 3, pp. 238–53.

HARRISON, R. J., HARRISON MATTHEWS, and
J. M. ROBERTS
1952. Reproduction in some *Pinnipedia*. *Trans. Zool. Soc. London*, vol. 27, pp. 437–540.

HARTMAN, CARL G.
1920. Studies in the development of the opossum, *Didelphis virginiana*: V. The phenomena of parturition. *Anat. Rec.*, vol. 19, pp. 1–11.
1933. On the survival of spermatozoa in the genital tract of the bat. *Quart. Rev. Biol.*, vol. 8, no. 2, pp. 185–93.
1952. *Possums*. Univ. Texas Press, Austin, 174 pp.

HARTRIDGE, H.
1920. The avoidance of objects by bats in their flights. *Jour. Physiol.*, vol. 54, pp. 54–7.
1945a. Avoidance of obstacles by bats. *Nature*, vol. 156, p. 55.
1945b. Acoustic control in the flight of bats. *Nature*, vol. 156, pp. 490–4.
1945c. Acoustic control in the flight of bats. *Nature*, vol. 156, pp. 692–3.
1946. Supersonic cries of bats. *Nature*, vol. 158, p. 135.

HATT, ROBERT T.
1929. The red squirrel: its life history and habits, with special reference to the Adirondacks of New York and the Harvard Forest. *Roosevelt Wild Life Annals*, vol. 2, no. 1, 140 pp.

1930. The biology of the voles of New York. *Bull. N.Y. State Coll. of Forestry*, vol. 3, no. 2c, *Roosevelt Wild Life Bull.*, vol. 5, no. 4, pp. 505–623.

1931. Habits of a young flying squirrel (*Glaucomys volans*). *Jour. Mamm.*, vol. 12, no. 3, pp. 233–8.

1938. Feeding habits of the least shrew. *Jour. Mamm.*, vol. 19, no. 2, pp. 247–8.

HAUGEN, ARNOLD O.

1942a. Home range of the cottontail rabbit. *Ecology*, vol. 23, no. 3, pp. 354–67.

1942b. Life history studies of the cottontail rabbit in southwestern Michigan. *Am. Midl. Nat.*, vol. 28, no. 1, pp. 204–44.

HAYCOCK, E.

1890. *Report of the Royal Commission on the mineral resources of Ontario and measures for their development*, Toronto, p. 58.

HEEZEN, B. C.

1957. Whales entangled in deep sea cables. *Deep-sea Res.*, vol. 4, pp. 105–15.

HEWER, H. R.

1957. A Hebridean breeding colony of grey seals *Halichoerus grypus* (Fab.) with comparative notes on the grey seals of Ramsey Island, Pembrokeshire. *Proc. Zool. Soc. London*, vol. 128, pp. 23–66.

HICKS, ELLIS A.

1949. Ecological factors affecting the activity of the western fox squirrel, *Sciurus niger rufiventer* (Geoffroy). *Ecol. Monog.*, vol. 19, no. 4, pp. 287–302.

HILDEBRAND, HENRY

1949. Notes on an abundance of shrews (*Sorex cinereus cinereus*) and other small mammals in the Ungava Bay region of far northern Quebec. *Jour. Mamm.*, vol. 30, no. 3, pp. 309–11.

HISAW, FREDERICK LEE

1923a. Feeding habits of moles. *Jour. Mamm.*, vol. 4, no. 1, pp. 9–20.

1923b. Observations on the burrowing habits of moles (*Scalopus aquaticus machrinoides*). *Jour. Mamm.*, vol. 4, no. 2, pp. 79–88.

HITCHCOCK, H. B.

1940. Keeping track of bats. *Can. Field-Nat.*, vol. 54, no. 1, pp. 55–6.

1941. *Myotis subulatus leibii* and other bats hibernating in Ontario and Quebec. *Can. Field-Nat.*, vol. 55, no. 3, p. 46.

1945. *Myotis subulatus leibii* in Ontario. *Jour. Mamm.*, vol. 26, no. 4, p. 433.

1949. Hibernation of bats in southeastern Ontario and adjacent Quebec. *Can. Field-Nat.*, vol. 63, no. 2, pp. 47–59.

1950. Sex ratios in hibernating bats. *Natl. Speleological Soc. Bull.*, no. 12, p. 26.

HITCHCOCK, H. B., and K. REYNOLDS

1940. *Pipistrellus* hibernating in Ontario. *Can. Field-Nat.*, vol. 54, no. 6, p. 89.

1942. Homing experiments with the little brown bat, *Myotis lucifugus lucifugus* (Le Conte). *Jour. Mamm.*, vol. 23, no. 3, pp. 258–67.

HOCK, R. J.

1951. The metabolic rates and body temperatures of bats. *Biol. Bull.*, vol. 101, no. 3, pp. 289–99.

HODGSON, ROBERT G.

1949. Farming nutria for profit. *Fur Trade Jour. Can.*, 110 pp.

HOFFMEISTER, DONALD F., and JOHN E. WARNOCK

1947. A concentration of lemming mice (*Synaptomys cooperi*) in central Illinois. *Trans. Ill. Acad. Sci.*, no. 40, pp. 190–3.

HOLLING, C. S.

1955. The selection by certain small mammals of dead, parasitized, and healthy prepupae of the European pine sawfly, *Neodiprion sertifer* (Geoff.). *Can. Jour. Zool.*, vol. 33, pp. 404–19.

1958. Sensory stimuli in the location and selection of sawfly cocoons by small mammals. *Can. Jour. Zool.*, vol. 36, pp. 633–53.

HOLLISTER, N.
  1911. A systematic synopsis of the muskrats. *N. Am. Fauna*, no. 32, pp. 7–38.
  1913. A synopsis of the American minks. *Proc. U.S. Natl. Mus.*, vol. 44, pp. 471–80.

HOOPER, EMMET T.
  1958. The male phallus in mice of the genus *Peromyscus*. *Misc. Pub., Mus. Zool., Univ. Mich.*, no. 105, 24 pp.

HOOPER, EMMET T., and BARBARA S. HART
  1962. A synopsis of recent North American microtine rodents. *Misc. Pub., Mus. Zool., Univ. Mich.*, no. 120, 68 pp.

HOOPER, EMMET T., and BURTON T. OSTENSON
  1949. Age groups in Michigan otter. *Occas. Papers Mus. Zool., Univ. Mich.*, no. 518, 22 pp.

HORNER, B. ELIZABETH
  1954. Arboreal adaptations of *Peromyscus*, with special reference to use of the tail. *Contrib. Lab. Vert. Biol., Univ. Mich.*, no. 61, 84 pp.

HOWARD, WALTER E.
  1949. Dispersal, amount of inbreeding, and longevity in a local population of prairie deermice on the George Reserve, southern Michigan. *Contrib. Lab. Vert. Biol., Univ. Mich.*, no. 43, 50 pp.

HOWELL, A. BRAZIER
  1926. Voles of the genus *Phenacomys*. *N. Am. Fauna*, no. 48, 66 pp.
  1927. Revision of the American lemming mice (genus *Synaptomys*). *N. Am. Fauna*, no. 50, 38 pp.
  1930. *Aquatic mammals: their adaptation to life in the water.* Charles C. Thomas, Baltimore, 338 pp.
  1935. Observations on the white whale. *Jour. Mamm.*, vol. 16, no. 2, pp. 155–6.

HOWELL, ARTHUR H.
  1901. Revision of the skunks of the genus *Chincha*. *N. Am. Fauna*, no. 20, 62 pp.

  1915. Revision of the American marmots. *N. Am. Fauna*, no. 37, 80 pp.
  1918. Revision of the American flying squirrels. *N. Am. Fauna*, no. 44, 64 pp.
  1929. Revision of the American chipmunks (genera *Tamias* and *Eutamias*). *N. Am. Fauna*, no. 52, 157 pp.
  1936. A revision of the American Arctic hares. *Jour. Mamm.*, vol. 17, no. 4, pp. 315–37.
  1938. Revision of the North American ground squirrels, with a classification of the North American *Sciuridae*. *N. Am. Fauna*, no. 56, 256 pp.

HUBBS, C. L.
  1951. Eastern Pacific records and general distribution of the pygmy sperm whale. *Jour. Mamm.*, vol. 32, no. 4, pp. 403–10.

JACKSON, C. F.
  1938. Notes on the mammals of southern Labrador. *Jour. Mamm.*, vol. 19, no. 4, pp. 429–34.
  1939a. Notes on the range of the Labrador shrew, *Sorex cinereus miscix*. *Can. Field-Nat.*, vol. 53, no. 1, pp. 7–8.
  1939b. A new species of *Peromyscus* from the north shore of the Gulf of the St Lawrence. *Proc. Biol. Soc. Washington*, vol. 52, pp. 101–4.
  1939c. Polar bear in Lake St John district, Quebec. *Jour. Mamm.*, vol. 20, no. 2, p. 253.

JACKSON, H. H. T.
  1915. A review of the American moles. *N. Am. Fauna*, no. 38, 100 pp.
  1925. Preliminary descriptions of seven shrews of the genus *Sorex*. *Proc. Biol. Soc. Washington*, vol. 38, pp. 127–30.
  1928. A taxonomic review of the American long-tailed shrews (genera *Sorex* and *Microsorex*). *N. Am. Fauna*, no. 51, 238 pp.
  1949. Two new coyotes from the United States. *Proc. Biol. Soc. Washington*, vol. 62, pp. 31–2.

1957. The status of *Eutamias minimus jacksoni*. *Jour. Mamm.*, vol. 38, no. 4, pp. 518–19.

1961. *Mammals of Wisconsin*. Univ. Wis. Press, Madison, 504 pp.

JACOBI, A.

1931. Das Rentier: eine zoologische Monographie der Gattung Rangifer. *Ergaenzungsband zum Zoologischen Anzeiger*, Leipzig, Bd. 96, 264 pp.

JAMESON, E. W., JR.

1943a. Source of food for chipmunks. *Jour. Mamm.*, vol. 24, no. 4, p. 500.

1943b. Notes on the habits and siphonapterous parasites of the mammals of Welland County, Ontario. *Jour. Mamm.*, vol. 24, no. 2, pp. 194–7.

1950. The external parasites of the short-tailed shrew *Blarina brevicauda* Say. *Jour. Mamm.*, vol. 31, no. 2, pp. 138–45.

JOHNSON, CHARLES E.

1925. The muskrat in New York: its natural history and economics. *Roosevelt Wild Life Bull. 3*, no. 2, pp. 205–320.

1927. The beaver in the Adirondacks: its economics and natural history. *Roosevelt Wild Life Bull. 4*, no. 4, pp. 501–641.

JOHNSON, DAVID H.

1951. The water shrews of the Labrador Peninsula. *Proc. Biol. Soc. Washington*, vol. 64, pp. 109–113.

JOHNSON, DONALD E.

1951. Biology of the elk calf, *Cervus canadensis nelsoni*. *Jour. Wildlife Mgt.*, vol. 15, no. 4, pp. 396–410.

JOHNSON, R. A.

1937. The food of the snowy owl (*Nyctea nyctea*) during a migration to the Gulf of St Lawrence. *Can. Field-Nat.*, vol. 51, no. 9, pp. 136–7.

JONSGÅRD, Å.

1951. Studies on the little piked or Minke whale (*Balaenoptera acutorostrata* Lacépède). *Norsk Hvalf.*, no. 40, Arg. (5), pp. 5–54.

JONSGÅRD, Å., and O. NORDLI

1952. Catch of white-sided dolphins. *Norsk Hvalf.*, no. 41, p. 229.

JUDD, W. W.

1950. Mammal host records of Acarina and Insecta from the vicinity of Hamilton, Ontario. *Jour. Mamm.*, vol. 31, no. 3, p. 357.

1953. Mammal host records of Acarina and Insecta from the vicinity of London, Ontario. *Jour. Mamm.*, vol. 34, no. 1, pp. 137–9.

KELKER, GEORGE H.

1937. Insect foods of skunks. *Jour. Mamm.*, vol. 18, no. 2, pp. 164–70.

KELLOGG, R.

1928. The history of whales, their adaptations to life in the water. *Quart. Rev. Biol.*, vol. 3, pp. 29–76; 174–208.

1938. Adaptation of structure to function in whales. *Carnegie Inst. Washington Pub.*, no. 501, pp. 649–82.

1940. Whales, giants of the sea. *Natl. Geogr. Mag.*, vol. 77, no. 1, pp. 35–90.

KELLOGG, W. N.

1953. Ultrasonic hearing in the porpoise, *Tursiops truncatus*. *Jour. Comp. Psychol.*, vol. 46, pp. 446–50.

1961. *Porpoises and sonar*. Univ. Chicago Press, 177 pp.

KELLOGG, W. N., R. KOHLER, and H. N. MORRIS

1953. Porpoise sounds as sonar signals. *Science*, vol. 117, pp. 239–43.

KELSALL, J. P.

1957. Continued barren-ground caribou studies. *Wildlife Mgt. Bull.*, ser. 1, no. 12, 148 pp.

KIMURA, S., and T. NEMOTO

1956. Note on a Minke whale kept alive in aquarium. *Sci. Repts. Whales Res. Inst. Tokyo*, vol. 11, p. 81.

KLUGH, A. BROOKER

1921. Notes on the habits of *Blarina brevicauda*. *Jour. Mamm.*, vol. 2, no. 1, p. 35.

1923. Notes on the habits of the chipmunk, *Tamias striatus lysteri. Jour. Mamm.*, vol. 4, no. 1, pp. 29–32.

1924. Notes on *Eptesicus fuscus. Jour. Mamm.*, vol. 5, no. 1, pp. 42–3.

1927. Ecology of the red squirrel. *Jour. Mamm.*, vol. 8, no. 1, pp. 1–32.

KNOTTNERUS-MEYER, THEODOR

1908. *Uber des Eisbären und seine geographischen Formen.* Sitzungsberichte der Gessellschaft Naturforschender Freunde zu Berlin, pp. 170–87.

KOMAREK, E. V.

1932. Distribution of *Microtus chrotorrhinus*, with description of a new subspecies. *Jour. Mamm.*, vol. 13, no. 2, pp. 155–8.

KRITZLER, H.

1952. Observations on the pilot whale in captivity. *Jour. Mamm.*, vol. 33, no. 3, pp. 321–34.

KRUTZSCH, PHILIP H.

1954. North American jumping mice (genus *Zapus*). *Univ. Kans., Pub. Mus. Nat. Hist.*, vol. 7, no. 4, pp. 349–472.

LAGLER, KARL F., and BURTON T. OSTENSON

1942. Early spring food of the otter in Michigan. *Jour. Wildlife Mgt.*, vol. 6, no. 3, pp. 244–54.

LANDIS, C. S.

1951. *Woodchucks and woodchuck rifles.* Greenburg, New York, 402 pp.

LANTZ, DAVID E.

1907. An economic study of field mice (genus *Microtus*). *U.S. Dept. Agr., Biol. Surv. Bull.*, no. 31, 64 pp.

LATHAM, ROBERT M.

1953. Simple method for identification of least weasel. *Jour. Mamm.*, vol. 34, no. 3, p. 385.

LAUN, H. CHARLES

1962. Loud vocal sounds produced by striped skunk. *Jour. Mamm.*, vol. 43, no. 3, pp. 432–3.

LAURIE, E. M. O.

1946a. The coypu in Great Britain. *Jour. Animal Ecol.*, vol. 15, pp. 22–34.

1946b. The reproduction of the house mouse (*Mus musculus*) living in different environments. *Proc. Roy. Soc. London, Ser. B, Biol. Sci. 133 (872)*, pp. 248–81.

LAWRENCE, BARBARA

1946. Brief comparison of the short-tailed shrew and reptile poisons. *Jour. Mamm.*, vol. 26, no. 4, pp. 393–6.

LAWRENCE, B., and W. E. SCHEVILL

1954. *Tursiops* as an experimental subject. *Jour. Mamm.*, vol. 35, no. 2, pp. 225–32.

1956. The functional anatomy of the Delphinid nose. *Bull. Mus. Comp. Zool.*, Harvard, vol. 114, no. 4, pp. 103–51.

LAWS, R. M.

1959. The foetal growth rates of whales with special reference to the fin whale, *Balaenoptera physalus* Linn. *Discovery Repts.*, vol. 29, pp. 281–308.

LAY, DANIEL W.

1942. Ecology of the opossum in eastern Texas. *Jour. Mamm.*, vol. 23, no. 2, pp. 147–59.

LAYNE, JAMES N.

1952. The os genitale of the red squirrel, *Tamiasciurus. Jour. Mamm.*, vol. 33, no. 4, pp. 457–9.

1954. The biology of the red squirrel, *Tamiasciurus hudsonicus loquax* (Bangs), in central New York. *Ecol. Monog.*, vol. 24, no. 3, pp. 227–67.

LEIGHTON, ALEXANDER H.

1932. Notes on the beaver's individuality and mental characteristics. *Jour. Mamm.*, vol. 13, no. 2, pp. 117–26.

1937. The twilight of the Indian porpoise hunters. *Nat. Hist.*, vol. 40, no. 1, pp. 410–16.

LEWIS, HARRISON F.
1942. Fourth census of non-passerine birds in the bird sanctuaries of the north shore of the Gulf of St Lawrence. *Can. Field-Nat.*, vol. 56, no. 1, pp. 5–8.

LEWIS, HARRISON F., and J. KENNETH DOUTT
1942. Records of the Atlantic walrus and the polar bear in or near the northern part of the Gulf of St Lawrence. *Jour. Mamm.*, vol. 23, no. 4, pp. 365–75.

LIERS, EMIL E.
1951. Notes on the river otter (*Lutra canadensis*). *Jour. Mamm.*, vol. 32, no. 1, pp. 1–9.
1953. *An otter's story.* Viking Press, New York, 191 pp.
1958. Early breeding in the river otter. *Jour. Mamm.*, vol. 39, no. 3, pp. 438–9.

LILLY, JOHN C.
1961. *Man and dolphin.* Doubleday, 312 pp.

LINDSAY, DAVID MOORE
1911. *A voyage to the Arctic on the whaler Aurora.* Dana Estes & Co., Boston, 223 pp.

LINSDALE, JEAN
1927. Notes on the life history of *Synaptomys*. *Jour. Mamm.*, vol. 8, no. 1, pp. 51–4.

LOCKLEY, R. M.
1954a. The Atlantic grey seal. *Oryx*, vol. 2, pp. 384–7.
1954b. *The seals and the curragh. Introducing the natural history of the grey seal of the North Atlantic.* J. M. Dent & Sons, London, 149 pp.

LOOMIS, F. B.
1911. A new mink from the shell heaps of Maine. *Am. Jour. Sci.*, 4th ser., vol. 31, no. 183, pp. 227–9.

LOUGHREY, ALAN G.
1959. Preliminary investigations of the Atlantic walrus *Odobenus rosmarus rosmarus* (Linnaeus). *Wild Life Mgt. Bull.*, ser. 1, no. 14, 123 pp.

LOW, A. P.
1889. Report of exploration in James Bay and country east of Hudson Bay, drained by the Big, Great Whale and Clearwater Rivers, 1887 and 1888. *Geol. and Nat. Hist. Surv. of Can., Ann. Report, New Ser.*, vol. 3, pt. 2, app. 3, pp.1J–94J.
1890. The Mistassini region. *Ottawa Nat.*, vol. 4, no. 1, pp. 11–28.
1896. List of mammalia of the Labrador Peninsula, with short notes on their distribution, etc. *Geol. Surv. of Can., Ann. Report*, vol. 8, pp. 313L–21L.
1906. *Report on the Dominion Government expedition to Hudson Bay and the Arctic islands on board of the D.G.S. Neptune, 1903–1904.* Government Printing Bur., 355 pp.

LOWER, A. R. M.
1915. A report on the fish and fisheries of the west coast of James Bay. *Ann. Report Dept. Naval Ser. for the fiscal year ending March 31, 1914, Sessional Paper*, no. 39a, Ottawa, pp. 33–67.

MACKENZIE, B. A.
1954. Green algal growth on gray seals. *Jour. Mamm.*, vol. 35, no. 4, pp. 595–6.

MACKINTOSH, N. A.
1946. The natural history of whalebone whales. *Smithsonian Inst. Ann. Report for 1946*, pp. 235–64.

MACLEOD, C. F.
1960. The introduction of the masked shrew into Newfoundland. *Bi-Monthly Progress Rept.*, Forest Biol. Div., Res. Br., Dept. Agr., vol. 16, no. 2, p. 1.

MACLEOD, C. F., and A. W. CAMERON
1961. Distribution records for mammals in west-central Quebec. *Jour. Mamm.*, vol. 42, no. 2, pp. 281–2.

MACLULICH, D. A.
1937. Fluctuations in the numbers of the varying hare (*Lepus americanus*). *Univ. Toronto Studies, Biol. Ser.*, no. 43, 136 pp.

MANNING, T. H.
1943. Notes on the mammals of south and central west Baffin Island. *Jour. Mamm.*, vol. 24, no. 1, pp. 47–59.
1947. Bird and mammal notes from the east side of Hudson Bay. *Can. Field-Nat.*, vol. 60, no. 4, pp. 71–85.
1948. Preliminary report on a background study of the caribou, *Rangifer caribou caribou* (Gmelin) and *Rangifer arcticus caboti* Allen of the Labrador Peninsula and the Province of Quebec north of the St Lawrence. *Ann. Report, Prov. Quebec Assoc. Protection Fish and Game*, pp. 20–1.

MANSFIELD, A. W.
1963. Seals of arctic and eastern Canada. *Bull. Fish. Res. Bd. Can.*, no. 137, 30 pp.

MANVILLE, R. H.
1942. Notes on the mammals of Mount Desert Island, Maine. *Jour. Mamm.*, vol. 23, no. 4, pp. 391–8.
1949. A study of small mammal populations in northern Michigan. *Misc. Pub., Mus. Zool., Univ. Mich.*, no. 73, 83 pp.
1961. Notes on some mammals of the Gaspé Peninsula, Quebec. *Can. Field-Nat.*, vol. 75, no. 2, pp. 108–9.

MANVILLE, R. H., and P. G. FAVOUR, JR.
1960. Southern distribution of the Atlantic walrus. *Jour. Mamm.*, vol. 41, no. 4, pp. 499–503.

MARKLEY, MERLE H., and C. F. BASSETT
1942. Habits of captive marten. *Am. Midl. Nat.*, vol. 28, no. 3, pp. 604–16.

MARSHALL, WILLIAM H.
1936. A study of the winter activities of the mink. *Jour. Mamm.*, vol. 17, no. 4, pp. 382–92.
1951a. An age determination method for the pine marten. *Jour. Wildlife Mgt.*, vol. 15, no. 3, pp. 276–84.
1951b. Pine marten as a forest product. *Jour. Forestry*, vol. 49, no. 12, pp. 899–905.

MARTIN, HORACE T.
1892. *Castorologia, or the history and traditions of the Canadian beaver.* Montreal and London, 238 pp.

MATHESON, COLIN
1950. Longevity in the grey seal. *Nature*, vol. 166, pp. 73–4.

MATHEWSON, S. J.
1935. Blackfish in the Gulf of St Lawrence. *Jour. Mamm.*, vol. 16, no. 3, p. 234.

MATSON, J. R.
1946. Notes on dormancy in the black bear. *Jour. Mamm.*, vol. 27, no. 3, pp. 203–12.
1954. Observations on the dormant phase of a female black bear. *Jour. Mamm.*, vol. 35, no. 1, pp. 28–35.

MATTHEWS, L. H.
1937. The humpback whale, *Megaptera nodosa*. *Discovery Repts.*, vol. 17, pp. 7–92.
1938a. The sperm whale, *Physeter catodon*. *Discovery Repts.*, vol. 17, pp. 93–168.
1938b. The sei whale, *Balaenoptera borealis*. *Discovery Repts.*, vol. 17, pp. 183–290.

MAYNARD, J. E.
1929. Oba area, District of Algoma—Game and Fish. *Report Ont. Dept. Mines*, vol. 38, pt. 6, p. 117.

MCBRIDE, A. F., and H. KRITZLER
1951. Observations on pregnancy, parturition and post-natal behaviour in the bottle-nose dolphin. *Jour. Mamm.*, vol. 32, no. 3, pp. 251–66.

MCLAREN, I. A.

1958a. The biology of the ringed seal, *Phoca hispida* (Schreber) in the eastern Canadian arctic. *Bull. Fish. Res. Bd. Can.*, no. 118, 97 pp.

1958b. Some aspects of growth and reproduction of the bearded seal, *Erignathus barbatus* (Erxleben). *Jour. Fish. Res. Bd. Can.*, vol. 15, no. 2, pp. 219–27.

1958c. The economics of seals in the eastern Canadian arctic. *Fish. Res. Bd. Can., Circ.*, no. 1, 94 pp.

MERRIAM, C. HART

1884. Seals in the upper St Lawrence. *Forest and Stream*, vol. 22, p. 124.

1895. Revision of the shrews of the American genera *Blarina* and *Notiosorex*. *N. Am. Fauna*, no. 10, 34 pp.

1896. Revision of the lemmings of the genus *Synaptomys*, with descriptions of new species. *Proc. Biol. Soc. Washington*, vol. 10, pp. 55–64.

1900. Preliminary revision of the North American red foxes. *Proc. Washington Acad. Sci.*, vol. 2, pp. 661–76.

1902. Four new Arctic foxes. *Proc. Biol. Soc. Washington*, vol. 15, pp. 167–72.

1903. Eight new mammals from the United States. *Proc. Biol. Soc. Washington*, vol. 16, pp. 73–8.

MERRILL, SAMUEL

1920. *The moose book.* 2nd ed., E. P. Dutton and Co., New York, 366 pp.

MIDDLETON, A. D.

1930. The ecology of the American grey squirrel (*Sciurus carolinensis* Gmelin) in the British Isles. *Proc. Zool. Soc. London, 1930*, pt. 3, pp. 809–43.

MILLER, GERRIT S., JR.

1896. Genera and subgenera of voles and lemmings. *N. Am. Fauna*, no. 12, 84 pp.

1897a. Notes on the mammals of Ontario. *Proc. Boston Soc. Nat. Hist.*, vol. 28, no. 1, 44 pp.

1897b. Revision of the North American bats of the family *Vespertilionidae*. *N. Am. Fauna*, no. 13, 144 pp.

1897c. Synopsis of voles of the genus *Phenacomys*. *Proc. Biol. Soc. Washington*, vol. 11, pp. 77–87.

1899. A new polar hare from Labrador. *Proc. Biol. Soc. Washington*, vol. 13, pp. 39–40.

1907. The families and genera of bats. *U.S. Natl. Mus. Bull.*, no. 57, 282 pp.

1912. *Catalogue of the mammals of western Europe (Europe exclusive of Russia) in the collection of the British Museum.* Brit. Mus. (Nat. Hist.), London, 1019 pp.

1924. List of North American Recent mammals. *U.S. Natl. Mus. Bull.*, no. 128, 673 pp.

MILLER, GERRIT S., JR., and GLOVER M. ALLEN

1928. The American bats of the genera *Myotis* and *Pizonyx*. *U.S. Natl. Mus. Bull.*, no. 144, 218 pp.

MILLER, GERRIT S., JR., and REMINGTON KELLOGG

1955. List of North American Recent mammals. *U.S. Natl. Mus. Bull.*, no. 205, 954 pp.

MILLS, ENOS A.

1913. *In beaver world.* Houghton Mifflin, Boston, 240 pp.

MØHL-HANSEN, U.

1954. Investigations on reproduction and growth of the porpoise (*Phocaena phocaena*) from the Baltic. *Vidensk. Medd. fra Dansk Naturh. Foren.*, Bd. 116, pp. 369–96.

MOHR, C. E.

1936. Notes on the least bat, *Myotis subulatus leibii*. *Proc. Penn. Acad. Sci.*, vol. 10, pp. 62–5.

MOISAN, GASTON

1956. Late breeding in moose, *Alces alces*. *Jour. Mamm.*, vol. 37, no. 2, p. 300.

1956–7. Le caribou de la Gaspésie. *Nat. Canadien*, vol. 83, pp. 225–34, 262–74; vol. 84, pp. 5–27.

MOODY, PAUL A.
1941. Identification of mice in genus *Peromyscus* by a red blood cell agglutination test. *Jour. Mamm.*, vol. 22, no. 1, pp. 40–7.

MOORE, JOSEPH C.
1949. Notes on the shrew, *Sorex cinereus*, in the southern Appalachians. *Ecology*, vol. 30, no. 2, pp. 234–7.
1953. Distribution of marine mammals to Florida waters. *Am. Midl. Nat.*, vol. 49, no. 1, pp. 117–58.
1958. A beaked whale from Bahama Islands and comments on the distribution of *Mesoplodon densirostris*. *Am. Mus. Novitates*, no. 1897, 12 pp.
1960. New records of the Gulf-stream beaked whale, *Mesoplodon gervaisi*, and some taxonomic considerations. *Am. Mus. Novitates*, no. 1993, 35 pp.

MOORE, JOSEPH CURTIS, and RALPH S. PALMER
1955. More piked whales from southern North Atlantic. *Jour. Mamm.*, vol. 36, no. 3, pp. 429–33.

MOORE, JOSEPH CURTIS, and F. G. WOOD, JR.
1957. Differences between the beaked whales, *Mesoplodon mirus* and *Mesoplodon gervaisi*. *Am. Mus. Novitates*, no. 1831, 25 pp.

MOORE, WILLIAM H.
1910. A shrew new to New Brunswick. *Ottawa Nat.*, vol. 23, no. 12, pp. 217–18.
1911. Notes from New Brunswick. *Ottawa Nat.*, vol. 25, no. 1, p. 13.
1928. Land mammals of New Brunswick. *Rod and Gun and Can. Silver Fox News*, vol. 30, pp. 238–40.

MORGAN, LEWIS H.
1868. *The American beaver and his works.* Lippincott, Philadelphia, 330 pp.

MORRIS, R. F.
1943. The small forest mammals of New Brunswick and the Gaspé. *Bull. Nat. Hist. Soc. New Brunswick*, vol. 1, no. 1, pp. 27–42.
1948. The land mammals of New Brunswick. *Jour. Mamm.*, vol. 29, no. 2, pp. 165–76.

MOULTHROP, PHILIP N.
1937. An insular form of white-footed mouse from Anticosti. *Sci. Pub. Cleveland Mus. Nat. Hist.*, vol. 5, no. 3, pp. 11–13.

MUELLER, H. C., and J. T. EMLEN, JR.
1957. Homing in bats. *Science*, vol. 126, pp. 307–8.

MURIE, ADOLPH
1936. Following fox trails. *Misc. Pub., Mus. Zool., Univ. Mich.*, no. 32, 45 pp.

MURIE, OLAUS J.
1951. *The elk of North America.* Stackpole Co., Harrisburg, Pa., and Wildlife Mgt. Inst. Washington, D.C., 376 pp.

MURPHY, R. C., and J. T. NICHOLS
1913. Long Island fauna and flora: I, The bats. *Sci. Bull.*, Brooklyn Inst. Arts and Sci., vol. 2, no. 1, pp. 1–15.

MURRAY, J., and J. HJORT
1912. *The depths of the ocean.* Macmillan, London, 821 pp.

MYERS, BETTY JUNE
1956. The rearing of a grey seal in captivity. *Can. Field-Nat.*, vol. 69, no. 4, pp. 151–3.

MYERS, RICHARD F.
1960. Lasiurus from Missouri Caves. *Jour. Mamm.*, vol. 41, no. 1, pp. 114–17.

NEEDLER, A. W. H.
1931. Blackfish (*Globiocephalus*) stranded on the south coast of Prince Edward Island. *Can. Field-Nat.*, vol. 45, no. 7, pp. 157–8.

NELSON, BERNARD A.
1945. The spring molt of the northern red squirrel in Minnesota. *Jour. Mamm.*, vol. 26, no. 4, pp. 397–400.

NELSON, E. W.

1909. The rabbits of North America. *N. Am. Fauna*, no. 29, 314 pp.

NEWSOM, WILLIAM MONYPENY

1937a. Winter notes on the moose. *Jour. Mamm.*, vol. 18, no. 3, pp. 347–9.

1937b. Mammals on Anticosti Island. *Jour. Mamm.*, vol. 18, no. 4, pp. 435–42.

NICHOLSON, A. J.

1941. The homes and social habits of the wood-mouse (*Peromyscus leucopus noveboracensis*) in southern Michigan. *Am. Midl. Nat.*, vol. 25, no. 1, pp. 196–223.

NORMAN, J. R., and F. C. FRASER

1937. *Giant fishes, whales and dolphins.* Adlard and Son, London (1938. W. W. Norton and Co., New York), 361 pp.

NORRIS, K. S., J. H. PRESCOTT, P. V. ASA-DORIAN and P. PERKINS

1961. An experimental demonstration of echo-location behavior in the porpoise, *Tursiops truncatus* (Montagu). *Biol. Bull.*, vol. 120, pp. 163–76.

NORTON, A. H.

1930a. The mammals of Portland, Maine, and vicinity. *Proc. Portland Soc. Nat. Hist.*, vol. 4, pp. 1–15.

1930b. A red bat at sea. *Jour. Mamm.*, vol. 11, no. 2, pp. 225–6.

NOVA SCOTIA

1932–48. *Ann. Reports, Dept. Lands and Forests,* for the years 1931–47.

NOVICK, A.

1955. Laryngeal muscles of the bat and production of ultrasonic sounds. *Am. Jour. Physiol.*, vol. 183, p. 648.

1957. Orientation in paleotropical bats, I. *Microchiroptera.* Abstract in *Federation Proc.*, vol. 16, pp. 95–6.

OLDS, J. M.

1950. Notes on the hood seal (*Cystophora cristata*). *Jour. Mamm.*, vol. 31, no. 4, pp. 450–2.

OLSON, SIGURD F.

1932. Fish-eating deer. *Jour. Mamm.*, vol. 13, no. 1, pp. 80–1.

1938. A study of predatory relationship with particular reference to the wolf. *Sci. Monthly*, vol. 4, pp. 323–6.

OMAND, D. N.

1950. The bounty system in Ontario. *Jour. Wildlife Mgt.*, vol. 14, no. 4, pp. 425–34.

OSGOOD, WILFRED H.

1907. Some unrecognized and misapplied names of American mammals. *Proc. Biol. Soc. Washington*, vol. 20, pp. 43–52.

1909. Revision of the mice of the American genus *Peromyscus. N. Am. Fauna*, no. 28, 285 pp.

PACKARD, ALPHEUS SPRING, JR.

1866. List of vertebrates observed at Okak, Labrador, by Rev. Samuel Weiz, with annotations by A. S. Packard, Jr., M.D. *Proc. Boston Soc. Nat. Hist.*, vol. 10, pp. 264–77.

PALMER, RALPH S.

1954. *The mammal guide. Mammals of North America north of Mexico.* Doubleday & Co., N.Y., 384 pp.

PANUSKA, JOSEPH A., and NELSON J. WADE

1956. The burrow of *Tamias striatus. Jour. Mamm.*, vol. 37, no. 1, pp. 23–31.

1957. Field observations on *Tamias striatus* in Wisconsin. *Jour. Mamm.*, vol. 38, no. 2, pp. 192–6.

PAYNE, F. F.

1887. Mammals and birds of Prince of Wales Sound. *Proc. Can. Inst.*, vol. 22, no. 148, pp. 111–123.

PEARCE, JOHN

1937. A captive New York weasel. *Jour. Mamm.*, vol. 18, no. 4, pp. 483–8.

PEARSON, OLIVER P.

1942. On the cause and nature of a poisonous action produced by the bite of a shrew (*Blarina brevicauda*). *Jour. Mamm.*, vol. 23, no. 2, pp. 159–66.

1944. Reproduction in the shrew (*Blarina brevicauda* Say). *Am. Jour. Anat.*, vol. 75, no. 1, pp. 39–93.

1945. Longevity of the short-tailed shrew. *Am. Midl. Nat.*, vol. 34, no. 2, pp. 531–46.

PEDERSON, T., and J. T. RUUD

1946. A bibliography of whales and whaling. *Hvalrådets Skrifter*, no. 30, pp. 5–32.

PETERSON, RANDOLPH L.

1947. Further observations on swimming and diving of meadow voles. *Jour. Mamm.*, vol. 28, no. 3, pp. 297–8.

1950. A new subspecies of moose from North America. *Occas. Papers Roy. Ont. Mus. Zool.*, no. 9, 7 pp.

1952. A review of the living representatives of the genus *Alces*. *Contrib. Roy. Ont. Mus. Zool. and Paleo.*, no. 34, 30 pp.

1953a. Studies of the food habits and the habitat of moose in Ontario. *Contrib. Roy. Ont. Mus. Zool. and Paleo.*, no. 36, 49 pp.

1953b. Notes on the eastern distribution of *Eutamias minimus*. *Contrib. Roy. Ont. Mus. Zool. and Paleo.*, no. 37, 4 pp.

1955. *North American moose.* Univ. Toronto Press, 280 pp.

1956a. *Phenacomys* eaten by speckled trout. *Jour. Mamm.*, vol. 37, no. 1, p. 121.

1956b. Ontario's big game. The deer family. *Roy. Ont. Mus. Zool. and Paleo.*, 16 pp.

1957. Changes in the mammalian fauna of Ontario. *Changes in the fauna of Ontario. Contrib. Roy. Ont. Mus., Div. Zool. and Paleo.*, pp. 43–58.

1962. Notes on the distribution of *Microtus chrotorrhinus*. *Jour. Mamm.*, vol. 43, no. 3, p. 420.

PETERSON, RANDOLPH L., and STUART C. DOWNING

1952. Notes on the bobcats (*Lynx rufus*) of eastern North America with the description of a new race. *Contrib. Roy. Ont. Mus. Zool. and Paleo.*, no. 33, 23 pp.

1956. Distribution records of the opossum in Ontario. *Jour. Mamm.*, vol. 37, no. 3, pp. 431–5.

PETERSON, RANDOLPH L., and J. K. REYNOLDS

1954. Taxonomic status of the European hare in Ontario. *Contrib. Roy. Ont. Mus. Zool. and Paleo.*, no. 38, 7 pp.

PETERSON, R. L., R. O. STANDFIELD, E. H. MCEWAN, and A. C. BROOKS

1953. Early records of the red and the gray fox in Ontario. *Jour. Mamm.*, vol. 34, no. 1, pp. 126–7.

PETERSON, RICHARD S., and ADAM SYMANSKY

1963. First record of the Gaspé shrew from New Brunswick. *Jour. Mamm.*, vol. 44, no. 2, pp. 278–9.

PIERCE, G. W., and D. R. GRIFFIN

1938. Experimental determination of supersonic notes emitted by bats. *Jour. Mamm.*, vol. 19, no. 4, pp. 454–5.

PIERS, H.

1923. Accidental occurrence of the pygmy sperm whale (*Kogia breviceps*) on the coast of Nova Scotia: an extension of its known range. *Proc. and Trans. Nova Scotia Inst. Sci.*, vol. 15, pp. 95–114.

PIMLOTT, DOUGLAS H.

1953. Newfoundland moose. *Trans. 18th N. Am. Wildlife Conf.*, pp. 563–79.

1959. Reproduction and productivity of Newfoundland moose. *Jour. Wildlife Mgt.*, vol. 23, no. 4, pp. 381–401.

1961. The ecology and management of moose in North America. *La Terre et la Vie*, no. 2, pp. 246–65.

PIMLOTT, D. H., and W. J. CARBERRY
1958. North American moose transplantations and handling techniques. *Jour. Wildlife Mgt.*, vol. 22, no. 1, pp. 51–62.

PIRLOT, P.
1962. Mammifères de la Province de Québec. *Nat. Canadien*, vol. 89, no. 4, pp. 129–47.

PO-CHEDLEY, DONALD S., and ALBERT R. SHADLE
1955. Pelage of the porcupine, *Erethizon dorsatum dorsatum. Jour. Mamm.*, vol. 36, no. 1, pp. 84–95.

POCOCK, R. I.
1935. The races of *Canis lupus. Proc. Zool. Soc. London*, pt. 3, pp. 647–86.

POLDERBOER, EMMET B.
1942. Habits of the least weasel (*Mustela rixosa*) in northeastern Iowa. *Jour. Mamm.*, vol. 23, no. 2, pp. 145–7.
1948. Late fall sexual activity in an Iowa least weasel. *Jour. Mamm.*, vol. 29, no. 3, p. 296.

POLDERBOER, EMMET B., LEE W. KUHN, and GEORGE O. HENDRICKSON
1941. Winter and spring habits of weasels in central Iowa. *Jour. Wildlife Mgt.*, vol. 5, no. 1, pp. 115–19.

POLLACK, E. MICHAEL, and WILLIAM G. SHELDON
1951. The bobcat in Massachusetts, including analyses of food habits of bobcats from other northeastern states, principally New Hampshire. *Mass. Div. Fish and Game*, 24 pp.

POMERLEAU, RENÉ
1950. Au sommet de l'Ungava. *Revue de l'Université Laval*, vol. 4, no. 9, pp. 775–91.

POOLE, E. L.
1932. Breeding of the hoary bat in Pennsylvania. *Jour. Mamm.*, vol. 13, no. 4, p. 365.

PORSILD, A. E.
1944. Notes from a Labrador peat bog. *Can. Field-Nat.*, vol. 58, no. 1, pp. 4–6.

PORSILD, MORTON P.
1922. Scattered observations on narwhals. *Jour Mamm.*, vol. 3, no. 1, pp. 8–13.

PREBLE, EDWARD A.
1899. Revision of the jumping mice of the genus *Zapus. N. Am. Fauna*, no. 15, 42 pp.
1902. A biological investigation of the Hudson Bay region. *N. Am. Fauna*, no. 22, 140 pp.

PREBLE, NORMAN A.
1956. Notes on the life history of *Napaeozapus. Jour. Mamm.*, vol. 37, no. 2, pp. 196–200.

PRENTISS, D. W.
1903. Description of an extinct mink from the shell-heaps of the Maine Coast. *Proc. U.S. Natl. Mus.*, vol. 26, pp. 887–8.

PRINCE, LESLIE A.
1941. Water traps capture the pygmy shrew (*Microsorex hoyi*) in abundance. *Can. Field-Nat.*, vol. 55, no. 5, p. 72.

PROVOST, E. E., and C. M. KIRKPATRICK
1952. Observations on the hoary bat in Indiana and Illinois. *Jour. Mamm.*, vol. 33, no. 1, pp. 110–13.

QUAIFE, M. M.
1921. *Alexander Henry's travels and adventures in the years 1760–1776.* Lakeside Press, Chicago, 340 pp.

QUAY, W. B.
1955. Histology and cytochemistry of skin gland areas in the caribou, *Rangifer. Jour. Mamm.*, vol. 36, no. 2, pp. 187–201.
1959. Microscopic structure and variation in the cutaneous glands of the deer, *Odocoileus virginianus. Jour. Mamm.*, vol. 40, no. 1, pp. 114–28.

QUAY, W. B., and JEROME S. MILLER
1955. Occurrence of the red bat, *Lasiurus borealis*, in caves. *Jour. Mamm.*, vol. 36, no. 3, pp. 454–5.

QUIMBY, DON C.

1951. The life history and ecology of the jumping mouse, *Zapus hudsonius*. *Ecol. Monog.*, no. 21, pp. 61–95.

QUIMBY, DON C., and J. E. GAAB

1957. Mandibular dentition as an age indicator in Rocky Mountain elk. *Jour. Wildlife Mgt.*, vol. 21, no. 4, pp. 435–51.

QUIMBY, DON C., and DONALD E. JOHNSON

1951. Weights and measurements of Rocky Mountain elk. *Jour. Wildlife Mgt.*, vol. 15, no. 1, pp. 57–62.

RAND, A. L.

1933. Notes on the mammals of the interior of western Nova Scotia. *Can. Field-Nat.*, vol. 47, no. 3, pp. 41–50.

1943. History of the raccoon (*Procyon lotor* L.) in Nova Scotia. *Can. Field-Nat.*, vol. 57, nos. 4 and 5, p. 95.

1944a. Canadian forms of the meadow mouse (*Microtus pennsylvanicus*). *Can. Field-Nat.*, vol. 57, nos. 7 and 8, pp. 115–23.

1944b. The recent status of Nova Scotia fur bearers. *Can. Field-Nat.*, vol. 58, no. 3, pp. 85–96.

1944c. The status of the fisher, *Martes pennanti* (Erxleben), in Canada. *Can. Field-Nat.*, vol. 58, no. 3, pp. 77–81.

1945. Mammals of the Ottawa district. *Can. Field-Nat.*, vol. 59, no. 4, pp. 111–32.

RAVEN, HENRY C.

1937. Notes on the taxonomy and osteology of two species of *Mesoplodon* (*M. europaeus* Gervais, *M. mirus* True). *Am. Mus. Novitates*, no. 905, 30 pp.

1942. On the structure of *Mesoplodon densirostris*, a rare beaked whale. *Bull. Am. Mus. Nat. Hist.*, vol. 80, no. 2, pp. 23–50.

RAVEN, HENRY C., and W. K. GREGORY

1933. The spermaceti organ and nasal passages of the sperm whale. *Am. Mus. Novitates*, no. 677, 18 pp.

REEKS, HENRY

1870. Notes on the zoology of Newfoundland. *The Zoologist*, orig. vol. 28, 2nd ser., vol. 5, pp. 2033–49.

1871. Notes on the zoology of Newfoundland. *The Zoologist*, orig. vol. 29, 2nd ser., vol. 6, pp. 2340–557.

REYNOLDS, J. K.

1942. Notes on homing and hibernation in *Eptesicus fuscus*. *Can. Field-Nat.*, vol. 55, no. 9, p. 132.

1955. Distribution and populations of the European hare in southern Ontario. *Can. Field-Nat.*, vol. 69, no. 1, pp. 14–20.

RHOADS, S. N.

1898. Contributions to a revision of the North American beavers, otters and fishers. *Trans. Am. Philos. Soc.*, vol. 19, pp. 417–39.

1902. Synopsis of the American martens. *Proc. Acad. Nat. Sci.* Philadelphia, vol. 54, pp. 443–60.

RICHARDS, STEPHEN H., and RUTH L. HINE

1953. Wisconsin fox populations. *Wis. Cons. Dept., Tech. Wildlife Bull.*, no. 6, 78 pp.

RIIS, PAUL B.

1938. Woodland caribou and time. *Parks and Recreation*, part 1, vol. 21, no. 10, pp. 529–35; part 2, vol. 21, no. 11, pp. 594–600; part 3, vol. 21, no. 12, pp. 639–45; part 4, vol. 22, no. 1, pp. 23–30.

ROBBINS, M.

1959. *An archaic village in Middleboro, Massachusetts*. Cohannet Chapter, Mass. Archaeol. Soc., 84 pp.

ROLLINS, CLAIR T.

1945. Habits, foods and parasites of the bobcat in Minnesota. *Jour. Wildlife Mgt.*, vol. 9, no. 2, pp. 131–45.

RUST, CHARLES CHAPIN

1962. Temperature as a modifying factor in the spring pelage change of short-tailed weasels. *Jour. Mamm.*, vol. 43, no. 3, pp. 323–8.

RYSGAARD, G. N.

1942. A study of the cave bats of Minnesota with especial reference to the large brown bat *Eptesicus fuscus fuscus* (Beauvois). *Am. Midl. Nat.*, vol. 28, no. 1, pp. 245–67.

SAINT-CYR, DOMINIQUE NAPOLEON

1887. Report of a voyage to the Canadian Labrador; also catalogue of plants and birds. Legislative Assembly, *Sessional Paper*, no. 17B, 217 pp.

SANDERSON, GLEN C.

1950. Methods of measuring productivity in raccoons. *Jour. Wildlife Mgt.*, vol. 14, no. 4, pp. 389–402.

1951a. Breeding habits and a history of the Missouri raccoon population from 1941 to 1948. *Trans. 16th N. Am. Wildlife Conf.*, pp. 445–61.

1951b. The status of the raccoon in Iowa for the past twenty years as revealed by fur reports. *Iowa Acad. Sci.*, vol. 58, pp. 527–31.

1961. Techniques for determining age of raccoons. *Ill. Nat. Hist. Surv., Biol. Notes*, no. 45, 16 pp.

SAUNDERS, W. E.

1902. Birds of Sable Island, Nova Scotia. *Ottawa Nat.*, vol. 16, no. 1, pp. 15–31.

1920. A new mammal for Canada. *Can. Field-Nat.*, vol. 34, no. 1, p. 17.

1927. *Phenacomys ungava* in Ontario. *Jour. Mamm.*, vol. 8, no. 4, pp. 305–7.

1930. Bats in migration. *Jour. Mamm.*, vol. 11, no. 2, p. 225.

1932. Notes on the mammals of Ontario. *Trans. Roy. Can. Inst.*, vol. 18, pt. 2, pp. 271–309.

SCHEFFER, VICTOR B.

1958. *Seals, sea lions and walruses. A review of the Pinnipedia.* Stanford Univ. Press, Stanford, Cal., 179 pp.

SCHEVILL, WILLIAM E.

1956. *Lagenorhynchus acutus* off Cape Cod. *Jour. Mamm.*, vol. 37, no. 1, pp. 128–9.

1961. *Cetacea. The Encyclopedia of the Biological Sciences.* Reinhold, New York, pp. 205–9.

SCHEVILL, WILLIAM E., and RICHARD H. BACKUS

1960. Daily patrol of a *Megaptera. Jour. Mamm.*, vol. 41, no. 2, pp. 279–81.

SCHEVILL, WILLIAM E., and BARBARA LAWRENCE

1949. Underwater listening to the white porpoise (*Delphinapterus leucas*). *Science*, vol. 109, pp. 143–4.

1953. High-frequency auditory response of a bottlenosed porpoise, *Tursiops truncatus* (Montagu). *Jour. Acoust. Soc. Am.*, vol. 25, pp. 1016–17.

1956. Food-finding by a captive porpoise (*Tursiops truncatus*). *Breviora*, Mus. Comp. Zool., Harvard Univ., no. 53, 15 pp.

SCHEVILL, WILLIAM E., and WILLIAM A. WATKINS

1962. Whale and porpoise voices. A phonograph record. Booklet (24 pp.) accompanying phonograph disc. Woods Hole Oceanographic Inst., Woods Hole, Mass.

SCHWARZ, ERNST

1945. On North American house mice. *Jour. Mamm.*, vol. 26, no. 3, pp. 315–16.

SCHWARZ, ERNST, and HENRIETTA K. SCHWARZ

1943. The wild and commensal stocks of the house mouse, *Mus musculus* Linnaeus. *Jour. Mamm.*, vol. 24, no. 1, pp. 59–72.

SCOTT, THOMAS G.

1947. Comparative analysis of red fox feeding on two central Iowa areas. *Iowa Exp. Sta. Res. Bull.*, no. 353, pp. 425–87.

1955a. Dietary patterns of red and gray foxes. *Ecology*, vol. 36, no. 2, pp. 366–7.

1955b. An evaluation of the red fox. *Ill. Nat. Hist. Surv., Biol. Notes*, no. 35, 16 pp.

SCOTT, THOMAS G., and WILLARD D. KLIMSTRA
1955. Red foxes and a declining prey population. *South Ill. Univ., Monog. Ser.*, no. 1, 123 pp.

SEAGEARS, CLAYTON B.
1944. The fox in New York. *Ed. Bull.*, N.Y. Cons. Dept., 85 pp.

SELWYN, A. H. C.
1883. Summary reports of the operations of the geological corps. *Geol. Surv. of Can., Rept. of Progress*, 1880–2, pp. 1–29.

SERGEANT, D. E.
1958. Dolphins in Newfoundland waters. *Can. Field-Nat.*, vol. 72, no. 4, pp. 156–9.
1962a. The biology of the pilot or pothead whale *Globicephala melaena* (Traill) in Newfoundland waters. *Bull. Fish. Res. Bd. Can.*, no. 132, 84 pp.
1962b. On the external characters of the blackfish or pilot whales (genus *Globicephala*). *Jour. Mamm.*, vol. 43, no. 3, pp. 395–413.
1963. Minke whales, *Balaenoptera acutorostrata* Lacepede, of the western North Atlantic. *Jour. Fish. Res. Bd. Can.*, vol. 20, no. 6, pp. 1489–504.

SERGEANT, D. E., and H. D. FISHER
1957. The smaller cetacea of eastern Canadian waters. *Jour. Fish. Res. Bd. Can.*, vol. 14, no. 1, pp. 83–115.
1960. Harp seal populations in the western North Atlantic from 1950 to 1960. *Fish. Res. Bd. Can., Circ.*, no. 5, 58 pp. (mimeographed).

SETON, ERNEST THOMPSON
1921. The sea mink, *Mustela macrodon* (Prentiss). *Jour. Mamm.*, vol. 2, no. 3, p. 168.
1925–28. *Lives of game animals.* Doubleday, Doran & Co., Garden City, N.Y. 4 vols.

SEVERAID, JOYE HAROLD
1942. *The snowshoe hare: its life history and artificial propagation.* Maine Dept. Inland Fisheries and Game, Augusta, Maine, 95 pp.

1945. Breeding potential and artificial propagation of the snowshoe hare. *Jour. Wildlife Mgt.*, vol. 9, no. 4, pp. 290–5.

SEVERINGHAUS, C. W.
1949. Tooth development and wear as criteria of age in whitetailed deer. *Jour. Wildlife Mgt.*, vol. 13, no. 2, pp. 195–216.

SHADLE, ALBERT R.
1950. Feeding, care, and handling captive porcupines (*Erethizon*). *Jour. Mamm.*, vol. 31, no. 4, pp. 411–16.
1951. Laboratory copulations and gestations of porcupine, *Erethizon dorsatum.* *Jour. Mamm.*, vol. 32, no. 2, pp. 219–21.
1952. Sexual maturity and first recorded copulation of a 16-month male porcupine, *Erethizon dorsatum dorsatum.* *Jour. Mamm.*, vol. 33, no. 2, pp. 239–41.
1955. Removal of foreign quills by porcupines. *Jour. Mamm.*, vol. 36, no. 3, pp. 463–5.

SHADLE, ALBERT R., and WILLIAM R. PLOSS
1943. An unusual porcupine parturition and development of the young. *Jour. Mamm.*, vol. 24, no. 4, pp. 492–6.

SHADLE, ALBERT R., WILLIAM R. PLOSS, and EUGENE M. MARKS
1944. The extrusive growth and attrition of the incisor teeth of *Erethizon dorsatum.* *Anat. Rec.*, vol. 90, no. 4, pp. 337–41.

SHADLE, ALBERT R., MARILYN SMELZER, and MARGERY METS
1946. The sex reactions of porcupines (*Erethizon d. dorsatum*) before and after copulation. *Jour. Mamm.*, vol. 27, no. 2, pp. 116–21.

SHAPIRO, JACOB
1949. Ecological and life history notes on the porcupine in the Adirondacks. *Jour. Mamm.*, vol. 30, no. 3, pp. 247–57.

SHAW, WILLIAM T.

1928. The spring and summer activities of the dusky skunk in captivity with a chapter on the insect food of the dusky skunk by K. F. Chamberlain. *N.Y. State Mus. Handbook*, no. 4, 103 pp.

SHELDON, CAROLYN

1934. Studies on the life histories of *Zapus* and *Napaeozapus* in Nova Scotia. *Jour. Mamm.*, vol. 15, no. 4, pp. 290–300.

1936. The mammals of Lake Kedgemakooge and vicinity, Nova Scotia. *Jour. Mamm.*, vol. 17, no. 3, pp. 207–15.

1938a. Vermont jumping mice of the genus *Zapus. Jour. Mamm.*, vol. 19, no. 3, pp. 324–32.

1938b. Vermont jumping mice of the genus *Napaeozapus. Jour. Mamm.*, vol. 19, no. 4, pp. 444–53.

SILVER, JAMES, W. E. CROUCH, and M. C. BETTS

1942. Rat proofing buildings and premises. *U.S. Dept. Int., Fish and Wildlife Serv., Cons. Bull.*, no. 19, 26 pp.

SILVER, JAMES, and F. E. GARLOUGH

1941. Rat control. *U.S. Dept. Int., Fish and Wildlife Serv., Cons. Bull.*, no. 8, 27 pp.

SILVER, JAMES, and A. W. MOORE

1941. Mole control. *U.S. Dept. Int., Fish and Wildlife Serv., Cons. Bull.*, no. 14, 17 pp.

SIMPSON, GEORGE GAYLORD

1945. The principles of classification and a classification of mammals. *Bull. Am. Mus. Nat. Hist.*, vol. 85, 350 pp.

1951. *Horses—The story of the horse family in the modern world and through sixty million years of history.* Oxford Univ. Press, New York, 247 pp.

SIVERTSEN, ERLING

1941. On the biology of the harp seal, *Phoca groenlandica* Erxl. *Hvalrådets Skrifter*, no. 26, 166 pp.

SLIJPER, E. J.

1962. *Whales.* Hutchinson & Co. (Publishers) Ltd., London, 475 pp.

SMITH, ALEXANDER H.

1901. Geologist's report of exploration survey party No. 8. *Report of the Survey and Exploration of Northern Ontario, 1900,* Toronto, pp. 198–207.

SMITH, E., and W. GOODPASTER

1958. Homing in nonmigratory bats. *Science,* vol. 127, no. 3299, p. 644.

SMITH, RONALD WARD

1939a. A new race of *Sorex arcticus* from Nova Scotia. *Jour. Mamm.*, vol. 20, no. 2, pp. 244–5.

1939b. A new geographic race of *Peromyscus leucopus* from Nova Scotia. *Proc. Biol. Soc. Washington,* vol. 52, pp. 157–8.

1940. The land mammals of Nova Scotia. *Am. Midl. Nat.*, vol. 24, no. 1, pp. 213–41.

SNEAD, EDWIN, and GEORGE O. HENDERSON

1942. Food habits of the badger in Iowa. *Jour. Mamm.*, vol. 23, no. 4, pp. 380–91.

SNELL, GEORGE D. (ed.)

1943. *Biology of the laboratory mouse.* 2nd ed., Blackiston Co., Philadelphia, 497 pp.

SNYDER, DANA P.

1954. Skull variation in the meadow vole (*Microtus p. pennsylvanicus*) in Pennsylvania. *Annals Carnegie Mus.*, vol. 33, no. 13, pp. 201–34.

1956. Survival rates, longevity, and population fluctuations in the white-footed mouse, *Peromyscus leucopus*, in southeastern Michigan. *Misc. Pub., Mus. Zool., Univ. Mich.* no. 95, 33 pp.

SNYDER, L. L.

1924. Some details on the life history and behaviour of *Napaeozapus insignis abietorum* (Preble). *Jour. Mamm.*, vol. 5, no. 4, pp. 233–7.

1929a. *Cryptotis parva*, a new shrew to the Canadian list. *Jour. Mamm.*, vol. 10, no. 1, pp. 79–80.

1929b. Records for *Phenacomys ungava* in Ontario. *Jour. Mamm.*, vol. 10, no. 4, pp. 81–2.

1929c. The mammals of the Lake Abitibi region. *Contrib. Roy. Ont. Mus. Zool.*, no. 2, pp. 7–15.

1930. A faunal investigation of King Township, York County, Ontario. II. The mammals of King Township. *Trans. Roy. Can. Inst.*, vol. 17, pt. 2, pp. 173–81. (*Contrib. Roy. Ont. Mus. Zool.*, no. 3.)

1931. A faunal investigation of Long Point and vicinity, Norfolk County, Ontario. II. The mammals of Long Point and vicinity. *Trans. Roy. Can. Inst.*, vol. 18, pt. 1, pp. 127–38.

1935. Another least weasel specimen from Ontario. *Can. Field-Nat.*, vol. 49, p. 169.

1938. A faunal investigation of western Rainy River District, Ontario. *Trans. Roy. Can. Inst.*, vol. 22, pt. 1, pp. 157–213. (*Contrib. Roy. Ont. Mus. Zool.*, no. 14.)

1941. The mammals of Prince Edward County, Ontario. A faunal investigation of Prince Edward County, Ontario. *Univ. Toronto Studies, Biol. Ser.*, no. 48, pp. 12–24. (*Contrib. Roy. Ont. Mus. Zool.*, no. 19.)

1942. Mammals of the Sault Ste. Marie region. *Trans. Roy. Can. Inst.*, vol. 24, pt. 1, pp. 105–20. (*Contrib. Roy. Ont. Mus. Zool.*, no. 21.)

SOLLBERGER, DWIGHT E.
1940. Notes on the life history of the small eastern flying squirrel. *Jour. Mamm.*, vol. 21, no. 3, pp. 282–93.

1943. Notes on the breeding habits of the eastern flying squirrel (*Glaucomys volans volans*). *Jour. Mamm.*, vol. 24, no. 2, pp. 163–73.

SOPER, J. DEWEY
1920. Notes on the mammals of Ridout, District of Sudbury, Ontario. *Can. Field-Nat.*, vol. 34, no. 4, pp. 61–9.

1921. Malformed hind foot of the common house mouse (*Mus musculus*). *Jour. Mamm.*, vol. 2, no. 4, p. 237.

1923a. A biological reconnaissance of portions of Nipissing and Timiskaming Districts, northern Ontario. *Can. Field-Nat.*, vol. 36, no. 9, pp. 175–6; vol. 37, no. 1, pp. 11–15.

1923b. The mammals of Wellington and Waterloo Counties, Ontario. *Jour. Mamm.*, vol. 4, no. 4, pp. 244–52.

1944. The mammals of southern Baffin Island, Northwest Territories, Canada. *Jour. Mamm.*, vol. 25, no. 3, pp. 221–54.

SOWLS, LYLE K.
1948. The Franklin ground squirrel, *Citellus franklinii* (Sabine), and its relationship to nesting ducks. *Jour. Mamm.*, vol. 29, no. 2, pp. 113–37.

SPENCER, DONALD A.
1950. The porcupine, its economic status and control. *U.S. Dept. Int., Fish and Wildlife Serv., Wildlife Leaflet*, no. 328, 7 pp.

SPENCER, MILES
1889. Notes on the breeding habits of certain mammals, from personal observations and enquiries from Indians. *Geol. and Nat. Hist. Surv. of Can., Ann. Report*, vol. 3, pt. 2, app. 3, pp. 76J–79J.

SPERRY, CHARLES E.
1941. Food habits of the coyote. *U.S. Dept. Int., Fish and Wildlife Serv., Wildlife Res. Bull.*, no. 4, 70 pp.

STAINS, HOWARD J.
1956. The raccoon in Kansas, natural history, management, and economic importance. *Univ. Kans., Mus. Nat. Hist. and State Biol. Surv. Kans., Misc. Pub.*, no. 10, 76 pp.

STARRETT, A., and P. STARRETT
1955. Observations on young blackfish *Globicephala*. *Jour. Mamm.*, vol. 36, no. 3, pp. 424–9.

STEARNS, W. A.
1883. Notes on the natural history of Labrador. *Proc. U.S. Natl. Mus.*, vol. 6, nos. 7–8, pp. 111–16.

STEGEMAN, LEROY C.
1930. Notes on *Synaptomys cooperi cooperi* in Washtenaw County, Michigan. *Jour. Mamm.*, vol. 11, no. 4, pp. 460–6.

1937. Notes on young skunks in captivity. *Jour. Mamm.*, vol. 18, no. 2, pp. 194–202.

1939. Some parasites and pathological conditions of the skunk (*Mephitis mephitis nigra*) in central New York. *Jour. Mamm.*, vol. 20, no. 4, pp. 493–6.

STENLUND, MILTON H.
1955. A field study of the timber wolf (*Canis lupus*) on the Superior National Forest, Minnesota. *Minn. Dept. Cons., Tech. Bull.*, no. 4, 55 pp.

STRECKER, R. L., and JOHN T. EMLEN, JR.
1953. Regulatory mechanisms in house-mouse populations: the effect of limited food supply on a confined population. *Ecology*, vol. 34, no. 2, pp. 375–85.

STRONG, WILLIAM DUNCAN
1930. Notes on mammals of the Labrador interior. *Jour. Mamm.*, vol. 11, no. 1, pp. 1–9.

STUEWER, FREDERICK W.
1942. Studies of molting and priming of fur of the eastern raccoon. *Jour. Mamm.*, vol. 23, no. 4, pp. 399–404.

1943a. Reproduction of raccoons in Michigan. *Jour. Wildlife Mgt.*, vol. 7, no. 1, pp. 60–73.

1943b. Raccoons: their habits and management in Michigan. *Ecol. Monog.*, no. 13, pp. 203–58.

SUTTON, GEORGE M., and W. J. HAMILTON, JR.
1932. The mammals of Southampton Island. *Mem. Carnegie Mus.*, Pittsburgh, vol. 12, pt. 2, sect. 1, 111 pp.

SVIHLA, ARTHUR
1930. Breeding habits and young of the red-backed mouse, *Evotomys. Papers Mich. Acad. Sci., Arts and Letters*, vol. 11, pp. 485–90.

1932. A comparative life history study of the mice of the genus *Peromyscus. Misc. Pub., Mus. Zool., Univ. Mich.*, no. 24, 39 pp.

1935. Development and growth of the prairie deer-mouse, *Peromyscus maniculatus bairdii. Jour. Mamm.*, vol. 16, no. 2, pp. 109–15.

SWANSON, GUSTAV, and P. O. FRYKLUND
1935. The least weasel in Minnesota and its fluctuation in numbers. *Am. Midl. Nat.*, vol. 16, no. 1, pp. 120–6.

TAVERNER, P. A.
1914. Geological survey museum work on Point Pelee, Ontario. *Ottawa Nat.*, vol. 28, no. 8, pp. 97–105.

TAVOLGA, MARGARET C., and F. S. ESSAPIAN
1957. The behaviour of the bottle-nosed dolphin (*Tursiops truncatus*): Mating, pregnancy, parturition and mother-infant behaviour. *Zoologica*, vol. 42, no. 2, pp. 11–32.

TAYLOR, WALTER P. (ed.)
1956. *The deer of North America. The white-tailed, mule and black-tailed deer*, genus Odocoileus, *their history and management.* Stackpole Co. and Wildlife Mgt. Inst., 668 pp.

TENER, J. S.
1955. Three observations of predators attacking prey. *Can. Field-Nat.*, vol. 68, no. 4, pp. 181–2.

THOMPSON, DANIEL Q.
1952. Travel, range, and food habits of timber wolves in Wisconsin. *Jour. Mamm.*, vol. 33, no. 4, pp. 429–42.

TODD, JOHN B.
1927. Winter food of cottontail rabbits. *Jour. Mamm.*, vol. 8, no. 3, pp. 222–8.

TOMILIN, A. G.
1957. *Kitoobraznye* [*Cetacea*]. *Zveri S.S.S.R. i prilezhashchikhstran*, tom. 9, Moskva Akademiia nauk S.S.S.R., 757 pp. (In Russian.)

TONER, G. C.
1956a. House cat predation on small mammals. *Jour. Mamm.*, vol. 37, no. 1, p. 119.
1956b. Some numbers for big game in Ontario. *Jour. Mamm.*, vol. 37, no. 1, pp. 119–20.

TOWNSEND, CHARLES WENDELL
1911. *Captain Cartwright and his Labrador Journal*. Dana Estes and Co., Boston, 385 pp.

TRODD, L. L.
1962. Quadruplet fetuses in a white-tailed deer from Espanola, Ontario. *Jour. Mamm.*, vol. 43, no. 3, p. 414.

TRUE, F. W.
1889. Contributions to the natural history of the Cetaceans, a review of the family *Delphinidae*. *U.S. Natl. Mus. Bull.*, no. 36, 191 pp.
1890. Observations on the life history of the bottlenose porpoise. *Proc. U.S. Natl. Mus.*, vol. 13, pp. 197–203.
1904. The whalebone whales of the western North Atlantic compared with those occurring in European waters, with some observations on the species of the North Pacific. *Smithsonian Contrib. Knowl.*, vol. 33, 332 pp.
1910. An account of the beaked whales of the family *Ziphiidae* in the collection of the United States National Museum, with remarks on some specimens in other American museums. *U.S. Natl. Mus., Bull.*, no. 73, 89 pp.

1913. Description of *Mesoplodon mirus*, a beaked whale recently discovered on the coast of North Carolina. *Proc. U.S. Natl. Mus.* vol. 45, pp. 651–7.

TUFTS, R. W.
1939. Newfoundland caribou liberated in Nova Scotia. *Can. Field-Nat.*, vol. 53, no. 8, p. 123.

TURNER, LUCIEN M.
1885. List of the birds of Labrador, including Ungava, East Main, Moose, and Gulf districts of the Hudson Bay Company, together with the island of Anticosti. *Proc. U.S. Natl. Mus.*, vol. 8, pp. 233–54.

ULMER, FREDERICK A., JR.
1941a. *Mesoplodon mirus* in New Jersey, with additional notes on the New Jersey *M. densirostris* and a list and key to the Ziphoid whales of the Atlantic coast of North America. *Proc. Acad. Nat. Sci.*, vol. 93, pp. 107–22.
1941b. *Kogia breviceps* in South Carolina and New Jersey. *Jour. Mamm.*, vol. 22, no. 4, pp. 450–1.

VAN DEUSEN, HOBART M.
1961. Yellow bat collected over South Atlantic. *Jour. Mamm.*, vol. 42, no. 4, pp. 530–1.

VERRILL, A. E.
1865. Notes on the natural history of Anticosti. *Proc. Boston Soc. Nat. Hist.*, vol. 9, pp. 132–6.

VIBE, CHRISTIAN
1950. The marine mammals and the marine fauna in the Thule District (Northwest Greenland) with observations on ice conditions in 1939–41. *Meddelelser om Grønland*, no. 6, pp. 21–53.

VLADYKOV, VADIM D.

1944. Chasse, biologie et valeur economique du marsouin blanc ou béluga (*Delphinapterus leucas*) du fleuve et du golfe Saint-Laurent. Prov. Que. Dépt. des Pêcheries, *Études sur les Mamm. Aquatiques*, no. 3, 194 pp.

1946. Nourriture du marsouin blanc ou béluga (*Delphinapterus leucas*) du fleuve Saint-Laurent. Prov. Que. Dépt. des Pêcheries, *Études sur les Mamm. Aquatiques*, no. 4, 155 pp.

WARBURTON, FRED

1950. Notes on the vertebrates, except fishes, of the Sault Ste Marie region of Ontario. *Can. Field-Nat.*, vol. 64, no. 6, pp. 192–200.

WARREN, EDWARD R.

1927. *The beaver: its work and its ways.* Monog. Am. Soc. Mamm., no. 2. Williams and Wilkins Co., Baltimore, 177 pp.

WATERS, JOSEPH H., and CLAYTON E. RAY

1961. Former range of the sea mink. *Jour. Mamm.*, vol. 42, no. 3, pp. 280–3.

WEAVER, RICHARD LEE

1940. Notes on a collection of mammals from the southern coast of the Labrador Peninsula. *Jour. Mamm.*, vol. 21, no. 4, pp. 417–22.

WETZEL, R. M.

1955. Speciation and dispersal of the southern bog lemming, *Synaptomys cooperi* (Baird). *Jour. Mamm.*, vol. 36, no. 1, pp. 1–20.

WHEELER, E. P. 2nd.

1930. Journeys about Nain. Winter hunting with the Labrador Eskimo. *Geog. Rev.*, New York, vol. 20, no. 3, pp. 454–68.

1953. Notes on Pinnipedia. *Jour. Mamm.*, vol. 34, no. 2, pp. 253–5.

WHITAKER, W. L.

1940. Some effects of artificial illumination on reproduction in the white-footed mouse, *Peromyscus leucopus noveboracensis. Jour. Exp. Zool.*, vol. 83, pp. 33–60.

WHITEMAN, ELDON E.

1940. Habits and pelage changes in captive coyotes. *Jour. Mamm.*, vol. 21, no. 4, pp. 435–8.

WHITLOCK, S. C.

1950. The black bear as a predator of man. *Jour. Mamm.*, vol. 31, no. 2, pp. 135–8.

WHITNEY, LEON F., and ACIL B. UNDERWOOD

1952. *The raccoon.* Practical Sci. Pub. Co., Orange, Conn., 177 pp.

WILLIAMS, M. Y.

1920. Notes on the fauna of the Moose River and the Mattagami and Abitibi tributaries. *Can. Field-Nat.*, vol. 34, no. 7, pp. 121–6.

1921. Notes on the fauna of Lower Pagwachuan, Lower Kenogami and Lower Albany Rivers of Ontario. *Can. Field-Nat.*, vol. 35, no. 5, pp. 94–8.

1942. Notes on the fauna of Bruce Peninsula, Manitoulin and adjacent islands. *Can. Field-Nat.*, vol. 56, no. 4, pp. 60–2; no. 5, pp. 70–81; no. 6, pp. 92–3.

WILLIAMSON, GORDON R.

1961. Winter sighting of a humpback suckling its calf on the Grand Bank of Newfoundland. *Norsk Hvalf.*, vol. 5, no. 8, pp. 335–41.

WIMSATT, W. A.

1942. Survival of spermatozoa in the female reproductive tract of the bat. *Anat. Rec.*, vol. 83, pp. 299–307.

1944a. Further studies on the survival of spermatozoa in the female reproductive tract of the bat. *Anat. Rec.*, vol. 88, pp. 193–204.

1944b. Growth in the ovarian follicle and ovulation in *Myotis lucifugus lucifugus*. *Am. Jour. Anat.*, vol. 74, pp. 129–73.

1945. Notes on breeding behavior, pregnancy, and parturition in some vespertilionid bats of the eastern United States. *Jour. Mamm.*, vol. 26, no. 1, pp. 23–33.

WIMSATT, W. A., and F. C. KALLEN

1952. Anatomy and histophysiology of the penis of a vespertilionid bat, *Myotis lucifugus lucifugus* with particular reference to its vascular organization. *Jour. Morphol.*, vol. 90, pp. 415–65.

WORTHINGTON, L. V., and W. E. SCHEVILL

1957. Underwater sounds from sperm whales. *Nature*, vol. 180, p. 291.

WRAGG, L. E.

1954. The effect of D.D.T. and oil on muskrats *Can. Field-Nat.*, vol. 68, no. 1, pp. 11–13.

WRIGHT, A. H., and S. E. R. SIMPSON

1920. The vertebrates of the Otter Lake region, Dorset, Ontario. *Can. Field-Nat.*, vol. 34, no. 8, pp. 141–5; no. 9, pp. 161–8.

WRIGHT, BRUCE S.

1948. Survival of the northeastern panther (*Felis concolor*) in New Brunswick. *Jour. Mamm.*, vol. 29, no. 3, pp. 235–46.

1951. A walrus in the Bay of Fundy, the first record. *Can. Field-Nat.*, vol. 65, no. 2, pp. 61–4.

1953. Further notes on the panther in the northeast. *Can. Field-Nat.*, vol. 67, no. 1, pp. 12–28.

1959. *The ghost of North America. The story of the eastern panther.* Vantage Press, New York, 140 pp.

1961. The latest specimen of the eastern puma. *Jour. Mamm.*, vol. 42, no. 2, pp. 278–9.

1962. Notes on North Atlantic whales. *Can. Field-Nat.*, vol. 76, no. 1, pp. 62–5.

WRIGHT, P. L.

1942a. Delayed implantation in the long-tailed weasel (*Mustela frenata*), the short-tailed weasel (*Mustela cicognani*), and the marten (*Martes americana*). *Anat. Rec.*, vol. 83, no. 3, pp. 341–53.

1942b. A correlation between the spring molt and spring changes in the sexual cycle in the weasel. *Jour. Exp. Zool.*, vol. 91, no. 1, pp. 103–10.

1947. The sexual cycle of the male long-tailed weasel (*Mustela frenata*). *Jour. Mamm.*, vol. 28, no. 4, pp. 343–52.

1948a. Breeding habits of captive long-tailed weasels (*Mustela frenata*). *Am. Midl. Nat.*, vol. 39, no. 2, pp. 338–44.

1948b. Preimplantation stages in the long-tailed weasel (*Mustela frenata*). *Anat. Rec.*, vol. 100, no. 4, pp. 593–608.

1950. Development of the baculum of the long-tailed weasel. *Proc. Soc. Exp. Biol. and Med.*, vol. 75, pp. 820–2.

WRIGHT, PHILIP L., and ROBERT RAUSCH

1955. Reproduction in the wolverine, *Gulo gulo. Jour. Mamm.*, vol. 36, no. 3, pp. 346–55.

WRIGHT, WILLIAM H.

1910. *The black bear.* Scribner's, New York, 127 pp.

YERGER, RALPH W.

1955. Life history notes on the eastern chipmunk, *Tamias striatus lysteri* (Richardson), in central New York. *Am. Midl. Nat.*, vol. 53, no. 2, pp. 312–23.

YOUNG, STANLEY P.

1941a. Hints on bobcat trapping. *U.S. Dept. Int., Fish and Wildlife Serv., Circ.*, no. 1, 6 pp.

1941b. Hints on wolf and coyote trapping. *U.S. Dept. Int., Fish and Wildlife Serv., Circ.*, no. 2, 8 pp.

1946. *The wolf in North American history.* The Caxton Printers, Caldwell, Idaho, 149 pp.

1958. *The bobcat of North America.* Wildlife Mgt. Inst., Washington, D.C., 193 pp.

YOUNG, STANLEY P., and EDWARD A. GOLDMAN

1944. *The wolves of North America.* Wildlife Mgt. Inst., Washington, D.C., 636 pp.

1946. *The puma, mysterious American cat.* Wildlife Mgt. Inst., Washington, D.C., 358 pp.

YOUNG, STANLEY P., and HARTLEY H. T. JACKSON

1951. *The clever coyote.* Stackpole Co. and Wildlife Mgt. Inst., Washington, D.C., 411 pp.

YOUNGMAN, PHILIP M.

1962. The spread of the European hare to the Ottawa region of Ontario. *Can. Field-Nat.,* vol. 76, no. 4, p. 223.

YOURANS, M.

1930. Un chéiroptère nouveau à Québec, *Myotis quebecensis. Nat. Canadien,* vol. 57, no. 3, pp. 65–6.

ZEUNER, FREDRICK E.

1963. *A history of domesticated animals.* Hutchinson & Co. (Publishers) Ltd., London, 560 pp.

LIST OF PUBLICATIONS AND SERIALS ABBREVIATED IN THE BIBLIOGRAPHY

Alaska Cooperative Wildlife Research Unit, Special Report. College, Alaska.

American Committee for International Wildlife Protection, Special Publication. New York, N.Y.

American Journal of Anatomy. Baltimore, Md.

American Journal of Physiology. Boston, Mass.

American Journal of Science. New Haven, Conn.

American Midland Naturalist. Notre Dame, Ind.

American Museum Novitates. New York, N.Y.

American Naturalist. Boston, Mass.

Anatomical Record. Philadelphia, Pa.

Animal Behaviour. London, Eng.

Annales, Association Canadienne-Française pour l'Avancement des Sciences. Montreal, Que.

Annals of Natural History. London, Eng.

Annals of the Carnegie Museum. Pittsburgh, Pa.

Annual Report, National Museum of Canada. Ottawa, Ont.

——, *Nova Scotia Department of Lands and Forests.* Halifax, N.S.

——, *Provancher Society of Natural History of Canada.* Quebec, Que.

——, *Province of Quebec Association for the Protection of Fish and Game Inc.* Quebec, Que.

——, *Smithsonian Institution.* Washington, D.C.

Arctic: Journal of the Arctic Institute of North America. Montreal, Que.

Australian Journal of Marine and Freshwater Research. Melbourne, Australia.

Bi-Monthly Progress Report. Forest Biology Division, Research Branch, Department of Agriculture. Ottawa, Ont.

Biological Bulletin. Woods Hole, Mass.

Breviora. Museum of Comparative Zoology, Harvard University. Cambridge, Mass.

Bulletin, American Museum of Natural History. New York, N.Y.

——, *Boston Society of Natural History.* Boston, Mass.

——, *British Museum (Natural History).* London, Eng.

——, *Fisheries Research Board of Canada.* Ottawa, Ont.

——, *Illinois Natural History Survey.* Urbana, Ill.

——, *Museum of Comparative Zoology.* Harvard University, Cambridge, Mass.

——, *National Museum of Canada.* Ottawa, Ont.

——, *Natural History Society of New Brunswick.* St John, N.B.

——, *New York State College of Forestry.* See *Roosevelt Wild Life Annals, Roosevelt Wild Life Bulletin.*

Canadian Field-Naturalist. Ottawa, Ont.

Canadian Journal of Research. Ottawa, Ont.

Canadian Journal of Zoology. Ottawa, Ont.

Canadian Naturalist and Geologist. Montreal, Que.

Carnegie Institution of Washington Publications. Washington, D.C.

Carnegie Magazine. Carnegie Museum, Pittsburgh, Pa.

Connecticut State Geological and Natural History Survey Bulletin. Hartford, Conn.

Contributions, Division of Zoology and Palaeontology. Royal Ontario Museum, Toronto, Ont.

——, *Laboratory of Vertebrate Biology.* University of Michigan, Ann Arbor, Mich.

——, *Royal Ontario Museum of Zoology.* Toronto, Ont.

——, *Royal Ontario Museum of Zoology and Palaeontology.* Toronto, Ont.

Deep-sea Research. Pergamon Press, London, Eng.

Discovery Reports. Cambridge, Eng.

Ecological Monographs. The Ecological Society of America, Brooklyn, N.Y.

Ecology. The Ecological Society of America, Brooklyn, N.Y.

Educational Bulletin. State of New York Conservation Department, Albany, N.Y.

Études sur les Mammifères Aquatiques. Département des Pêcheries, Quebec, Que.

Experientia. Basel, Switzerland.

Federation Proceedings. Federation of American Societies for Experimental Biology, Baltimore, Md.

Field Columbian Museum Publications, Zoological Series. Chicago, Ill.

Field Museum of Natural History, Zoological Series. Chicago, Ill.

Fisheries Research Board of Canada, Circular. Arctic Unit, Montreal, Que.

——, *General Series.* Atlantic Biological Station, St Andrews, N.B.

Forest and Stream. New York, N.Y.

Fur Trade Journal of Canada. Oshawa and Toronto, Ont.

Geographical Review. New York, N.Y.

Geological and Natural History Survey of Canada, Annual Report, New Series. Ottawa, Ont.

Geological Survey of Canada, Annual Report. Ottawa, Ont.

——, *Report of Progress.* Ottawa, Ont.

Handbook, Royal Ontario Museum of Zoology. Toronto, Ont.

Hvalrådets Skrifter. Scientific results of marine biological research. Oslo, Norway.

Illinois Natural History Survey, Biological Notes. Urbana, Ill.

Intermediate Naturalist. Toronto, Ont.

Iowa Academy of Science. Ames, Iowa.

Iowa Experimental Station Research Bulletin. Iowa State College of Agriculture and Mechanic Arts. Ames, Iowa.

Journal of Agricultural Research. Washington, D.C.

Journal of Anatomy. London, Eng.

Journal of Animal Behavior. Cambridge, Mass.

Journal of Animal Ecology. Cambridge, Eng.

Journal of Comparative Psychology. Baltimore, Md.

Journal of Experimental Zoology. Philadelphia, Pa.

Journal of Forestry. Washington, D.C.

Journal of Mammalogy. Lawrence, Kan.

Journal of Morphology. Philadelphia, Pa.

Journal of Physiology. London and Cambridge, Eng.

Journal of the Acoustical Society of America. Menasha, Wis.

Journal of the Fisheries Research Board of Canada. Ottawa, Ont.

Journal of Wildlife Management. Menasha, Wis.

Meddelelser om Grønland. Kommissionen for Videnskabelige Undersøgolser I Grønland, Copenhagen, Den.

Memoir, Cornell University Agricultural Experiment Station, New York State College of Agriculture. Ithaca, N.Y.

Memoirs, American Museum of Natural History. New York, N.Y.

——, *Boston Society of Natural History*. Boston, Mass.

——, *Carnegie Museum*. Pittsburgh, Pa.

——, *Wistar Institute of Anatomy and Biology*. Philadelphia, Pa.

Michigan Department of Conservation Game Division Publication. Lansing, Mich.

Minnesota Department of Conservation, Technical Bulletin. St Paul, Minn.

Miscellaneous Publications, Museum of Zoology, University of Michigan. Ann Arbor, Mich.

National Geographic Magazine. Washington, D.C.

National Museum of Canada, Bulletin (Biological Series). Ottawa, Ont.

——, *Natural History Papers*. Ottawa, Ont.

National Speleological Society Bulletin. Washington, D.C.

Natural History. American Museum of Natural History, New York, N.Y.

Naturaliste Canadien, Le. Quebec, Que.

Nature. London, Eng.

New York Fish and Game Journal. Albany, N.Y.

New York State Museum Bulletin. Albany, N.Y.

New York State Museum Handbook. Albany, N.Y.

Norsk Hvalfangst-Tidende, (The Norwegian Whaling Gazette). Sandefjord, Norway.

North American Fauna. United States Department of Agriculture [Interior], Washington, D.C.

Notulae Naturae. Academy of Natural Science, Philadelphia, Pa.

Occasional Papers, Museum of Zoology, University of Michigan. Ann Arbor, Mich.

Occasional Papers, Royal Ontario Museum of Zoology. Toronto, Ont.

Ohio Journal of Science. Columbus, Ohio.

Ontario Department of Lands and Forests, Technical Bulletin. Toronto, Ont.

Ontario Natural Science Bulletin. Guelph, Ont.

Oryx. Journal of the Fauna Preservation Society. London, Eng.

Ottawa Naturalist. Ottawa, Ont.

Papers, Michigan Academy of Science, Arts and Letters. Ann Arbor, Mich.

Parks and Recreation. Rockford, Ill.

Proceedings, Academy of Natural Sciences. Philadelphia, Pa.

——, *American Philosophical Society*. Philadelphia, Pa.

——, *Biological Society of Washington*. Washington, D.C.

——, *Boston Society of Natural History*. Boston, Mass.

——, *Canadian Institute*. Toronto, Ont.

——, *Linnean Society of London*. London, Eng.

——, *New England Zoological Club*. Cambridge, Mass.

——, *Nova Scotian Institute of Natural Science*. Halifax, N.S.

——, *Pennsylvania Academy of Science*. Harrisburg, Pa.

——, *Portland Society of Natural History*. Portland, Me.

——, *Royal Society, London, Series B, Biological Sciences.* London, Eng.

——, *Society for Experimental Biology and Medicine.* New York, N.Y.

——, *United States National Museum.* Washington, D.C.

——, *Washington Academy of Sciences.* Washington, D.C.

——, *Zoological Society of London.* London, Eng.

Proceedings and Papers, 5th Technical Meeting, International Union for the Protection of Nature, Copenhagen, 1954. Brussels, Belgium.

Proceedings and Transactions, Nova Scotia Institute of Science. Halifax, N.S.

Quarterly Review of Biology. Baltimore, Md.

Recent Memoirs on the Cetacea. The Ray Society Institute, London, Eng.

Report of the Ontario [Bureau] Department of Mines. Toronto, Ont.

Revue de l'Université Laval, La. Quebec, Que.

Rod and Gun in Canada. Toronto, Ont.

Roosevelt Wild Life Annals. New York State College of Forestry, Syracuse, N.Y.

Roosevelt Wild Life Bulletin. New York State College of Forestry, Syracuse, N.Y.

Science. Cambridge, Mass.

Science Bulletin. Museum of the Brooklyn Institute of Arts and Science, New York, N.Y.

Scientific Monthly. Washington, D.C.

Scientific Publications of the Cleveland Museum of Natural History. Cleveland, Ohio.

Scientific Reports, Whales Research Institute. Tokyo, Japan.

Sessional Papers. Government of Canada, Ottawa, Ont.

Smithsonian Contribution to Knowledge. Washington, D.C.

Southern Illinois University, Monograph Series. Carbondale, Ill.

Systematic Zoology. New Haven, Conn.

Telegram Weekend Magazine. Toronto, Ont.

Terre et la Vie: Revue d'Histoire Naturelle, La. Paris, France.

Transactions, American Philosophical Society. Philadelphia, Pa.

——, *Illinois Academy of Science.* Springfield, Ill.

——, *North American Wildlife Conference(s).* Washington, D.C.

——, *Nova Scotian Institute of Natural Science.* Halifax, N.S.

——, *Royal Canadian Institute.* Toronto, Ont.

——, *Royal Society of Canada.* Ottawa, Ont.

——, *Zoological Society of London.* London, Eng.

United States Department of Agriculture, Biological Survey Bulletin. Washington, D.C.

——, *Bulletin, Division of Ornithology and Mammalogy.* Washington, D.C.

——, *Circular.* Washington, D.C.

—, *Farmers' Bulletin.* Washington, D.C

——, *Technical Bulletin.* Washington, D.C

United States Department Interior, Fish and Wildlife Service, Circular. Washington, D.C.

——, *Conservation Bulletin.* Washington, D.C.

——, *Wildlife Leaflet.* Washington, D.C.

——, *Wildlife Research Bulletin.* Washington D.C.

United States Geological and Geographical Survey of the Territories. Miscellaneous Publications. Washington, D.C.

United States National Museum Bulletin. Washington, D.C.

University of California Publications in Zoology. Berkeley, Calif.

University of Kansas, Publications of the Museum of Natural History. Lawrence, Kan.

University of Toronto Studies, Biological Series. University of Toronto Press, Toronto, Ont.

Videnskableige Meddeleleser fra Dansk Naturhistovisk Forening, Copenhagen, Den.

Wildlife Management Bulletin. Canadian Wildlife Service, Department of Northern Affairs and National Resources, Ottawa, Ont.

Wisconsin Conservation Department, Technical Wildlife Bulletin. Madison, Wis.

Zeitschrift für Säugetierkunde. Berlin, Germany.

Zoologica. New York, N.Y.

Zoologist, The. London, Eng.

Index

Scientific names are set in capitals, French names in italics; page numbers in bold type denote illustrations and/or maps. The Index includes page references to the scientific names in the Contents list (pages vi to xvii) in order to direct the reader to authorities for the races and to type localities.

Aardvarks 18
ABIETORUM, NAPAEOZAPUS INSIGNIS xi, **186-7**
  PEROMYSCUS MANICULATUS ix, **142-3**
  VULPES VULPES xii, 210
ABROCOMIDAE, Family 17
ACADICUS, CASTOR CANADENSIS ix, 133, **135**
  MICROTUS, PENNSYLVANICUS x, 161, **163**
  SOREX CINEREUS vi, **35**
  ZAPUS HUDSONIUS xi, 182, **183**
ACUTOROSTRATA, BALAENOPTERA xvi, 383, 388, **389**
ACUTUS, LAGENORHYNCHUS xvi, 369, **371-2**
Adouris 16
African water shrews 14
Agoutis 16
ALBIBARBIS, SOREX PALUSTRIS vi, 44
ALBIROSTRIS, LAGENORHYNCHUS xvi, 369, **370**, 372
ALBUS, ONDATRA ZIBETHICUS xi, 171
ALCES 318, 326-30
  ALCES 326, **327-9**, 330
  ALCES AMERICANA xv, 328
  ALCES ANDERSONI xv, 328
ALEXANDRINUS, RATTUS RATTUS xi, 177
ALGONQUINENSIS, NAPAEOZAPUS INSIGNIS xi, **186-7**
Alisphenoid 20, **21**, 22, **23**
ALLOTHERIA, Subclass 10, 13
ALNORUM, MICROSOREX HOYI vi, 46
ALOPEX 195, 205-10
  LAGOPUS 25, 205, **206-7**
  LAGOPUS INNUITUS xii, 205
  LAGOPUS UNGAVA xii, 205, **207**
Ambergris 353
American disc-winged bats 15
American elk 318
American grey squirrel 108
American opossums 27
AMERICANA, ALCES ALCES xv, 328
  MARTES 252, **253-4**, 255
  MARTES AMERICANA xiii, 252

AMERICANUS, LEPUS 85, **86-8**, 89
  LEPUS AMERICANUS viii, 87
  OREAMNOS 339
  URSUS 218, **219-20**, 221-2
  URSUS AMERICANUS xii, 221
AMPHIBIA 6
Amphibians 8
AMPULLATUS, HYPEROODON xv, **349-50**, 351
ANDERSONI, ALCES ALCES xv, 328
Anes 313-14
Angular process 20, **21**, 22, **23**
ANGUSTA, BLARINA BREVICAUDA vi, **48**, 49
ANOMALURIDAE, Family 16
Anteaters 8, 15
  scaly 16
  spiny 9, 13
Antelopes 19, 335
ANTICOSTIENSIS, PEROMYSCUS MANICULATUS ix, **142-3**
ANTILOCAPRIDAE, Family 19, 315, 317
Antilopes 335
Antorbital process 20, **21**
Aortic arch 6
APLODONTIDAE, Family 16
Aquatic mammals 8
AQUATICUS, SCALOPUS 25, 52, **53**, 54
AQUILONIUS, ONDATRA ZIBETHICUS xi, **170-1**
Arboreal mammals 8
Arctic fox 25, 149, 205, **206-7**, 208-10
Arctic hare 25, **85**, 87, 89, **90-1**
Arctic shrew **33**, 38, **39**, 40
ARCTICUS, LEPUS 25, **85**, 89, **90-1**
  RANGIFER 332
  RANGIFER ARCTICUS 333
  SOREX 32, **33-4**, 37-8, **39**, 40
  SOREX ARCTICUS vi, 38, **39**
ARCTOS, URSUS 218
ARGENTATUS, PEROMYSCUS MANICULATUS ix, **142-3**
ARIES, OVIS xv, **338**, 339
Armadillos 15

ARTIODACTYLA, Order 19, 26, 315-39
Asian dormice 16
ASINUS, EQUUS 312, 314
Ass 312, 314
ASTRAPOTHERIA, Order 18
Atlantic killer whale 373, **374-5**
Atlantic walrus 291
Atlas **24**
ATRATA, MARTES AMERICANA xiii, 252, **254**
AUDITORY BULLA 20, **21**, 22, **23**
AUSTRALIS, EUBALAENA 399
Axis **24**
Aye-aye 15

Badger 17, **263-4**, 265
BAIRDII, PEROMYSCUS MANICULATUS ix, **141-2**, 143
BALAENA 397, **400-3**
  GLACIALIS 398
  MYSTICETUS xvii, 398, 400, **401-2**, 403
BALAENIDAE, Family 17, 381, 397-403
BALAENOPTERA 382-90, 394
  ACUTOROSTRATA xvi, 383, 388, **389**
  BOREALIS xvi, 383, 386, **387**, 388
  MUSCULUS 383, 391
  PHYSALUS xvi, 383, **384-5**, 386
BALAENOPTERIDAE, Family 17, 381-97
Baleen whales 17, 340, 381-403
Baleines à bec 342
Baleine à bec commune 349
Baleine à bec de Blainville 345
Baleine à bec de Sowerby 343
Baleine à bec de True 347
Baleine à bosse 394
Baleine bleue 391
Baleine boréale 397, 400
Baleine noire 397-8
Bamboo rats 16
Bandicoots 14
BANGSI, MUSTELA ERMINEA xii, 233
  VULPES RUBRICOSA **212**

452 – INDEX

BANGSII, LEPUS ARCTICUS viii, 89,
91
BANTENG, BOS 337
BARBATUS, ERIGNATHUS xiv, 302,
303–4, 305
Barren-ground caribou 333
Barren grounds 25
Basioccipital 20, **21**, 22, **23**
Basisphenoid 20, **21**, 22, **23**
Bastard samson fox 210
BATHYERGIDAE, Family 17
Bats 8, 59–83, 367
American disk-winged 15
big brown 74, **75–6**
common 15, 60–83
crest-nosed 15
disk-winged, American 15
ears **61**
eastern long-eared **66–7**
evening **77**
fish-eating 14
free-tailed 15
fruit-eating 14
golden 15
hispid 14
hoary **81–2**, 83
hollow-faced 14
horseshoe-nosed 15
Keen **66–7**
large-winged 14
leaf-nosed 15
least **68–9**
little brown **63–4**, 65
long-legged 15
long-tailed 14
Madagascarian 15
mouse-eared 62–9
mouse-tailed 14
moustache-lipped 15
pig 15
red 78, **79–80**
sac-winged 14
short-tailed 15
silver-haired 70, **71**
small-footed **68–9**
smoky 15
smooth-faced 15
sucker-footed 15
thumbless 15
valve-nosed 14
vampire 8, 15
yellow 15
Beaked whales 17, 342–51
Blainville **345–6**
Sowerby **343–4**
True **347–8**
Bearded seal 302, **303–4**, 305
Bears 8, 17, 218–25
black 218, **219–20**, 221–2
blue 219
cinnamon 219

glacier 219
grizzly 218
Kermode 219
polar 206, 218–19, 222, **223–4**,
225
Beaver 16, **103**, 133, **134–5**, 136–7,
192, 257
Behaviour 3
Belettes 232
Belette, petite 241
Belette à longue queue 239
Beluga 17, 357–9
Beluga 357
BEOTHUCUS, CANIS LUPUS xii, 200,
202
BIDENS, MESOPLODON xv, 342,
343–4
Big brown bat 74, **75–6**
Big short-tailed shrew **47–8**, 49
Biological products 3
Biotic areas 25
Biscayan right whale **398–9**, 400
BISON 4, 335, **336**, 337
BISON **336**
Bison 335
Bison d'Amérique 336
Black bear 218, **219–20**, 221–2
Black fox 210
Black rat **175**, 177
Blackfish 376–8
Bladdernose seal 309–11
Blainville beaked whale **345–6**
Blaireau 263
BLARINA 31, 47–9
BREVICAUDA **47–8**, 49
BREVICAUDA ANGUSTA vi, **48–9**
BREVICAUDA HOOPERI vi, 49
BREVICAUDA PALLIDA vii, **48–9**
BREVICAUDA TALPOIDES vii, 47,
48
Blood cells 6
Blue bear 219
Blue fox 208
Blue whale 7, 340, 383, 386, 388,
391–3
Boar, wild 316
Bobcat **284–5**, 286
Boeufs 335
Bog lemming **150–1**, 152
BONARIENSIS, MYOCASTOR COYPUS
xi, 192
Bones:
ear 7
skeleton **24**
skull 20, **21**, 22, **23**
Boreal forest 25
BOREALIS, BALAENOPTERA 383, 386,
387, 388
LASIURUS **61**, 78, **79–80**, 81
LASIURUS BOREALIS vii, 78
ODOCOILEUS VIRGINIANUS xv, 323

SYNAPTOMYS **138**, 149–50, 152,
153–4, 155
UROCYON CINEREOARGENTEUS xii,
217
BOS 335–7
BANTENG 337
PRIMIGENIUS 337
TAURUS **337**
Bottlenose whale **349–50**, 351
Bottle-nosed dolphin **366–8**
BOVIDAE, Family 19, 315, 317,
335–9
Bowhead whale 383, 397, 400,
401–2, 403
BRADYPODIDAE, Family 15
BRADYPUS 7
BREDANENSIS, STENO 362
BREVICAUDA, BLARINA **47–8**, 49
BREVICEPS, KOGIA xvi, 354, **355–6**
BREWERI, PARASCALOPS 54, **55–6**
Brown bat, big 74, **75–6**
little **63–4**, 65
BRUMALIS, MARTES AMERICANA xiii,
252, **254**
Brush wolf 197, **198–9**, 200–1, 203
Buffalo, North American 336
Bulla, auditory 20, **21**, 22, **23**
tympanic 20, **21**, 22, **23**
Burro 314
Bush babies 15

CABALLUS, EQUUS 312, **313**, 314
CABOTI, RANGIFER 332–3
RANGIFER ARCTICUS 333
Cachalots 351
Cachalot macrocéphale 351
Cachalot pygmée 354
CAECATOR, CASTOR CANADENSIS ix,
133, **135**
CAENOLESTIDAE, Family 14, 27
Calcaneum **24**
CALLITHRICIDAE, Family 15
CAMELIDAE, Family 19
Camels 3, 19
Campagnols 161
Campagnol à dos roux 155
Campagnol à dos roux de Gapper
155
Campagnol des champs 161
Campagnol des rochers 164
Campagnol sylvestre 167
Campagnol-lemmings 149
Campagnol-lemming boréal 152
Campagnol-lemming de Cooper 150
CAMPANIUS, LEPUS TOWNSENDII
viii, 92
Canada lynx 280, **281–2**, 283–4,
286
CANADENSIS, CASTOR 133, **134–5**,
136–7
CASTOR CANADENSIS ix, 133

CERVUS 318, **319–20**, 321–2
CERVUS CANADENSIS xv, 321
LUTRA **271–2**, 373–4
LUTRA CANADENSIS xiii, 273
LYNX 275, 280, **281–2**, 283
LYNX CANADENSIS xiii, 280
MARMOTA MONAX ix, 116, **117**
OVIS 338
ZAPUS HUDSONIUS xi, 182, **183**
Canadian biotic area 25
Canadian shield 25
Cane rats 17
CANESCENS, GLAUCOMYS
    SABRINUS ix, 132
CANIDAE, Family 17, 194–217
Canine teeth 7, 22, **23**
CANIS 195–204
    FAMILIARIS 196, 203, **204**
    LATRANS 196–7, **198–9**, 200
    LATRANS THAMNOS xii, 197
    LUPUS 196, 200, **201–2**, 203
    LUPUS BEOTHUCUS xii, 200, **202**
    LUPUS HUDSONICUS xii, 200
    LUPUS LABRADORIUS xii, 200, **202**
    LUPUS LYCAON xii, 200, **202**
CAPEREA 397
CAPRA 335, 339
    HIRCUS **339**
CAPROMYIDAE, Family 16, 104,
    192–3
Capybaras 16
Carcajou 260, 262
Caribou 201, 262, 317, 330–2, **333**,
    334
    barren-ground 333
    woodland 201, **331**, 333–4
Caribou 330
CARIBOU, RANGIFER 332
    RANGIFER TARANDUS xv, **331–3**
CARNIVORA, Order 8, 17, 26,
    194–287
Carnivores 4, 8, 171, 194–287
    marine 288–311
Carolinian life-zone 25
CAROLINENSIS, MICROTUS
    CHROTORRHINUS 166
    SCIURUS 106, **107**, 108, **109**
Carpals **24**
CASTOR 133–7
    CANADENSIS 133, **134–5**, 136–7
    CANADENSIS ACADICUS ix, 133, **135**
    CANADENSIS CAECATOR ix, 133,
    135
    CANADENSIS CANADENSIS ix, 133
    CANADENSIS LABRADORENSIS ix,
    133, **135**
    CANADENSIS MICHIGANENSIS ix,
    133
Castor 133
CASTORIDAE, Family 16, 103–4,
    133–7

CATADON, PHYSETER xv, 351,
    352–3, 354
Cats 2, 17, 275–87
    domestic 10, 22, **23–4**, 276, **279**,
    280, 286
Cattle (cow):
    domestic 3, 19, 286, 335–6, **337**
    polled 335
CATUS, FELIS xiii, **23–4**, 275, **279**
Caudal vertebrae 7, **24**
CAUDATUS, PEROMYSCUS LEUCOPUS
    x, **145–6**
Cavies 16
CAVIIDAE, Family 16
CEBIDAE, Family 15
CERCOPITHECIDAE, Family 15
Cerfs 317, 322
Cerf de Virginie 322
Cervical vertebrae 7, **24**
CERVIDAE, Family 19, 315, 317–34
Cervides 317
CERVUS 318–22
    CANADENSIS 318, **319–20**, 321–2
    CANADENSIS CANADENSIS xv, 321
    CANADENSIS MANITOBENSIS xv,
    321
    CANADENSIS NELSONI xv, 321
CETACEA, Order 8, 17, 26, 340–403
Cétacés à baleine 381
Cétodontes 341
Chat domestique 279
Chats 275
Chauve-souris 60
Chauve-souris à queue velue 78
Chauve-souris argentée 70
Chauve-souris brune 63
Chauve-souris brune, grande 74
Chauvre-souris cendrée 81
Chauve-souris commune 62
Chauve-souris de Keen 66
Chauve-souris pygmée 68
Chauve-souris rousse 78
Chauve-souris vespérale 77
Cheval domestique 313
Chevaux 312–13
Chèvres 335, 339
Chèvre domestique 339
Chevreuils 317
Chevrotains 19
Chien 195–6, 203
CHIMO, LUTRA CANADENSIS xiii,
    272–3
Chimpanzees 15
Chinchillas 16
CHINCHILLIDAE, Family 16
Chipmunk 105, 114, 253
    eastern **121–2**, 123, 126
    least **124–5**, 126
    western **124–5**, 126
CHIROPTERA, Order 8, 14, 26,
    59–83

CHOLOEPUS 7
CHORDATA, Phylum 10
CHROTORRHINUS, MICROTUS **138**,
    161, 164, **165–6**, 167
    MICROTUS CHROTORRHINUS x,
    164, 166
CHRYSOCHLORIDAE, Family 14
CICOGNANII, MUSTELA ERMINEA xii,
    233
CINEREOARGENTEUS, UROCYON
    215–16, 217
    UROCYON CINEREOARGENTEUS xii,
    217
CINEREUS, LASIURUS **61**, 78, **81–2**,
    83
    LASIURUS CINEREUS vii, 81
    SOREX 32, **33–5**, 36, 41, 44
    SOREX CINEREUS vi, **35**, 37
Cinnamon bear 219
CITELLUS 106, 118–20
    FRANKLINII ix, 118, **119–20**
    TRIDECEMLINEATUS
        TRIDECEMLINEATUS 120
Civets 17
Class (classification) 10, 12
    MAMMALIA 6, 10, 13
Classification 9–19
CLETHRIONOMYS 139, 155–7, 161
    GAPPERI **138**, 155, **156–7**
    GAPPERI GAPPERI x, 155, **156**
    GAPPERI GASPEANUS x, **156–7**
    GAPPERI HUDSONIUS x, **156–7**
    GAPPERI LORINGI x, 157
    GAPPERI OCHRACEUS x, 155
    GAPPERI PALLESCENS x, **156–7**
    GAPPERI PROTEUS x, **156–7**
    GAPPERI UNGAVA x, **156–7**
Climatic factors 25
Climatic regions 8
Clothing 2
Coatis 17
Cochons 315
Cochon domestique 316
Cohort (classification) 12
Coloured fox 210–14
Colugos 14
Common bats 15, 60–83
Common dolphin **364–5**, 367, 393
Common dormice 16
Common finback whale 383,
    384–5, 386
Common muskrat **169–70**, 171–2
Common opossum 27, **28–9**, 30
Common porpoise **379–80**
Common shrew **33–5**, 36, 38, 40,
    44
Common weasel 233
CONCOLOR, FELIS 275, **276–7**, 278
    PHOCA VITULINA xiv, 294, 296
CONDYLARTHRA, Order 17
Condyles, occipital 7, 20, **21**, 22, **23**

CONDYLURA 52, 56–9
  CRISTATA 54, 56, **57–8**, 59
  CRISTATA CRISTATA vii, 57
  CRISTATA NIGRA vii, 57, **58**
Condylure étoilé 56
Coneys 16
Conservation 3
COOPERI, SYNAPTOMYS **138**, 149,
  150–1, 152–3, 155
  SYNAPTOMYS COOPERI x, 150
Coronoid process 20, **21**, 22, **23**
Costal cartilage **24**
Cottontails 87, 96–7, **98–9**, 251
  New England **100–1**
Cougar 276–7, 278, 280
COUGAR, FELIS CONCOLOR xiii, 277
Couguar 276
Cow, domestic 336, **337** (*see also*
  Cattle)
Coyote 195–200, 204
Coyote 195–7
Coypu 188, 192, **193**
COYPUS, MYOCASTOR 192, **193**
Cranium **24**
CRASSIDENS, PSEUDORCA 362
CRASSUS, PHENACOMYS UNGAVA xi,
  159–60
Crest-nosed bats 15
CRICETIDAE, Family 16, 104,
  138–73
CRICETINAE, Subfamily 138
CRISTATA, CONDYLURA 54, 56,
  57–8, 59
  CONDYLURA CRISTATA vii, 57
  CYSTOPHORA xiv, **308**, 309, **310**,
  311
Cross fox 210, 214
CRYPTOTIS 31, 50–1
  PARVA 25, 50, **51**
  PARVA PARVA vii, 50
CTENODACTYLIDAE, Family 17
CTENOMYIDAE, Family 16
Cultural development 5
CUNICULAS, ORYCTOLAGUS 20, **21**,
  102
CUNICULIDAE, Family 16
CYNOCEPHALIDAE, Family 14
CYSTOPHORA 293, 308–11
  CRISTATA xiv, **308**, 309, **310**, 311
Cytology 3

DACOTENSIS, ODOCOILEUS
  VIRGINIANUS xv, 323
Darwin, Charles 11
Dassie rats 17
Dassies 18
DASYPODIDAE, Family 15
DASYPROCTIDAE, Family 16
DASYURIDAE, Family 14
DAUBENTONIIDAE, Family 15
Dauphins 362

Dauphin à flancs blancs 371
Dauphin à gros nez 366
Dauphin à nez blanc 369
Dauphin commun 364
Dauphins à côtés blancs 369
Deer 4, 19, 197, 221, 257, 262,
  317–34
  mule 326
  red 318
  white-tailed 286, 322, **323–5**,
  326, 330
Deer mouse 140, **142**, 144, 146
  prairie **141–2**, 143
  woodland 140, **141**, **143**
DEGENER, LUTRA CANADENSIS xiii,
  272–3
DELETRIX, VULPES **212**
DELPHINAPTERIDAE, Family 357
DELPHINAPTERINAE, Subfamily
  357–9
DELPHINAPTERUS 357–9
  LEUCAS xvi, 357, **358–9**
DELPHINIDAE, Family 17, 341,
  362–80
DELPHINUS 363–5
  DELPHIS **364–5**
DENSIROSTRIS, MESOPLODON xv,
  342–3, **345–6**
Dentary 20, **21**, 22, **23**
Denticètes 341
DERMOPTERA, Order 8, 14
DESMODONTIDAE, Family 8, 15
Diaphragm 6
Diastema 20, **21**
DICROSTONYX 25, 139, 147–9, 153
  GROENLANDICUS 147, 149
  HUDSONIUS x, 25, **138**, **147–8**, 149
DIDELPHIDAE, Family 14, 27–30
DIDELPHIS MARSUPIALIS 27, **28–9**,
  30
  MARSUPIALIS VIRGINIANA vi,
  29–30
Digits 7, **24**
DINOCERATA, Order 18
DINOMYIDAE, Family 16
DIPODIDAE, Family 16
Diseases, infectious 3
Disk-winged bats, American 15
DISPAR, SOREX vi, 32, **34**, 40, **41–2**
DIVERGENS, ODOBENUS ROSMARUS 291
Dogs 2, 17, 195–6, 211, 265, 269,
  278
  domestic 200, 203, **204**, 205
  German shepherd 197, 200
  mongrel 197
  spaniel 260
Dolphins 17, 340, 362, 375
  bottle-nosed **366–8**
  common **364–5**, 367, 393
  freshwater 17
  Risso 362

river 17
  white-beaked 369, **370**, 372–3
  white-sided 369, **371–2**, 373, 393
Domestic animals:
  cat 10, 22, **23–4**, 276, **279**, 280,
  286
  cattle (cow) 3, 19, 286, 335–6, **337**
  dog 200, 203, **204**, 205
  goat 3, **339**
  horse 3, **313**
  livestock 4, 197, 201, 221
  pig **316**
  rabbit 20, **21**, **102**
  sheep **338**, 339
Domesticated ferret 231, 245, **251**
Domestication 2
DOMESTICUS, MUS MUSCULUS xi, 178
Donkey 312, 314
Dormice, Asian 16
  common 16
  spiny 16
DORSATUM, ERETHIZON 188,
  189–90, 191
  ERETHIZON DORSATUM xi, 191
Draft animals 3
DRUMMONDII, MICROTUS
  PENNSYLVANICUS x, 162
Duck-billed platypus 9, 13
DUGONGIDAE, Family 18
Dugongs 18

Ear bones 7
Eared seals 17
Eastern chipmunk **121–2**, 123, 126
Eastern flying squirrel **127–9**, 132
Eastern fox squirrel **110–11**
Eastern gray squirrel **107**, 108,
  109, 110–11, 118, 239
Eastern long-eared bat **66–7**
Eastern mole 25, 52, **53–4**
Eastern phenacomys **158–9**, 160
Eastern pipistrelle 72, **73**
Echidnas 9, 13
ECHIMYIDAE, Family 17
Echo-location 59, 340
Ecology 3
Ecureuils 105–6
Ecureuil fauve 110
Ecureuil gris 108
Ecureuil roux 112
Ecureuils de terre 118
EDENTATA, Order 15
Egg-laying mammals 9
Elephant shrew 14
ELEPHANTIDAE, Family 18
Elephants 18, 393
Elk, American 318
  European 318
EMBALLONURIDAE, Family 14
EMBRITHOPODA, Order 18
Embryology 3

Endocrinology 3
ENHYDRA 231
ENIXUS, MICROTUS PENNSYLVANICUS
    x, 162, **163**
Environment 3
Épaulard 373
Epiphyses 7
EPTESICUS 61, 74–6
    FUSCUS **61**, 74, **75–6**, 81
    FUSCUS FUSCUS vii, 74
    FUSCUS PALLIDUS vii, 74
EQUIDAE, Family 19, 312–14
EQUUS ASINUS 312, 314
    CABALLUS 312, **313**, 314
EREMUS, PEROMYSCUS MANICULATUS
    x, **142–3**
ERETHIZON DORSATUM 188, **189–90**,
    191
    DORSATUM DORSATUM xi, 191
    DORSATUM PICINUM xi, 190–1
ERETHIZONTIDAE, Family 16, 104,
    188–91
ERIGNATHUS 293, 302–5
    BARBATUS xiv, 302, **303–4**, 305
ERINACEIDAE, Family 14
Ermine 233, **234–5**, 236–7, 239–40,
    243, 259
ERMINEA, MUSTELA 232–3, **234–5**,
    236, 239–41
ESCHRICHTIIDAE, Family 17
EUARCTOS, Subgenus 218–19
EUBALAENA 397–400
    AUSTRALIS 399
    GLACIALIS **398–9**, 400
    SIEBOLDII 399
EUROPAEUS, LEPUS 85, 92, **94–6**
    MESOPLODON 348
European elk 318
European hare 89, **94–6**
EUTAMIAS 105, 124–6
    MINIMUS 121, 123, **124–5**, 126
    MINIMUS HUDSONIUS ix, 126
    MINIMUS NEGLECTUS ix, **125–6**
EUTHERIA, Infraclass 10, 14
Evening bat 77
EVERSMANI, MUSTELA 251
    MUSTELA PUTORIUS 251
Evolution 9, 11, 13
Exoccipital 20, **21**, 22, **23**
External auditory meatus 20, **21**,
    22, **23**
Extinction 11, 13

False killer whale 362
False paca 16
FAMILIARIS, CANIS 196, 203, **204**
Family (classification) 10–12
Family:
    ABROCOMIDAE 17
    ANOMALURIDAE 16
    ANTILOCAPRIDAE 19, 315, 317

APLODONTIDAE 16
BALAENIDAE 17, 381, 397–403
BALAENOPTERIDAE 17, 381–97
BATHYERGIDAE 17
BOVIDAE 19, 315, 317, 335–9
BRADYPODIDAE 15
CAENOLESTIDAE 14, 27
CALLITHRICIDAE 15
CAMELIDAE 19
CANIDAE 17, 194–217
CAPROMYIDAE 16, 104, 192–3
CASTORIDAE 16, 103–4, 133–7
CAVIIDAE 16
CEBIDAE 15
CERCOPITHECIDAE 15
CERVIDAE 19, 315, 317–34
CHINCHILLIDAE 16
CHRYSOCHLORIDAE 14
CRICETIDAE 16, 104, 138–73
CTENODACTYLIDAE 17
CTENOMYIDAE 16
CUNICULIDAE 16
CYNOCEPHALIDAE 14
DASYPODIDAE 15
DASYPROCTIDAE 16
DASYURIDAE 14
DAUBENTONIIDAE 15
DELPHINAPTERIDAE 357
DELPHINIDAE 17, 341, 362–80
DESMODONTIDAE 8, 15
DIDELPHIDAE 14, 27–30
DINOMYIDAE 16
DIPODIDAE 16
DUGONGIDAE 18
ECHIMYIDAE 17
ELEPHANTIDAE 18
EMBALLONURIDAE 14
EQUIDAE 19, 312–14
ERETHIZONTIDAE 16, 104, 188–91
ERINACEIDAE 14
ESCHRICHTIIDAE 17
FELIDAE 17, 194, 275–87
FURIPTERIDAE 15
GEOMYIDAE 16
GIRAFFIDAE 19
GLIRIDAE 16
HETEROMYIDAE 16
HIPPOPOTAMIDAE 19
HIPPOSIDERIDAE 15
HOMINIDAE 15
HYAENIDAE 8, 17
HYDROCHOERIDAE 16
HYSTRICIDAE 16
INDRIDAE 15
INIIDAE 17
KOGIIDAE 17, 341, 354–6
LEMURIDAE 15
LEPORIDAE 16, 83–102
LOPHIOMYIDAE 16
LORISIDAE 15
MACROPODIDAE 14

MACROSCELIDIDAE 14
MANIDAE 16
MEGADERMATIDAE 14
MOLOSSIDAE 15
MONODONTIDAE 17, 341, 357–62
MURIDAE 16, 104, 173–80
MUSTELIDAE 17, 194, 231–74
MYRMECOPHAGIDAE 15
MYSTACINIDAE 15
MYZOPODIDAE 15
NATALIDAE 15
NOCTILIONIDAE 14
NOTORYCTIDAE 14
NYCTERIDAE 14
OCHOTONIDAE 16, 83
OCTODONTIDAE 16
ODOBENIDAE 17, 288–92
ORNITHORHYNCHIDAE 13
ORYCTEROPODIDAE, 18
OTARIIDAE 17, 288, 292
PEDETIDAE 16
PERAMELIDAE 14
PETROMYIDAE 17
PHALANGERIDAE 14
PHASCOLOMIDAE 14
PHOCIDAE 17, 288, 292–311
PHYLLOSTOMIDAE 15
PHYSETERIDAE 17, 341, 351–4
PLATACANTHOMYIDAE 16
PLATANISTIDAE 17
PONGIDAE 15
POTAMOGALIDAE 14
PROCAVIIDAE 18
PROCYONIDAE 17, 194, 226–30
PTEROPIDAE 14
RHINOCEROTIDAE 19
RHINOLOPHIDAE 15
RHINOPOMATIDAE 14
RHIZOMYIDAE 16
SCIURIDAE 16, 103–32
SELEVINIIDAE 16
SOLENODONTIDAE 14
SORICIDAE 14, 30–51
SPALACIDAE 16
SUIDAE 19, 315–16
TACHYGLOSSIDAE 13
TALPIDAE 14, 30, 52–9
TAPIRIDAE 19
TARSIIDAE 15
TAYASSUIDAE 19, 315
TENRECIDAE 14
THRYONOMYIDAE 17
THYROPTERIDAE 15
TRAGULIDAE 19
TRICHECHIDAE 18
TUPAIIDAE 15
URSIDAE 17, 194, 218–25
VESPERTILIONIDAE 15, 60–83
VIVERRIDAE 17
ZAPODIDAE 16, 104, 181–7
ZIPHIIDAE 17, 341–51

Feet 7
  DICROSTONYX HUDSONIUS **148**
  northern lemming mouse **153**
FELIDAE, Family 17, 194, 275–87
FELIS CATUS xiii, **23–4**, 275, **279**
  CONCOLOR 275, **276–7**, 278
  CONCOLOR COUGAR xiii, 277
  CONCOLOR SCHORGERI 277
Femur **24**
Ferrets 232
  domesticated 231, 245, **251**
Fever, rabbit 99
Fibula **24**
Fin whales 382–6
Finback whales 383–90, 395–6
  common 383, **384–5**, 386
Fin-backed whales 382–96
Fish-eating bats 14
Fisher 252, **256–8**, 259
Flight 8
Flora 25
FLORIDANUS, SYLVILAGUS 96–7,
  98–9, 100–1
Flying foxes 14
Flying lemurs 14
Flying squirrels 105, 126
Flying squirrel, eastern **127–9**,
  132
Flying squirrel, northern 114,
  128–9, **130–1**, 132
FONTIGENUS, MICROTUS
  PENNSYLVANICUS x, 162, **163**
Food habits 8
Foramen magnum 20, **21**, 22, **23**
Fox squirrel 108, 111
  eastern **110–11**
Foxes 17, 91, 164, 195, 205–17,
  282, 378
  Arctic 25, 149, 205, **206–7**, 208,
    210
  bastard Samson 210
  black 210
  blue 208
  coloured 210–14
  cross 210, 214
  gray 210, **215–16**, 217
  red 210, **211–12**, 213, 215, 217
  silver 210, 214
  tree 217
  tree-climbing 217
Franklin ground squirrel 118,
  119–20
FRANKLINII, CITELLUS ix, 118,
  119–20
Free-tailed bats 15
FRENATA, MUSTELA 232–3, **238–9**,
  240–1
Freshwater dolphins 17
Frontal 20, **21**, 22, **23**
FRONTALIS, STENELLA 362
Fruit-eating bats 14

FRUTECTANUS, NAPAEOZAPUS
  INSIGNIS xi, 187
FULVA, VULPES VULPES xii, 210
FUMEUS, SOREX 32, **33–4**, 36, **37**,
  38, 41
  SOREX FUMEUS vi, 37–8
FURIPTERIDAE, Family 15
FURO, MUSTELA 251
  MUSTELA PUTORIUS xiii, 251
FUSCUS, EPTESICUS **61**, 74, **75–6**, 81
  EPTESICUS FUSCUS vii, 74

Galagos 15
GAPPERI, CLETHRIONOMYS **138**, 155,
  156–7
  CLETHRIONOMYS GAPPERI x,
    155, **156**
Gaspé shrew **33**, 40, **41**
GASPEANUS, CLETHRIONOMYS
  GAPPERI x, **156–7**
GASPENSIS, NAPAEOZAPUS INSIGNIS
  xi, 186–7
  SOREX vi, 32, **33**, 40, **41**, 42
Genetics 3
Genus (classification) 10–12
Geographic races (list) vi–xvii
GEOMYIDAE, Family 16
German shepherd dog 197, 200
Giant otter 231
Gibbons 15
GIGAS, LYNX RUFUS xiv, **285**
Giraffes 19
GIRAFFIDAE, Family 19
Girdle, pelvic 7
  shoulder 7
GLACIALIS, BALAENA 398
  EUBALAENA **398–9**, 400
Glacier bear 219
Glands, mammary 6
GLAUCOMYS 105, 126–32
  SABRINUS 114, 126, 128–9,
    130–1, 132
  SABRINUS CANESCENS ix, 132
  SABRINUS GOODWINI ix, **131–2**
  SABRINUS GOULDI ix, **131–2**
  SABRINUS MACROTIS ix, 132
  SABRINUS MAKKOVIKENSIS ix,
    131–2
  SABRINUS SABRINUS ix, **131–2**
  VOLANS 126, **127–9**
  VOLANS VOLANS ix, 128
Glenoid fossa 22, **23**
Gliders 8
GLIRIDAE, Family 16
GLOBICEPHALA 363, 376–8
  MELAENA xvi, 364, **376–7**, 378
Globicéphale noir 376
Glossary 404–8
GLOVERALLENI, SOREX PALUSTRIS
  vi, **43–4**
Goats 19, 335, 337

domestic 3, **339**
  mountain 339
Golden bat 15
  mole 14
GOODWINI, GLAUCOMYS SABRINUS
  ix, **131–2**
Gophers, grey 118
Gophers, pocket 8, 16
Gorillas 15
GOULDI, GLAUCOMYS SABRINUS ix,
  131–2
GRACILIS, PEROMYSCUS MANICULATUS
  x, 140, **141**, **143**, 146
GRAMPUS 362, 374
  GRISEUS 362
Grand polatouche 129
Grande chauve-souris brune 74
Grande musaraigne 47
Gray (*see also* Grey):
  fox 210, **215–16**, 217
  long-tailed shrew **41–2**
  seal 305, **306–7**, 308
  squirrel, eastern **107**, 108, **109**,
    110–11, 118, 239
  whale 17
Greenland right whale 400–3
Greenland seal 299–302
Grey (*see also* Gray):
  gopher 118
  squirrel, American 108
GRISEUS, GRAMPUS 362
  TAMIAS STRIATUS ix, 123
Grizzly bear 218
GROENLANDICA, PHOCA
  (PAGOPHILUS) xiv, 293, 299,
    300–1, 302
GROENLANDICUS, DICROSTONYX
  147, 149
  RANGIFER TARANDUS xv, 332–3
Ground hog 115
Ground squirrel 105
  Franklin 118, **119–20**
GRYPUS, HALICHOERUS xiv, 305,
  306–7, 308
Guinea pigs 16
GULO 231, 252, 260–2
  LUSCUS **260–1**, 262
  LUSCUS LUSCUS xiii, 262
Gundis rats 17
GYMNICUS, TAMIASCIURUS
  HUDSONICUS viii, 114

Haematology 3
Hair 6
Hair seals 17, 293–302
Hairy-tailed mole 54, **55–6**
HALICHOERUS 293, 305–8
  GRYPUS xiv, 305, **306–7**, 308
HAMILTONI, URSUS AMERICANUS xii,
  220–1
Harbour porpoise **379–80**, 393

Harbour seal **394–5**, 296
Hares 16, 83–4, 282, 286
 Arctic 25, **85**, 87, 89, **90–1**
 European 89, **94–6**
 snowshoe **86–8**, 89, 257
 varying **86–8**, 89
Harp seal 299, **300–1**, 302, 311
Heart 6
Hedgehogs 14
HEMIONUS, ODOCOILEUS HEMIONUS
 326
Hermine 233
Heterodont (dentition) 7
HETEROMYIDAE, Family 16
Hibernation 60, 64–5, 67–9, 72, 74,
 105, 116, 120, 123, 126, 182,
 184
Hierarchy 10–12
Hinney 312
Hippopotami 19
HIPPOPOTAMIDAE, Family 19
HIPPOSIDERIDAE, Family 15
HIRCUS, CAPRA **339**
HIRTUS, PROCYON LOTOR xii, 226
Hispid bats 14
HISPIDA, PHOCA (PUSA) 293–4, 296,
 297–8, 299
 PHOCA (PUSA) HISPIDA xiv, 297
Histology 3
Hoary bat **81–3**, 83
Hollow-faced bats 14
HOMINIDAE, Family 15
Hooded seal **308**, 309, **310**, 311
HOOPERI, BLARINA BREVICAUDA vi, 49
Hormones 3
HORRIBILIS, URSUS 218
Horsehead seal 305–8
Horses 19, 312
 domestic 3, **313**
Horseshoe-nosed bats 15
House mouse **178–9**, 180
HOYI, MICROSOREX **33–4**, 44, **45**,
 46
 MICROSOREX HOYI vi, 46
Hudson seal 171
Hudsonian life-zone 25
HUDSONICA, MEPHITIS MEPHITIS
 xiii, 267
HUDSONICUS, CANIS LUPUS xii, 200
 TAMIASCIURUS **112–13**, 114
 TAMIASCIURUS HUDSONICUS viii,
 113–14
HUDSONIUS, CLETHRIONOMYS
 GAPPERI x, **156–7**
 DICROSTONYX x, 25, **138**, **147–8**,
 149
 EUTAMIAS MINIMUS ix, 126
 ZAPUS 181, **182–3**, 184–5
 ZAPUS HUDSONIUS xi, 182, **183**
HUMERALIS, NYCTICEIUS 77
 NYCTICEIUS HUMERALIS vii, 77

Humerus **24**
Humpback whale 386, **394–5**, 396
Husbandry, animal 3
 swine 2
Hutias 16
HYAENIDAE, Family 8, 17
HYBRIDUS, LEPUS EUROPAEUS viii,
 95
HYDROBADISTES, SOREX PALUSTRIS
 vi, 44
HYDROCHOERIDAE, Family 16
Hyenas 17
Hyoids **24**
HYPEROODON 342, 349–51
 AMPULLATUS xv, **349–50**, 351
 PLANIFRONS 350
HYPOPHAEUS, SCIURUS CAROLINENSIS
 viii, 108
Hyraxes 18
HYROCOIDEA, Order 18
HYSTRICIDAE, Family 16
HYSTRICOMORPHA, Suborder 104,
 188–93

IGNAVA, MARMOTA MONAX ix,
 116–17
Incisive foramen 20, **21**, 22, **23**
Incisor teeth 7, 20, **21**, 22, **23**, 85
INDRIDAE, Family 15
Infectious diseases 3
Infraclass (classification) 12
 EUTHERIA 10, 14
 METATHERIA 10, 14
 PANTOTHERIA 13
Infraorbital canal 22, **23**
Infraorder (classification) 12
INIIDAE, Family 17
Innominate bones 7
INNUITUS, ALOPEX LAGOPUS xii, 205
 SYNAPTOMYS BOREALIS x, **153–4**
INSECTIVORA, Order 8, 14, 26,
 30–59
INSIGNIS, NAPAEOZAPUS 181, **185–6**
 NAPAEOZAPUS INSIGNIS xi, **186–7**
Interparietal 20, **21**, 22, **23**
INTERVECTUS, MICROSOREX HOYI vi,
 46

Jack rabbit 89, 95
 white-tailed **92–3**, 95
Jaw, lower 6
Jerboas 16
JOHNSONI, MARMOTA MONAX ix,
 116, **117**
Jugal 22, **23**
Jugular process 20, **21**
Jumper (whale) 373
Jumping mice 16, 181–7
 meadow 181, **182–3**, 184, 187
 woodland **185–6**, 187
Jumping shrew 14

Kangaroo rats 16
Kangaroos 14
Keen bat **66–7**
KEENII, MYOTIS **61**, 62–3, **66–7**
Keewatin mink 245
Kermode bear 219
Killer whale, Atlantic 373, **374–5**
 false 362
Kingdom (classification) 10, 12
Kinkajous 17
KOGIA BREVICEPS xvi, 354, **355–6**
KOGIIDAE, Family 17, 341, 354–6

Labba 16
Laboratory mammals 3
LABRADORENSIS, CASTOR CANADENSIS
 ix, 133, **135**
 SOREX PALUSTRIS vi, **43**, 44
 THALARCTOS 224
 THALARCTOS MARITIMUS 223
LABRADORIUS, CANIS LUPUS xii, 200,
 202
 LEPUS ARCTICUS viii, 89, **91**
 MICROTUS PENNSYLVANICUS x,
 162–3
Lachrymal (Lacrimal) bone 20, **21**,
 22, **23**
LACUSTRIS, MUSTELA VISON xiii, 245
LADAS, ZAPUS HUDSONIUS xi, 182,
 183
LAGENORHYNCHUS 363, 369–73
 ACUTUS xvi, 369, **371–2**
 ALBIROSTRIS xii, 369, **370–2**, 372
 OBLIQUIDENS 372
LAGOMORPHA, Order 16, 26, 83–102
LAGOPUS, ALOPEX 25, 205, **206–7**
Lambdoidal crest 22, **23**
Lapins 84
Lapin à queue blanche 96–7
Lapin de garenne 102
Lapin de Nouvelle-Angleterre 100
Large-winged bats 14
LARICORUM, SOREX ARCTICUS vi, 40
LASIONYCTERIS 60, 70–1
 NOCTIVAGANS vii, **61**, 70, 71
LASIURUS 60, 78–83
 BOREALIS **61**, 78, **79–80**, 81
 BOREALIS BOREALIS vii, 78
 CINEREUS **61**, 78, **81–2**, 83
 CINEREUS CINEREUS vii, 81
LATRANS, CANIS 196–7, **198–9**, 200
LAURENTIANUS, TAMIASCIURUS
 HUDSONICUS viii, **113–14**
Leaf-nosed bats 15
Least bat **68–9**
Least chipmunk **124–5**, 126
Least shrew 50
Least weasel 231, **241–2**, 243
LEIBII, MYOTIS SUBULATUS vii, **68–9**
Lemming, bog **150–1**, 152
 Ungava varying 25, **147–8**, 149

Lemming d'Ungava 147
Lemming mice 149–55
    northern 152, **153–4**, 155
    southern **150–1**, 152
Lemmings variés 147
LEMURIDAE, Family 15
Lemurs 15
    flying 14
    woolly 15
LEPORIDAE, Family 16, 83–102
LEPUS 84–96
    AMERICANUS 85, **86–8**, 89
    AMERICANUS AMERICANUS viii, 87
    AMERICANUS PHAEONOTUS viii, 87, **88**
    AMERICANUS STRUTHOPUS viii, 87
    AMERICANUS VIRGINIANUS viii, 87
    ARCTICUS 25, **85**, 89, **90–1**
    ARCTICUS BANGSII viii, 89, **91**
    ARCTICUS LABRADORIUS viii, 89, **91**
    EUROPAEUS 85, 92, **94–6**
    EUROPAEUS HYBRIDUS viii, 95
    TOWNSENDII 85, **92–3**, 95
    TOWNSENDII CAMPANIUS viii, 92
LEUCAS, DELPHINAPTERUS xvi, 357, **358–9**
LEUCOPUS, PEROMYSCUS 140, 144, **145–6**
LEUCOTIS, SCIURUS CAROLINENSIS 108, **109**
Lièvres 84, 85
Lièvre arctique 89
Lièvre d'Amérique 87
Lièvre d'Europe 95
Lièvre de Townsend 92
Life-zone areas 25
Linnaeus, Carl von 10
LITOPTERNA, Order 18
Little brown bat **63–4**, 65
Little piked whale 388, **389**, 390
Little short-tailed shrew 25, 50, **51**
Livestock 4, 197, 201, 221
Llamas 19
Long-eared bat, eastern **66–7**
Long-legged bats 15
Long-tailed bats 14
Long-tailed paca 16
Long-tailed shrew, gray **41–2**
Long-tailed shrews 32–44
Long-tailed weasel **238–9**, 240, 243, 251
LOPHIOMYIDAE, Family 16
LOQUAX, TAMIASCIURUS HUDSONICUS viii, 114
LORINGI, CLETHRIONOMYS GAPPERI x, 157
LORISIDAE, Family 15
LOTOR, PROCYON 226, **227–8**, 229–30
LOTOR, PROCYON LOTOR xii, 226
Loups 195–6

Loup 200
Loutres 271
Loutre de rivière 271
LOWII, MUSTELA VISON xiii, 245, **246**
LUCIFUGUS, MYOTIS **61**, 62, **63–4**, 65, 67–70, 72, 74
    MYOTIS LUCIFUGUS vii, 63
Lumbar vertebrae 7, **24**
LUPUS, CANIS 196, 200, **201–2**, 203
LUSCUS, GULO **260–1**, 262
    GULO LUSCUS xiii, 262
LUTRA 231, 245, **271–4**
    CANADENSIS **271–2**, 373–4
    CANADENSIS CANADENSIS xiii, 273
    CANADENSIS CHIMO xiii, **272–3**
    CANADENSIS DEGENER xiii, **272–3**
    CANADENSIS PREBLEI xiii, 273
LYCAON, CANIS LUPUS xii, 200, **202**
Lynx, 276, 279
    Canada 280, **281–2** 283–4, 286
LYNX CANADENSIS 275, 280, **281–2**, 283
    CANADENSIS CANADENSIS xiii, 280
    CANADENSIS SUBSOLANUS xiii, 280, **282**
    RUFUS 275, 280, **284–5**, 286–7
    RUFUS GIGAS xiv, **285**
    RUFUS RUFUS xiv, 285
    RUFUS SUPERIORENSIS xiv, **285**
Lynx 280
Lynx du Canada 280
Lynx roux 284
LYSTERI, TAMIAS STRIATUS ix, **122–3**

MACHRINUS, SCALOPUS AQUATICUS vii, 54
MACKENZII, PHENACOMYS UNGAVA x, 160
MACRODON, MUSTELA xiii, 232, 245, **250**
MACROPODIDAE, Family 14
MACROSCELIDIDAE, Family 14
MACROTIS, GLAUCOMYS SABRINUS ix, **132**
Madagascarian bat 15
MAKKOVIKENSIS, GLAUCOMYS SABRINUS ix, **131–2**
Malar 22, **23**
Malocclusions, tooth **85**, 103
MAMMALIA, Class 6, 10, 13
Mammalogy 2, 5
Mammals, order and classification of 9–19
Mammary glands 6
Manatees 7, 18
Mandibles 20, **21**, 22, **23–4**
Mandibular condyle 20, **21**, 22, **23**
Mandibular fossa 20, **21**
Maned rats 16

MANICULATUS, PEROMYSCUS 140–4
    PEROMYSCUS MANICULATUS x, 140, **142–3**
MANIDAE, Family 16
MANITOBENSIS, CERVUS CANADENSIS xv, 321
Maps, distribution (list) xxiv–xxvi
Marine carnivores 288–311
Marine mammals 8, 288–311, 340–403
MARITIMENSIS, SOREX ARCTICUS vi, **39**, 40
MARITIMUS, THALARCTOS 218, 222, **223–4**, 225
    THALARCTOS MARITIMUS xii, **223–4**
Marmosets 15
Marmot 105, 115
MARMOTA 106, 115–18
    MONAX 115–16, **117–18**
    MONAX CANADENSIS ix, 116, **117**
    MONAX IGNAVA ix, 116, **117**
    MONAX JOHNSONI ix, 116, **117**
    MONAX RUFESCENS ix, 116
Marmottes 115
Marmotte commune 115
'Marsh rabbit' 171
Marsouins 362
Marsouin blanc 357
Marsouin commun 379
Marsupial mole 14
MARSUPIALIA, Order 8, 14, 26–30
MARSUPIALIS, DIDELPHIS 27, **28–9**, 30
Marsupials 9, 14
Marsupium 29
Marten 114, 252, **253–4**, 255–7
MARTES 231, 252–9
    AMERICANA 252, **253–4**, 255
    AMERICANA AMERICANA xiii, 252
    AMERICANA ATRATA xiii, 252, **254**
    AMERICANA BRUMALIS xiii, 252, **254**
    PENNANTI 252, **256–8**, 259
    PENNANTI PENNANTI xiii, 256
Martres 252
Masked shrew **34–5**, 36
Mastoid process 20, **21**, 22, **23**
Maxilla 20, **21**, 22, **23**
Meadow jumping mouse 181, **182–3**, 184, 187
Meadow vole 161, **162–3**, 164, 166
MEARNSII, SYLVILAGUS FLORIDANUS viii, 97
Medical research 3
MEDIOXIMUS, SYNAPTOMYS BOREALIS x, 153, **154**
MEGADERMATIDAE, Family 14
MEGAPTERA 382, 394–6
    NODOSA 394
    NOVAEANGLIAE xviii, **394–5**, 396

Mégaptère 394
MEGAPTERINAE, Subfamily 382
MELAENA, GLOBICEPHALA xvi, 364, 376–7, 378
MELLONAE, PHOCA VITULINA xiv, 294, 295–6
MEPHITIS 231, 266–70
  MEPHITIS **266–7, 368–9**
  MEPHITIS HUDSONICA xiii, 267
  MEPHITIS MEPHITIS xiii, 267
  MEPHITIS NIGRA xiii, 267
MESOPLODON 342–8
  BIDENS xv, 342, **343–4**
  DENSIROSTRIS xv, 342–3, **345–6**
  EUROPAEUS 348
  MIRUS xv, 342, **347–8**
Mesozoic 9
Metacarpals **24**
Metatarsals **24**
METATHERIA, Infraclass 10, 14
Mice (Mouse) 16, 211, 253
  deer 140, **142**, 144, 146
  house **178–9**, 180
  jumping 16, 181–7
  lemming 149
  meadow jumping 181, **182–3**, 184
  native 138
  northern lemming 152, **153–4**, 155
  Old World 16, 173, 178
  pine 25, **167–8**
  pocket 16
  prairie deer **141–2**, 143
  red-backed 155, **156–7**
  southern lemming **150–1**, 152
  white-footed 140, 144, **145–6**
  woodland deer 140, **141**, 143
  woodland jumping **185–6**, 187
MICHIGANENSIS, CASTOR CANADENSIS ix, 133
MICROSOREX 31, 34, 44–6
  HOYI **33–4**, 44, **45**, 46
  HOYI ALNORUM vi, 46
  HOYI HOYI 46
  HOYI INTERVECTUS vi, 46
  HOYI THOMPSONI vi, 46
Microtine rodents, tooth enamel patterns **138**
MICROTUS 139, 161–8
  CHROTORRHINUS **138**, 161, 164, **165–6**, 167
  CHROTORRHINUS CAROLINENSIS 166
  CHROTORRHINUS CHROTORRHINUS x, 164, 166
  CHROTORRHINUS RAVUS x, **165–6**
  PENNSYLVANICUS **138**, 161, **162–3**, 164, 167
  PENNSYLVANICUS ACADICUS x, 161, **163**

PENNSYLVANICUS DRUMMONDII x, 162
PENNSYLVANICUS ENIXUS x, 162, **163**
PENNSYLVANICUS FONTIGENUS x, **163**
PENNSYLVANICUS LABRADORIUS x, 162, **163**
PENNSYLVANICUS PENNSYLVANICUS x, 161–2
PENNSYLVANICUS TERRAENOVAE x, 162, **163**
PINETORUM 25, **138**, 161, 164, **167–8**
PINETORUM SCALOPSOIDES xi, 167
XANTHOGNATHUS 166
MICTOMYS, Subgenus 152
Milk teeth 7
MINIMUS, EUTAMIAS 121, 123, **124–5**, 126
Mink, 171, 232, **244**, 245, **246–9**, 251–2, 259, 378, 390
  Keewatin 245
  sea 231–2, 245, **250**
Minke whale 388, **389**, 390
MINNESOTA, TAMIASCIURUS HUDSONICUS viii, 114
MIRUS, MESOPLODON xv, 342, **347–8**
MISCIX, SOREX CINEREUS vi, **35**
Molar teeth 7, 20, **21**, 22, **23**
Mole rats 16, 17
Mole shrew 49
Moles 8, 14, 52–9
  eastern 25, 52, **53–4**
  golden 14
  hairy-tailed 54, **55–6**
  marsupial 14
  star-nosed 56, **57–8**, 59
MOLOSSIDAE, Family 15
MONAX, MARMOTA **115**–16, **117–18**
Mongooses 17
Mongrel dog 197
Monkeys, New World 15
  Old World 15
MONOCEROS, MONODON xvi, **360–1**, 362
MONODON 357, 360–2
  MONOCEROS xvi, **360–1**, 362
MONODONTIDAE, Family 17, 341, 357–62
MONODONTINAE, Subfamily 357, 360–2
MONOTREMATA, Order 9, 13
Monotremes 6, 9
Moose 221, 257, 262, 317–18, 326, **327–9**, 330, 337
Morse 288–9
Mouffettes 267
Mouffette rayée 267

Mountain beavers 16
Mountain goats 339
Mountain sheep 317
Mouse-eared bats 62–9
Mouse-tailed bats 14
Moustache-lipped bats 15
Moutons 335, 338
Mouton domestique 338
Mule 312
Mule deer 326
Multituberculates 10
MULTITUBERCULATA, Order 13
MURIDAE, Family 16, 104, 173–80
MUS MUSCULUS **178–9**
  MUSCULUS DOMESTICUS xi, 178
Musaraignes 31
Musaraigne, petite 50
Musaraigne arctique 38
Musaraigne cendrée 34
Musaraigne de Gaspé 40
Musaraigne fuligineuse 36
Musaraigne, grande 47
Musaraigne gris longicaude 41
Musaraigne longicaude 32
Musaraigne palustre 42
Musaraigne pygmée 44
MUSCULUS, BALAENOPTERA 383, 391
  MUS **178–9**
  SIBBALDUS xvi, 340, 383, **391–3**
Muskoxen 335, 337
Muskrat 147, 172, 192, 245, 247, 273
  common **169–70**, 171–2
MUSTELA 231–51, 267
  ERMINEA 232–3, **234–5**, 236, 239–41
  ERMINEA BANGSI xii, 233
  ERMINEA CICOGNANII xii, 233
  ERMINEA RICHARDSONII xii, 233
  EVERSMANI 251
  FRENATA 232–3, **238–9**, 240–1
  FRENATA NOVEBORACENSIS xiii, 240
  FRENATA OCCISOR xiii, 240
  FURO 251
  MACRODON xiii, 232, 245, **250**
  PUTORIUS 231–2, 245, **251**
  PUTORIUS EVERSMANI 251
  PUTORIUS FURO xiii, 251
  PUTORIUS PUTORIUS 251
  RIXOSA 232–3, **241–2**, 243
  RIXOSA RIXOSA xiii, 243
  VISON 232, **244–5**, **246–50**
  VISON LACUSTRIS xiii, 245
  VISON LOWII xiii, 245, **246**
  VISON VISON xiii, 245
MUSTELIDAE, Family 17, 194, 231–74
MYOCASTOR COYPUS 192, **193**
  COYPUS BONARIENSIS xi, 192
MYOMORPHA, Suborder 103, 138–87

MYOTIS 61–9, 77
  KEENII **61**, 62–3, **66–7**
  KEENII SEPTENTRIONALIS vii, **67**
  LUCIFUGUS **61–2**, **63–4**, 65, 67–70,
    72, 74
  LUCIFUGUS LUCIFUGUS xii, 63
  SODALIS 60–2
  SUBULATUS **61–2**, **68–9**
  SUBULATUS LEIBII vii, 68–9
MYRMECOPHAGIDAE, Family 15
MYSTACINIDAE, Family 15
MYSTICETI, Suborder 340, 381–403
MYSTICETUS, BALAENA 398, 400,
    401–2, 403
MYZOPODIDAE, Family 15

NAPAEOZAPUS INSIGNIS 181,
    185–6, 187
  INSIGNIS ABIETORUM xi, **186–7**
  INSIGNIS ALGONQUINENSIS xi,
    186–7
  INSIGNIS FRUTECTANUS xi, 187
  INSIGNIS GASPENSIS xi, **186–7**
  INSIGNIS INSIGNIS xi, **186–7**
  INSIGNIS SAGUENAYENSIS xi,
    186–7
Narval 357, 360
Narwhal 17, **360–1**, 362
Nasal 20, **21**, 22, **23**
NATALIDAE, Family 15
Native mice 138
NEGLECTUS, EUTAMIAS MINIMUS ix,
    125–6
  NELSONI, CERVUS CANADENSIS xv,
    321
  New England cottontail **100–1**
  New World monkeys 15
  New World porcupines 16, 188
NIGER, SCIURUS 106, 108, **110–11**
NIGRA, CONDYLURA CRISTATA vii,
    57, **58**
  MEPHITIS MEPHITIS xiii, 267
NOCTILIONIDAE, Family 14
NOCTIVAGANS, LASIONYCTERIS vii,
    61, 70, **71**
NODOSA, MEGAPTERA 394
North American buffalo 336
North American porcupines 188–91
North Atlantic right whale **398–9**,
    400
Northern flying squirrel 114,
    128–9, **130–1**, 132
Northern lemming mouse 152,
    153–4, 155
NORVEGICUS, RATTUS xi, 173,
    174–6
Norway rat **103**, **174–5**, 176–7, 180
NOTORYCTIDAE, Family 14
NOTOUNGULATA, Order 18
NOVAEANGLIAE, MEGAPTERA xvii,
    394–5, 396

NOVEBORACENSIS, MUSTELA FRENATA
    xiii, 240
  PEROMYSCUS LEUCOPUS x, 144,
    146
Nutria 16, 192, **193**
Nutria 192
NYCTERIDAE, Family 14
NYCTICEIUS 61, 77
  HUMERALIS **77**
  HUMERALIS HUMERALIS vii, 77

OBLIQUIDENS, LAGENORHYNCHUS 372
OBSCURUS, ONDATRA ZIBETHICUS xi,
    169, **170**
  PIPISTRELLUS SUBFLAVUS vii, 72
Occipital condyles 7, 20, **21**, 22, **23**
OCCISOR, MUSTELA FRENATA xiii,
    240
OCHOTONIDAE, Family 16, 83
OCHRACEUS, CLETHRIONOMYS
    GAPPERI x, 155
Octodont rats 16
OCTODONTIDAE, Family 16
OCYTHOUS, UROCYON
    CINEREOARGENTEUS xii, 217
ODOBENIDAE, Family 17, 288–92
ODOBENUS ROSMARUS 25, **289–90**,
    291–2
  ROSMARUS DIVERGENS 291
  ROSMARUS ROSMARUS xiv, 291
ODOCOILEUS 322–6
  HEMIONUS HEMIONUS 326
  VIRGINIANUS 322, **323–5**, 326
  VIRGINIANUS BOREALIS xv, 323
  VIRGINIANUS DACOTENSIS xv, 323
ODONTOCETI, Suborder 340–81
Old World mice, 16, 173, 178
Old World monkeys 15
Old World porcupines 16
Old World rats 16, 173, 178
Omnivores 8
ONDATRA 139, 169–72
  ZIBETHICUS **169–70**, 171–2
  ZIBETHICUS ALBUS xi, 171
  ZIBETHICUS AQUILONIUS xi,
    170–1
  ZIBETHICUS OBSCURUS xi, 169, **170**
  ZIBETHICUS ZIBETHICUS xi, 169
Opossum 8, 14, 27–30
  American 27
  common 27, **28–9**, 30
Opossum commun 27
Opossum d'Amérique 27
Optic foramen 20, **21**
Orbitosphenoid 20, **21**, 22, **23**
ORCA 374
  ORCA 374
ORCINUS 363, 373–5
  ORCA xvi, 373, **374–5**
  RECTIPINNA 374
Order (classification) 10–12

Order:
  ARTIODACTYLA 19, 26, 315–39
  ASTRAPOTHERIA 18
  CARNIVORA 8, 17, 26, 194–287
  CETACEA 8, 17, 26, 340, 403
  CHIROPTERA 8, 14, 26, 59–83
  CONDYLARTHRA 17
  DERMOPTERA 14
  DINOCERATA 18
  EDENTATA 15
  EMBRITHOPODA 18
  HYRACOIDEA 18
  INSECTIVORA 8, 14, 26, 30–59
  LAGOMORPHA 16, 26, 83–102
  LITOPTERNA 18
  MARSUPIALIA 8, 14, 26–30
  MONOTREMATA 9, 13
  MULTITUBERCULATA 13
  NOTOUNGULATA 18
  PANTODONTA 18
  PANTOTHERIA 13
  PERISSODACTYLA 19, 26, 312–14
  PHOLIDOTA 16
  PINNIPEDIA 8, 17, 26, 288–311
  PRIMATES 15
  PROBOSCIDEA 18
  PYROTHERIA 18
  RODENTIA 8, 16, 26, 103–93
  SIRENIA 8, 18
  SYMMETRODONTA 13
  TAENIODONTA 15
  TILLODONTIA 15
  TRICONODONTA 13
  TUBULIDENTATA 18
Orders (key) 26
OREAMNOS AMERICANUS 339
Orignal 326
ORNITHORHYNCHIDAE, Family 13
Orque 373
ORYCTEROPODIDAE, Family 18
ORYCTOLAGUS 84, 87, 102
  CUNICULAS 20, **21**, **102**
OTARIIDAE, Family 17, 288, 292
Otter, 17, 245, 257, **271–2**, 273–4
  giant 231
  sea 231
Ours 218
Ours noir 219
Ours polaire 222
Ovibos 335
OVIS 335, 338
  ARIES **228**, 339
  CANADENSIS 338
Oxen 335

Pacas 16
  false 16
  long-tailed 16
PAGOPHILUS, Subgenus 293,
    299–302

Palaeontology 3
Palate 7
Palatine bone 20, **21**, 22, **23**
Palatine fissure 22, **23**
PALLESCENS, CLETHRIONOMYS
    GAPPERI x, **156–7**
PALLIDA, BLARINA BREVICAUDA vi,
    48–9
PALLIDUS, EPTESICUS FUSCUS vii, 74
PALUSTRIS, SOREX 32, **33–4**, 41–2,
    43–4
    SOREX PALUSTRIS vi, 44
Pangolins 16
PANTODONTA, Order 18
Pantotheres 10
PANTOTHERIA, Infraclass 13
PANTOTHERIA, Order 13
PARASCALOPS 52, 54–6
    BREWERI 54, **55–6**
Parasites 3
Parasitology 3
Parietal 20, **21**, 22, **23**
Paroccipital process 22, **23**
PARVA, CRYPTOTIS 25, 50, **51**
    CRYPTOTIS PARVA vii, 50
PASTEURELLA TULARENSIS 99
Patella **24**
Peccaries 19
PEDETIDAE, Family 16
Pékans 252, 256
Pelts, Production of:
    Arctic fox 209
    beaver 137
    bobcat 287
    cross fox 214
    ermine 237
    fisher 259
    lynx 283
    marten 255
    mink, ranch 248
    mink, wild 249
    muskrat 172
    otter 274
    raccoon 230
    red fox 214
    silver fox 214
    striped skunk 270
Pelvic girdle 7
Pelvis **24**
PENNANTI, MARTES 252, **256–8**, 259
    MARTES PENNANTI xiii, 256
PENNSYLVANICUS, MICROTUS **138**,
    161, **162–3**, 164, 167
    MICROTUS PENNSYLVANICUS x,
    161–2
    SCIURUS CAROLINENSIS viii,
    108, **109**
PERAMELIDAE, Family 14
PERISSODACTYLA, Order 19, 26,
    312–14
PEROMYSCUS 138–46, 178

LEUCOPUS 140, 144, **145–6**
LEUCOPUS CAUDATUS x, **145–6**
LEUCOPUS NOVEBORACENSIS x,
    144, 146
MANICULATUS 140–4
MANICULATUS ABIETORUM ix,
    142–3
MANICULATUS ANTICOSTIENSIS ix,
    142–3
MANICULATUS ARGENTATUS ix,
    142–3
MANICULATUS BAIRDII ix, **141–2**,
    143
MANICULATUS EREMUS x, **142–3**
MANICULATUS GRACILIS x, 140,
    141, **143**, 146
MANICULATUS MANICULATUS x,
    140, **142–3**
MANICULATUS PLUMBEUS x,
    142–3
Petit polatouche 128
Petit rorqual 388
Petite belette 241
Petite musaraigne 50
PETROMYIDAE, Family 17
PHAEONOTUS, LEPUS AMERICANUS
    viii, 87, **88**
Phalangeal formula 7
PHALANGERIDAE, Family 14
Phalangers 14
Phalanges **24**
PHASCOLOMIDAE, Family 14
Phenacomys **138**, 139, 158–60
    eastern **158–9**, 160
Phenacomys d'Ungava 158
PHENACOMYS UNGAVA **138**, **158–9**,
    160–1, 164
    UNGAVA CRASSUS x, **159–60**
    UNGAVA MACKENZII x, 160
    UNGAVA SOPERI x, 160
    UNGAVA UNGAVA x, **159**, 160
PHOCA 293–302
    GROENLANDICA 293, 299, **300–1**,
    302
    (PAGOPHILUS) GROENLANDICA
    xiv, 293, 299, **300–1**, 302
    (PUSA) HISPIDA 293–4, 296,
    297–8, 299
    (PUSA) HISPIDA HISPIDA xiv, 297
    VITULINA 293, **294–5**, 296–7
    VITULINA CONCOLOR xiv, 294, 296
    VITULINA MELLONAE xiv, 294,
    295–6
    VITULINA RICHARDII 294
PHOCA, Subgenus 293–6
PHOCIDAE, Family 17, 288, 292,
    311
PHOCOENA 363, 379–80
    PHOCOENA xvi, **379–80**
PHOLIDOTA, Order 16
Phoques 292–3

Phoque à capuchon 309
Phoque annelé 296
Phoque barbu 302
Phoque commun 294
Phoque du Groenland 299
Phoque gris 305
PHYLLOSTOMIDAE, Family 15
Phylogenetic relations 10
Phylum (classification) 12
    CHORDATA 10
PHYSALUS, BALAENOPTERA 383,
    384–5, 386
PHYSETER CATODON xv, 351, **352–3**,
    354
PHYSETERIDAE, Family 17, 341,
    351–4
Physiology 3
PICINUM, ERETHIZON DORSATUM
    xi, 190–1
Pig bats 15
Pigs 19, 286, 315
    domestic **316**
    puffing 380
Pikas 16, 83
Piked whale, little 388, **389**, 390
Pilot whale 364, **376–7**, 378
Pine mouse 25, **167–8**
Pine vole **167–8**
PINETORUM, MICROTUS 25, **138**,
    161, 164, **167–8**
    PITYMYS 167
PINNIPEDIA, Order 8, 17, 26,
    288–311
Pipistrelle, eastern 72, **73**
Pipistrelle de l'Est 72
PIPISTRELLUS 61, 72–3, 83
    SUBFLAVUS **61**, 72, **73**
    SUBFLAVUS OBSCURUS vii, 72
    SUBFLAVUS SUBFLAVUS 72
PITYMYS PINETORUM 167
Placental mammals 9
PLANIFRONS, HYPEROODON 350
PLATACANTHOMYIDAE, Family 16
PLATANISTIDAE, Family 17
Platypus, duck-billed 9, 13
Pleistocene 9
PLUMBEUS, PEROMYSCUS
    MANICULATUS x, **142–3**
Pocket gophers 8, 16
Pocket mice 16
Polar bear 206, 218–19, 222,
    223–4, 225
Polatouches 126
Polatouche, grand 129
Polatouche, petit 128
Polecat 251
Pollack whale 386, **387–8**
Polled cattle 335
Polled sheep 335
PONGIDAE, Family 15
Porc-épic 188

Porc-épics d'Amérique 188
Porc-épics du Nouveau Monde 188
Porcupines 188, **189–90**, 191, 262, 282
  New World 16, 188
  North American 188–91
  Old World 16
Porpoises 17, 340, 362, 375
  common **379–80**
  harbour **379–80**, 393
  rough-toothed 362
Postorbital process:
  of the frontal 22, **23**
  of the jugal 22, **23**
  of the malar 22, **23**
  of the supraorbital 20, **21**
POTAMOGALIDAE, Family 14
Pothead whale **376–7**, 378
Pottos 15
Pourcil 379
Prairie deer mouse **141–2**, 143
Prairie dog 105
PREBLEI, LUTRA CANADENSIS xiii, 273
Predators 4
Prehistoric animals 9
Premaxila 20, **21**, 22, **23**
Premolars 7, 20, **21**, 22, **23**
Presphenoid 20, **21**, 22, **23**
PRIMATES, Order 15
PRIMIGENIUS, BOS 337
PROBOSCIDEA, Order 18
PROCAVIIDAE, Family 18
PROCYON LOTOR 226, **227–8**, 229–30
  LOTOR HIRTUS xii, 226
  LOTOR LOTOR xii, 226
PROCYONIDAE, Family 17, 194, 226–30
Pronghorns 4, 19, 317
PROTEUS, CLETHRIONOMYS GAPPERI x, **156–7**
PROTOTHERIA, Subclass 9, 13
PSEUDORCA CRASSIDENS 362
PTERONURA 231
PTEROPIDAE, Family 14
Pterygoid 20, **21**, 22, **23**
Puffing pig 380
Puma 276–8
PUSA, Subgenus 293, 296–9
(PUSA) HISPIDA HISPIDA, PHOCA xiv, 297
Putios 232, 251
PUTORIUS, MUSTELA 231–2, 245, **251**
  MUSTELA PUTORIUS 251
Pygmy shrew 7, **33–4**, 44, **45–6**
Pygmy sperm whale 354, **355–6**
PYROTHERIA, Order 18

Quadrate (bone) 7

QUEBECENSIS, TAMIAS STRIATUS ix, **122–3**

Rabbit fever 99
Rabbits 4, 16, 83–4, 197, 211, 240, 245, 253, 286
  cottontail 87, 96–7, **98–9**, 251
  domestic 20, **21**, **102**
  jack 89, 95
  white-tailed jack **92–3**, 95
Rabies 76
Raccoons 8, 17, 226, **227–8**, 229, 257
Races, geographic (list) vi–xvii
Radius 24
RANGIFER 318, 330–4
  ARCTICUS 332
  ARCTICUS ARCTICUS 333
  ARCTICUS CABOTI 333
  CABOTI 332–3
  CARIBOU 332
  CARIBOU SYLVESTRIS 333
  TARANDUS 330–2, **333–4**
  TARANDUS CARIBOU xv, **331–3**
  TARANDUS GROENLANDICUS xv, 332–3
  TERRAENOVAE 333
Rat chinchillas 17
Ratons 226
Raton laveur 226
Rats 16–17, 138, 173–7
  bamboo 16
  black **175**, 177
  cane 17
  dassie 17
  gundis 17
  kangaroo 16
  maned 16
  mole 16–17
  Norway **103**, **174–5**, 176–7, 180
  octodont 16
  Old World 16, 173, 178
  rock 17
  roof 177
  spiny 17
Rats 138
Rat des toits 177
Rat musqué 169
Rat noir 177
Rat surmulot 179
Rats d'Ancien Monde 173
RATTUS 173–8
  NORVEGICUS xi, 173, **174–6**
  RATTUS 173–4, **175**, 176–7
  RATTUS ALEXANDRINUS xi, 177
  RATTUS RATTUS xi, 177
RAVUS, MICROTUS CHROTORRHINUS x, **165–6**
RECTIPINNA, ORCINUS 374
Red bat 78, **79–80**
Red deer 318

Red fox 210, **211–12**, 213, 215, 217
Red squirrel 108, **112–13**, 114, 129, 253
Red-backed mouse 155, **156–7**
REGALIS, TAMIASCIURUS HUDSONICUS viii, **113–14**
  VULPES VULPES 210
Regions, climatic 8
Reindeer 317, 330
Religion 4
Renards 195
Renard arctique 205
Renard gris 215
Renard roux 210
Reptiles 6, 8
  mammal-like 9
Rhinoceroses 19
RHINOCEROTIDAE, Family 19
RHINOLOPHIDAE, Family 15
RHINOPOMATIDAE, Family 14
RHIZOMYIDAE, Family 16
Ribs 24
RICHARDII, PHOCA VITULINA 294
RICHARDSONII, MUSTELA ERMINEA xii, 233
Right whales 397–403
  Biscayan **398–9**, 400
  Greenland 400–3
  North Atlantic **398–9**, 400
Ringed seal 296, **297–8**, 299
Risso dolphin 362
River dolphins 17
RIXOSA, MUSTELA 232–3, **241–2**, 243
  MUSTELA RIXOSA xiii, 243
Rock rats 17
Rock vole 164, **165–6**
Rodent tooth enamel patterns, microtine **138**
RODENTIA, Order 8, 16, 26, 103–93
Rodents 4, 8, 103–93, 240, 273
Roof rat 177
Rorquals 382–3
Rorqual, petit 388
Rorqual commun 383
Rorqual sei 386
ROSMARUS, ODOBENUS 25, **289–90**, 291–2
  ODOBENUS ROSMARUS xiv, 291
Rough-toothed porpoise 362
RUBRICOSA, VULPES VULPES xii, 210, **212**
RUFESCENS, MARMOTA MONAX ix, 116
RUFIVENTOR, SCIURUS NIGER viii, 111
RUFUS, LYNX 275, 280, **284–5**, 286–7
  LYNX RUFUS xiv, 285
RUMINANTIA, Suborder 315, 317–39

Sable 259
SABRINUS, GLAUCOMYS 114, 126, 128–9, **130–1**, 132
   GLAUCOMYS SABRINUS ix, **131–2**
Sacral vertebrae 7, **24**
Sac-winged bats 14
Saddle-back shrew 38, **39**, 40
Sagittal crest 22, **23**
SAGUENAYENSIS, NAPAEOZAPUS
   INSIGNIS xi, **186–7**
Samson fox, bastard 210
SCALOPSOIDES, MICROTUS
   PINETORUM xi, 167
SCALOPUS 52–4
   AQUATICUS 25, 52, **53**, 54
   AQUATICUS MACHRINUS vii, 54
Scaly anteaters 16
Scapula **24**
SCHORGERI, FELIS CONCOLOR 277
SCIURIDAE, Family 16, 103–32
SCIUROMORPHA, Suborder, 103, 105–32
SCIURUS 106–11
   CAROLINENSIS 106, **107**, 108, **109**
   CAROLINENSIS HYPOPHAEUS viii, 108
   CAROLINENSIS LEUCOTIS 108, **109**
   CAROLINENSIS PENNSYLVANICUS
      viii, 108, **109**
   NIGER 106, 108, **110–11**
   NIGER RUFIVENTOR viii, 111
SCROFA, SUS **316**
Sea lions 17
Sea mink 231–2, 245, **250**
Sea otter 231
Seal, Hudson 171
Seals, 7, 25, 223, 291–311, 375
   bearded 302, **303–4**, 305
   bladdernose 309–11
   eared 17
   gray 305, **306–7**, 308
   Greenland 299–302
   hair 17, 293–302
   harbour **294–5**, 296
   harp 299, **300–1**, 302, 311
   hooded **308**, 309, **310**, 311
   horsehead 305–8
   ringed 296, **297–8**, 299
Sei whale 386, **387**, 388
SELEVINIIDAE, Family 16
SEPTENTRIONALIS, MYOTIS KEENII
   vii, **67**
Serums 3
Sheep 3, 19, 286, 335, 337
   domestic **338**, 339
   mountain 317
   polled 335
Shepherd dog, German 197, 200
Short-tailed bats 15
Short-tailed shrew, big 47–8, 49
Short-tailed shrew, little 25, 50, **51**

Short-tailed weasel 233, **234–5**, 236–7
Shoulder girdle 7
Shrew teeth **34**
Shrews, 8, 14, 31–51, 253
   African water 14
   Arctic **33**, 38, **39**, 40
   big short-tailed 47–8, 49
   common **33–5**, 36, 38, 40, 44
   elephant 14
   Gaspé **33**, 40, **41**
   gray long-tailed 41–2
   jumping 14
   least 50
   little short-tailed 25, 50, **51**
   long-tailed 32–44
   masked **34–5**, 36
   mole 49
   pygmy 7, **33–4**, 44, **45–6**
   saddle-back 38, **39**, 40
   smoky **33–4**, 36, **37–8**, 40
   water **33**, 41–2, **43**, 44
SIBBALDUS 382, 391–4
   MUSCULUS xvi, 340, 383, **391–3**
SIEBOLDII, EUBALAENA 399
Silver fox 210, 214
Silver-haired bat 70, 71
SIRENIA, Order 8, 18
Skeleton 6, **20**
   parts labeled **24**
Skull 20
   parts labeled **21**, **23**
Skunk 17, 266–9
   striped **266–7**, **268–9**
Sloths 7–8, 15
Slow loris 15
Small-footed bat **68–9**
SMITHI, SYNAPTOMYS BOREALIS x, 153
Smoky bat 15
Smoky shrew **33–4**, 36, **37–8**, 40
Smooth-faced bats 15
Snowshoe hare **86–8**, 89, 257
SODALIS, MYOTIS 60–2
Soils 25
Solenodons 14
SOLENODONTIDAE, Family 14
SOPERI, PHENACOMYS UNGAVA x, 160
SOREX 31–44
   ARCTICUS 32, **33–4**, 37–8, **39**, 40
   ARCTICUS ARCTICUS vi, 38, **39**
   ARCTICUS LARICORUM vi, 40
   ARCTICUS MARITIMENSIS vi, **39–40**
   CINEREUS 32, **33–5**, 36, 41, 44
   CINEREUS ACADICUS vi, **35**
   CINEREUS CINEREUS vi, **35**, 37
   CINEREUS MISCIX vi, **35**
   DISPAR vi, 32, **34**, 40, **41–2**
   FUMEUS 32, **33–4**, 36, **37**, 38, 41
   FUMEUS FUMEUS vi, **37–8**
   FUMEUS UMBROSUS vi, **37**, 38

GASPENSIS vi, 32, **33**, 40, **41**, 42
PALUSTRIS 32, **33–4**, 41–2, **43–4**
PALUSTRIS ALBIBARBIS vi, 44
PALUSTRIS GLOVERALLENI vi, **43–4**
PALUSTRIS HYDROBADISTES vi, 44
PALUSTRIS LABRADORENSIS vi, **43–4**
PALUSTRIS PALUSTRIS vi, 44
PALUSTRIS TURNERI vi, **43**, 44
SORICIDAE, Family 14, 30–51
Souris 138
Souris à pattes blanches 144
Souris commune 178
Souris d'Ancien Monde 173
Souris sauteuses 181
Souris sauteuse des bois 185
Souris sauteuse des champs 181
Souris sylvestre 140
Southern bog lemming **150–1**, 152
Southern lemming mouse **150–1**, 152
Sowerby beaked whale **343–4**
SPALACIDAE, Family 16
Spaniel dog 260
Speciation 17
Species (classification) 10–13
Sperm whale 351, **352–3**, 354, 383, 386, 396
Sperm whale, pygmy 354, **355–6**
Spermaceti 351, 354
Spermophile de Franklin 118
SPHAGNICOLA, SYNAPTOMYS
   BOREALIS x, 153
Spiny anteater 9, 13
Spiny dormice 16
Spiny rats 17
Spiny-tailed squirrels 16
Spring haas 16
Squamosal 20, **21**, 22, **23**
Square-flipper **302–5**
Squirrels 16, 105–14, 118–20, 126–32
   American grey 108
   eastern flying **127–9**, 132
   eastern fox **110–11**
   eastern gray **107**, 108, **109**, **110–11**, 118, 239
   flying 105, 126
   fox 108, 111
   Franklin ground 118, **119–20**
   ground 105
   northern flying 114, 128–9, **130–1**, 132
   red 108, **112–13**, 114, 129, 253
   spiny-tailed 16
   tree 105–11, 114
Stag 318
Star-nosed mole 56, **57–8**, 59
STENELLA FRONTALIS 362
   STYX 362
STENO BREDANENSIS 362

Sternum 7, **24**
STRIATUS, TAMIAS **121–2**, 123–4, 126
Striped skunk **266–7, 268–9**
STRUTHOPUS, LEPUS AMERICANUS
    viii, 87
STYX, STENELLA 362
Subclass (classification) 12
    ALLOTHERIA 10, 13
    PROTOTHERIA 9, 13
    SYNAPSIDA 9
    THERIA 10, 13
Subfamily (classification) 12
    CRICETINAE 138
    DELPHINAPTERINAE 357–9
    MEGAPTERINAE 382
    MONODONTINAE 357, 360–2
SUBFLAVUS, PIPISTRELLUS **61**, 72, **73**
    PIPISTRELLUS SUBFLAVUS vii, 72
Subgenus (classification) 12
    EUARCTOS 218–19
    MICTOMYS 152
    PAGOPHILUS 293, 299–302
    PHOCA 293–6
    PUSA 293, 296–9
    SYNAPTOMYS 152
Suborder (classification) 12
    HYSTRICOMORPHA 104, 188–93
    MYOMORPHA 103, 138–87
    MYSTICETI 340, 381–403
    ODONTOCETI 340–81
    RUMINANTIA 315, 317–39
    SCIUROMORPHA 103, 105–32
    SUIFORMES 315–16
Subphylum (classification) 12
    VERTEBRATA 6, 10
SUBSOLANUS, LYNX CANADENSIS
    xiii, 280, **282**
Subspecies (list) vi–xvii
    classification 12
Subtribe (classification) 12
SUBULATUS, MYOTIS **61**, 62, **68–9**
Sucker-footed bats 15
SUIDAE, Family 19, 315–16
SUIFORMES, Suborder 315–16
Suisse 121
Suisse de l'ouest 124
Sulphur-bottom whale 340, **391–3**
Superclass (classification) 12
Superfamily (classification) 12
SUPERIORENSIS, LYNX RUFUS xiv, **285**
Superorder (classification) 12
Supraoccipital 20, **21**, 22, **23**
Supraorbital processes 20, **21**
Survival 11
SUS SCROFA **316**
SYLVESTRIS, RANGIFER CARIBOU 333
SYLVILAGUS 84, 96–102
    FLORIDANUS 96–7, **98–9**, 100–1
    FLORIDANUS MEARNSII viii, 97
    TRANSITIONALIS viii, 96–7,
      100–1

SYMMETRODONTA, Order 13
Symmetrodonts 10
SYNAPSIDA, Subclass 9
SYNAPTOMYS 139, 149–55, 161
    BOREALIS **138**, 149–50, 152,
      153–4, 155
    BOREALIS INNUITUS x, 153, **154**
    BOREALIS MEDIOXIMUS x, 153,
      154
    BOREALIS SMITHI x, 153
    BOREALIS SPHAGNICOLA x, 153
    COOPERI **138**, 149, **150–1**,
      152–3, 155
    COOPERI COOPERI x, 150

TACHYGLOSSIDAE, Family 13
TAENIODONTA, Order 15
Taiga 25, 408
TALPIDAE, Family 14, 30, 52–9
TALPOIDES, BLARINA BREVICAUDA
    vii, 47, **48**
Tamia mineur 124
TAMIAS 105, 121–3
    STRIATUS **121–2**, 123–4, 126
    STRIATUS GRISEUS ix, 123
    STRIATUS LYSTERI ix, **122–3**
    STRIATUS QUEBECENSIS ix, **122–3**
TAMIASCIURUS 106, 108, 112–14,
    129
    HUDSONICUS **112–13**, 114
    HUDSONICUS GYMNICUS viii, 114
    HUDSONICUS HUDSONICUS viii,
      113–14
    HUDSONICUS LAURENTIANUS viii,
      113–14
    HUDSONICUS LOQUAX viii, 114
    HUDSONICUS MINNESOTA viii, 114
    HUDSONICUS REGALIS viii, **113–14**
    HUDSONICUS UNGAVENSIS **113**, 114
TAPIRIDAE, Family 19
Tapirs 19
TARANDUS, RANGIFER 330–2, **333**
Tarsals **24**
Tarsiers 15
TARSIIDAE, Family 15
Taupes 52
Taupe à queue glabre 52
Taupe à queue velue 54
Taupe de l'est 52
TAURUS, BOS **337**
TAXIDEA 231, 263–5, 267
    TAXUS **263–4**, 265
    TAXUS TAXUS xiii, 263
TAXUS, TAXIDEA **263–4**, 265
    TAXIDEA TAXUS xiii, 263
TAYASSUIDAE, Family 91, 315
Teeth 7, 176
    canine 7, 22, **23**
    incisor 7, 20, **21**, 22, **23**, 85
    milk 7
    molar 7, 20, **21**, 22, **23**

premolar 7, 20, **21**, 22, **23**
RATTUS **176**
shrew **34**
    tooth enamel patterns (microtine
      rodents) **138**
    tooth malocclusions 85, **103**
Temporal bone 22, **23**
TENRECIDAE, Family 14
Tenrecs 14
TERRAENOVAE, MICROTUS
    PENNSYLVANICUS x, 162–3
    RANGIFER 333
THALARCTOS LABRADORENSIS 224
    MARITIMUS 218, 222 **223–4**, 225
    MARITIMUS MARITIMUS xii, 223–4
    MARITIMUS UNGAVENSIS 223, **224**
THAMNOS, CANIS LATRANS xii, 197
THERIA, Subclass 10, 13
THOMPSONI, MICROSOREX HOYI vi,
    46
Thoracic vertebrae 7, **24**
THRYONOMYIDAE, Family 17
Thumbless bats 15
THYROPTERIDAE, Family 15
Tibia **24**
TILLODONTIA, Order 15
Timber wolf 197, 200, **201–2**, 203,
    222, 325
Toothed whales 341–80
TOWNSENDII, LEPUS 85, **92–3**, 95
TRAGULIDAE, Family 19
TRANSITIONALIS, SYLVILAGUS viii,
    96–7, **100–1**
Tree fox 217
Tree 'shrews' 15
Tree squirrels 105–11, 114
Tree-climbing fox 217
Tribe (classification) 12
TRICHECHIDAE, Family 18
TRICHECHUS 7
TRICONODONTA, Order 13
Triconodonts 10
TRIDECEMLINEATUS, CITELLUS
    TRIDECEMLINEATUS 120
True beaked whale **347–8**
TRUNCATUS, TURSIOPS xvi, **366–8**
TUBULIDENTATA, Order 18
Tucu tucus 16
Tularemia 99
TULARENSIS, PASTEURELLA 99
TUPAIIDAE, Family 15
TURNERI, SOREX PALUSTRIS vi, **43**,
    44
TURSIOPS 363, 366–8
    TRUNCATUS xvi, **366–8**
Tympanic bulla 7, 20, **21**, 22, **23**
Type localities vi–xvii

Ulna **24**
UMBROSUS, SOREX FUMEUS vi, **37**,
    38

UNGAVA, ALOPEX LAGOPUS xii, 205, 207
  CLETHRIONOMYS GAPPERI x, 156–7
  PHENACOMYS 138, 158–9, 160–1, 164
  PHENACOMYS UNGAVA x, 159, 160
Ungava varying lemming 25, 147–8, 149
UNGAVENSIS, TAMIASCIURUS HUDSONICUS 113, 114
  THALARCTOS MARITIMUS 223, 224
Ungulates 4
Unicorn 360
UROCYON 195, 210, 215–17
  CINEREOARGENTEUS 215–16, 217
  CINEREOARGENTEUS BOREALIS xii, 217
  CINEREOARGENTEUS CINEREO-ARGENTEUS xii, 217
  CINEREOARGENTEUS OCYTHOUS xii, 217
URSIDAE, Family 17, 194, 218–25
URSUS AMERICANUS 218, 219–20, 221–2
  AMERICANUS AMERICANUS xii, 221
  AMERICANUS HAMILTONI xii, 220–1
  ARCTOS 218
  HORRIBILIS 218
Uterus 6

Vaches 337
Vache domestique 337
Valve-nosed bats 14
Vampire bats 8, 15
Varying hare 86–8, 89
Varying lemming, Ungava 25, 147–8, 149
Vertebrae:
  caudal 7, 24
  cervical 7, 24
  lumbar 7, 24
  sacral 7, 24
  thoracic 7, 24
VERTEBRATA, Subphylum 5, 10
VESPERTILIONIDAE, Family 15, 60–83
VIRGINIANA, DIDELPHIS MARSUPIALIS vi, 29–30
VIRGINIANUS, LEPUS AMERICANUS viii, 87
  ODOCOILEUS 322, 323–5, 326
Viscachas 16
VISON, MUSTELA 232, 244–5, 246–50
  MUSTELA VISON xiii, 245
Visons 232, 245
Vison de mer 250
VITULINA, PHOCA 293, 294–5, 296–7

VIVERRIDAE, Family 17
Viviparous 6
VOLANS, GLAUCOMYS 126, 127–9
  GLAUCOMYS VOLANS ix, 128
Voles 161–8
  meadow 161, 162–3, 164, 166
  pine 167–8
  rock 164, 165–6
  yellow-cheeked 166
  yellow-nosed 164, 165–6
Vomer 20, 21, 22, 23
VULPES 195, 205, 210–14
  DELETRIX 212
  RUBRICOSA BANGSI 212
  VULPES 210, 211–12, 213–14
  VULPES ABIETORUM xii, 210
  VULPES FULVA xii, 210
  VULPES REGALIS 210
  VULPES RUBRICOSA xii, 210, 212

Walrus 17, 25, 288, 289–90, 291–2, 375
  Atlantic 291
Wapiti 4, 317–18, 319–20, 321–2, 337
Wapiti 318
Water shrew 33–4, 41–2, 43–4
Water shrews, African 14
Weasels 17, 164, 232–43
  common 233
  least 231, 241–2, 243
  long-tailed 238–9, 240, 243, 251
  short-tailed 233, 234–5, 236–7
Western chipmunk 124–5, 126
Whalebone whale 381–403
Whales 8, 25, 223, 340–403
  Atlantic killer 373, 374–5
  baleen 17, 340, 381–403
  beaked 17, 342–51
  Biscayan right 398–9, 400
  Blainville beaked 345–6
  blue 7, 340, 383, 386, 388, 391–3, 396
  bottlenose 349–50, 351
  bowhead 383, 397, 400, 401–2, 403
  common finback 383, 384–5, 386
  false killer 362
  fin 382–6
  finback 383–90, 395–6
  fin-backed 382–96
  gray 17
  Greenland right 400–3
  humpback 386, 394–5, 396
  killer, Atlantic 373, 374–5
  killer, false 362
  little piked 388, 389, 390
  Minke 388, 389, 390
  North Atlantic right 398–9, 400
  pilot 364, 376–8
  pollack 386, 387–8

pothead 376–8
pygmy sperm 354, 355–6
right 397–403
sei 386, 387–8
Sowerby beaked 343–4
sperm 351, 352–3, 354, 383, 386, 396
sulphur-bottom 340, 391–3
toothed 341–80
True beaked 347–8
whalebone 381–403
white 357, 358–9
White whale 357, 358–9
White-beaked dolphin 369, 370, 372–3
White-footed mouse 140, 144, 145–6
White-sided dolphin 369, 371–2, 373, 393
White-tailed deer 286, 322, 323–5, 326, 330
White-tailed jack rabbit 92–3, 95
Wild boar 316
Wolverine 231, 241, 260–1, 262
Wolves 91, 195–204, 223
  brush 197, 198–9, 200–1, 203
  timber 197, 200, 201–2, 203, 222, 325
Wombats 14
Woodchuck 103, 105, 115–16, 117–18, 197
Woodland caribou 201, 331, 333–4
Woodland deer mouse 140, 141, 143
Woodland jumping mouse 185–6, 187
Woolly lemurs 15

XANTHOGNATHUS, MICROTUS 166
Xiphoid process 24

Yellow bats 15
Yellow-cheeked vole 166
Yellow-nosed vole 164, 165–6

ZAPODIDAE, Family 16, 104, 181–7
ZAPUS 181–4, 187
  HUDSONIUS 181, 182–3, 184–5
  HUDSONIUS ACADICUS xi, 182, 183
  HUDSONIUS CANADENSIS xi, 182, 183
  HUDSONIUS HUDSONIUS xi, 182, 183
  HUDSONIUS LADAS xi, 182, 183
Zebra 312
ZIBETHICUS, ONDATRA 169–70, 171–2
  ONDATRA ZIBETHICUS xi, 169
ZIPHIIDAE, Family 17, 341–51
Zygomatic arch 20, 21, 22, 23

M

N